DELIVERANCE
Mary Fields

First African American Woman Star Route
Mail Carrier in the United States

A MONTANA HISTORY

MIANTAE METCALF MCCONNELL

Huzzah Publishing
P. O. Box 684
Columbia Falls, MT 59912

Printed in the United States of America
Second Edition

Visit www.miantaemetcalfmcconnell.com for news and updates

Publisher's Cataloging-In-Publication Data

Names: McConnell, Miantae Metcalf.
Title: Deliverance : Mary Fields : first African American woman star route mail carrier in the United States : a Montana history / Miantae Metcalf McConnell.
Description: Columbia Falls, MT : Huzzah Publishing, [2016] | Includes bibliographical references.
Identifiers: ISBN 978-0-9978770-0-7 (paperback) | ISBN 978-0-9978770-1-4 (ebook)
Subjects: LCSH: Fields, Mary, approximately 1832-1914. | Letter carriers--Montana--Biography. | African American women--Montana--Biography. | Star routes--History--19th century. | Frontier and pioneer life--Montana--History--19th century. | Ursulines--Montana--History--19th century. | Women--Suffrage--Montana--History. | LCGFT: Biographies.
Classification: LCC HE6385.F54 M33 2016 (print) | LCC HE6385.F54 (ebook) | DDC 383.14309209786--dc23

Includes Bibliography
ISBN 978-0-9978770-0-7 (paperback)
ISBN 987-0-9978770-1-4 (eBook)
PCN 2016913128

To my family
past, present and future

CONTENTS

PART FOUR

PROLOGUE

PLACE

THE BIRDTAIL, MONTANA TERRITORY

*S*eventy million years ago, two of planet earth's continents trembled. Tectonic forces caused the vast bodies of crust, plates and mantle, above and below sea level, to shift and course slowly through disparate gravities of ocean and atmosphere.

The two landmasses collided and kept moving—crushing, burning, splitting, bashing and scraping—until what had been solid became chaos, a co-mingled mass in flux. Unique formations of crust, mineral and seabed oolites emerged, rearranged and reconstituted by geothermic melting and orogenic thrust faulting. The activity birthed an abundance of structural transformation; most evident, a gargantuan expanse of mountain peaks docked north to south, the spired backbone of a new continent and the geologic wonder that would later be called *The Great Rocky Mountains* and *The Continental Divide*.

Millenniums passed. Compressed snow had accumulated and crystallized. Glaciers cloaked pinnacles, sculpted ravines, etched cirques and crowned glistening wilderness atop territorial landscapes, such as the *American West*.

Eastern rocky mountain slopes stretched downward to hills and prairies cut by scant numbers of archetypal anomalies left behind: steep, molar-shaped buttes and elevated arrangements of statuesque stone—pillars that mystified and compassed direction—one in particular, that inadvertently inspired a name for itself and the region surrounding its thousand-foot-high summit: *Birdtail Rock* and *The Birdtail*, respectively.

Imagine, if you will, that you have journeyed, committed to a quest. You pull your gaze from lengths of *Rocky Mountain* peaks and America's *Continental Divide*, the forested watershed of watersheds that towers above, and scan what appears to be an infinite distance of knee-deep grass: *the Great Plains*. Your footprints leave no tangible trace in the continent-sized meadow. It is hot. Your sight blurs when you strain to identify manifest horizons: north, south and straight ahead, where the sun rose earlier. You look closer and notice that the prairieland surface is not entirely flat. There are curvatures, ridges, like that of coastal ocean floors.

A soft breeze lifts. Your skin feels the change. Swishing sounds rustle your senses and you begin to sway, taken by prairie grass reverie. Overhead, sunlight shifts. Flamboyant gusts of wind swoop in. Swells of green and gold shimmer. Elements consort, whispering, whirling—sheaths and grains and the invisible, dancing. You are holding your breath. Your legs give way, and you plop upon dusty earth. Suddenly, you are jolted—you realize that you are alone in the place where dinosaurs romped and ran and ate trees at their leisure.

Fuzzy stalks tickle. You feel better camouflaged, but from whom, you wonder. A high-pitched buzz catches your attention. Some kind of insect, you deduce as you swing an obtuse glance. Color flashes—a small bright bird. Clutching a reed at the edge of your focal length, it sings the most astounding melody, in perfect tone. Your eyelids close.

All this while, you realize, you have been gaping. You ponder the importance of premonition, unaware of genetic sine qua non within, primeval instincts passed down. You breathe a deep breath, inhale aged pollen and essence of Pterodactyl as you relax, imagine. You wet your finger and savor the taste of dirt.

Sometime later, you push up from your haunches, stretch toward cumulus clouds and amble forward, resolved to prove your grit. The flat in-between country is pristine, you think, or is it? You stumble, catch the bulk of your body, turn your eyes and unwittingly redirect your path.

Confident, you proceed at a buoyant pace, cast sight to choose a reference point and halt. A solid portent interrupts your intention; the rock formation is epic in size and design. Cataclysmic fusion shaped the prehistoric stone, etched the distinctive patterns into an intriguing arced crest. Wonderstruck, you stare from base to apex, and eventually, further, blinking at lapis blue sky. You step back.

"It's a birdtail!" you exclaim.

A pair of eagles drop from mystic heights, talons clasped to one another, spiraling, spinning in centrifugal abandon.

Your heart quickens.

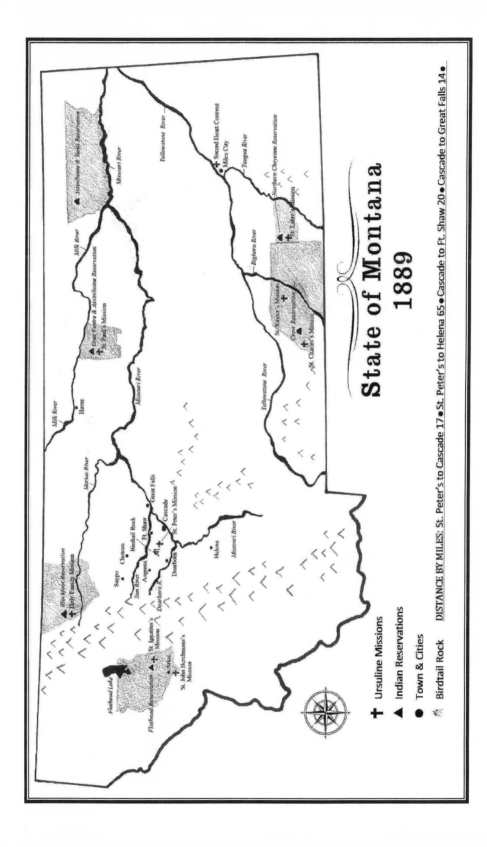

State of Montana
1889

Ursuline Missions ✝

Indian Reservations ▲

Town & Cities ●

Birdtail Rock 🌲

DISTANCE BY MILES: St. Peter's to Cascade 17 ● St. Peter's to Helena 65 ● Cascade to Ft. Shaw 20 ● Cascade to Great Falls 14 ●

Part One

1

HOME

WINTER 1893, THE BIRDTAIL PRAIRIE, MONTANA

*M*ary looked at her right hand and grumbled, "Should have known better than to use gloves out of the scrap pile—" Blood oozed from the shard of wood wedged deep in her palm. "I'll cut it out later—"

She peeled remnants of blood-soaked leather away from the wound, grabbed a hoof clipper from her toolbox, severed the jagged stick close to skin. A single snap. The other glove was easy to pull off and she clipped the sheath's nebs, all five—flipped it over and eased the makeshift casing across knuckles and the bothersome injury—pulled the cuff above her wrist.

A gust of wind sent shivers and she glanced upward. Glazed streaks of sky had assembled. Dogs barked in the distance. She tightened layers of crocheted wool about her neck, pursed her lips and examined the condition of her hitch wagon, gave its side a tap. A flat thud confirmed suspicions. "Rods are flexed, and the bunk is sagging."

She considered the contents—hand-hewn timber sent by a railroad man, a rich tycoon—the donation meant to replace the chapel's primary posts, and to complete ongoing construction of the Indian girl's boarding house before temperatures plummeted. She wiped her brow and leaned against the siding she'd crafted to upgrade the buckboard years earlier, shook her head and thought about the girls who had died needlessly. "Nuns can't ward off disease without warmth … If I leave the load here, half of it even, might not be able to haul the rest in time."

Hamstrings pulled as she bent over and hefted the last twelve-foot beam, steadied it upright against the tailgate, shouldered its straight edge single-handedly into the empty slot, second row up. "I asked them not to send wet cedar," she grieved. "Weighs close to marble. That's the problem." She stooped beneath the overhang, pressed her back against the timber and calculated poundage by the pressure laid onto her spine. "Like I said, too heavy."

She sighed and tossed thick straps across the felled grove of mighty giants, cinched and tied them off double, wet her lips and looked northwest. "Seventeen miles. Hauling freight on slathered ice is like stepping on eggs in a hurry. Wish Mr. Shepherd would hurry up with our supplies. He knows I'm out here waiting—" She reached beneath the wagon cross-seat, exchanged clippers for a hoof pick and attended to her team, ready and waiting. Bending into a straddled squat, she coaxed one horse after another to lift each leg, resting it upon her thigh while she scraped pebbles from the hoof's interior. Pushing upright, her comely figure camouflaged under layers of cotton, fleece and wool, she grazed her hip to make sure her pistol was in place, concealed in the goatskin lining of her skirt pocket.

Lightning, her favorite and lead of the four-horse team, nickered. She stroked his rippled neck and tousled his mane, ragged from rubbing against pine bark. "Looking a little scruffy, boy, but you need your extra fur coat." He struck his pedicured hoof against the ice-laden earth, tossed his head with a snort. "I know, you're ready. We'll get back to the mission soon."

The region's wagoner glanced across the street—to Cascade's cornerstoned building at the intersection of Front Street and Central, a pioneer reference point that housed two prominent establishments: the Odd Fellows Lodge upstairs, and beneath, filling the entire ground floor, the Shepherd & Flinn Mercantile. "Our merc is busier than a cattle drive," she said, as if Lightning was interested. "More customers crossing that threshold than all the saloons combined." She ran her hand across the length of his soft coat, patted his rump. "Most folks trek to town hungrier for company than supplies— huddle, they do, around the potbelly dawdling, competing to spin the tallest tale. Maybe that's what John Shepard is doing instead of packing my order."

Sudden movement darted across a second-story window. Mary straightened her skirt and crossed her arms. "Clara the busybody, up to it again. Trying to hide her meddlesome self behind lace curtains."

Acrid wood burned inside her palm. "Grates on my nerves, but I admit, I've got the advantage. She's inside tethered to a husband's domain, and as she is quick to point out, Mary Fields, the only colored citizen in our Birdtail territory, runs wild and free. Amok is her word. Only freighter worth a tinker, too, and I'm proud of it." Casting her gaze to the stationary silhouette, Mary waved, circumflexed a quarter-turn and surveyed the length of Central Avenue.

Noting decreased activity as time ticked by, she tapped her foot and sipped the day's frigid cold, tasted its burn and held it captive as she stared at the roadway's sleek shine built by iced layers—level, like prairie from a distance. Frozen swash had settled, filled the pits and shallows. "Street looks like one of those ice rinks back East. Wouldn't that be a sight, us wilderness dwellers skating in downtown Cascade—as if there's an up or down part." She lifted one foot and then the other, trod in place to keep warm. "Guess it's a bona fide town with the new post office. Got one store, one church, one schoolhouse, two sheep sheds and three saloons—looks like a tintype of life sequestered in the wild and wooly. Yep." She shot a glance toward the mercantile entrance, noticed that the summer screen door had not been removed. That fancy emporium took years to get here, she reminisced, built long after those abandoned shacks tailing the end of Central: shelter tacked up by folks waylaid—the seasonal Missouri River rise, and wagon train drifters. Hand raised to forehead, she squinted. "Those walls are gonna collapse before the next bitterroot bloom. Should rescue boards to patch the henhouse." Soothed by her own voice, she checked the weight and color of sky and sighed again.

Lightning lifted his head and whinnied, rubbed his face against her arm. Mary leaned in and whispered, "This stogie-sized splinter hurts like the dickens, boy. My pistol hand."

The mercantile door flew open. John Shepherd stepped across its threshold, slipping as he turned to close the solid window shutters he had built to swaddle heat inside. Secured to his satisfaction, the shop-keep paused to examine his prized addition, a large tin thermometer attached to the crossbeam above the steps—a beacon enlisting patronage and a contribution to the community, of sorts; everyone wanted to know how hot or cold it could get. Detained by glacial chills that squeezed his lungs and fogged his spectacles, he pulled the lenses from his brow and wiped the glass with a blue bandana tied loose around his neck. He set the bridge across his nose, checked to be sure that Mary had cleared the lumber from the street and efforted a ragged holler, "Nineteen below!" Adjusting temple ends across his ears, he added, "That's all, Black Mary. Tell Mother the girls' fabric is backordered. Sugar and everything else."

Mary raised her gloveless hand and nodded.

Irritated, she turned away, blew an even channel of breath and watched. The warmth did not follow the usual thermal path upward; instead, the opaqued breath feathered and dimmed. "Don't like the look of it," she said, recalling savage winds that had dumped nugget—no, fist-sized—chunks of hail that consequently chiseled unpredictable sinkholes—quagmires in her road that lurked, in her opinion, like ranch hand drifters—riff-raff who cluttered an otherwise pristine landscape.

Launching her strong body onto the cross-seat, she adjusted the length of her newly shod feet into place. Stuffed rags filled the toes of the machine-stitched, factory-tanned work boots branded personal by someone who had burned the capital letter initials L. C. M. into the cowhide. Tracking bull elk days earlier, Mary had spotted the treasure under thickets of kinnikinnik after pausing to admire the evergreen's blood-red berry clumps. Pulling on the bill of her tattered Union cap, she fingered wiry salt and pepper hair beneath its mottled leather band, dark from sweat and saddle soap. "Last check," Mary muttered, "Pistol? Yes. Rifle? Yes. Whiskey? Yes. Jerky? Yes." Holding her tongue in place, she twisted chapped lips to sound a practiced timbre that mobilized horsepower at will. "Chiick-chiick."

Reins snapped.

Outside of town, the Birdtail freighter and her team passed the cemetery, slowed for a sharp curve, and picked up speed on the road's gradual rise. The familiar eye-stretching panorama came into view, Montana's stretch of the Great Rocky Mountains—mighty glaciers and majestic pinnacles towering above all else, a monumental spine-tipped range extending past limits of human sight to the north and to the south—a wilderness, which by its very nature, provided and divided sustenance. *The Birdtail*, pristine land unfurled to the east, donned its own array of natural splendor—a vast extrapolation of primal, odd-shaped summits, prairie and buttes. "Glorious, no matter what," Mary whispered.

Miles of ice-cracking rhythm eventually lulled the driver into musings from her past. She ached for hardships endured by brave souls come to the region early on. Ursuline sisters had confided details of their arrival: outfitted with faith but with no firearms, money or food, they had spent their first winter crouched under a wagon bed, resigned to surrender frostbit toes and fingers to the barbarous blizzards. Other wayfarers recounted equally sorrowful chronicles.

"Folks came thinking it was gonna be easy," Mary said, and lifted her buttocks off the seat to avoid a hard bounce, an upcoming gully cut deep by subterranean hot springs. The load thumped. Wood scraped, the wagon swerved. Mary glimpsed back, snapped the reins and shouted, "Go! Giddyup!"

Hooves dug in for traction. Lightning lunged to toggle the course.

As the rig slowed, the driver settled her gear in place, grabbed a strip of jerky and returned to her musings: most of us struggled too hard already—and the Army didn't help—those poor Indian children—bad enough they were yanked from around here—babes shipped all the way from back East—that's just wrong. She exhaled and sunk her teeth into a strip of Angus loin, chewed while she listened to the crisp ra-ta-tat rumble that steadied as wagon wheels straightened into an open stretch of prairie, the easier part of the ride.

She rekindled a memory—herself and Mother Amadeus huddled in the front section of chapel, shortly after Mother had recovered from pneumonia—the reason Mary had jumped on the train in Toledo, determined to save her friend's life. Mother had squeezed Mary's hands and proclaimed: *It's true what the sisters declare—that my recovery is a miracle. A miracle born from the benevolent power of your healing abilities, once again. Thank you.*

Mary remembered her answer: *You'd do the same for me. You looked like one of those nativity figurines, fragile as porcelain lying on that straw bed. Sisters thought you were ready for last rites, but I knew different.*

She thought about the medicinals—how she had organized the remedies, the formulas, the constant administering—and revisited the unexpected moment when Mother proffered the precious covenant, a privilege shared by no one else. She had bid: *Just between us, when we're alone you don't have to call me Mother Amadeus. We're old friends and, after all, you're eleven years older than me. I could hardly be your mother. Since you're not a nun, and since no one else calls me Mary, it will be our... Just call me Mary, if you like.*

Mary smiled, thinking how stunned she had been to receive such an invitation from the Ursuline Reverend Foundress.

"Lord."

She grabbed another piece of jerky and recalled her reply: *Well, just between us then. I don't want anyone else thinking they can call you Mary. And I appreciate short words. Mary rolls off the tongue a whole lot easier than Mother Amadeus of the Heart of Jesus.*

We giggled like schoolgirls ... "It was our blood-sister pact," she said as she adjusted the harness reins through paired fingers. "Eight years ago."

Approaching her favorite panorama, anticipation stirred. She stretched forward to greet her beloved touchstone, the highest crag. Bruised clouds pulped by the brewing storm had tumbled across its belly and hovered, leaving only the mountain's peak in view. Disappointed, Mary slumped back and slowed the team for the next bend, the journey's halfway mark. Streaks of sun flashed through a rift. Glare blinded, stabbed her vision. Whipping sounds snaked a frightful snap—the kind of snap a strike of lightning makes when it splits trees.

The wagon's tongue had cracked.

The rig jack-knifed. Blasts of noise screeched. Flesh lunged, shrieks wailed. Beams and wagon parts flew upended—bashed mid-air, crashed below. Mary watched her body flail, helpless. Shiny particles blurred past. The voice in her mind begged for the safety of her horses—and fell away.

When she woke, she heard the sound of hollow tapping—hooves on ice. Flickering light coaxed her eyes to focus. She saw that her skirt was torn and thought blood was holding her knees together. Beads of sweat pimpled her forehead. She wondered why she was hot. Releasing the grip that bound her fetus curl, she viewed her body, sunk deep in slush—below fractured wood, jackstrawed. She scanned for open cavities, a way to the surface, and forced her mind to understand: the wagon rolled ... the horses ... how bad?

She heard herself bark, "Move!"

Sharp pain gripped her head, seared through her neck and shoulders. Nausea spiked. She swallowed, clenched a metal rod, sucked in and pulled up—squeezed and twisted her bulk through narrow crevices.

Once emerged, she jockeyed balance, broke a length of wood split from the doubletree. Only snowflakes moved, crystallized doilies dropping in silence. Relieved, she spotted the horses nearby—compassed at random, surprisingly tranquil.

Lightning whinnied.

"Come on, boy. Mary's here. You're a dandy, you are."

She coaxed the team together methodically, cautiously. There was no time to chase a runaway. She struggled to craft make-do halters from broken straps tangled in debris, slipping and stumbling until at last she had the horses tied off in pairs: Lightning with Bigg, Cricket with Blaze.

A trail of red splatter directed her to the gash in Cricket's hind leg. After examination, she assured, "Not too deep, missed the tendon, you'll make it, girl."

Mary extricated an ivory-handled sailor knife from trousers buttoned snug under skirt layers, cut an arms-length-strip of cotton from the hem of her slip and wrapped the mare's leg from fetlock to knee. Suddenly dizzy, she eased herself upright. "Where's my cap?"

She maneuvered the horses into line formation and faced them, leads coiled tightly in her ungloved hand, numb from fingertips to knuckles. She dug her boot beneath recent veils of snowdrift, located the frozen stratum, looked around. The dilemma offered no witnesses, no testimony, no rescue. She surveyed the snowscape—no bluff or gully to offer shelter. More than eight miles to safety, she calculated. We could stay here, try to get a fire going ...

Blaze came forward. Nuzzled against her.

The freighter closed her eyes. A sudden twinge prodded. She clutched her rifle—dropped the reins, searched for the whiskey vial she'd tucked in her overcoat pocket. Heat will help, she thought, touching the glass. How can it not be broken? She gazed ahead, aware of imminent dangers. This could be bad, real bad—can't do anything about the freight—can't be afraid, not one bit—my team will smell it. She stretched her muffler across her face and around her head. "Gotta pull foot, y'all. Let's get home."

The horses perked, hearing mention of home.

They shuffled through knee-deep powder, to the curve from which they had flung, the evidence now mantled with snow fluff, an idyllic familial scene accented by a smooth soft-ribboned promenade that wound gracefully along wilderness curves.

Mary ordered, "We've got to go by instinct. You lead the way, Lightning. I'll walk alongside." No search party's gonna chance what's coming, she kept to herself.

"Come on now—gotta walk. We'll turn into tombstones if we stay here."

Overhead, an onslaught of pewter clouds gestated into columns. Whiffs of dry air whirled across snow mounds, quipping tiny crystals airborne. Dusk retreated. Legendary north winds, known for hurling glaciers, amassed and fisted, launched into fury.

Hours passed.

Progress was slow. Mary and her champions battled the course, crimped between slipshod ice and arrows of sleet that pierced and pummeled. High-pitched wind-born howls besieged her throbbing head, numb and swathed in soggy homespun. Attempts to sing, console her comrades, were aborted.

"Hope someone locked the hen house door—girls better sleep in one room, stay warm." She seeped a thin breath. "Gonna have a cigar when I get home. Sisters can't come looking—I have all the horses!"

The team slowed and huddled, heads together.

Mary chided, "Not now! Come on, Bigg—all of you. Move! Sorry, Cricket, I know it hurts." She rubbed the mare's cramped hamstrings. "Please. We can't stop. You're strong—come on—hay and oats waiting. Hay and oats!"

They inched apart and bowed their necks to the storm, shivering. Mary praised, "Good girls, good boys, go home now."

Good girls, good boys at the mission, love them so. Especially when we picnic in summer—wildflowers so pretty—so warm—telling tales to the little ones. Six-year-old Annie's face pressed into Mary's mind; her image clear. "Sweet child, can't help but love her—she'll be worried. Don't worry, Annie."

Lightning bolts sparked the turbid blackness, allowing split seconds to identify landmarks. Gusts imploded, sucked brush in fitful bursts. She waited for another glimpse. A wave of hail hit from behind, knocked her reeling.

Bigg pulled the reins taut. She drew herself up, tripped and grabbed his mane. *These ice bullets are hitting a pattern. I can't see it, but I feel it,* her mind rallied. *Can't feel the cold now either, but I feel the pattern, like in snowflakes, like when I was cloaked in branches, invisible to the bounty hunters.*

A rabid howl cut the gale. Hearts seized.

She ordered without sound: *Stop. Wolves!*

They stopped.

Wait. Listen. Be invisible!

Panic gripped. Adrenaline surged. Arrested bodies hunched to restrain action.

A roll of thunder prolonged anxiety, giving unseen stalkers the advantage. A slurry of howls repeated their leader's declaration.

Sweat stung. Mary felt the feral lust, tongues wet for the taste. *Where are they?* She tucked down.

The pack flanked their prey—calibrated, camouflaged.

Have to put an end to it before … did they move? They're close. She held steady. *If the horses spook it'll be the end.*

The alpha leader signaled. Canis lupus warriors closed in.

Mary reached for the flask and sipped. As heat seeped down, she slid the bottle inside and pushed cartridges into the rifle chamber. Stretching her fingers open and shut, she pulsed heat to surface veins. She pulled halter leads close and instructed without words: *we are strong.*

Horseflesh pressed together.

She lodged the Winchester into her armpit, cocked the hammer and squinted.

Lightning reared and thrust a ferocious scream, hoofs aimed.

Mary spotted movement cutting the sleet, squeezed the trigger.

An ear-piercing squeal trilled beyond the blast.

"Wait! Come back!"

Rumbling aftershocks shimmied through the ice.

She scrambled to chase the stampeding team. Her boot caught and she stumbled, then touched, to verify. *Wolf. Warm, furry, dead. One carrion down.*

Retreating yips scattered.

She spun around.

Which way? "Not my horses!"

Her voice ricocheted.

"Lightning, Bigg!" she yelled, spun a half-turn. "Cricket, Blaze!"

She crouched, listened for the echo, uncovered and cradled her ear to catch sound waves altered by the gale.

"Has to be," she gasped, "sound is bouncing off the Belt Mountains. I know the way!"

Cinching last-chance-certainty to heart, she set course.

"Lightning—Bigg—Cricket—Blaze—I'm coming!

2

INTROSPECTION

SAINT PETER'S MISSION, MONTANA 1893 - 1894

Cloaked in pervasive darkness, a six-winters-old orphan edged her slender body against a narrow chapel window and looked out. There was no reflection, only cold blackness that seeped and grabbed. Angry at the blizzard, she sent her message into its confluent twist of fury, demanding one small favor—passage for her only friend, the dark elder called Mary.

Since arriving at the mission three months past, she had maintained a vow of silence weakened only when lulled in Mary's embrace. If she knew the English words, it remained her secret. According to Army documents, her name was Annie Saint Germain, classified as "survivor" rescued in a redskin uprising near Syracuse, New York.

Shortly after bedtime, the petite girl with waist-long braids had escaped the dormitory, dashed across the torrent-swept compound and slipped into the chapel. Water puddled beneath wet socks and her drenched nightgown. She kept watch at the strange portal made with white-medicine, fire and sand. Hours of vigil delivered no sign of Mary or her wagon. The girl wished she could see her friends the stars who would at least give her the time. Stricken by melancholy, she pressed her cheek against the frozen pane, strained to identify constellations or signs of human life. Past traumas sparked renewed sadness and a stream of tears melted ice crystals, bound her soft skin to the frigid glass.

Yanking free, she faced the black night again and willed her vision to see beyond. She composed a petition: Sky Woman and Great Turtle, please, I already lost everyone. You do not need her. I do. Consummating her prayer, she whispered the sacred words, "Ha Wen Neyu, Ha Wen Neyu, Ha Wen Neyu" (Creator, Creator, Creator).

"My goodness child, you startled me," gasped Mother Mary Amadeus on her knees at the altar. Prayer beads in hand, sheepskin draped over chilled joints, she relit her candle and turned to locate the source of intrusion. Rising to reprimand the girl from "tribe unknown," she moved closer and placed a hand on the child's shoulder.

"My dear, you're ice cold." The small sentinel made no reply, remained still and did not look up. Mother knelt next to the newcomer. "Don't worry," she said as she wrapped the wooly hide around her, "Mary Fields will come home. She always does." The voice was kind. Annie allowed her body to feel the touch.

Sister Gertrude limped up twelve steep, coarsely-cut stairs, to the chapel bell tower. As she stepped into the alcove, one leg hurled upward, apart from the other that slid on hardened ice until her gloved hand slammed against a wall. Beneath, the lantern puckered a last flicker. Squinting into blackness, she groped for the bell pulley and fingered instead, a solid shaft of ice that had coated the fibrous rope. She wrapped her shawl around it and launched. Her grip slid. She bent over and unlaced her boot, used it to fracture the slick seal, force breaks she could hear. Again, she flung herself, latched and let her full-weight fall, a human drop-pin.

A dull clang moaned in the pummeling sleet. Gertrude was glad this once, for a body heavier than those of her sisters. She knew the iron bell must rock into full swing before it could sound above the yowling wind and thunderclaps. In a hasty prayer she implored: Holy Mother, muscles like barbell men, please, and wrenched with divine power, she was certain. Chunks fell from the icicled rope, reclaimed. She yanked again. The bell lifted. Its knocker struck a victorious ring. "This will herald her home," Gertrude called as she steadied her strength into rhythm.

Immense quiet loomed. Morning calls from livestock were absent. A queer translucence glowed beneath tarnished clouds stretched sheer on the horizon. The numbing freeze had dropped to minus thirty-seven. There was no time to waste; Mary had to be found.

Inside the Indian girls' dormitory, roommates crouched into a huddle. Peeps of anxiety squeaked above heavy shushes and serious tones. One voice fell upon the other, each given equal weight of respect: "If they know how much I care for Mary, will they say I'm sinful—just pray for her—what if something bad has happened—keeps my secrets—tells me how to ask the nuns—gives my messages—send her strength—but is it a sin to love her so much? Shush. It isn't a sin to love the one that loves us."

Gertrude jogged back to the tower. She slung her weight against the still frozen yet operable rope and tolled the bell with renewed fervor, believing Mary would hear across the eerie silence.

Mother Amadeus and three sisters had left before light. Taking the lead, Mother had broken into a heavy trot and plowed through snowfields, undaunted. They knew that frostbite may have taken hold—or worse— could feel each other's silent prayers and listened as they traversed the altered landscape, desperate to hear Mary Fields' familiar holler: *Good morning sisters!*

"She's not where the road was," Mother huffed as she struggled to catch breath. "Most people circle to the right when they're lost—that would be to our left. Let's go."

"How do you know that?" asked one of the nuns.

"Margaret's father is a Blackfeet scout. He told me."

As the quartet of determined believers pushed on, they listened with strained acuity and realized, eventually, that the only sound disturbing the blizzard aftermath was they, themselves. Undeterred, eight feet crunched through the brittle-topped snow, hollowed a bass rhythm joined by higher-toned melodies of rustling and swishing—triad chords of garment layers moving across the other: thin cotton on thick wool thrusting, shifting. A third level of harmony peaked, barely audible: crosses scaling each necklace chain—private pendulums of faith connected.

Two hours passed. The sisters tramped up a small rise that led toward a valley gulch and the Sun River tributary Mother had christened Ursula's Creek. Panting, Sister Anna covered her mouth to minimize the burn of alpine air. Clara tightened her grip on the knapsack of provisions. Hooding their eyes to see through glare, the team spotted something. A dark lump. Halfway down.

"Mary!" they screamed.

She had collapsed face-first. An etched rim of crusted snow darkened the outline of her tragedy; layers beneath stole her sustenance and trickled downstream.

Black skirts swirled. Carefully, they rolled her over to examine. Sister Seraphine covered the body with a blanket; Mother squeezed a bare wrist; Anna laid an ear to Mary's chest. Clara stared, trembling, overcome with fear.

Motionless, Mary's flesh had turned pallid. Her thick black eyelashes and eyebrows lay encased in strips of clear freeze. Crows flew about, cawing. A pulse was detected. "She's alive," Mother whispered. "Mary, wake up!" Hearing desperation in her own voice, she quivered and barked, "Let's get her home. Now!"

The nuns slid her stiff body onto three layers of army issued bedrolls; they stretched socks and mittens over grayed frostbit toes and fingers and eased a wool cap over hair matted in hard blood. Mother ordered, "Anna, here. Carry this side." She pointed. "And you, Seraphine, grab that side. I'll hold the top." They moved into position. "We're going to carry her home. Don't let her neck push up. We must be strong to keep her supine. Clara, to her feet. Clara, hold both ends of the blankets and don't let her drag. We'll move in unison, fast. One, two, lift. Go."

They forged ahead, a trained regiment maneuvering like clockwork—gears and cogs rotating in synchronized formation, keenly aware how each linked moment could determine destiny.

Meanwhile, Gertrude coddled frayed nerves into purpose, directing: prepare warm shelter for Mary, for her consecrated body no matter its condition. Alive or dead, she'll need a comfortable place to heal. Or transcend.

Blankets in hand, she opened the door to Mary's cabin and discovered patches of ice adhered to the flat-board walls. Dismayed, she rushed back and prepared the mission guest room instead. Fanning flames under split logs stacked in the potbelly, a crackling fire soon devoured dense tamarack and supplied chunks of red coal to radiate. An iron kettle filled with water, sizzled on the stove's griddle, spouting mist into the arid air. She pondered over what kind of herbal medicine Mary might prescribe if she were doctoring. Perhaps their neighbor Sycowastakapi would know; the daughter of a local Piegan-Blackfeet chief and wife of Scottish homesteader Ed Lewis, Sycowastakapi had provided roots and herbs for healing before, and they had worked. Gertrude instructed one of the girls to sled to the Lewis ranch, promised cookies for a swift return.

Extreme weather frequently forced travelers to take shelter at Saint Peter's Mission. Joseph Bickett, an ex-military man employed part-time as a farrier in Cascade, had bunked with the Jesuits and overslept. Having been waylaid before, he preferred taking his meals with the sisters, a field's length away. He'd locate Sister Gertrude, whose name he had memorized in appreciation of her cooking, beg some grits.

After listening to the sisters' concerns, he decided to head out, find the mission horses and their driver, the Nigger Mary. He thought the retrieval might be a good Christmas gift for the nuns—a man named Joseph rescuing a gal named Mary. He grinned and adjusted his faded regulation cap above his ears.

Having saddled his mount, the former army scout slipped a shiny boot into the stirrup, pressed and swung upward. Immediately, he spotted four Ursulines in familiar yards of garb struggling to transport a large object above thigh-high snow. He kicked the broad ribs beneath him, and his horse complied—lunged through blizzard mounds and barricades of ice that cost him precious time. He jumped from this horse, looked at Mary and masked his concern for the sake of the nuns. Her grayed complexion spiked memories from blood-soiled battlefields.

Desperate voices begged him to hurry. All resource shot to his legs. He scooped the cocooned body into his arms. Holding Mary less the radiance of life, heavy from soaked coverings and lost consciousness, he loped across the final stretch of snow and deposited her in a heated cell at the end of the nuns' cavernous stone building.

Finding his way back to Gertrude's kitchen, Joseph draped his jacket over a chair and devoured leftovers, lingered long enough to learn that Mary was alive. He sipped a long drink of water and stacked biscuits around the ham hock he'd placed in the center of a dishcloth—provisions for his self-appointed reconnaissance mission. Square knotting opposite corners, he pulled the bundle taut, filled his canteen with vinegar-laced water that would not freeze, then looped the items together with a leather strap he'd attach to his saddle. Rushing outside he whistled for his steed. The nuns' horses were still on the loose and daylight was waning.

It was well over an hour before Joseph sited signs that piqued his interest.

Wolf tracks, on the run, without prey. He followed. Evidence on a prevalent slope showed two wolves gaining speed. He reckoned that their marks would lead to more wolves, a pack at large, hungry—suspected the pair was among those involved in Mary's misfortune. Only last week he had tracked a seven-foot gray wolf in the Belt Mountains. He narrowed his brow, patted his horse.

For Joseph, tracking was the compass of life, the center from which all truth could be discovered. Unraveling mystery by understanding sole prints was satisfying, often surprising. He challenged himself to ferret the whole tale that could only be understood if one interpreted the details correctly—the nuances laid visible to those with the knowing and the patience. Identifying beasts was the mere beginning; a true story emerged with subjective examination: on which edge were the tracks weighted, caved or ridged—distance between and patterns thereof, changes made when mingled with weather and time and countless other variables—where the animal traveled and why.

He became irritated when he thought about scientists and preachers who declared, presumptuously in his opinion, that beasts were brainless and inferior, limited to action and reaction. Joseph's conclusions were based on experienced observation and he believed that it wasn't the four-legged animals who lacked common sense.

As beams of sunlight sliced through laden strata, the edges of Joseph's mouth curled—tracks were easier to read with shadows to mark the borders of boot, hoof and paw indents. He cornered the next bend. There it was—the braided interplay of species—star-crossed imprints of battle. Death.

Primal senses heightened, Joseph circled the scene on foot, kneeled to the ice for details. The vivid drama unraveled. He confirmed that the carcass belonged to the alpha wolf after comparing its size, sex, and age to the others; this evidence proved that Mary's sharp shooting had diverted a well-executed ambush. Rising familiarity made his bones ache. He felt for them all.

Backtracking both parties, Joseph deciphered: wolves had stalked Mary and her team for hours—just far enough away so that the horses didn't pick up their scent. He thought them fortunate not to have realized the magnitude of peril shadowing every move.

Returning to the battle scene, he appraised: would have been a victorious kill for the wolves, their territory, nine of them. Took terrified horses to bolt and split-scatter after working as a team for years. A darkening sky chilled. Joseph fastened his jacket, untied the cache of food. In the saddle once more, he tracked the horses' escape, examining ice hacked by the rawest impulse.

By dusk, Joseph returned to the mission with a forensic account and three horses. The Mother Superior met him at the door. She took his dripping overcoat and greeted, "Thank goodness you're back. Would you like your boots dried? We can put them by the stove."

"No, but thank you Ma'am, I mean Sister." Joseph became nervous in cramped quarters, particularly when flanked by what appeared to be herds of women underfoot. He wished for his hat so he could cock the rim low over his brow, but the nun had hung it on a peg by the door. Worried faces wrapped in cloth flocked toward him. He looked to his boots and crossed his arms. "I came to report on my tracking, Mother Amadeus, Ma'am."

"Yes, thank you, Joseph. Would you mind if we go to the chapel to talk?" She didn't want the entire mission family listening to what might be a gory exposition.

Joseph was relieved—more space, less women. Sisters Seraphine and Clara grabbed their wraps and hurried behind. He kicked ice from the chapel door sill, waved the nuns through and slammed the door shut. He rushed his words, "Well, Ma'am, lucky that it were a blizzard, yes'm, cause the sleet done froze the details clear."

Mother questioned the tracker's perception of luck but remained silent, waited for more.

"Found most the horses at the Moran place. They fed 'em and brushed 'em down—real neighborly. Offered me beef stew and a seat by the fire. Real shame Nigger Mary collapsed only an acre or so east of his place— close, but far enough to die just the same."

The lines of Mother's forehead deepened. "Where's Bigg?" she asked. We saw you bring the three, but there—"

Joseph coughed and fixed a gaze on the bronze statue of Jesus centered on the altar. "Well, yes'm, Ma'am, the sorrel mare you calls Bigg, I'm sorry, Ma'am, she didn't make it. The wolves got her. They dragged chunks of her—" He noticed a young woman twisting her lips. "Oh, sorry. Well, some of her is left. I'd bury her for ya, but the ground is hard as an axe." When there was no reply and three pairs of eyes continued to gawk, he offered more. "Well, she put up a good fight. Tracks showed her rearing and bucking in the gully, where the creek narrows. She was surrounded. Wolves is hungry too."

"Could you tell what happened to Mary?" Seraphine asked.

He looked at his boots, listened to mice scurry. "Them wolf tracks circled Nigger Mary and her team for miles—like the wolves were escorting them—like royalty or something 'cept they was being hunted. Real lucky you only lost one. Tracks tell me there were nine wolves, and that's a lot of fight." He rubbed his arm. "The other mare is lame; rear leg is cut. Looks like it'll heal up with some tending."

"Thank you Joseph. Bless you for your kindness," Mother said, suddenly exhausted.

"How's Nigger Mary doin'? I seen blood where she fell. She walked long and far, after. She took that alpha wolf down with one shot through the heart."

"She did? My ..." Mother noticed the posture of her associates stiffen. "Mary is resting. The wound on her head isn't deep. Frostbit hands and feet."

"She's a great gal, Nigger Mary. Well, I'll be gettin' on now. Will stay with the Jesuits if they ... would you let Sister Gertrude know to expect me for breakfast, if that's all right?" He nodded and reached for the rim of his hat, pinching air.

"Good night," the women murmured, grateful for but reeling from distressing facts that could make tired bodies want to curl up under warm covers and sleep past noon.

Mary Fields began to surface from dreams of Big Dipper constellations where family and friends were alive and talkative. Bright air fluttered. She felt her eyelids blink and caught a reflection of herself in luminous orbs she recognized. Annie.

"Mary. Ucsote (Grandmother)," Annie whispered. She touched Mary's arm above the dark engorged hands Gertrude had been soaking with herbal wraps. In her heart, Annie thanked Great Turtle. A single tear slid to the tip of her chin.

Mary thought she was watching herself cry over the death of her parents. She felt breath rise to her chest and drifted back into sleep.

Annie bolted toward the door. Spotting Mother Superior at the end of the corridor she called, "Mother! Mother!"

The nun rushed to Mary's bedside, fearing the worst. She checked for a pulse and turned to Annie. "Nothing's changed. She's just sleeping."

"She was awake. Will she stay alive?"

Mother waited for the pounding in her chest to stop. She knew Annie spoke the truth—only something paramount would break the child's resolve to remain silent. She watched Annie twist a strand of loose hair. "Mary Fields will be fine."

Annie moved toward the end of the bed, placed her hand near Mary's leg.

"I think she could use some help, though," the nun suggested.

Annie's trust teetered. She gave the nun a blank gaze and waited for orders she would not like.

"Would you stay with her, let me know when she is awake?"

Surprised, she nodded.

"Do you understand?"

Annie's throat itched. She swallowed deep and spoke clearly, "I understand. Thank you."

When Mary woke the second time it was midnight. She recognized her friend Mary Amadeus, who was smiling. Each searched the other for information. "Mary," Mother said, "I am so thankful. You're home safe and sound." Annie sat cross-legged in the shadows.

"Oh my God, I couldn't save them!" Mary gasped. "Are they all right?"

Mother patted Mary's shoulder. "Yes." All right is relative, she thought, knowing that one of the horses was "all right" in God's hands.

"Are you sure?" Mary insisted, trying to sit up.

"Yes." She glanced to the girl. "Everything is fine. I want you to take this—arnica powder, under your tongue. Open up."

"Oh," she groaned, "bruised but not broken?"

"You'll heal. You are going to rest, just like you forced me to, remember? No arguing. You are to stay in this bed and sleep. I mean it."

Mary dozed off before she could rally the energy to disagree.

Waning moonlight offered solace when she opened her eyes again. She lifted her rifle arm, seeking the source of pain. Swollen fingertips reached a bandage at the back of her head; blood oozed at her touch. She heard crackling and glanced to identify the source glowing in the corner. Her head ached. It hurt to breathe. Blizzard memories toppled forward: the wagon crashing, horses on the run, wolf howls. Heat burst into veins. She kicked covers off and was shocked to see her palms and forearms wrapped like amputated stumps. A wave of fear gripped. What would I do, she thought, if I'd been hurt really bad? She dropped into fitful sleep as embers turned to ash.

She didn't remember those thoughts the next morning, but they returned when Mother Amadeus entered the room and began talking. "Mary, I don't want to worry you, but when you are feeling better I want us to make a plan about your future. If anything happens while I'm gone to the other missions, the sisters will care for you of course, but I think more security is in order."

"What?" Mary swooned.

Gaining momentum, Mother emphasized, "I want you to be taken care of if ever you need help—including the help of Christ our Lord, who I know always assists you. Will you come to chapel when you're able? It would be a good example to the girls, as well—to see you humble yourself before the Lord Almighty. We are so grateful you survived." She paused, recalling moments when each had shared private thoughts to the other and composed a particular prayer: Dear Lord, I don't know how to define Mary's style of religion—I just ask that you reserve her reception in Heaven. You know how good she is.

Mary closed her eyes but Mother knew she was still listening. "The Lord Jesus wants to save your body *and* your soul. As your friend, Mary, I ask you to consider your spiritual salvation. You are always saving us from catastrophe; let us comfort you. Will you come to Mass? Partake in communion?"

Mary raised her head. "I hear you, my friend. I'll give your words serious thought." Security, she rankled, surely she remembers I'm to live here the rest of my life. And I thought we'd agreed on religious rights.

Four strangers loitered at the edge of the mission grounds, hands waving and heads bobbing. "Are you sure this is the right building?" barked a cowhand perched upon a draft horse, legs spread and aching from the long ride on stock not intended for saddles.

His friend seated on the flatbed wagon shot back, "Yes sir, we want the Ursuline Academy, not the Jesuits'." He pointed to the large stone building on their left. "Saint Angela's. The one they gave a keystone ceremony for last year—"

"What do it matter what building is what? We're going to the barn anyways," bellowed the other rider.

"It'll matter, wait and see."

"Let's move," the driver ordered, snapping his whip.

A short time later, heavy knocks pounded on the back door—the entrance for deliveries and friends who knew the way. Gertrude hurried from the chopping block and pried the door ajar—ice had begun to seal.

"Ruthless cold it is," she claimed to the man who filled her doorway. His beard was dark and spongy, laced with ice, dripping. Hazel eyes caught her attention and when he squinted, she noticed crow's-feet nested permanent.

"Top of the morning to you," the man greeted.

"Come in, come in," Gertrude bid, unsure if she had met him before. She twitched as three more men shuffled into view but continued to wave them indoors. They lowered their heads as if the entrance was cut for a cabin and kept their eyes to the floor.

She led them to her kitchen, eager to share the spacious warmth of hearth and home. The crew cowered awkwardly and glanced to the tall man in charge who said, "I don't know if you remember me, Mother. I'm Iain, from east of town—the lumber mill. We all heard about Nigger Mary's crash and went to check on damage done. If there was food, it's gone. We salvaged the timber, fine wood it is, brung it here for you ladies, Ma'am. Afraid the wagon is busted. Where should we stack them pillars?"

"I'm Sister, Sister Gertrude; Ursuline Mothers teach." She straightened her apron and fiddled with a pair of clothespins in her pocket. "All of you sit down, please. I'll get something to take the chill out." She didn't appreciate him addressing her Mary as "Nigger Mary" and wished she could set him straight without getting into trouble. But they had gone out of their way…

The foursome waited. They stared at skillets and pots hung from heavy iron hooks that protruded through ancient granite. Massive blocks of sculpted stonework sparked visions of castles, knighthood, and torture chambers. Also intriguing to the laborers, was an enormous fire pit cut into the wall that featured an unusual roasting device with adjustable clamps, prongs and grills.

"This kitchen is bigger than my whole place," the short man declared.

"Must be Catholics everywhere to raise enough money to build a mansion like this: three stories, good masonry. Stark from Sun River did it, I heard tell. Look how high the ceilings are."

Gertrude ignored their jabbering as she clanged iron efficiently, prepared a simple meal from leftovers.

Iain's cousin whispered, "Hope we are lucky enough to get some of that yeast bread they make." He rubbed his belly.

"Yeah, I heard it was good."

"So that's what you meant," said the one who had questioned their destination.

His comrades grinned. The cousin explained, "Had some at the Jesuit place yonder once. His tongue slid across his upper lip. "They said the girls bake it twice a week—figured this place would be more likely to serve it up."

His buddy laughed, "Must 'a been really good for you to remember all that. Is that why you came with us?"

"Want I should tie ya up on that spit there?" He motioned to the hearth. "Big enough for two hogs or you."

"That's enough fellas or they'll throw us out," Iain barked. "Ain't used to roughhousing here, I imagine."

When Iain and his men, stuffed full from the windfall of corned beef, toast, and currant jelly, excused themselves to stack the wood and return to Cascade, Gertrude took a moment to gather her thoughts. She couldn't remember the task they had interrupted—surely it had to do with food. She sat down, frowning. From her vantage point at the head of the twenty-foot table, formerly a sweet-scented yellow pine, she pulled a worn Christmas postcard from the other pocket of her apron—correspondence from her birth sister, Vera, postmarked Rome, Italy. Italian script, translated, declared: … *I'm proud you're an Ursuline, offering Christian education and culture to Amerika's uncivilized heathens* …

"I'm not sure they're all heathens," Gertrude fussed, imagining her distraught sister twisting a hankie, worried that Gertrude was toiling over an open campfire, forever smudged with charcoal and bear fat, fending off wild beasts and redskins. Should tell her it isn't like the old days, she mused, when snow blew through our shack walls and hunger pains crushed like menstrual cramps.

She considered Mother's claim—that the new academy house shone as testimony from devout faith and the generosity of loyal supporters. Drumming her fingers, Gertrude concluded: took us years of life and death struggle, living in accommodations disgraceful and unsanitary—that's more upsetting than confronting frostbite and wolves and grizzlies. Vera would agree: seven years' penance merits a glorious kitchen, from God's grace.

She set her clothespins on the table, crossed her right leg and swung it to a childhood tune. Having scrubbed her new commercial ovens with cider vinegar, she admired their capacity, glad for the saving of precious time and labor they would provide, as it was her responsibility to bake for the entire Saint Peter's community, including the expected increase of mouths to feed now that Saint Angela's qualified for federal funding. Each morning Gertrude sent a prayer of gratitude to Heaven and to Miss Katharine, the rich lady who had donated the kitchen money. She knew it was greedy, but she also wished for a mattress, and likewise for her sisters, though Mother Superior had said that if sleeping on the floor provided young women with an education, it was a victorious sacrifice.

As for contributions from the Birdtail, Gertrude had an inkling that Mary Fields solicited help from the locals. She recalled several conniption fits when Mary riled on about the Indian girls' living conditions, failing to see reason until the wood flat board dormitory called *The Opera House,* was under construction. Don't know why it's called Opera, she mused. "Oh! It's the tally, the tally of sundries—that's what I was doing."

Gertrude's suspicions were correct. Mary didn't share the Ursuline perspective on voluntary suffering. She claimed she'd already had her plateful while serving in slavery most of her life. When detained in Cascade, she made it a point to casually convey the sisters' immense need for basic necessities at Saint Angela's. Angling proprieties of religion, she cast, "Something more comfortable than a frozen plank to sleep on might lighten the nuns' burdens, earn generous parishioners extra attention in the hereafter."

Mary woke sweating with fever. She thought it was her first night back (it was the third) and was upset to discover bruises on all limbs. And what was she doing in the guest room? Pleased to find her little companion wrapped tight in a quilt beside her, Mary pulled the bed covers up and imagined

Annie's former family snuggled under warm furry hides inside a tribal longhouse, though that kind of life was gone for good. Then she remembered Mary's words about confession and communion, and her chest hurt.

Mother Mary worked long after the moon had passed its apex, stationed at her oval mahogany desk—a peace offering sent from the Cleveland Motherhouse after its Superior had adamantly refused to send more Ursuline novices to Montana. By flickering candlelight, Mary Amadeus scrutinized the docket of monthly reports dispatched from each of her Montana missions. That meant seven reports to read and one to compose for Saint Angela's Academy at Saint Peter's Mission.

The first three relayed satisfactory progress. As she opened the fourth parcel, poor penmanship flagged her attention. A plea for help from the housemother at Saint Francis Xavier Mission on the Crow Reservation read:

> *Agnes Brewer, our newest Sister who arrived six months past, told Emma Collins, a white boarding student, to tell her parents that she, Agnes, is forced to work and gets nothing to eat. What should I do?*

Mother heaved a tired sigh and reminded herself that situations such as this were unavoidable. Progress was easily sabotaged, given the temperamental relations between Indians, Army, Church, and State. She decided to travel across the vast Territory as soon as passage was possible, regretting how sequestered life amidst deplorable conditions and hostile environments could drive even the sweetest demeanor to delirium. If only she could convince sisters to remain for a decade, secure divine tenure for themselves as they protected and educated the savage innocents in their time of need … She paused to admit to her Savior: if I did not receive immense solace and reinforcement through prayer, I would have gone mad by now, too. I'll take a moment, go to chapel. Perhaps prayer will bring an inspired solution to Agnes's affliction.

She dashed across the compound, gripping her cape blown open from blasting winds. The chapel door creaked as she pulled. Scents of burnt wick and paraffin wax calmed a chilled quiver. She eased through the dark guided by memory and touch—located matchsticks—struck friction. Candlelit auras sweetened the night's solitude.

She slid the wrap from her shoulders, shook it, spread the wet wool over the end of a pew and stepped to her usual spot, front and center. She began with the Lord's Prayer, proceeded by composing particulars, and then entered a relaxed silence that would in time, usher in a timeless serenity. Tension subsided, and her body rocked gently—until she felt a presence.

Startled, she pulled back to identify an unexpected image rising from the stillness; it was her child-self christened Sarah Theresa Dunne, an apparition of the young woman prior to her vows, her commitment to Christ and the Ursuline order—a union that had necessitated a new name of religion.

Mother Mary challenged the presence: What are you doing here? I am praying.

She heard Sarah's voice, a tender intonation that had belonged to her:

I am here because there is still hurt inside you. To be a true servant of God you cannot have personal desires mixed in your heart.

To examine the furtive chance that the claim might hold merit, Mary Amadeus took a deep breath and bowed, releasing judgment and ideas.

The young woman's voice advised:

Do you realize that your search for God was driven in part by your-our need for love and acceptance from family, corrupted by hurtful feelings of abandonment? That is the reason you chose to help young girls—so that they don't feel pain in their hearts as we did.

Mary adjusted the weight on her knees and dove towards holy surrender, the promise of truth.

The spirit of Sarah continued:

But they do feel pain in their hearts. You must follow the Lord's guidance through prayer and purity of surrender without question, the way the first Ursuline women tended their destiny toward a higher purpose.

The darkness under her closed eyes spiraled deeper, inviting entry into passageways of sacred time, available by and in direct proportion to her ability to trust unconditionally. Her body softened and swayed gently.

The sweet voice assured:

Not everyone is a soldier like you. Some are not orators, scholars. Some learn by doing, by relationships with family and the earth, like Mary Fields. She follows a path of spirit as sacred as your own. Likewise for the Indian girls. Give them more than an education. If you pray deeply you will see their true needs.

Mother shivered. She felt full, malleable, liquid even, like wine runneth over ... and grateful. She began a new prayer, promising to remember and love her childhood self, Sarah. She beseeched her Lord God for guidance to learn how to love with heightened compassion and awareness and added, "And I pray that I may surrender all judgment for the way in which I attempt to bring Mary Fields to her soul. Perhaps you have given me Mary's friendship as a way to experience religious faith from a broader point of view. Amen."

Half-awake, Mary squinted at stars through half-drawn curtains. Raw and exhausted, she considered a single thought: What if Mother's right? What if my soul will be damned and gone to Hell if I don't embrace the church and confess, commune, pray their way? They have, after all, spent their whole lives practicing religion, and maybe they do know best. "I am not perfect, far from it," she mumbled, thinking, maybe my cigar smoking and impatience are my sins, my pitfalls … but I can't be a nun. Can't help them that way. Communion, confession, she mused, staring at red coals. Love and compassion come from looking at the big picture, living best as one can. Making rules and forcing obedience is too much like slavery, and I don't believe the wonder of life can be ordered—divided into categories of good, evil, white, colored. I pray a different way. I aim to stay here with the girls who need love as much as education; they need to remember their families and roots, in my opinion. This is my family—everyone except for Reverend Brondel. Still, maybe I should do as Mary says, I don't know. I did join the church in Toledo.

It was another weekday and mission life had returned to its routine. By nine-thirty, Indian girls had attended mass, finished morning chores, and were mid-way through breakfast. Classes would begin at ten o'clock. As they gulped the last of their porridge, a deep-throated voice boomed from out-of-sight, "Good morning mothers, sisters and young ladies!"

Anxious to see everyone, Mary limped down the corridor wearing an ensemble resembling a patchwork in-progress. Unable to locate her wool britches, she had thrown a faded green skirt and torn red sweater over her pink polka-dot nightgown and topped her bandaged head with her favorite herringbone cap, gingerly affixed.

Passed through the doorway, she swerved into an empty chair and waved her arms to the throng of women who appeared delighted to see her. She sipped a breath and continued, her voice strong as ever, "I'm up and ready—repaired and restored. I'll be dancing a jig in a couple of days!" She scanned the room. "Are the horses tended? My chickens? Have you been collecting the eggs?" Heads bobbed, some making mental notes to learn the meaning of jig. Glances to the nuns sought permission to respond.

"Mary!" sisters exclaimed, Mother Amadeus loudest of all. Shouting at the table was forbidden, but when the nuns broke the rule, the girls kept to their seats and dared, "Good morning, Mary!" Postulants and sisters scurried to greet their brave soldier.

"Stay put for awhile, Mary," Gertrude huffed, arriving first, "you're still quite bruised."

Mary folded her arms to avoid contact.

"You're a sight for sore eyes," said Sister Clara, beaming.

Sister Anna grimaced, unable to move her stare from the patch of bloody blisters that pocked Mary's fingers where the freeze had taken its bite. She stepped back.

"We're happy to see you up," Sister Seraphine cried, pushing into Anna's place.

"Mary!" young voices cheered in the background, longing to break from the bench and run to her arms.

"I've got to go check on the horses. Are they all right? Blaze, Lightning—?"

A hand touched her shoulder. "In due time," Mother said. "First thing you're going to do is enjoy a hearty breakfast. "Sister Gertrude would you—"

"I'd be happy to."

Mother stepped away, clapped her hands and instructed, "Girls, stack your dishes and get to class." Skirts twirled to the clamor of footsteps. Annie cowered at the sideboard's end, her intent obvious. "You too, Annie," Mother bade.

Annie left but hid behind the door, listening.

"Sister Gertrude, do you know what happened to my clothes? I need them."

"They're being stitched. They were torn and dirty."

Gertrude slipped her own homespun knitted shawl from her shoulders and tenderly placed it on Mary who gladly accepted, pulled it snug around her neck. "Well, can I help you fix that hearty meal Mother mentioned? I'm mighty hungry."

"No, you come sit by the oven and get warmed up. Come on." She extended her arm. "Take it slow, lean on me." As they inched toward the kitchen, the Ursuline cook chatted, "I'll fry some of those tasty Rhode Island browns you and your hens provide so well. And some bacon—this is a special occasion!"

Mary settled at the kitchen table, dizzied by the flurry of activity.

Proud to have come from strong peasant stock, Gertrude pushed up her sleeves and clanked her original "bacon and eggs" tempo at the griddle. She had coveted a desire to play the kettledrum and had been disappointed to learn that the instrument was not among those included in Saint Angela's music program. Let's see now, she organized: bacon crispy, biscuits left over. "Oops," she said. Having begun kitchen duty before dawn when she had offered up her usual petition, her kyrie eleison that asked for the Lord's forgiveness, now she whispered an abridged version as she set to work: "Sorry, Lord, can't keep my sleeves over my hands like a good Ursuline when I'm cooking—you understand—forgive me?"

Yielding to the unusual separation from routine, Mary explored a moment of detached objectivity. She examined the physical habitat of the home she had fought so hard to return to and wondered whether the tremendous resolve and energy required to survive would ever become easier.

The convent, bare and utilitarian in its beginning, had become homey. Handcrafted additions had been added to its walls. Embroidered Bible parables, cross-stitched with colorful thread and mounted into homemade wooden frames, were displayed in every room. Lace curtains had been fashioned from remnants of hand-me-down tablecloths. The creative works had been constructed by students learning new skills. Copper pots and kettles almost too pretty to use, hung above cast iron stoves.

Could see your face in them, if you had a mind to and scrubbed long enough, she mused. Those special ovens donated by Miss Drexel are good, too—reminds me of the ovens lined up in the ex-master's kitchen. *Big enough to bake you in*, gnawed an unwanted memory. This kitchen is cozy, she decided as she rested one arm on the table, the right equipment and a welcome place to feast eyes and appetite.

Abruptly, her foreman-self interrupted. She looked to Sister Gertrude. "Is the freight all right? Did anyone pick it up? Was anyone else hurt? Tell me what happened, Gertrude."

Gertrude faced Mary, wet hands on sturdy hips. "Well, Mary, you were in bad shape. We thanked the Almighty to have found you alive. You were face down in the snow, you were. That little one, Annie, has been by your side ever since we got you back, and you won't believe it, but she spoke, spoke English, she did! Said to me clear as day, 'Don't worry, I will feed her.' I didn't even realize it at first because it sounded so normal-like, you know? I think she only talked so she could be with you. She's been by your side for the past five days."

"Five days! It's been five days? Oh my—"

Mary struggled to stand.

"Don't you even think about it," Gertrude ordered. "Everything is taken care of, and your eggs are done."

She eased down. Gertrude placed a mug of hot coffee on the table followed by a large steaming platter, the aromas sumptuous. "Mary, did you hear the bell tolling?"

Mary stared, her expression, blank—then frowned attempting to recall as she took a bite of toast, set it down. "I remember bells ringing in my dream, over and over. They wouldn't let me fall asleep."

"No, not a dream. That was us, Mary! We were ringing the bell for you, praying that you would hear and find your way home."

"Oh. The church bell, in the steeple." She stroked her forehead. "I think I remember. That was you, Sister Gertrude?"

Gertrude smiled.

Memories began to crystallize. "Thank you."

Using fingertips, the only parts of both hands not wrapped, to lift the mug, she sipped the aromatic drink, thought some more.

"I knew you would find me when I heard that bell. Couldn't tell where or how far away it was, though—weather was fearsome. Forgot until you just asked. Yes, the bell."

Struggling to maneuver the fork and spoon, anxious to devour every last morsel of her breakfast, Mary looked up and asked, "Gertrude, before the blizzard, a chunk of cedar found its way into this hand." She raised her right palm. "Who cut it out and wrapped it this way? And what day of the week is it?"

"Sister Clara and Friday."

"All right."

Minutes later, only scattered crumbs and smeared egg yolk remained on her plate. She set her napkin on the table, scooted the smooth-log bench, built by herself, back. "That was delicious, Sister." Starting to push up, she winced, and winced again.

"Mary, there's just one other thing." Gertrude untied her apron. "I don't think you ought to go outside yet—" Gertrude started toward the door.

Mother Amadeus entered, list in hand.

"Mother," Gertrude said, "I was just going to tell Mary about the horses."

"What?" Mary hollered. Tearing through pain to stand, she glared from one to the other. "What about the horses?" She fixed her eyes on Mary Amadeus. "I thought you said they were all right!"

Mother rushed to her friend, held her shoulders, looked her squarely in the eyes. "Mary, it's no news to you, after the life you've lived, that there is a time and season for everything."

"What? Who's dead?"

"I'm sorry, Mary. Bigg didn't make it."

"But you—"

"I couldn't tell you when you were still in shock and in danger. I'm sorry, but you would—"

"Was it the wolves? Did they get her?"

"Yes. She's been buried. One of the town men, Mr. Cornell, buried her. The blacksmith, Mr. Bickett, found her and brought the rest of the team home."

Mary shrank. Her favorite mare, named after the talisman Big Dipper that guided her escape from Tennessee to Ohio, to freedom. Dead. She dropped to the bench. Nausea gripped.

Mother and Sister Gertrude stood by, silent. Though wanting to soften the blow, they understood that loss was personal and there would be shock waves to endure. Gertrude had adopted western imagery for their times of hardship—imagined a bronco-busting cowboy sticking to his mount until it tuckered, exhausted. Mother's mind pulsed from echoes of Sarah's advice— *pray deeply, you will see their true needs*—She turned to her suffering friend.

"Mary, could you rest for awhile before you go out into the cold?"

Mary sucked a deep breath and said, "No."

"All right. Would you let Annie keep you company?"

"I guess so."

"Sister, go get Annie, please."

Pleasantly surprised to have been released from class, Annie accompanied her Ucsote to the henhouse. At the sound of Mary's footsteps and the usual greeting, "Howdy girls, Mary's here," hen hullabaloo broke loose. The layers sprinted, screeched, cackled and flapped, creating a cacophony accompanied by feathers and dust and feet flying. After scattering handfuls of cracked corn, she watched the frenzied competitors angle to peck the highest number of kernels, and sighed, "All right girls, I give up. You win!" Dust settled, she forced herself to do what she always did for her ladies—sang a lullaby. Annie witnessed the hens strut to their nests, clucking with satisfaction.

Mary's song came to its end. Bigg dead, she grieved, don't want it to be true.

Her heart thumped harder by the time she reached the corral. Lightning and Blaze whinnied and trotted toward her. Cricket limped behind. Mary slid the gate latch open and entered. "Careful Annie, they won't hurt you, stick to me." Annie gripped Mary's skirt, eyes wide at horses that came to their master willingly, not like the mounts kept by cavalrymen she had observed.

Mary hugged Lightning tight, then stroked and patted, ignoring the pain in her fingers and hands. She lavished the same affections on Blaze and Cricket. Tears rained free, and she labored, "I'm so sorry, y'all. Our Bigg. Lost your partner didn't you, Lightning? Good boy, yes, good boy." He stood beside her as she repeated over and over, "We're back, we made it, we're all right." Needing more time to sooth her heart, she stroked him again and wiped her eyes on strips of gauze pulled from her bandaged arm. "Bigg is free now," she intoned.

Oncoming cold seemed to drill through flesh. Striated layers of mist hung at ground level. It seemed to Annie, shivering, that the sky was weeping. Mary and the team hovered above her, giants to her view. She pressed against the thigh of her strong dark Ucsote friend and felt homesick. Yearning to be a warrior like her brother had been, she imagined herself on the back of the black horse Lightning, galloping east toward the rising sun, to her real home.

"Are you all right little one?" Mary asked tenderly. "You look tuckered out. Me too. Let's go inside."

Mary rubbed her chest as she headed toward the convent door—questioned why she had remained in Montana's frozen white tundra. She hadn't planned to stay. "I love you, Bigg," she whispered. "Hope you're at peace, loping through green pastures somewhere."

Escorted by Annie, she limped to her own lodging, a deteriorated temporary cabin built by the Jesuits thirty years prior. As she collapsed onto her tatted-straw mattress, she hoped for a good dream, a restful sleep that would bring her back to herself.

Annie unlaced Mary's boots, set them by the small potbelly and added another log from the stack outside. Cuddling next to her Ucsote, she pretended she would be home in her tribe's longhouse when she woke.

At dawn, Annie rejoined the mission schedule. After chores and breakfast, she took her place at mass, a new member in the chorus Mother had christened *Sparrows of God*. She stood in the long queue of choir robes—gathered fabric that reminded her of white-necked quail when they puffed feathers during spring rituals. Knees stiff, she mouthed awkward-shaped sounds—syllables and verse, she was told to call them—wondering why singers faced walls and objects rather than each other, wondering if the God they preached about wanted them to be lonely. It made no sense—birds sang to one another. Her thoughts drifted to Mary and the clucking hens.

Mother Superior had been detained. As she pushed the chapel door ajar, she regarded the sisters administering, the congregation engaged. Noticing a bright blue anomaly, front and left, she gaped: Mary Fields in the first pew, wearing a dress. Flinging decorum aside, she rushed down the center aisle to hug her. She gushed, "God bless your strong hearted spirit, Mary. Let's pray together and ask for the Holy Mother's blessing."

Mary Fields smiled. She had no words to speak, but she was glad to be alive.

After the wagon crash, Mary Fields spent more time alone. To her mission companions, she appeared to be lost in thoughts or daydreams. She failed to be the effervescent source of humor they had come to rely on. This change was attributed to the loss of her horse, but Mary knew better—it took more than that to draw her inward and keep her there. She began to seek quiet corners where she could enjoy solitude without distraction, and preferred reading by her lantern rather than participating in social activities. She skipped the school spelling bees but attended musical and theatrical performances, aware that they required dedicated hours of rehearsal.

Mary thought about her parents and the family of friends she'd had in Tennessee. She took long walks. Routinely borrowing books from Mother Mary's personal library, she discovered stories she had never heard—tales involving myths and pirates and sea creatures. Pleased that she had broadened her literary reach, she burrowed now, into a new frontier—poetry—words that to her thinking, painted and crunched and cried and left open-prairie spaces on the page where one might ponder.

She fancied stories of her own fitting inside various book chapters—overlooks that, powered by imagination, propelled her out of the Birdtail at will. Sometimes, while she repaired fences, buildings and whatever else needed fixing, she wondered if other continents or centuries might feel more natural.

"I'm seeing things different," she told her hens as she slipped a hand beneath to gather warm eggs. "It's the silent underbelly to watch—pardon the pun. Got on that train thinking it was for Mother Mary, and my prayers for a new life got answered without me knowing." Her leghorn layer squawked and flapped away. "I'm talking about freedom with purpose," she uttered. "That's what I want. And time to see it through."

NAMES

SPRING 1894

*T*hough page three of the 1894 calendar announced the arrival of March, winter maintained its numbing presence. Occasionally, bouts of rain passed through, florid signs of weakening weather fronts. Ice began a slow retreat leaving residue, soaked surfaces that sunk when trodden upon.

Mucking out the milking shed, Mary heard whirring sounds approach. She looked down the rise, recognized the buggy and its driver. "That would be Mary Ann," she said, as she hung the pitchfork in its place. "Early to pick up her girls—"

Mrs. Moran maneuvered her buggy up the drive's muddy incline, but lost control when two wheels slid into ruts at the curve. "Good Morning, Black Mary," she hollered, unaware that she had splashed muck onto Mary's skirt. Sliding to a halt near the mission's holding pen, a small coral used for guest livestock, she declared, "The only good thing about winter is that it can't last forever," and waited for help.

"Amen to that, Mrs. Moran. Winter can adios." Mary grabbed the harness reins, led the mare to the back door and helped the mistress who clutched a cloth-covered box ease down from the buggy. Mary wondered why their neighbor was so gussied up and adamant about keeping her package level, figured that Mary Ann was missing city life again. As she led the well-bred quarter horse toward the barn, she couldn't resist likening Mary Ann to a chickadee—a high-strung little bit of a bird—the ones that chirped and hopped from branch to branch, vulnerable yet stronger than appearance would suggest. She supposed that it was difficult for the Birdtail wife to shine next to her boisterous husband, well known and charitable;

both the nuns and Jesuit fathers counted on him, for good reason. A born and bred Catholic, Thomas Moran reliably donated labor and supplies. He had helped the sisters build the original wood-planked schoolhouse and was among the first to enroll his white daughters.

It had been weeks since Mary Ann ventured out. Bored and rattled by winter's cold shoulder, she pined for the company of women. Since the Ursulines' arrival years earlier, she had guarded a selfish secret—delight in the fact that the brutal wilderness had forced these Ursulines to deviate from traditional sequestered communities.

Convincing gossip had informed that her heroine, the Mother Superior, who was highly educated and fluent in several European languages, occasionally bent the rules if the ends justified the means. Rumors of Amadeus entering teepees alone, where she addressed Indian chiefs in their native tongue, consolidated impressive agreements with relative ease and reappeared victorious—this had inspired Mary Ann to dream beyond her homestead acres.

That summer and many that would follow, Mrs. Moran postured a calling of her own. She collected household survival tips and, when weather allowed, volunteered as a frontier hostess to welcome first-time Birdtail homesteaders. Though she had been raised a Lutheran, she promoted Catholic Church membership, Ursuline-Jesuit education and non-denominational Christian community. She knew all too well—every homesteader needed help.

Montanans understood the need for layers. Mary Ann opened the academy door, paused to slip her shoes from an oversized pair of work boots and straightened her white-going-to-church gloves, essential for the protection of her fair skin, much the same as the embroidered dishtowel protected the contents of her package firmly gripped. She listened to layers of netting swish against her mail-order brocade skirt as she strolled down the hallway and into the area most congregated, the kitchen. Mother Sebastian, the academy's seamstress instructor, welcomed Mary Ann with a polite embrace and peck on the cheek.

"Mother, hide this fast," Mary Ann whispered, handing her the bundle.

Sebastian leaned against the cupboard, detecting no reason to hurry. She prepared herself for a long chat, as it was Mary Ann's habit to discuss the latest women's fashion styles, sharing periodicals sent by her cousin in Boston.

"It's Mary's birthday cake," Mary Ann insisted.

The nun squeezed her toes, unable to squelch rising irritation. She had, after all, stayed up late the night before to finish a lovely cake, Mary's cake.

They had agreed on this arrangement several weeks prior. How could Mary Ann have forgotten?

"Mother, hide it now! Mary is coming, and you know nothing gets by her."

Sebastian lifted the bundle and placed it in the pantry—a good place for it to remain permanently, she thought, considering how long it had taken her to harvest and dry the delicate wild rose petals that she had artfully sprinkled onto pink frosting, icing she had cleverly tinted with beet root powder.

She sighed and offered Mary Ann tea, the special Assam variety shipped from India to England to America and unbeknownst to Sebastian, an annual Christmas gift from the Moran family.

Mary Ann sipped her tea sparingly, striving to emulate English high society that she had served earlier in life as a parlor maid. Hoping that the nun would recognize blue-blood posture, she forced her pinky finger upward.

"Mother, would you remind me when it's four o'clock?" she asked.

Sebastian looked at her, waiting for the reason she knew would follow. "I want to get home before dark. Mr. Moran gets upset when supper is late."

Perturbed to be delegated into the role of timepiece, but reconciled by the belief that it was better to consummate religious vows than marital ones, Sebastian answered, "Of course, Mary Ann. We wouldn't want to upset Mr. Moran." She decided to display the mistress's cake as the featured birthday dessert and present hers afterward, thinking that they would likely need two cakes anyway.

While Sebastian shushed the large crowd of Saint Peter's inhabitants, that included the Jesuits and their boy student-boarders, Gertrude hurried outside, anxious to lure Mary into her lair. She called, "Mary, could you help me in the kitchen?"

"Surely," Mary hollered over her shoulder, hoping Gertrude hadn't broken the rotisserie again.

She hung a halter on the fence post, wiped muddy hands on her apron and tugged her wool cap over numbed ears. A crow flew overhead, and Mary stopped to watch. "Thank you for showing me the beautiful sky—hadn't even noticed, Mister Crow."

"Mary, come here! I have to show you something before Mother sees it!" Gertrude tiptoed into the mud. Pretending to be upset, she swung an arm around her catch, pressed Mary toward the door and after they had wiped their shoes, goaded her the distance of the stone house, swung the parlor doors open and waved the birthday girl through.

"Happy Birthday!" pitched dozens of passionate well-wishers, "Happy Birthday!"

Mary stepped back, mouth ajar, realized then, that it was, actually was, her birthday. Flustered, she felt heat rise to her face as she identified each of the voices cheering. She waved her healed-hands high, gazed at the happy assembly and stood tall.

"Thank you, everyone. I forgot. Honestly!"

Guests shuffled as they vied for a better view of their friend, confidante, helper, whose birthday was the only birthday celebrated with fanfare. Little girls pushed through channels of legs and hugged Mary's waist.

Mary spied a double-layered vanilla coconut cake with a white tapered candle flaming from its center. Me and the coconut, she thought, the least native pair of nuts ever seen in the Birdtail. On the other hand, one could call us exotic. She smiled.

"Make a wish, make a wish!" the crowd chanted.

Before she squeezed both eyes shut, she cast a glance across the assembly, consciously gathering prairie dog numbers of brown, and some blue, eyes, into a singular wish: Dear Lord, on my sixty-second year, let the children and I find a more normal life, and a bigger one, whatever that looks like, and let everybody be healthy and strong, including my team.

An able blow turned fire into smoke.

Robust plants pushed through the earth's warming crust. Most everyone devised reasons to go outside and point skin allowed to be bare toward soft sunrays that filtered through forest peaks and into the slight rise of valley where the mission stood isolated in ancient terrain. At dawn, steam rose above thin ice that coated the width of tributaries. Glacial melt rippled and gurgled beneath, released, at last, from the long hard freeze.

Mother Amadeus took a moment to peer through her binoculars. She observed a gang of elk arcing cloven hooves above snow on a mountain precipice, envious of the leisurely pace with which they traversed the tree line, one behind the other and returned to her office, set the eyepiece down and thumbed through the Ursuline Mission post.

She found what she had been waiting for—a letter from the U.S. Commissioner of Indian Affairs. Anxious to know if funding had been approved, she tore its flap and scanned the single sheet of stationery, a brief paragraph. The Saint Angela's Academy application had been received and was currently under consideration. Yes, they had met the criteria for federal subsidies, nine dollars per pupil per month, and appropriations would be forthcoming contingent upon the inspector's interview and report. The correspondence did not mention when to expect the Bureau representative.

Relieved, she felt sure they would receive the allocations, particularly after they had completed construction of a three-story building to house the Ursuline academy. She relayed the news, cautioning the sisters' excitement though she could barely contain her own.

Mother Superior instructed the mothers to outline their respective curriculums and proceed on the assumption that federal funds would arrive. She had recently made a commitment to local chiefs: Saint Angela's would accept up to two-hundred additional girls before winter. In the interim, she would borrow money to purchase seed for wheat and vegetables, fabric for clothing, leather for shoes, perhaps a few Jersey milk cows. More young women would be rescued, trained to assimilate and achieve—fewer would die.

After mid-day dinner she pulled Mary aside and asked her to mark extended boundaries for the herb and vegetable gardens. Whisking a first-of-the-season mosquito from her shoulder, she emphasized the importance of this task—burgeoning numbers of pupils would not survive without increased yields—and asked Mary to apportion labor among the hired hands.

Later that afternoon, Mary and her assistant, Annie, ventured outside. After assessing the factors involved: seed quality, hours of seasonal light, wind dynamics and the condition of unworked soil, Mary flagged new perimeters. Annie watched her adopted Ucsote push boulders to mark the boundary corners, her dark brown skin steeped darker from sweat and ceaseless labor, the brave tender one who told her tales during the long winter darkness. She had confided to Annie that there were other lands, far away, where no white people lived. The earth was rich and fertile, she had said, a red rust color, and the sun was hot and bright and hugged the happy people all year round. A place where lush giant plants grew colorful sweet fruits and where animals, bigger and taller than teepees, roamed and roared and people were kind, lived together peacefully. She had added, that if one were to listen heart-fully, any plant could speak loud and clear if it wanted to, share all kinds of information for the asking—if one had the ability to hear. Annie had given these stories a great deal of thought.

"Come on," Mary called, shovel in hand, "Let's start on the herb garden."

Annie followed to the plot near the academy building.

"All these weeds need pulling out." Mary handed her a short-handled spade.

Annie was glad to be outside, not scrubbing or sewing like the other girls, but she took her time, tilted her head, begged to hear a voice explain who they were and why they had the right to survive. Nothing happened, so she did as she was told, dug and yanked the tallest perennial, its taproot bound to clay and stone. Broad leaves were ripped and mashed as she wrestled, her face and hands splattered with green blood that oozed between fingers.

"You're as persistent as those weeds," Mary said with a wink.

Annie didn't reciprocate as expected. "I think weed is a word for something you don't know," she said, angry and wrought with guilt she couldn't explain. "I don't want to do this." She sat down, wiped the goo on her skirt and stared at the green stain on her arm. "Oh," she heard Mary say.

"Well," the voice she had come to rely upon continued, "how about if I do the digging, and you chop up the dirt with a hand hoe? Or you can take a break if you want."

"Can we feed the plants to the chickens?"

"Yes. A good way to honor them, Annie. Thanks for reminding me."

A hand hoe was placed on the ground beside the girl, and she picked it up, turned away and thwacked a steady rhythm. She struggled with unkept feelings, closed her eyes and traveled to touchstone memories within, frayed visions and voices that fused as she beckoned them. Soon she could hear the familiar voices of elders, and saw herself sitting, listening. They, the elder men and women, spoke in deep, moving tones as they shared reverent history passed down by beloved ancestors, the sacred stories and tales about life before the white people.

Sometime later, Annie raised her head and asked, "Mary, did your Ucsote teach you how to make the plant medicines?"

Mary squatted beside her young friend, fingered the leaves of volunteer plantain she had slipped into her pocket and said, "No. My mother and someone else's Ucsote. Never knew my own grandmother. She lived in a place called Africa. Far, far away." She put her arm around Annie's shoulders. "We got to do the best we can, Annie. You're stronger than you know." She decided to ask the question she'd been wondering about. "Why didn't you speak when you got here, Annie? I suspect you knew how."

Annie sighed. "When they heard us speak *our* words, they kicked us and spit on me and shouted, '*No speak Indian*.' So I learned the English and waited."

"For what?"

"To see how the ones that take me, are."

"What do you think?"

She hugged her knees. "Better than the soldiers."

"Do you know the name of your family, your tribe?"

"Onon—People of Hills. I heard the English call our home, 'Finger Lakes.'" She rubbed an eye. "Please don't tell, Mary."

"I won't."

"At Fort Shaw they put us in a dark room with bars and we waited. Mother Amadeus brought me here. Just me. Maybe because I was the only girl. My family is gone." Annie drew a circle in the dirt, drew larger ones around it.

"I'm sorry Annie, real sorry."

"Do you want to hear one of our stories, Mary?"

"Yes, of course I do." She touched Annie's chin and arranged herself directly across.

Annie had practiced these particular English words so that the story would live on, in case her tribal language died, like her family had. She held Mary's gaze and began, "The name of this story is 'Sky Woman Creates the Earth'.

Before the world was born, Sky Woman fell through a hole in the sky. She splashed into water where the animal spirits live. A flock of geese spirits saw Sky Woman fall. They pulled her from the water with their wings and put her on Great Turtle, who was swimming. Animal spirits dove through the darkness. They found mud on the water floor. Muskrat spirit died when he was gathering mud, but beaver found the mud in muskrat's little paws and mouth."

Annie studied the mud in her fingernails and sipped another breath.

"Beaver gave the mud to Sky Woman. She put it on Great Turtle's back, very careful. Then Sky Woman took a drum from her bag. When she drummed and danced and sang songs, Great Turtle grew and the earth was made. Sky Woman and Muskrat and Beaver and Geese Spirits and Great Turtle gave us the world."

She searched Mary's expression to see if she understood. "When I have my hands in earth, I remember all of them. I asked them to bring you home that night."

"Thank you, Annie," Mary replied, slipping Annie's hand in hers. "I was thinking of you that night, too. Thank you for telling me about Sky Woman and everyone. That was a story I never heard before. I'll remember it with you."

"My real name is Onatah."

She scooted into Mary's open arms, buried her face.

"O—na—tah," Mary pronounced slowly, stretching the syllables as they rocked together. "What a beautiful name. What does it mean?"

"I can't remember."

"It will come to you."

Mary Fields had supervised the Indian girl's laundry production for years, until eventually one of the sisters took over. She'd taught pioneer stain removal in addition to ironing techniques and soap making. Working in teams, the girls laundered Ursuline faculty and student attire as well as the cassocks, rabbis, birettas, shirts and pants for the Jesuits and boy students in their charge. That left the Mother Superior's vestments. Aware that they were precious to her friend, part of sacred rituals and nearly impossible to replace, Mary continued to wash those items herself.

On Monday morning, as usual, Mother handed Mary a linen sack of soiled vestments. Mary tucked the bundle under her arm and said, "Friend Mary, can we talk for a moment?"

Mother nodded with a smile; she understood by Mary's tone that the exchange would be one of privities and welcomed the distraction. She had just returned from two weeks at Saint Ignatius Mission, the Canadian Ursuline establishment situated on the other side, the western side, of the Rocky Mountains. The facility housed Flathead Salish Indian pupils who were enrolled in elementary and secondary schools. Aware of the tribes' request to board younger children, Mother Amadeus had volunteered to establish an adjoining kindergarten which would be run by her American Ursulines. Construction was underway, but mudslides had delayed Mother's return, an arduous journey even by train.

Mother and Mary headed toward the chapel, sidestepping to avoid puddles. Noticing shades of blue reflected from the sky above, Mary said, "I loved the stained glass at the Toledo chapel, especially Mary Magdalen holding the baby Jesus."

"Me, too," Mother replied. "That window faced east, so beautiful at dawn."

Mary held the chapel door open, waited for her friend to pass through and got to the point. "I've been wondering about little Annie's name. Didn't you say the Army ledger listed her as *Annie Saint Germain?*" The door clunked behind.

"Yes."

They stood in the tallow-scented sanctum while their eyes adjusted, then made themselves comfortable on the last pew.

"Do you know what her name was before it was changed—her birthing name?" Mary set the sack of vestments to her side.

"Why the interest? You know that the girls are given Christian names." Chagrined at her reactionary response, Mother Mary took a breath and glanced to see if Mary had taken offense.

"I just wonder how they go about selecting surnames for the girls. Saint Germain sounds so noble, like a Catholic Saint."

"You're right. It is unusual." She scooted back against the wood. "I have no idea why the authorities chose that name. But I do know of a famous man by the name of Saint Germain."

"Who was he?" Mary leaned in.

"Comte de Saint Germain. It means, the Count of Saint Germain. He was a man of mystery, not a man of the cloth.

"Oh. Important sounding name."

"Yes. There are legends about his expertise in politics, alchemy and music. People claimed he had a powerful gift for healing. In fact, they said he made potions and elixirs that retained youth and beauty."

"A fountain of youth?" Mary Fields posed.

Mary Amadeus raised an eyebrow and nodded.

"He was said to look forty years old for over a hundred years." Mother Mary stretched her legs and wondered how Comte de Saint Germain had managed to escape the long arm of the church. Surely, he had been decreed a heretic. She couldn't remember. "He was born of royalty—well, even that is debated. His origins were, some say, from Spain, others say from Germany, others from France. The dates of his birth and death are also disputed, but he lived in the eighteenth century."

"I see why you say 'legend.'" Mary Fields shook her head, captivated.

"Yes. He was a wealthy aristocrat, a close companion to kings and queens: Louis XV and Francis Racoczi II. He wore huge precious jewels and knew how to make diamonds and gold—at least that is the tale."

"Make them—like from rocks or something?"

"Yes. Alchemy. He had a reputation that ran the gamut, from soothsayer to prophet. Even his death was mysterious—his body was never found, and sightings of him persisted for another fifty years. Quite an esoteric intrigue."

Mary envisioned aristocrats in fancy clothes wearing jewels on skin that didn't wrinkle. What did a royal household look like, and Europe for that matter? What kind of medicine, and music? Was a royal horse made royal by ownership, confirmation or the garb it wore? And Annie's home … was there a link from one to the other? No. Yes. The power of healing, maybe.

She fidgeted. "That's a handful to be named after. Why do you think they gave his name to Annie? Maybe her kin was the medicine healer of the tribe?"

Mother straightened. "I have no idea. It could have been for any reason. Maybe it was a family name of the person who was appropriating names, or someone who liked history."

"Well, whatever it is, it's a big name for a little girl. Did you ever find out which tribe she comes from?"

"No, but since she was found in New York, I'm assuming one of the Iroquois tribes."

Mary rubbed her forehead.

"How is the garden coming?" Mother stood and pressed on the pleats of her skirt. "I'm hoping to get tomato seeds from the Ohio Motherhouse, from Sister Helena. Do you think we'll be planted by mid-May?"

"I doubt it. Depends. I'm looking forward to nature's *first* crop, the wildflowers!"

"Oh, yes."

"Well, speaking of the garden, I'll get back to it. Thanks for telling me the Count story. Do you mind if I tell Annie?"

"No. Haven't thought of that tale for ages."

Mother pushed the door open. Sun blinded. Mary Fields helmeted her eyes and charged ahead, an old habit from years spent rushing; her destination, the barn. A breeze nudged her attention, and she realized she had left the laundry sack on the pew. The barn door was wide open, a violation of Mary's policy.

She shouted, "Mr. Mosney!" Hearing no answer from the hired hand, she bellowed full force, "Mosney!"

She marched into the gullet of the splintered barn, its walls permanently slanted by blizzards. The interior, dark from lack of windows, was cluttered with straw, tools and broken items tossed into corners. "What a mess," she grumbled as she rounded the corner, spotted Mosney in the tack room hunched on a milking stool, puffing a cigar butt.

"What are you doing, smoking in here? Outside with you! You know darn well it's too risky to be smoking by the feed and these dry old boards. You know we've had too many fires already. You were here—"

"I was the one who done rescued the fire in the stone house, if'n you don't remember, Fields."

"Rescued! Only thing you did was get water and tarps like I told you—if you can wring your wet brain out long enough to recollect."

"Don't tell me what to do, you ugly old nigger. You know wha—"

"I sure will tell you what to do! You're a hired hand, and those hands are supposed to be working, not setting the place on fire. I came in here to tell you the buggy seat and the harness need mending. Take care of it, Mr. Mosney. I trust you'll do a good job. I know you can when you want to."

He sucked hard and spat. "Burns said he was takin' care of the harness, not that *you* need to know."

Mary stomped outside, slurring, "I'm sick of this idiot excuse for a man. Can't find anybody to work without giving me lip."

John Mosney snorted and kicked the nearest tin can—one of many he had tossed on the barn floor. It clanged against a stack of horseshoes and set off a flurry of pigeons. "Dang rats with wings—get out'a my barn!" he hollered. "Soon as Burns gets back, I'm giv'n him an earful." He dropped the stogie, stepped on it, twisted his boot heel with vengeance. "Bad enough to be taking orders from *any* woman. I've had my fill of taking orders from some darkie nigger hired hand who thinks she knows it all. If'n he don't listen, I'm gone."

Wish Mosney and Burns would both disappear, Mary ranted in her mind. And it's a load of hooey—calling Mr. Burns the foreman—he's not here half the time, ain't worth shucks, either—if it wasn't for the womenfolk, I'd tell those lazy scalawags where to go.

Temperatures finally inched into the upper fifties on the last day of April. Nancy and Lizzie, boarding students who had been assigned to kitchen duty, clocked their required three hours of daily labor in the morning, baking bread—loaves and loaves of delicious mission grown cracked-wheat bread. Generally, two-person teams were paired by grade level and ethnicity, and it was the Indian girls who did the baking. This morning, Nancy's partner had fallen ill, and Lizzie, a wiry blonde of Anglo-Saxon descent, one of the few non-Indian boarders, volunteered to substitute.

Baking reminded Lizzie of her mother, and she liked kneading dough. "Don't you just love this gigantic kitchen?" she asked the Indian girl upon entry.

Nancy, a Piegan Blackfeet, thought the metal utensils foreign and weapon-like, but she enjoyed the sequential mindlessness of their task. "It's good to have three ovens so we get done sooner," she answered, intentionally vague.

The reply left Lizzie confused. She counted cups of flour, emptied them into a huge ceramic bowl and thought about her parents. Her father, Moses Tully, had opened a gunsmith shop in Ulm, a settlement northeast of Saint Peter's. Business hadn't soared the way he had promised Lizzie's mother it would when they sold everything and set out from Saint Louis, Missouri three years earlier. When Moses discovered it was less expensive to send his daughter to the Ursulines than to care for her at home, he enrolled her in the academy, making another promise to his wife: it was only temporary. Nell Tully, a devout Methodist, was broken-hearted. Alone in a foreign place, she had lost her only child, twice, she claimed. First in body and secondly in soul, to the other religion—all for a pittance of ten dollars per month.

Once more, Lizzie tried to make conversation. "Nancy, have you ever thought of traveling abroad, on a ship, like Mother Amadeus does when she goes to Europe?"

Nancy gagged on a yelp. "You must be joking," she scoffed, pulling dough apart. "An Indian girl traveling to Europe. How? As a servant?"

"It's not that crazy. Maybe Mother Amadeus will take one of you to Italy next time."

"One of us?"

"No offense, but Indians are quite the curiosities in Europe. That's what Papa says. Not like us Americans who just came from there."

"Why would Mother take—" Nancy's hands stopped. Curiosities. Wasn't Europe where the Ursuline sect began? Are they still there? Would she? Warm dough webbed her fingers together. She added more flour and worked the mass, pushed her weight into the kneading.

"Well, anyway," Lizzie said, "I'd like to go to England and meet my grandparents, and who knows, maybe I could stay with them. I love music and theatre, at least I think I do, and they all live in London. Maybe I could be a debutante in society and be presented in a formal cotillion. When I was in Helena, at the First National Bank with my Papa, I read in a magazine that in London, aristocrat lords and ladies attend the opera and theatre and balls, and travel to country estates to visit royalty. Maybe I would meet a handsome lord and he would ask me to marry him. I would be called Lady Elizabeth, not Lizzie."

Nancy continued to smack, fold and press the dough, louder than necessary, watching for the required emergence of smooth elastic texture and the end of the girl's romantic fantasy.

"Names. Now that's a subject," she began, redirecting the conversation. "Have you ever noticed that everyone here except you white girls has had their name changed at least once, some twice?"

"You have to have a Christian name, that's why."

"The sisters had Christian names before they professed their vows, and they changed them when they entered the Ursuline Cloister."

"I didn't know that. Are you sure?"

"Yes. That's because there's supposed to be an important meaning behind the gift of a new name. In our tribe, a person is given a name for something they have done, or to describe their natural talent. Names are an honor that call to a person's core, help us grow in spirit." She warned herself to be cautious.

"What was your name, Nancy?"

"Nadie. It means 'wise one.'"

"That's pretty. What tribe are you from?"

"Piegan. The Blackfeet tribe from the north." "Tribe" was an English word Nancy didn't like. She felt that it divided the Blackfeet people into pieces. She longed to speak her native tongue.

Lizzie glanced toward the window, noticed Mary on her knees working in the garden. "What about Mary Fields? Where did she get that nickname 'White Crow'?"

Nancy wondered whether the name "Mary" was given by parents or a slave owner. "White Crow is a name of honor," she said, "not a nickname."

Aromas of bread had escaped through the opened windows, ridden on crisp air that swirled low to the ground. Distracted from planting, Mary White Crow paused to savor the heady scent. "That bread smells sumptuous," she bellowed for the benefit of the bakers. "I can see it sliced up, ready for a picnic!"

Nancy looked at the blonde girl who was grinning. "Mary, or White Crow," Lizzie said, "is like sunshine after a blizzard. She helped me when I got here."

Surprised to witness the genuine affection, Nancy followed suit. "Like chickadees singing in the morn."

"We should be going on a picnic before long," Mary's voice rang as she strolled toward the kitchen. Bending over the water bucket by the door, she washed dirt from her hands.

Verses welled like the rising yeast. "Like horses and the wind, always moving," Lizzie pitched.

"Like magpies and rivers, always talking."

"Like a mother hen, taking us under her wings."

"What's that you're singing?" Mary asked as she opened the door and pulled her feet from the heavy work boots.

Nancy slung, "It's a new song, Mary, sheet music from San Francisco."

Enthusiasm creased Mary's broad face; she loved a new tune. "Well, you'll have to teach it to me, haven't heard that one."

Lizzie couldn't stop. "Like a buffalo stampede thundering across the plains." The girls giggled, delighted by their witty tit for tat and their fib.

"Think you could slip me one of those staffs of life?" Mary asked.

Lizzie shrunk back.

"Don't worry, if you're questioned, report that I requisitioned it."

Nancy chose the finest looking loaf, handed it to Mary and said, "I can't wait to go on the next picnic, White Crow."

"Me, too! We'll go on May Day as long as the weather's good. Maybe before. More picnics the better." Mary straightened her herringbone cap, tugged its bill and went outside.

Lizzie looked at Nancy. "You said the name 'White Crow' is a title of honor. I don't understand. I never heard of a white crow."

Nancy, having decided that the girl was harmless enough, answered, "It's hard to translate. Crows are mystical birds of creation. The color black is all colors mixed together and is the color of birth, of what came before light. Crows are clever. They watch out for other birds and animals and warn them if enemies approach. They are brave and loyal and like to joke and have fun. Like Mary."

"But why *white* crow then?"

"The Blackfeet had never seen a person the color of Mary. She talks like a white person and seems to know things the same as whites, but she is black. It's like she is from two worlds—holds secrets from the black creation world and the white people's world. This is powerful medicine and special, like Mary is special. So she was gifted the name, 'White Crow.'"

Lizzie didn't respond. She brushed butter on dough raised in the loaf pans and loaded them into the oven. She wanted to say that she understood, but she was confused, and she'd never heard her race called *whites* before.

"I have to think about it. Is it because she takes care of us and makes us medicine when we are ailing?"

"Partly."

"I know most settlers call your people heathens and savages and call coloreds niggers and think you aren't civilized like us, but I don't think that, Nancy."

"I wouldn't have told you what White Crow means if I thought you were, like them."

"I won't be spreading anything you said around in case it might get you in trouble. Not that it would, but just—"

"Thanks. Let's clean up. It will be time for class when this batch is done."

Nancy shot a glance outside. She watched Mary pat sifted earth over the furrowed row, wondered where the new seeds came from and whether the people there were free.

The night of the new moon, Nancy, who went by Nadie in the privacy of her sleep, dreamed a familiar scene. It began with heartbeats merged into drumbeats that sounded in cadence. She stood in long shadows, deep within a pristine forest where she heard water gurgling in the distance. Stepping tenderly, she arrived at the earth's damp edge and peered beneath currents that swirled within a deep pool. Long shafts of light reached through thinning autumn leaves. Clumps of red mountain-ash berries caught reflections from a smooth contoured object laid naked in the pool's bed of algae, stick and stone. Her stomach lurched. The source of sheen came from an object attached to an ear, a human ear hanging loose from its dead owner's face. White opaque pods sat in the eye sockets, and flesh swiveled where a mouth had been. Remnants of scalp pushed against knotted sticks. Hair from the corpse's severed head clung to moss and waved in ripples. The drumming stopped. It was then she realized that the protrusion from the victim's skull was not a branch; it was an antler.

The dream skipped to Nadie crouched at the edge of a meadow. She felt strong, inhaled crisp air and the scent of decaying leaves. Bow in hand and arrows in the sheath strapped across her back, she stalked. Drumming beats began, the same as before. She waited in a thicket of tall reeds. First rays of light lit the heavy mist. Tingling, she felt the presence of her target. Easing an arrow into her bow, she leaned forward, ready.

Her body jerked and she woke. It was bright, and she was holding her breath.

The drumbeats reverberated in Nancy's mind throughout the day. She imagined birds and bears and buffalo and humans dancing a drumming song together. It was the dance of life, the sacred heritage of roots and earth and sky and medicine that could not be broken, no matter where she was or what happened to her. She couldn't say it in English and didn't want to. She knew that others held the connection, too, along with the good sense not to mention it.

Forced to spend hours in class, her body corseted, her mind free, she kept her shoulders up, her stomach in, like a lady. They could teach her their etiquette, but they couldn't make her want it or believe it. As one hand scribed the English cursive letters, the other, her free hand, tapped the dream beat on her lap, steady and steadfast. She felt protected in the afterglow of her dream.

It was the way she sometimes felt during music lessons Mother Amadeus had initiated. They called it her musical aptitude, the thing that had singled Nadie out, gave her the privilege to choose her instrument first, before her peers. She chose the violin. When she plucked and stroked the strings, she could feel herself inside its wooden belly, not unlike the hollowed trees wrapped with hide—the drums that sounded and resounded.

April 5, 1894

My dear friend Katharine,

... I have lately been ill-of-heart, lamenting with lingering sorrow, the passing of a profusion of young souls flown to Heaven during our cruel winter. I wonder if they died needlessly; had we provided better provisions and medical care for these innocent children, could we have saved them? Not only has the cold stolen the souls of more than one Indian student per month—some of our most prized postulants, novices and sisters here at Saint Peter's have been whisked away, delivered to sublime salvation. We pray that their souls will rest in the hands of our Merciful Lord in Heaven.

Winter has not let up, and March delivered riveting sub-zero temperatures, hail and snowstorms. If it had not been for Mary Fields and the hired hands, we would not have been able to give proper burials. The ground is frozen deep. I worry that our resources will not cover our medical and burial expenses. We are suffering.

I believe that keeping the Indian girls busy is the best protocol for good health; work keeps the body warmer, stronger and less likely to succumb to such things as croup, diphtheria and other maladies. Still, we lose too many of them.

You have heard my charge more than once: "It is the Ursuline calling to educate young women of any color so that they may become women trained to fill, acceptably, any station in life." Is there anything you can do to shepherd more sisters to our outposts?

Thank you for your commendable support of our humble mission in the West. I fear that our contract schools would not have survived without you, dear Sister. If there is additional funding available for the welfare of our children, we would be most grateful to receive it. I look forward to our next visit.

Yours in faith and appreciation,
Sister Mary Amadeus

4

RENEWAL

MAY DAY 1894

*S*ixty lucky pupils would win the Saint Peter's lottery, awarding them a place in Mary Fields' May Day Expedition. Over two-hundred contestants printed their names on leftover train ticket stubs and placed them in the designated milk can. Father Rebmann picked the winning tickets, and Mary Fields recorded each name in her ledger.

The mission's annual romp had originated seven years earlier when Mary proposed the spring outing. She had begun her several-month campaign by voicing seasonal yearnings shared by all Birdtail inhabitants: "We need something to look forward to on those frozen, confined, never ending winter days."

She cited Mother's philosophy on fitness, claiming that such an excursion into the hills would provide the perfect measure of physical stamina and exertion, the type of exercise that the Superior, in her wisdom, believed necessary to maintain the population's health. "Also," Mary declared, "the endeavor will render the students physically fit in time for planting crops. And as a bonus, they'll learn more about European culture."

Mother didn't consider May Day cultural, given its pagan origin, but she relented after weeks of Mary's ceaseless prodding and promised to convince the Jesuit Fathers on one condition: that no history of May Day be imparted. Only the civilized merits of May Day would be memorialized, she mandated: the selfless delivery of floral bouquets.

Stories of previous May Day rollick circulated. Anticipation of play inspired daydreams. Participating students attended classes on Saturday in order to be excused for Tuesday's field trip.

Before roosters crowed on May 1st, forty-two girls gathered at the back door of Saint Angela's, engaged in fanciful chatter. Giggles peaked when male lottery winners came jogging across the field from the Jesuit sector. The door burst open. Their leader, Mary Fields, squeezed through, donning a broad smile and loads of gear wrapped across her strong square shoulders. Heavy sacks, satchels and baskets were distributed. Mary raised her walking stick and hollered, "This is a grand expedition. Let's go!"

Sisters Gertrude and Anna watched the long line of bodies march toward the nearby mountain. Gertrude likened the group to a mother duck and her ducklings wandering off on an adventure. Anna said she hoped they wouldn't get lost, like in *Alice's Adventures in Wonderland.*

Mary set an exuberant pace, matched by gleeful followers. Hair escaped her cap as she continually glanced back to track the slow pokes. She had knotted her checkered apron over a heavy muslin skirt, its bulging pockets swinging as she trotted purposefully to higher ground. "Panoramas deliver joy to the heart," she extolled, suspecting that most of the children who accompanied her, felt the same way. It was her experience that elevated overviews were "getaways to infinity" that gifted calm and the clarity to make important decisions.

Debates over the contents of Mary's pockets buzzed. "I'll bet you two bits that Mary has rock peppermint candies in both pockets," John Lewis challenged his friends.

"You don't have two bits," schoolmate George guffawed, holding his belly.

"Well then, I'll bet you two hours of shoveling manure," John dared.

"Nah, I don't think so."

"Chicken—blaac, buc-buc,"

A husky redhead named Mabel skipped at Mary's side, said between gasps, "My mother told me that her village in England had a May Pole."

"What's a May Pole?" Nancy asked as she joined the crowd at the forefront.

Mabel repeated her mother's words, "It's a tall evergreen tree striped of its branches. It's erected in the town square and decorated with leaves and flowers. People tie colored ribbons to its top. Is that right, Mary?"

"Yes."

"Why do they do that?" Nancy asked, fondly recalling the smooth inner bark of teepee poles, and attempting to imagine what a town square might be.

Mabel squealed, "Each person holds a ribbon, and then they dance, weaving in and out, around each other, making some kind of pretty braid. And they're singing while the piper is playing the flute, and men in costumes with jingle bells dance around. Sounds grand, but my mother said that it was outlawed and now, no dancing is allowed but it's all right to give flower bouquets or baskets of flowers."

"Why is it against the law?" Nancy asked Mabel with the spots called freckles.

The girl shrugged. Nancy looked to Mary who intensified her search for flowers in the brush, avoiding eye contact.

"Mary, do you know why it's not allowed anymore?"

The leader kneeled to pluck violets. "That's a question you best ask someone else. The way I heard it, folks were having too much merriment, and other folks thought it wasn't respectful. Not sure that it's really against the law."

Nancy said, "I don't understand why the Sisters say dancing is sinful. I love to dance, and it makes me happy. It's like singing, and how can you do one without the other?"

Mary looked up. "Let's just find our flowers. They make my heart dance, and the sun feels so good!"

Sometime later, after patches of sweat had doused backs and brows, Mary declared a sit-a-spell at the crest of a steep hill. Droves of young faces squeezed tight, flushed and panting for breath. One boy's voice rose above the rest. "Mary White Crow, can we go to the pishkun, the buffalo jump? Balsam flowers will be there, and probably yarrow and glacier lilies."

The boy knows his flower habitats, Mary admired, knows that balsam and yarrow grow in heavy rock. But it's a long way for the group, five miles. We'd have to keep a fast pace to make it back by dinner. She lifted both arms above overhead and lowered her palms slowly, a signal for the group to be quiet. Chatter subsided and she asked, "Would you like to go to Buffalo Falls?"

Rowdy whoops cheered.

"All right then. Break into groups of ten with at least one tall person who's responsible for the rest. Count off before we go. Does everyone understand?"

"Yes," the swarm shouted.

"And you understand that we have to be mindful, no mishaps so we can keep our picnics coming? We'll need to clip at a good pace."

A high-pitched majority agreed.

"All right. Don't step on any flowers, and see if you can remember where they are in case you need more on the way back."

She took the well-trodden path along the ridge, then a narrower trail that descended into a canyon. The hikers proceeded, single file. Gurgling echoes disclosed the presence of water, which as they rounded a horseshoe curve, was spotted rising through fissured slabs of rock. The effervescent seltzer cascaded into a shallow basin of chipped gravel.

Gulps were sipped. Thirst was quenched.

Renewed, the May Day troop tromped upward, to and fro on switchbacks crossing heavy breasted mounds and steep inclines. Fortitude was rewarded when they reached the top, a second summit. Explorers scooted on their bellies to the cliff's edge where they ogled a sheer drop-off. Cataclysmic events had severed the mountain peak eons past; mineral wreckage lay strewn in the pit below. A chiseled gap revealed the crag's interior—jagged slate slabs torqued from a mammoth quake, most likely.

Annie called, "This must be the buffalo jump, but where's the pishkun and what is it?"

"Who will answer Annie's question?" Mary called.

Gerald Brave, the Blackfeet boy who had suggested the detour, raised his hand. "I will. See there?" He pointed to a massive lichen-covered rock wall in the distance. "A pishkun has two sides that form the shape of a 'V' or an arrowhead." He demonstrated with his hands. "The walls are strong, built as broad as a man is tall. The wider end is the beginning of the pishkun. It's usually built by a stream where buffalo go to drink. See those two walls, far apart?" He pointed to one, then to the other. Annie and the younger children nodded. "There's a spring near the rise, in the center. The grass grows thick there, sheltered from wind, a favorite place for buffalo to graze. When the people need meat, we make noise near the water when they are drinking. Upset, the buffalo stampede. The walls block their escape and they are forced this direction. See how the pishkun narrows as it comes this way, to the cliff?" He pointed again. "They are running fast and don't see the drop. They run over the edge and fall to their death. We bless them, use their meat and hides and bones and don't waste anything. At least that's what we used to do."

Annie's eyes widened. She didn't know if buffalo roamed in her homeland. She tugged his shirt and said, "I saw buffalo on the way here," and gazed at the boy who clearly had more tribal memories than she.

"There used to be buffalo for as far as you could see. My family told me about the great hunts."

"That's horrible," Mabel the red-head shrieked, "running an animal off the cliff!"

Gerald bristled. "Kinder than shooting it, stripping off its robe and leaving the flesh to rot without honor, without purpose!"

Fueled with contempt, the two locked eyes. Mary intervened, "All right, that's enough. Stop it." She pointed by their feet. "Look here, everyone, glacier lilies!"

"Can I pick one?" a nearby voice asked.

"No," Mary said, "they don't last, cut down."

Like the buffalo," Gerald muttered.

"Let's see what else we can find. There's a big bunch of balsam sunflowers on the incline. Pick some of those—they're hardy, like the buffalo."

The group marched on until they reached a wide plateau feathered in green softness, a mantle that offered far-reaching vistas to the east and west. "Here we are," Mary declared. She waited for her brood to collect themselves around her. "Set your things down and fan out. Take the sacks and baskets and pick away. We need lots and lots of flowers for our bouquets!" She straightened her cap. "Come back in a half hour and we just might have ourselves a picnic. Get going!" Bodies sprinted like spooked quail. "Wait!" Mary called, "I forgot to say, I see buttercups, red paintbrush and lupine from here—" Only a handful of listeners lingered. "And if you heard me earlier, you know to head downhill on that path," she pointed, "for forget-me-nots, iris and violets. Orchids, too, maybe." Annie lingered at Mary's side. "Onatah, see those tall bright pink flowers with the tall stalks? We call them fireweed. Go get us some, please."

While gatherers rushed from color to color, Mary pulled yards of cotton cloth from her sacks. She drew pleats on one edge of the yardage, laid it down on the weathered crest and shaped circular rows to hug the convex curve of earth and stretched yards of cloth around, one circle and then another, leaving body-room between. Looks like a labyrinth, she mused, a simple one, or a target. She anchored edges with small stones and decided to place herself in the center, the place where an imaginary object plopped into water, creating rings.

As her flock returned, they placed their treasure in Mary's inner circle, under a tent she had crafted to keep the flowers cool. She instructed her flock to sit facing the center, anywhere along the contoured picnic tablecloth. Lured by savory aromas, most settled next to the food baskets. She sent the older boys to get water and counted to make sure all sixty of her brood were present.

Quick to respond, the boys placed buckets of water throughout and joined their friends. Mary stood up to say grace. "We thank the Lord for this glorious May Day of sunshine, flowers, food and friends. Give your neighbor a smile and share the bounty. We've got second helpings.

Amen!" Scanning the gleeful expressions, she added, "You can eat with your hands."

The pleasure of feasting on fried chicken (Tennessee style), potato salad, candied yams and Macintosh apple turnovers in the open air was heightened by the freedom to jabber while doing so. An older boy named Isaiah wiped apple drippings from his face and stood up. After shushing the picnickers, he made an announcement.

"Mary White Crow, we thank you for this special day of wandering and flower gathering and good cooking. I look forward to this all winter. It makes my heart happy. We love you this much—" He spread his arms wide.

Thank you God in Heaven for times like this, Mary thought, tears welling. In that moment she realized that she had been cradling remorse for months, cocooning herself, healing—from something more than frostbite and Bigg's death. Bruised feelings lifted. There she was, in the center, unencumbered, part of the green grass and blue-sky and the best company in the world. She dipped a ladle into the water bucket, splashed water onto her face.

Moments later she grabbed a gunnysack from behind the baskets and carefully removed a cherished companion she had purchased in Toledo: her five-string banjo. Raucous subsided. Most youngsters had never seen such a curiosity. Aware of the crowd's attention, she plucked more treasure from her sack: a shiny harmonica set in the scale of D and a tin pennywhistle. She handed the flute and mouthpiece to the girls with whom she had been practicing. The trio tapped toes to set the beat and began to play, *Mary Had A Little Lamb,* followed by a little ditty written by Olive Wadsworth. Mary cheered, "See if you can guess the name of this one. It goes like—" She plucked the melody, strummed a few chords and sang the first verse.

"Join in," she hollered, "sing the words or hum along."

Over in the meadow,
In the sand in the sun
Lived an old mother toadie
And her little toadie one.

"Wink!" said the mother;
"I wink!" said the one,
So they winked and they blinked
In the sand in the sun.

The audience was tongue-tied, but not for long. Mary belted:

Over in the meadow,
Where the stream runs blue
Lived an old mother fish
And her little fishes two.

"Swim!" said the mother;
"We swim!" said the two,
So they swam, and they leaped
Where the stream runs blue.

Harmony and verse resonated. Delighted, Mary sang:

Over in the meadow,   *"Sing!" said the mother;*
In a hole in a tree   *"We sing!" said the three,*
Lived an old mother bluebird   *So they sang and were glad*
And her little birdies three   *In a hole in the tree ...*

Caroling to the nineteenth verse and improvising when Olive's lyrics had been completed, Mary ended the sing-along with:

Over in the meadow,
In a hole in a tree
... Lived a big old Mama toad
And her baby toads, sixty toads!
"Croak!" said the mama
We're croaking!" croaked the sixty baby toads,
So they croaked singing songs til sunshine rose.

"Wish we could spend the night," one enthusiast shouted.

Mary glanced at the sun's angle, reluctantly slid her banjo back into the duffel and announced, "All right, time to bundle our wildflowers so we can share them with folks who don't get to go to the wild places, like us! Break into circles by the dozen."

It had taken months to accumulate hard-to-find decorative garnishments that would accent each bouquet. Following Mary's directions, picnickers wrapped and tied pretty ribbon bows around each bunch of flower stems. Greetings came next. Cutting and folding precious paper scraps into gift cards, Mary instructed the assembly to compose greetings that were as cheerful as the flowers, and reminded, "Do not sign your name!"

An avid listener, one of the Jesuit students, showed Mary his first attempt: *May your days be filled with spring.* He asked, "Is that good, White Crow?"

"You have a polished writing voice, young lad," she declared, thinking how nice it was to be called White Crow ... how on May Day, the children could call her White Crow without fear of consequence.

The trip home was effortless, a brief duration, mostly downhill. The group arrived with enough daylight to spare—time to deliver bouquets and attend to evening chores and prayers as usual.

Expedition members and students who hadn't won the lottery shared the privilege of gifting May Day posies. First, a giver knocked on someone's door and high-tailed it to hide. Though everyone knew the flowers had come from the students, May Day tradition was honored: recipients pantomimed efforts to search for the gift giver and repeatedly pitched gratitudes, pretending they had no idea why such a special gift had been delivered, who brought it or where it had come from. The words, "Thank you, they are lovely," were hailed repeatedly, from doorways opened by Mothers, Fathers, Sisters and the hired help.

A spectacular fuchsia sky glowed behind the glacier-capped mountains, drawing May Day to its closure. Mary tromped to her quarters, settled into her rocker, lit a cigar and propped her aching feet onto a slatted crate.

Shortly after, three soft knocks sounded. Footsteps pattered. Annie crouched behind the dovetailed corner of the cabin.

Mary opened the door and mimicked the pose of a stereotyped frontier scout scouring the horizon. Fingers pressed together, she lifted her right hand to the crest of her forehead and squinted, pretending to hunt for the anonymous giver of the posy bouquet. She exaggerated a slow turn from one side to the other and called, "I don't know who gave me this splendid, beautiful bouquet, but it's absolutely gorgeous, and I thank you with my biggest heart!" She picked it up and cradled it like a babe, calling, "Oh my, a gentian flower! Happy May Day to you!"

"Bet they're from Annie," she said after she closed the door. "Though they could be from any of my little angels." She lifted the blossoms to her nose and filled her senses with memories, enough to last through another winter. "What a precious day," she cooed, admiring the colors.

Glowing, Annie sprinted back to her duties, unnoticed.

While Mary and her brood were gathering wildflowers, hired hand John Mosney had engaged in a May Day activity of his own. He borrowed pen and paper from Sister Gertrude and marched to the workbench in the barn. Pushing mice droppings aside, he squared his stance and struggled to print legibly. Sweaty fingers and a bandaged thumb handicapped his effort—he had hammered his own nail instead of an iron one positioned on a fence post the day before.

Annoyed after aligning so many alphabet letters, a chore that strained his mental and physical aptitudes, he began to wheeze. Shorty, the Jesuit's mongrel, had wandered in and rubbed against Mosney's overalls, whimpering for attention.

Mosney scribbled his signature and barked, "Shut up, Shorty. What you want?" He checked his composition:

Dear Honor Reverend Brondel Sir,

I been working hear at Saint Peters for months now and I aim to make a formal complaint to you about this nigger woman Mary Fields who been bossing folks like me around for two long in my opinion. Things will go much better for us hired help if she was gone. It aint right that a woman, particular a darkie nigger woman tell a white man what to do. And the Nuns they don't listen to me. I aim to quit if you keep her.

Respectful, John Mosney

Pushing the creased paper into a small envelope, he transferred his say-so to his interior vest pocket and patted his chest. Concerned that his written-on-the-page personal business could fall into wrong hands, he was reluctant to trust the local mail carrier with his message, capped and sealed or not. He decided to wait, hand his post to the Cascade postmaster who had sworn an oath to mind government privacy regulations.

Days later, Reverend Brondel opened the missive from John Mosney and groaned. Rubbing his balding head, he asked the Almighty to eliminate the diocesan controversy without his help, and concluded, after further thought, that he might have to take care of it if Divine intervention did not occur within a reasonable period of time. "Mary Fields," he grumbled. "It's one thing after another with those Ursulines."

John Baptist Brondel was well aware that Montana posts, whether of state or church affiliation, constantly struggled to keep hired help. Remote locations and limited social exchange were the most common complaints. Experience had taught him that pious company was hard for most drifters to handle without engaging in occasional diversions. He couldn't imagine diversions one could perpetrate near Saint Peter's. His head began to ache. The Bishop's priority must remain, he consigned, dedicated to the propagation of Catholicism, an outlook comprehensive to the whole.

To that end, he prioritized. Montana Indian school certifications and the immediate procurement of federal subsidies were most essential. Competition was fierce. The entire Montana Catholic mission educational system could crumble without that funding—along with his personal hope for promotion. Having been assigned the position of first state bishop was a godsend. To retain the post, his term of leadership had to demonstrate substantial success.

One of his parishioners, a well-informed Montana legislative constituent, had recently advised him of national statistics that indicated a decline—Catholic missions were no longer ahead, monetarily. Adding insult to injury, the A.M.E., African Methodist Episcopal Church in Helena, his

city of residence and the state's capitol, had been growing fast—faster than
the local Catholic Church where he ministered. At present, the boisterous-
singing A.M.E. congregation numbered over five hundred colored citizens.
Thoughts circled back to Mary Fields and the Ursuline sisters. Irritated, the
Reverend decided to investigate Mosney's claim—find out what the nuns
and their colored woman were really up to at Saint Peter's.

Sister Juliana, absorbed in meditative reflection as she plucked slugs from
lettuce shoots in the garden, flinched when she heard the rumbling of
hooves approaching so early in the morning. Looking up, she recognized
the black buggy with the extra-large wheels and panicked. The Bishop had
arrived two days early. Juliana sprinted to the kitchen and sounded the alert.

"Girls, sit down at your tables," Sister Gertrude ordered. "The Reverend
Lordship is here. I want you to eat your breakfast with well bred, lady-like
manners. Quiet! Now! "

Bodies squirmed into position along the lengthy juxtaposed tables,
another gift from Katharine Drexel. One hundred and nine Indian girls
sitting erect in western attire would be an impressive cultural victory for
the Bishop's eyes to behold. Nimble fingers fussed with hair and buttons to
avoid the eagle eye of Sister Gertrude who scrutinized the assembly while
she straightened her apron and pulled her sleeves down.

Reverend Brondel stayed for a week. On day one he inspected every
corner and cubby of the Ursuline domain: the academy, opera house,
cabins, stable, barn and hennery. He carried a notebook and pencil and
paused often to make notations. Concerned, Mother Superior appraised
the bishop's demeanor as atypically formal and self-absorbed; she asked
Gertrude to indulge the Reverend's sweet tooth. Bishop Brondel's favorite
desserts were served following each meal for the duration.

It was his lordship's routine to take a constitutional stroll after breakfast.
The sisters sighed relief when they heard the door shut behind him.

The Reverend noticed Mary Fields lumbering across the compound
with a fifty-pound feed sack poised on one hip. He watched her push
through the hennery doorway. A latch clanked shut. Strolling closer, he
loitered, pretending to deliberate. He leaned over to pick up a rusty tin,
stared at the cloudless sky.

"Good morning, my chicks and ducklings," Mary called, unaware
of the Reverend's presence. "Hallelujah, it's another new morn!" She
poured feed into the troughs, flung corn into a small outdoor area she had
constructed, and broke into song:

"Hallelujah, Hallelujah,
Warm seasons are coming,
Morning is here."

The reverend frowned, thinking she behaved like those A.M.E. members, shouting hymns to God-knows-what. He ground his teeth. A meadowlark trilled.

"Sun is rising,
Your friend Mary is here."

The Bishop confessed to his momentary diversion: scorn. He had transgressed—accused Mary of flinging self-professed, unsanctified blessings to mission livestock. He bowed to his trespass, admitted his impious sin: judgment.

But, he objected as he tossed the eroded tin onto the ground, treating lowly fowl as though they have souls, or reason, clearly challenges the Almighty's decrees. There should be consequence, he resolved. Men are the caretakers of God's—

A gristly hum came from behind. Brondel winced as he turned to find himself facing a short, rough whiskered, middle-aged cowhand who slouched to the right.

"Mister-Lordship-Brondel-Sir?"

The reverend nodded, suddenly thirsty.

"Good Morn to you, Sir. I's John Mosney, ranch hand for the mission, sir, and hoping to talk with you a stretch, if'n you please." He lifted a torn hat above his head, revealing a tangled mat of brown fuzz.

"Ah, yes, Mr. Mosney. Are you the same Mr. Mosney from whom I received correspondence of late?"

"I don't know about that, didn't send no core-spawn-dent, sir. But I did send ya a letter speaking concerns about the Nigger Mary, sir. Was it late?" Mosney postured a cunning smile, intending to look clever, unaware that his teeth, worn from bearing down on jerky, and dark from tobacco and neglect, could cause a gentleman to recoil.

"Shall we take a stroll, Mr. Mosney, stretch our legs?" John Brondel asked as he launched forward.

Mosney followed in tow.

Gertrude noticed them from her kitchen window and thought that the unlikely comradery, indicated by mouths flapping, hands moving and shoulders rounding forward, was cause for suspicion. She pursed her lips and muttered, "Mary Fields should be supervising Mr. Mosney, not his Lordship." The discordant association gave her an itch.

While Mosney rambled on about his superior skills and experience, Reverend Brondel appraised the man's obvious desire to advance. Though normally, the Reverend would feel disinclined to encourage such aspirations, due to the uncouth personal hygiene and the man's grandiose assessment of his ability, he wondered: was he competent enough to manage the place? Brondel met the ranch hand's stare and acknowledged the brazen closure: "So that's why I think you'd be real smart to get rid of the nigger woman, sir. Ain't no reason to have a nigger woman in a place like this, anyways, not when you could have myself, in her stead."

5

LOVE AND BETRAYAL

SUMMER 1894

Mother Amadeus had business in Cascade and wanted to do it herself. She asked Mary Fields to take her, and Mary heartily agreed, glad for the opportunity to get some tobacco.

Mr. Burns, Mosney's boss and the official mission ranch foreman, overheard. He was a wiry, brittle man, dark haired with high cheekbones and a tendency to disappear when questions rose. He seldom spoke, and when he did his taut eyes flickered from side to side. At times his head would droop, displaying the bald spot at its top, the size and shape of a fried egg and oddly edged by a handsome mane that hung to his shoulders. A dense mustache bowed downward, fusing into a fibrous untamed beard useful for concealing occasional facial tics.

Pretending he had not heard words pass between them, he broached, "Morning Mother Superior, I needs to pick up some horse shoes in town." He shot Mary a glance. "Would you like me to take you along, Mother?" Pressing his tongue against his palate, he sounded a series of hollow clicks and pointed at Mary, "She's got chores to do."

"How serendipitous, Mr. Burns."

He shifted his weight and scowled, unsure of the word and her meaning.

Not in the mood for fiddle-faddle, Mother clarified, "Mr. Burns, you're welcome to come to town with Mary Fields and I, if you like, within the hour. You can ready the team and wagon." She pulled her shawl tighter and strode briskly toward her office.

Burns smacked his right fist into his left palm and flung his hair back.

Mary ignored him and hurried to finish her chores. Pinching eggs from the old hen Martha, who pecked as fast of one of those treadle sewing machines donated by Miss Drexel, was never simple. "Two big ones. Good girl, Martha," she praised as she slid her hand out from under the seat of feathers. Unscathed, Mary trotted to the academy kitchen, handed the egg basket to Gertrude and rushed to her cabin where she threw on a clean skirt and grabbed her Winchester. "Bullets," she muttered, "have to buy bullets."

As Mother lunged upward, squeezed onto the buckboard plank next to Mr. Burns, now moved to the middle, she wished they had a buggy for day errands. Mary Fields signaled the team. The wagon, front-heavy with three people and no freight, rolled through the mission gate and past a thick row of lilac bushes that spiked seasonal pheromones capable of rousing inklings. Both Marys agreed that the scent was hypnotically fragrant and fell silent.

After a few miles, Burns could no longer tolerate being sandwiched between two women and asked if they could let up long enough for him to jump in the back. He regretted tagging along but reconciled his irritation by stretching out for a quick nap that he planned to follow with a dram or two of moonshine at Ludwig's place.

Mary maneuvered a smooth ride from the team who sported occasional snorts and blows, frisky head tossing and prancing she believed to be natural longings for freedom. It was early summer, after all. Revived earth warmed her progeny of grains, and sweated carbon musk, breathing deeply once more. Sapling leaf buds timidly unwound, and songbirds clung to weathered cattails, yodeling melodies to prospective mates. Melted ice trickled beneath the marsh, rechanneling trout avenues that would flow into the Dearborn River.

This landscape, designated Sun River Valley on government survey maps, ran from the Sun River in the north to the Dearborn River in the south. Locals preferred to call their region The Birdtail, named after an astounding lone monolith that marked the halfway point between the two cherished waterways. Birdtail Rock towered one thousand feet above the valley floor and featured a limestone-ridged summit, glacially sculpted into mammoth fanned-tail-feathers—a landmark from all directions.

Mary heard that generations of sacred ceremonies and vision quests had taken place on its elevated ledge. Beneath the quilled heights, a magnificent swath of earth lay prostrated. Each spring, seasonal winds and a variety of birds delivered seed to the ridge. Rain sprouted and seedlings flourished, making a thick green headband that adorned the mythic headdress, phoenix feathers sparkling in limitless acres of sky.

To Burns, the massive rock was simply a compass point, nothing more. He claimed that it looked like an upside-down eyetooth—but he was not known for sensitivities.

Cascade was less than an hour away. Burns pulled himself up and kneeled behind the cross-seat, squared close to Mother's black habit, what he thought of as a head tent. Attempting to sound solicitous, he asked how long she would be and suggested that she take "high tea," being the gentile lady that she was.

He intended to enjoy an undisturbed afternoon of leisure with whatever company he could rustle, sip that moonshine and get away from pious women for as long as possible. Unconvinced that she would heed his advice, he sighed, lifted a hand to scratch his bald spot, saw the harness break and screamed, "Look!"

The black mare fell to her knees. "Jump!" Mary yelled. The wagon lurched, then tilted on two wheels. Mother leaped as far as she could.

Mary flung herself, throwing the reins loose. She saw Burns hit the ground, yards back. Her boots slammed into gravel and she tucked, rolled against the grade. A quick glance assured that Mother was intact and she ran after the horses who were wide-eyed and trapped between straps and wheel spokes. Bursts of fright wet their nostrils, and they squealed and shook while Mary cooed and hurried to unleash unpredictable horsepower from anchors of wood.

Mother Mary eased herself upright and watched, taking care to be still.

Mary untangled hooves and legs from broken harness parts and a cracked singletree. Cautiously, she coaxed each horse from the shamble and walked them down the road and back to calm their nerves and check for injuries. She uncoiled the rope looped across her shoulder and tied the team to a tree ringed by knee-high grass.

"Are you all right, Mary?" she called, limping toward her, stretching muscle cramps.

Mother nodded and dusted off her many yards of cloth.

Burns rolled back from his fixed position and barked, "How dare you call the Mother Superior by her first name!"

"Relax, Mr. Burns. Help with the wagon, please," Mother shot.

Searching for the cause of the crash, Mary knelt to examine pieces of gear flung about. The harness straps were shredded, severed between rivets, where the leather had cracked previously—it had not been repaired as ordered.

Mary turned to face Burns who had finally risen and was casually inserting a pinch of tobacco into his mouth. "You no good excuse of a foreman," she yelled, "Look what you've done to Mother Mary. She could have died all because of you! Your leg better be broke from doing nothing—shirking *again*. I asked Mosney to repair this harness weeks ago, and he said you'd already done it!"

"Mary, it's all right," Mother said from the sidelines.

Burns, who had indeed not made the repair and played possum on the ground while Mary risked injury to save the horses, straightened his crumpled straw hat and tongued his chaw. With a flaunting twist of the hand, he signaled her dismissal and grunted, "You stupid nigger, shut your dirty mouth."

Mary grabbed a rock the size of her palm. "No one puts my friend in danger. You shut up." She aimed and watched the stone spin past his ear.

"Missed, ya dumb cluck," the high-pitched scratchy voice retaliated. Burns drew his pistol and pointed it.

"Go ahead, you coward," she dared. "Then at least you'd be hanged and the mission would finally be rid of you! If I wanted that rock to hit you dead, it would have. I'm warning you!"

Mother charged forward, planted herself between them, arms outstretched as if she could push them apart with willpower. "Mr. Burns, I beg you, put that gun away. I need you to go to town and get help." She lowered her arms and stepped toward him. "Please."

Burns' face, the side Mother could see, was purple with rage. He leveled his pistol at Mary a moment longer, savoring his hatred and the thrill of control. He spat on the ground and turned his back, shoved his gun into the holster. Starting off in a slow swagger, he calculated earshot distance and cursed loud enough to get the last word, "Women too big for their britches should realize their place is married, serving their master—not roaming the world."

He worked his tongue to muster more saliva and realized that he had mocked Black Mary as intended, and also the Mother Superior. A quiver spasmed

Mary turned to Mother Mary. "Have you seen my rifle?"

"Over there." She pointed towards a ditch. "Did you really ask them to repair the harness weeks ago?"

"You know I did if I said so. Mosney and Burns are no good, plain and simple." She adjusted her cap. "Like I said from the get go, Burns is an ungroomed mule's tail, to put it politely. You need better, Mary."

Mother rubbed dust from her eyes. "You know we don't have much to choose from. You're the best caretaker we could ever have. No hired help works like you. If you were a man, Reverend Brondel would tell me to give you a raise."

"They could at least do their job without whining about it."

"Let's sit in the shade for a moment."

By mid-summer, Saint Angela's two-acre vegetable garden burst with potatoes, turnips, beans, pumpkins, corn, tomatoes, squash, carrots, collards, peas, chard, onions, garlic and lettuce. The neighboring herb garden flourished too: comfrey, fennel, thyme, rosemary, capsicum, lemon balm, lavender, lovage, savory, oregano, tarragon, feverfew—domestic varieties combined with natives—cultivated spice bordered by marigolds and nasturtiums to fend off insects.

Sizzling July heat energized.

When the Indian boys assigned to sheep duty herded the mission flocks down from the hills nearby, Annie counted sixty-four wooly bodies that were to be dipped and sheared by Mosney and Burns, who thought Mary Fields ought to do it.

Other mission livestock included twenty pigs, two-hundred head of cattle, two-dozen horses and four-hundred foul. Grain was equally crucial for Saint Peter's survival; the Jesuit's workforce planted one-hundred acres of oats and seventy-five acres of wheat when classes ended in June.

Mary cherished the long hours of sun that lasted near to midnight. Frustration over Mosney and Burns receded as she cared for her herbs and flowers, and harvested fresh vegetables.

Nancy, like most of the Indian girls, resented being forced to remain at the mission during summer, severed from all family contact while nearly all of the white children went home to their parents. Even if they had to labor long hours, like us, she considered, it was still unfair. She sulked, longing for her parents, her brother and her friends, anxious at the uncertainties—who was alive or dead?

During afternoon break, Annie looked for Mary, anxious to ask a question she'd been mulling over. She found her on her knees in the garden, nosing through chard leaves, inspecting insect holes. Annie tapped her Ucsote's shoulder.

"Well look who's here," Mary said, grinning, "was just thinking about you." She handed Annie a harvest basket, its width half the girl's height. "Would you pick the reddest tomatoes for me? Right there—aren't they glorious?"

Annie squeezed her fingers around the basket's cool antler handle and inspected the tightly woven willow shoots skillfully patterned into an interesting shape—deep, plump and oval, like a gourd. "This basket is beautiful," she said, examining the intricacies. "Don't you think so?" She glanced to Mary who hadn't heard, engrossed in the thinning of carrots—deciding which were the strongest, pulling the others with apologies.

Annie wondered why the nuns let the older girls weave baskets, when no other native tradition was allowed. Snapping tomato stems at their notches, she lined the basket's interior with ripe produce and dragged it toward Mary. "White Crow, do you think that the name Saint Germain was given to me because my grandmother was a medicine woman? I remember she was important. Do you think the name giver tried to match the meaning of my family name into English—saint for healer?"

"Maybe, but how would he know? Your family lines were—I mean are, maternal, and I don't think your people used last names, did they?" Landing "Saint Germain" was more likely the luck of the draw, Mary thought, having altered her theory after quizzing Mother Amadeus. She envisioned a late-night Calvary poker game—the winner who picked the next captive's name.

"I don't understand."

"Never mind, sweet girl." Mary gazed at Annie, thinking it novel, nonetheless, that they had had the same inkling. A large green grasshopper jumped from beneath the chard. She pounced, squished the invader with a rock.

"White Crow, did the elders women teach you how to grow the plants? Did you learn anything from books? How did you learn to make the medicines?"

Mary laughed. "Didn't learn about plants from books. The remedies I know were passed from one woman to another, by story and song, women sticking together." She pulled the bandana off her head and wiped sweat from her face, recalling sweltering Tennessee heat and rows of tobacco plants, women whispering among them. Yet she had learned some helpful treatments watching white doctors treat the white people she worked for, was owned by. "All cures were spoken before they were written. Good to write it down, too, Annie. You learn how to write." She fanned her face and looked up. "Mother's doctor prescribes Actia Racemosa tincture for diphtheria. Actia Racemosa is Latin for Black Snake Root, and that's the same plant native folks around here used for ages. He added a powder called potash ..."

"I don't know everything you said. Will you teach me about the healing plants?"

"My, been rattling, haven't I? Yes, Onatah, I will. Sometimes I forget you're little."

"That's all right, White Crow. Sometimes I forget you're big. I love you, Ucsote."

Mary glanced, smiling for the bravery it had taken for an orphan to offer such a thing. "I love you too, Onatah. You remind me of a bird in spring with a magic song—she travels with sky woman and the animals."

"That's funny, White Crow. Do you think I could work on my own like you, when I am older? That's what I want—and to go back to my tribe. Do you think I can?"

Mary pushed the basket aside and sat down.

"It's possible. When I grew up is already a long time ago. Things change slow, but they change." She pulled weeds within reach. "You can do more than anyone thinks, Annie. Start by listening, and watch—you do that already. Learn their words. And the rhythm. And read." She leaned back, crossed her legs beneath her skirt and looked long at Annie. "I don't think the white name giver tried to honor your grandma, but I do know a story about the name Saint Germain. Want to hear it?"

"Yes!"

"Have a seat." She patted the soil next to her. "Turns out that there was a special fella, long time ago, called Comte de Saint-Germain. That means the Count of Saint Germain."

"What does Count mean?"

"It's kind of like being a chief or at least one of the important braves in the tribe."

"Oh. Where did he live?"

"Somewhere in Europe. He moved around a lot."

"What does his name mean—the Saint Germain part?"

"His name means great healer, magician, artist, you name it. It's like he could do everything better than anyone else, and somehow he stayed young, on top of it. He healed lots of people and spoke many languages."

"Oh, then it's a good name, as long as we are made to have white names, isn't it, White Crow?"

"Yes, I think it's a mighty fine name, especially the medicine healing part. Just like you said."

Annie looked to distant tree lines, drew a circle around herself with her finger.

Mary thought about the surname "Fields"—slaves had always been forced to answer to their master's surname, as far as she could recollect. Could have changed it once freed, legal, she considered, but by then, I'd worn it for more than half a century. Like to think of my former master's ancestors who begot the name "Fields" by laboring hard in them, same as we were put to laboring in those endless sweltering fields. Rather be named after plants than the trades, though. Better than Miller, Smith or Taylor. Wonder what my family's real name was.

Annie uttered, "Medicine healer, artist, magician," putting the words to memory.

"Annie, go get us something to tie up these tomatoes. Ask Sister Gertrude."

Mary watched the girl scamper toward the kitchen, quickened by the spoken words of love. She wished for a thundershower to escape watering rows of vegetables bucket by bucket.

"You done fixed the fence wrong, Nigger Mary," a voice rabid as a mad dog accused.

"Oh God, that pain in the neck," Mary murmured to the cabbage in her hand. Her grip tightened. She envisioned herself throwing it at Mosney as she stood up and mentally bore a hole through his forehead.

"What ya lookin at? Need me to show ya? Or do I need to do your work for ya on top of mine own?"

Mary glanced toward her rifle propped against the shed five feet away. Mosney caught her glance, cocked his pistol and pointed it at her. "Don't be thinking of shootin' me, Nigger."

She let the cabbage drop and glared at him, daring with an equal force of loathing, daring him to make it equal—each shooter, aiming, firearm in hand—if he had the guts for a showdown. She knew he wouldn't. She was the better shot. She considered her choices—how much time to reach her rifle? Was it worth the risk?

Seeing only Mary outside, Annie skipped from the pantry doorway calling, "Here's the string, Whi—"

Mary's look stopped her.

Annie saw the gun. She cast her sight to the ground and slumped, posturing submission.

Mosney saw the concern in Mary's eyes and followed her gaze, pointed his pistol at the girl with the happy voice.

Recoiling her manner, Mary spoke with neutrality—limp, as if she had surrendered, defeated. "I hear you, Mosney. I'll take care of that fence." She moved forward, planted herself between Annie and the weapon, tipped her eyes away from his.

Mosney snickered and spouted a victorious reprisal, "All right then, Nigger Mary. Get right to it. The fence is waiting." He uncocked the Colt, shoved it into his holster.

She sizzled, wished the man would trip and fall into a well with no water.

Spinning a half turn, Mosney paraded a victorious strut to the barn where he celebrated with a shot of corn whiskey, smug with new ammunition he'd relay to the reverend: *the darkie had threatened him at gunpoint!*

Annie recaptured her voice and asked, "Are you all right?"

Mary motioned Annie to come. Pulled her close. "Yes, course I am. Never let scum hurt you, Annie." She felt the pace of her heart, still pounding, stroked Annie's hair and looked down. "How about you, you all right?"

"Fine," Annie said, "I'm going to be like you, White Crow."

A chuckle murmured. "Well, not exactly, I hope." She lifted her darling into her arms and walked toward the house, uttering, "Thank you, Lord Almighty."

Reverend Brondel rested leisurely in his opulent library. He leaned back into his forest-green leather smoking-chair, cigar in hand. His housekeeper, a nervous woman coping with a torso twisted from arthritis, knocked on her master's door. Gaining permission, she entered gripping a silver tray upon which a single white envelope lay, addressed, "Master Reverend Brondel, URGENT."

Brondel took the correspondence and dismissed her. He leaned across the sixteenth century English parliament desk, grabbed his inlaid tortoise-shell letter opener and cut the fold with adept expertise, the kind acquired by gentleman hunters accustomed to slitting pheasant throats. He scanned the smudged letter.

-Collection or Prosecute, your Choice-

July 13, 1894

Honorable Reverend Brondel Sir,

> *Pay up the $400 the Ursuline Convent owes me for labor done and legal written promise to pay $400 for labor and travel expense for me and my family to come to the Saint Peter's Mission from New York and work for them, which I did, but will not stay any longer, or else I am sure that the Great Falls and Helena papers and the Federal Commission of Indian Affairs and the Bureau of Catholic Indian Missions would like to know about how the Catholic church doesn't*

*respect the working man and breaks contracts whenever it feels like it.
The same kinds of contracts you have with the America government to
get money for your Indian schools. Telegram me by the end of today or
I start talking. Send train tickets for three to me at Saint Peter's and
$400 cash.*

Mr. Lewis Walmert

"What a weasel," he snarled, "this is the one Mother hired to eliminate
the help problems. She was right. Asked me to talk to him." He lifted his
head, swore he could almost hear blood swishing inside his pulsing veins,
the tips of which had already burst into scarlet spider-web-marks on both
cheeks and earlobes.

"Haven't had time," he grumbled, darting a hot stare through the
statuesque bay window, taking a deep breath and brief moments to visit
his state bishop obligations. He reconsidered Mother's grievance. She
had expected the applicant to keep his word when she had agreed to pay
for his, and his family's, travel expenses from New York in return for the
commitment to work as ranch manager for a minimum of six months—
assuming, considerately, that the employee would be more likely to stay if
his family lived on site—believing the initial expense would be justified if
he managed the property's work force during months when she was absent
supervising her other missions.

He'd worked for half of the agreed upon term, collected his forty-five
dollar wage for each of three months, claiming, according to Mother, that
neither the place nor the work (the little accomplished thus far), met his
standards, and managed to instigate, by means of poor leadership skills,
additional conflict between Mosney and Burns. Clearly, he had not earned
the $400 she had invested to obtain his services.

She requested me, her bishop, to represent her, he recalled—believing,
after certain undisclosed behavior, that Mr. Walmert would disregard
confrontation coming from a woman of the cloth. She asked *me* to rally to
the Ursuline cause, admonish the cunning opportunist and persuade him
to keep his commitment. Now this half-cocked illegitimate threat forces
the issue—necessitates immediate action. Pacing, he concluded: Wally,
or whatever his name is, (he glanced to the letter) is obviously trying to
take advantage, his timing abundantly opportune considering the current
political upheaval over appropriations, all of us competing to provide Indian
schools.

He grabbed a cigar from his humidor, rolled it between thumb and finger.

I should have done as she asked, he admitted. But damages to the Church's reputation could easily exceed $400 if the kind of rumors Walmert threatens to make are picked up by the press—who knows what ramifications would follow—it could be disastrous.

He returned the cigar to its case.

Though Mary Amadeus was the one who pioneered the nine Montana Ursuline missions single-handed, and in truth, was the shining star responsible for most of the federal dollars and political support for Catholic presence in Montana for which he, as the state's Catholic Bishop, had received valuable accolades—this time he would abstain from championing her petition.

He spoke the words out loud to fuel his resolution. "It's the way it has to be.

He looked outside and glanced around his study, assembling details he would need to communicate before closing the matter, and concluded: I'll advise Mother Amadeus to meet the extortionist's demands—the tickets and the cash—immediately. Tell her not to offer likewise contracts in the future. Easing into the chair behind his desk, he tapped his foot and penned his judgment posthaste, aware that Mary Amadeus didn't have the funds to fulfill his mandate.

After fastening the many buttons of his vest, the reverend bishop pushed himself up and squeezed the smooth head of his walking stick—the beginning of his personal ritual adopted to create the Sabbath homily, a moral exhortation.

He embarked on his Friday afternoon promenade about Helena—a private processional—listening, observing and composing. When his feet began to hurt, he relied upon memorized scripture to distract himself from poundage pressing upon his fallen arches. This exercise, he believed, aided his ability to empathize with those who suffered, and he contemplated doctrine-driven lessons, parables for his hard-working membership. The Bishop could be counted on to quote relevant scripture. The Holy Bible was, in his opinion, the exemplar to combat all manner of temptations during the many trials of life. He reminded faithful parishioners, "If you falter there is always absolution."

Turning homeward, he recited, as was his habit, the twenty-third Psalm. This day, as he reached "… the valley of the shadow of death," he prayed simultaneously for God to sweep Ursuline problems away. "Perhaps by the lifting of the Holy staff that comforted," he digressed.

Days later, on July 25th, the Right Reverend Lordship Brondel, Catholic Bishop of Montana, received another urgent letter, this time from the Ursuline Saint Francis Xavier Mission, also within his jurisdiction. His countenance soured as he read:

Dear Honorable Bishop Reverend Brondel,

We are sorry to concern you with this, but we think you should be aware that one of our sisters, Sister Agnes, formerly Genevieve Brewer, is spreading rumors that Sister Rose has not received proper medical care or food or clothing. The claim states that Sister Rose has been left to die in our mission, with no concern or effort to assist on our part. What shall we do about—

Mother Scholastica
Saint Francis Xavier Mission, Crow Reservation

Ashamed of his volatile resentments, Brondel rubbed his topaz ring and lamented: when are these women going to do what they vowed to do—remain in cloisters and stop making problems for the church and their bishop? Why hasn't Mother Superior taken care of this?

He rubbed his head.

It all started with that colored woman, Mary Fields, he ruminated. She's the fly in the ointment. Mosney and Burns have a point. A negress shouldn't be giving orders to white men. God only knows what she'll do next. She was supposed to work for redemptive privileges. She's more trouble than she's worth, no matter the history between her and Mary Amadeus. And that's another thing: gives me the bejesus, their odd-fellow friendship. Best to cut machinations of the devil out before Mother Mary gets the opportunity to protest.

With harried hand he scribbled on official letterhead stationery and dispatched an envelope addressed: "Miss Mary Fields, Laundress, Saint Peter's Mission."

The Reverend scribed likewise correspondence to The Reverend Mother Mary Amadeus, Mother Superior of Montana Ursulines:

July 25, 1894

Dear Sister Mary Amadeus,

After careful consideration, I instruct you to enforce my directive, as scribed to Miss Mary Fields this same date. My decision, based on testimony of disruptive and violent behavior, is final.

We must place our religious commitments before personal associations. I am confident that you will implement the terms categorically.

Sincerely,
Reverend Bishop John Baptist Brondel

cc: Reverend J. Rebmann
Society of Jesus
Saint Peter's Mission

P.S. I trust you will resolve the problems at Saint Francis Xavier Mission immediately.

That same morning, Mother Amadeus had risen early and asked Mr. Burns to prepare the wagon and drive her to Great Falls. Stomach pain had necessitated her confinement for several weeks, and accounts were delinquent. She needed to make bank deposits and planned to make private inquiries to secure a Birdtail mining claim, believing that she may have discovered a vein of gold. Perhaps lying ill, vomiting on my birthday, was the opportunity for the Almighty to deliver this plan; it could provide financial independence, she pined. She informed the nuns that she would return before the agent from the Board of Indian Affairs arrived to inspect the mission, three days hence.

Mary mended fence where horns had pulled a post loose. Managing wire and wood and torn gloves to conform, similar to embroidery, she mused, she noticed how much bigger the place seemed without Burns. Breathing summer scents deep down, she hummed the melody "Follow the Drinking Gourd," and congratulated herself for making that run from Tennessee to Ohio, all those years ago.

Her stomach growled, which led her to imagine Gertrude simmering a thick venison stew, rich and tender, and she licked her lips, anticipating the taste. Afterwards she would enjoy her evening ritual—rocking in her rocking chair, her stomach full, puffing on one of those delicious cigars Mother Mary would bring from the smoke shop in Great Falls, as she had promised.

A familiar voice surprised her from behind. "How did you come to acquire so many skills usually owned by white men?" Nancy asked, observing Mary twist the barbed wire with adept skill. She knelt to search Mary's leather tool bag for the cutters she would surely request.

"Nancy, you gave me a start."

"Sorry, White Crow. Didn't mean to."

"No matter."

Mary took the cutters and clipped. "What did the Sisters teach you about emancipation?" she asked, deciding whether to share a personal chronicle.

"They taught us that slaves were freed in 1865. Is that right?"

"That was when the law was passed on paper, but it didn't mean anything yet. There were slave catchers everywhere. They hunted us like animals, and if we got caught they sold us back into bondage, into chains, making money for our suffering. That provided plenty of incentive to learn how to survive out-of-sight." She handed the cutters back and adjusted her cap. "You know how the government gave the tribes big blocks of reservation land, then changed the boundaries, made them smaller or moved tribes somewhere different?"

"Yes."

"Well, it was the same thing. I don't trust words on paper. I think folks are going to do what they want, no matter what they write down. A promise of the heart doesn't need to be written."

"That's what our chief said."

"Then I agree with your chief. Learn as much as you can about the world—I learned how to shoot, freight, raise stock, cook and launder—all so I could get work and survive alone if I needed to move on. Don't think all your academics would have helped me, but maybe they'll build an arsenal for you girls. I'm real glad I learned to read and write—was a lot older than you. You'll do all right, Nancy. I know it in my heart."

Nancy looked toward the three-story stone fortress, aware that she should hurry to perform the task she had been sent to accomplish—bring Mary in for supper. Twisting her braid, she looked to her companion. "I don't know what tools I'm going to need. I don't know what kind of choices I'll have."

"That's right. You don't even have rights on paper, let alone in the hearts of white folks and the government, so you have to create more than one plan and make the best choices possible. See what's coming before the rest of—"

The supper bell rang.

Mary considered her own advice. *Have I gotten lazy? Haven't made any backup plans myself, lately.* She slung her tool bag over her shoulder and wrapped an arm around her distressed friend. They looked to the mountains, to each other, and headed in.

Sister Gertrude stopped barking orders when she saw Mary. Rushing with propelled urgency, eyes wide and words quick to follow, she huffed, "Mary, I have something for you. Look!"

A glance to her apron revealed a paper corner jutting above the pocket edge—fine quality, weighted texture. "It's a letter addressed to you!" Fumbling to free the missive from her clothespins, she reported dutifully, "Father Rebmann just now brought the post."

Mary smiled at Gertrude's genuine devotion to efficiency and her loyalty. "My word. What's for supper?"

Gertrude's jaw dropped. "Mary, open your letter—then you get supper."

"Let me wash my dirty hands." Heading to the water basin she asked Gertrude, close behind, "Who is it from?"

"It doesn't say. Sure looks fancy."

The post released at last from her keeping, Gertrude watched Mary struggle with the well-sealed flap. "Want a knife?"

"No, but can I borrow your spectacles?"

Gertrude pulled the twine loop that kept hers handy, over her head, gave them and gaped, as did Nancy, ignoring the raucous activity behind, anxious to hear exciting news from somewhere.

Mary propped the spectacles on her nose, pulled a single sheet of folded cardstock from the envelope, and angled her head to bring the handwriting into focus. Long moments expired. Gertrude and Nancy grew concerned by frown lines cutting into the face they loved. They looked to each other.

Gertrude asked, "What is it?"

Mary, rereading the message, lifted her palm and held it there.

Nancy drew a breath.

Finally, Mary raised her head, stared at Gertrude, mouth open. No words.

"Who is it from?" Gertrude demanded.

Mary grunted, cleared her throat. "Brondel."

She handed the paper over, looked to the ceiling, looked to the floor, bit her lip to stop it from quivering, restrained herself momentarily, before exploding, "How dare him!"

A tick of time passed. She stomped her right foot and shouted again, "How dare him!" Her nails had cut into the palms of her fisted hands.

Nancy grabbed Mary's arms and pleaded, "Mary, what's wrong?"

Face contorted, she made no answer.

Gertrude struggled to read without her spectacles. She passed the letter to Nancy, ordering, "Read me what it says!"

Having heard Mary shout, students fled their places in the dining room and ran into the kitchen, the three words, *how dare him,* ringing in their young bones. Mary had never shouted anger before. Who was him? What horrible thing had he done? Where was the faceless attacker?

Nancy forced her voice to elocute:

July 25, 1894

To Mary Fields
Laundress, Saint Peter's Ursuline Mission

It has come to my attention that you have been exhibiting inappropriate behavior: to wit, violence and vulgarity. This immoral conduct is not conducive to a school environment.

Therefore, by my authority as Catholic Bishop of Montana, you are hereby dismissed of your employment at Saint Peter's Mission and are instructed to leave the premises immediately.

Henceforth, your relationship with the Sisters and Brothers at Saint Peter's is forever severed. You will not associate with the school, the instructors or its students from this time forward. You are instructed to leave with any and all of your possessions immediately. Do not return.

Reverend J. Brondel
Catholic Bishop of Montana
Helena, Montana

An uncomfortable silence trespassed against them. Whispers surfaced and repeated the horrible words: dismissed—severed—violence—do not return—Reverend Brondel. They added their own: Mary leaving? No, that can't be right. Can Mother Superior stop it? Those unable to speak buried fear in the pits of their stomachs.

Growing nervous, Sister Anna came forward. "Articles in the American Constitution promise protection from moral turpitude. Don't they? How can the church allow this to happen?"

Mary's indignation flared, "How *dare* him call my name in vain! How *dare* him accuse me without witness! He can't do this. *He has no right!*" She gripped her gut as though she had been stabbed.

"The devil's invaded our house," a young voice pronounced.

Gertrude cried out, "It has to be a mistake! You didn't do those things. We—"

Mary surveyed the nuns' paralyzed expressions. Knowing it was futile to ask, she did nonetheless as she beseeched, "Who's been saying I'm violent and vulgar? Do you know who it is?"

Darting looks indicated no insights. Suspicions leaned toward the men.

"Let me see the coward's face! Let them prove it!"

She paced a tethered course, a victim falsely accused, a warrior without status or means.

Nancy wadded the letter into a ball and heaved it to the floor. Annie, riveted mute from the beginning, forced her terror-struck body to leap. She grabbed the paper ball and threw it. Gertrude visioned the dispatch from hell fires bursting into flames. Sister Seraphine saw the coterie of girls bonded together as if bound, martyred. The girls, jarred as they re-grasped the scope of their tenuous predicament, waited to see if something would be done.

"Of all times for Mother to be gone," Gertrude wailed.

Mary's angst welled again.

"Says I'm fired, Gertrude." She crossed her arms, still standing in the center of the large room. "Says I have to leave y'all right this minute, for no reason. Just like that." She looked at each girl and each woman, all members of her family. "What a coward," she accused, disgusted. "Doesn't have the guts to be clear, cause he can't. He alludes, accuses, condemns—claims *I'm* violent while he spears me in the back." She stomped, smashing his dirty rotten words into the ground.

"I think you're right," Gertrude said. "You've been charged and convicted with two minutes of scribble. Sit down by me." She patted the table she had perched herself upon, pleading with tired eyes. "Girls, leave us now." She waved a hand. "Except you two," pointing a finger toward Nancy and Annie.

Mary sat down and closed her eyes. Thoughts skidded, and she went blank. Seconds passed. She pictured a lone mallard swooping down to enter a still lake—the moment just above water, when the flyer meets her reflection—open wings and sky visible above and below, about to merge ...

She saw it. She herself, the bird in flight. The bird surrenders, trusts the immersion, the collision into self ... or is she colliding into another self, an underbelly? And when her landing proves smooth, entering water that yields, folds into, becomes a part of her with the sky ... is she home? And what does that mean?

Sipping a breath, she felt warm steam rising to her face. Gertrude had brewed tea in a cup. For her. Set it on the table that she, Mary, had built. Resting elbows to hold the cup steady, she swallowed, lifted her chin, pushed her hoarse voice into a matter-of-fact tone and stated, "Mosney and Burns must have made up a whopper."

Annie scooted beside Mary, leaned her head on her Ucsote's shoulder and asked, "What's a whopper, White Crow?" The women chuckled, glad for some relief.

"It's a big fat lie."

She kissed Annie's head and said, "Don't you worry."

A covey of skirts rushed into the kitchen. The door shut. An informal conference began.

"Mary, wait until Mother returns. She'll know what to do," said Clara, frightened that Mary might do something wild and get hurt.

"There must be procedure to contest such an unwarranted order," said Sebastian. "Who would know the procedure?"

"Mother will know," Anna said. Doubt tested her certainty, and she blinked.

"When is she returning?" Sebastian demanded.

"Anytime now," Gertrude replied, rubbing a cramp.

"He should have to provide proof to *someone*," Anna insisted.

"Should, yes, but he can falsify his claims," Sebastian answered.

The newest novice, arrived from Toledo, rushed in, a book in hand. Eyes followed her. She asked the sisters to close them in prayer as she recited what she believed would solve the problem. With sober resolve she spoke, "The darkness of obedience will be lights in the next world."

Nancy glared, thinking, how could you possibly believe that? She wanted to shout: *Do you have any idea what you're saying?*

Gertrude said to the novice, "Thank you, dear. Shut the door, please, on your way out."

The young woman blushed and did as she was told.

Mary railed, "He has to charge me face to face, at least! Cowardice is not, as he said, conducive to school environment."

Annie imagined a buffalo charging her Ucsote, horns plunging, blood and guts spewing across Saint Angela's compound. Tears welled. She clung to her Ucsote's skirt.

Mary's blistered scorn fired, "Inappropriate behavior, he says. I'll challenge his, any day. Can't just destroy a person's life with words on paper!"

She scanned the company of faces. Nancy's penetrating gaze righted her compass: *of course he can ruin a person's life*. My life. Executing scribbles of ink with pious white authority. Isn't that what they all do in fits of disdain?

She stood up. "I'm going to Helena. I'm gonna see him face to face. He can prove his claims or back off."

Numb, Nancy said, "You know he isn't going to do that, Mary."

Mary looked at her young friend who had apparently been listening to her all along.

"He's at least going to have to look me in the eyes and lie before the Almighty God he professes to know so well. I hope the Almighty is gazing down when he makes false charges with the same voice that claims the right to forgive sins and preach compassion."

The base pulse in Mary's neck punched. She sat down.

The nuns clung in static positions, groping with the injustice, the unexplained tragedy forced upon their loyal friend who had always been the mission cornerstone in one way or another, since its beginning. Most of them firmly believed it wrong for the Bishop to have been given power over their Ursuline mission in the first place. They also knew if they did not obey him, their community was at risk of removal, just like Mary Fields.

"God forbid," Clara murmured.

"This slaps the face of Ursuline tradition," Gertrude wailed, "We are ordained to help women in trouble."

Sebastian pressed her temples.

Sister Anna looked at the floor.

Mary restated her course of action with chilling resolve. "This is what's going to happen. I'm leaving for Helena tomorrow to see the Reverend Brondel who will have to stand up to *me*. *Prove* his accusations."

No one responded.

"I need to go to bed now. Good night, sisters."

Nancy and Annie followed her outside.

Gertrude rallied. She bade the sisters to gather at the table and think. Think of ways to help. "She's bent and determined to confront the Reverend Lordship, and no one's going to stop her."

"We need to do something, whatever we can," Anna whimpered.

Clara asked, "Shouldn't we wait for Mother?"

"There is no time," Gertrude stated, rolling her eyes.

Seraphine, who had kept her tongue, declared, "We need to provide Mary with the support Mother would give." She crossed her arms, resolved.

Sebastian said, "Mr. Flinn is leaving for Helena tomorrow. He's at the Jesuit's house."

"Mary will take that as a sign of predestination," Gertrude sighed.

Clara had a thought. "If she is going to confront the Reverend Lordship, she needs to be dressed properly. It may help her cause."

"Now you're thinking," Gertrude praised. "Is there time to sew her a dress tonight, Sebastian?"

Sebastian looked at her watch, a prized possession. "Yes."

"Will you do it?"

"Yes, if someone stays up to keep me company."

"We must let Mr. Flinn know before dawn, so he doesn't leave without her," Seraphine said, tying shoelaces that had come undone.

"I'll go," Anna volunteered, glad to escape.

"Do you think Mother Superior will really be able to change the Lordship's mind?" Clara asked.

Heads wobbled.

Gertrude stood up, put her hands on her hips. "We need to be champions. We'll keep faith, make Mother proud. I'll brew some coffee."

Sebastian said, "Who's going to get the parlor curtains down? It's the only yardage we have at the moment."

6

PURSUIT

SUMMER 1894

*M*ary lifted her gathered skirt of floral chintz, yesterday's pleated window dressing, above her boot as she stepped into Mr. Flinn's buggy. She insisted on driving the team, wishing to mentally prepare for confrontation and avoid chitchat. It would take up to seven hours to rein the distance, five if lucky. She headed south to Dearborn, then to Wolf Creek, flanking the *Missouri's* western bank until arriving, at last, in Helena, Montana's cosmopolitan capital perched on a fortuitous roost under chunky spires of the continental divide, where one could hang one's hat and look east, down to Canyon Ferry Dam, a corralled water source that would soon supply the region's electric lights.

Should have put this garb on later, Mary thought, examining creases from the day's ride, but it was important to show the sisters how much I appreciate their good will. Don't like the idea of dressing up to defend myself. It's ironic—I'm headed to where I first arrived in Montana.

That night Mary bunked with kitchen staff in quarters at the Hotel Broadwater. She had befriended a number of the help during previous visits to the state capital. Once, they had included her in a late night escapade to soak in one of the hot spring baths, a luxury that had risked their jobs in the doing.

Grisly yet contained, Mary relayed her predicament to her city-friends and summarized, "I'm ready now. The question is, is he ready for me!"

In the cool of morning, she wrapped an old black cotton shawl tight around the bodice of her fancy dress and clonked down a wide sidewalk that continued past Main Street to the Catholic Church on the corner of First

Avenue East. She stood before the vicarage steps recently scrubbed, eyed the varnished door which displayed a prominent brass plaque inscribed "The Honorable Reverend Lordship Brondel" and stepped up, pounded its mid panel with a heavy hand, intending to sound like an invited male caller.

A fair-skinned, white-haired woman opened the massive door and looked up. "May I help you?" she asked politely.

Mary wondered how the woman could see with irises the color of bone. "Yes, Ma'am, you may. I would like to speak to the Reverend Brondel, please."

"I'm sorry," the tired domestic reported, "he is out, and I'm told that he will not be in his office today."

"Then why is his buggy in the barn?"

"I don't know. Perhaps he has gone afoot." She closed the door.

More deceit, Mary assumed. Returning every hour on the hour, she was given the same response. She felt sorry for the old woman who apparently had been forced to lie, breaking one of the church's commandments.

By sunset, Mary was livid.

The following morning, she marched to Helena's Department of Police. Leaning a forearm on the marble-top counter, she identified the sheriff by his badge and countenance. She called politely across twelve feet of open space, "Sheriff, I'm here to place charges against the Reverend John Brondel, the Bishop of Montana. I charge him with slander and breach of contract."

The sheriff set his coffee cup down and stared long—long enough for the wet edge of his mustache to dry. Deputies attended to paperwork and skirted about, glancing catawampus.

Sheriff Johnson made a point of identifying this woman by taking in her details, as it was his responsibility to do, same as any farmer would, should he be called upon to recount the marks of his milking cow. He would browse through the stack of wanted posters, later, if he wanted, see if he found a likeness, just in case.

"Well, I'd like to help you, I surely would," he said, "but according to the law, a negress is incompetent to testify against a white gentleman. That means—"

"I know what it means." Panicked, she wondered whether his words were true. Had she made a false assumption without checking the facts? Colored persons are freed—free to make charges like whites. She held her breath.

"According to Montana state law, and laws just like them all across

America, no coloreds, mulatto, Indian or Chinese, is permitted to give evidence against a white person." He took a swallow of dark liquid and made her wait. "Fact is, in most places, no woman is allowed to give testimony against any man. Just cause you aren't slaves anymore doesn't make you equal. You ought to know that."

Mary wished she was close enough to spit in his face, throw the desk he hid behind out the door and throw him onto a rock pile, stack stones to his neck along with his bedfellow, the monster Brondel. Instead, she postured her dignity, imagined it to be a real object she could embrace, a double bouquet of red roses, for example.

Once outside and down the street, she stared at shadows beneath the sidewalk boards as she lunged forward, berating herself for such a shortsighted mistake. How could she have neglected to research the laws? She needed to know—could she make charges against her assailant or not? Was such a despicable miscarriage of justice written in the constitution that ruled this young state, the land of opportunities? She was in the state capitol; there had to be a way to find out.

After walking for miles, she returned to Broadwater Hot Springs Hotel just before supper. Grateful for the invitation to sit at the table with affable company, she shared the events of her plight as they supped on chicken, potatoes and greens. She appreciated the opportunity to speak unedited, shared details of her day and rehashed the inherent injustices, concluding: "That cowardly sanctimonious priest hasn't got a fingertip of courage like the savior Lord Jesus he preaches about. What a pitiful Lordship. Hate to be on the ship sailed by him—the 'sail to redemption'. He hasn't got a chance of landing a spot on that island. Lies and deceit are tickets to damnation— according to *his own* words." She took off her shawl and tossed it on the chopping block. "I heard him preach that, over and over at the mission, for years. And the law—more broken promises. Sheriff claims that coloreds can't testify in court against any white person. How's that for justice? Have to find out if it's true or not."

"Mary, you know all that," bellowed the sous-chef, a large Tahitian woman who had introduced her to the staff. "And you might as well give it up. Plenty folks in this town happy to kill us at the blink of an eye. There's a whole club, a 'Gentleman's Club,' she advised, "that wants everyone *not* white gone and dead." Leaning back, she crossed her arms. "So you best stop your demands, less you be shushed permanent. We'd like you to stay alive." Affirmative grunts squawked.

Mary didn't reply. She realized, soberly that she might be gambling the safety of these good people. She got up, grabbed her satchel and went for the door.

"Mary Fields, wait."

"No. You're right," she said, turning back. "Going out. That's all."

She entered the darkness, cognizant of the city's dangers. She could rely on her shooting skills and her town handgun, the Ladysmith pistol already pocketed in the apron knotted tight around her waist. Rubbing the smooth arc of its pearl grip, she approached the vicarage again. She pressed details of the property to memory, clinging to a diminishing hope —that she would report his wrongful act, give testimony, and detail the confrontational scene she so yearned to appropriate.

The barn door had been left ajar. She peeked in, confirmed her suspicions. The horses and buggy were in place. Lights in an upstairs room glowed, and she caught a glimpse of John Brondel robed, pipe in hand.

I'd love to pitch a big rock through that window, she raged. Hear the crash, see the look of fear in his eyes when I march in and tell him what a lowdown coward he is—for my satisfaction and for having my old-age plans stolen. She clenched molars and glowered.

He'd be calling that poor old serving-woman to rescue him, she steamed. Would be turnabout right to hang him upside down like the tobacco plants, let *him* go hungry and dry up—but before he wrinkled to shreds I'd make him admit the truth—that Mary Fields didn't commit wrongs against anybody. His unfit power would crumble along with his sacrilegious transgressions. And he won't be hurting innocent sisters and children ever again. Yes.

A dog's bark flicked her mind to the present, and she realized that she had been pacing. "Better get," she mumbled. "He'll be having me arrested for breathing in front of his house."

She started back, feeling moderately vindicated. Ducking through alley shadows, she confronted her emotions. There's something else thundering down beneath. What is it that truly plagues me about all this?

She rubbed an eye and stepped onto the sidewalk, judging the remaining distance safest if she navigated amongst the rowdy saloon goers.

It's not the false accusations, she divined. It's that I don't have the right to claim injustice, speak the truth and have it heard before God and everyone. Don't have the centuries old right to a duel. They treat mules and automobiles and dogs better than women and children.

Amends in public. That's mostly what I want.

Brondel would like nothing better than for me to turn tail and disappear—well, short of getting arrested, thrown out of town, or worse.

I'd probably have it easier somewhere like Seattle, higher numbers of coloreds … but then I'd lose Mary and Onatah and Nadie, and I'm not leaving the Birdtail.

All the better—it'll stick in his craw.

When Mary woke the next morning she knew exactly what to do. A friend of a friend at the supper table had mentioned a rumor spreading amongst the A.M.E. church congregation. Word was, that a man from Ohio, a political type, had begun what would be the first newspaper for Helena coloreds—he was setting up shop in the back room of Ball's Portrait Photography. She decided that such a man was likely to have the answers she sought.

She followed directions to North Main Street, located the painted numbers: 1-3-7 and entered the studio. After brief discussion with a young man who wore an apron, she was directed to the end of a narrow corridor. She smelled paint. Her nose led her to shiny green letters recently applied to the door's upper panel. Gold flourishes accented the cursive lettering, shaping words into a stylish trademark: *The Colored Citizen.*

She turned the knob, entered, and was immediately greeted by a formidable man—clearly the one in charge. Like his trademark, the entrepreneur, dressed in couture clothing, had striking style—a pronounced contrast to that of his ink-splattered, sweaty workforce who labored to operate the printing press behind him.

He introduced himself from a height taller than average, exerting a baritone voice that emphasized each corner of vowel and syllable, revealing eloquent innuendos of cultured charisma. Her heart gaped. His sonorous pitch resonated familiarity. It was the same tone of choice Mary conjured to play the lover's part in her imaginary phantasms enjoyed while commandeering wagons across waves of grain.

"Good Morning, Madame," he assigned. My name is James Presley Ball, and I am the editor of our new, and eminently vital, publication: *The Colored Citizen.*"

He could model the African Hermes, Mary thought, losing focus. She said, "Good morning, fine proprietor. I am grateful that you're here."

"I cannot imagine a lady as lovely as you finding reason to languish me with gratitude for my mere presence alone. Might you have a question or quest I can equip myself to challenge this fine morn?"

She smiled. It had been ages since she'd engaged in flirtatious repartee. "I am hoping that you can tell me with certainty, what the law says, exactly."

"Exactly about what, dear lady?"

She explained her situation. Having memorized the sheriff's words, she recited them with impartial accuracy, all the while letting her eyes slide along the brawny physique of an ideal champion. He was the perfect shade of brown, she thought, dazzling dark eyes thickly lashed and firmly set against broad cheekbones chiseled proportionally above a strong square jaw that voiced articulate answers to each of her concerns.

She fussed with her hair. It was a beautiful thing to watch manliness flit between lines of articles, ordinances and stipulations, coherently articulating current standings of due process. When he told her with regret that the sheriff was correct, that she couldn't press charges or testify or contest her dismissal, she didn't mind quite so much, because he kissed her hand and she felt thirteen, weak in the knees.

While riding back to the mission with Mr. Flinn, she told herself to look at things different—a puzzle could be put together different ways— all that mattered was that it came out all right. This was a new chance to walk free, start something new, her mind shuffled. Maybe it's time to stop rattling my behind on the cross-seat, driving freight and lifting heavy feed sacks and all those chores I've been shouldering, she posed. How old am I now? She did the calculations. Sixty-two. My gosh, sixty-two. Maybe it wouldn't hurt to find an easier way. But what? Her thoughts drifted to James Ball, now recorded in her heart as the gracious man in Helena who'd found her attractive. Helena was, after all, named after a miner's sweetheart. A town christened for love—

That's kindred, she thought, and then imagined an embrace, a kiss.

Revisiting the prolonged intimate gaze when his hand had lifted hers, ungloved and unprepared, she'd panicked and made reason for a hasty exit. He had, she assigned, respected her choice to depart—take care of her own business. He didn't force his attentions. He was a gentleman. She smiled, recalling his last words, "If you ever find that you should need me, for anything, Miss Mary Fields, write, and I will come to you with all due haste, precious lady. Do not hesitate." She took his words to heart, and it cushioned the blow of losing place and home.

I was going to live there for the rest—

The snap of reins startled. She looked to the white man beside her, and to herself, the girls' confidante, the nuns' Rock of Gibraltar, riding in a buggy that hastily sped toward the scene of heartbreak—hers, and theirs too, she suddenly realized. Sadness weighed heavy as she cradled visions of children and herself, abandoned.

Have to leave quick or it will tear my heart to pieces, she remedied.

I'll sleep in my cabin one or two more nights. Sisters aren't anxious to be rid of me; if Brondel wants me out sooner, he can knock on *my* door. She pulled her cap into position, caught a whiff of apple blossoms. How much influence would Brondel's forked tongue have in Cascade—might end up being a catacomb of trouble. Will anyone take me in for a few days? Chilled, she turned her collar up and decided, someday I'll sew curtains out of this merry-go-round dress—when I have a place of my own.

Arriving at the mission an hour past dusk, Mary went directly to her cabin, preferring not to talk until she had rested. She pulled blankets over her head and fell asleep immediately.

Before sunrise, knocking awakened her. She fumbled, opened the door.

"Mary," Mother Amadeus groaned, anxious to face her namesake, bear witness to the aftereffects of an unthinkable tumultuous catastrophe her Bishop had created, "I am so very sorry. Did you talk to him?"

"No. Come in."

They anchored a sedately earnest hug. Mother suggested a walk to the nearby, mutually favored overlook on a dwarfed but charming peak she had named *Mount Angela*. They left before anyone stirred. The path's steep incline discouraged conversation—each Mary examined emerging feelings, primary views that if spoken, could either cement or sever the course of their relationship.

Approaching the third switchback, Mother Superior slipped and skinned her knee. Immediately, she drew a parallel, associating physical pain with the crueler situation at hand, decided that she deserved such a scrape—penance.

Mary Fields longed to gaze into distance and stretch her mind, maybe even her heart.

They reached the anticipated plateau and were rewarded by morning light, vistas of benched prairie to the east and peaks spiking the continent's backbone to the west. The nun leaned against a large boulder. Guilt for behavior less than perfect weighed heavy on her mind, equally matched by the burning desire to be forgiven by a friend, her friend.

Mary Fields sat on the damp ground and scooted to dangle her legs over the ledge.

Mary Amadeus spoke plainly, tendering regrets for her absence at the mission when the eviction dictum had arrived—a platform from which she would bare the more difficult burden—admission of failure, inasmuch as it was her fault, or responsibility, to stop unfair treatment from happening at her mission.

"I was unable to protect you, Mary." She hoped for atonement and blurted, "We had an agreement, and now I am unable to keep it." Rubbing her forehead, she added, "I find my word nullified by the powers that govern me, confiscate my freedom to choose. Here I am in the remote frontier, charged to provide education and immersion training for hundreds of young women, yet I am not allowed to fulfill an executive commitment."

Mary wished her Ursuline blood sister would stick to personal issues between them and shelve administrative conflict. She tossed a stone over the edge.

"This inequity is vast. As vast as this view. I hate to admit it—that I cannot honor my most heartfelt and genuine promise to you, my dear friend." She limped toward Mary's back and put a hand on her shoulder. "I am so sorry. I can't imagine how upset you must be. This is your *home*. You were to stay here for the rest of your life. I promised you."

A long silence ensued. Mary Fields was torn between recounting her indignation and offering forgiveness. She struggled to find words that would speak her meaning.

Sarah Theresa Dunne, now Mary Amadeus, sank into a dark childhood place, invoking the pivotal promise unkept: "We won't be gone for long," her parents had promised, "You'll come live with us when we're settled in California. Then we'll be a family again." They deposited her and her older sister in a parochial boarding school in Cleveland, took their sons and did not return. It stays forever, the desertion, she thought, feeling depressed and constricted. Mary has so many scars, and now I've added another.

Mary Fields closed her eyes and steeped in the sun's rising heat. Abruptly, she spun around and declared, "Maybe I'll go west." She stared at the Rockies, fantasizing an expedition through ominous wilderness.

Mother's first reaction was to insist that her friend remain, but she squelched the response, reminding herself that she didn't have the right to make requests when she couldn't keep her promise.

"I only want you to be happy, Mary. I am so sorry. I am so very sorry."

Their eyes found each other for the first time since the hug earlier.

"I'd like to sue the profane lordship," Mary huffed. "Wouldn't that be a first—a colored woman suing a Catholic Bishop! Wish it were possible. Maybe someday it will be. If I knew of a place where it's legal now, I'd move there."

Mary Amadeus looked down and waited for more.

"I was happy right where I am."

"I was happy with you here, too, Mary. I never wanted you to go. You mean so much to me, to all of us. I hope you can forgive me."

Mary said, "I know you don't have the power to change it—so I'm not angry with you." She stroked her chin, reassessing options. "I don't know what to do. Maybe set up a restaurant—you know I'm the best cook in the world."

The tension eased. "In Cascade?"

"Probably."

"It was always wrong that you weren't paid a salary, Mary, and I'm sorry I took so long to remedy that situation. You've only been paid for, what is it, five months? I didn't see the need to hurry, since you would always be with us. You would have had savings. I've been thinking about it, and you need to receive compensation, no matter what anyone thinks."

"That would be nice."

"It would help you set up a restaurant, if that's what you want to do."

"Do you really mean it? I don't want to hear any hot-air promises right now. You understand."

"Yes. I am serious. It will have to wait until after the harvest, but I will reimburse you for past wages already earned. It's not a gift. It's a debt that we need to honor."

"Well, if you mean it from that angle, I accept. Thank you, Mary."

Mary Amadeus took a deep breath, watched a chipmunk scurry across pine needles, its tail held upright, which reminded her, "Remember that beaver coat I promised? I finally received it—I had planned on giving it to you for Thanksgiving. Let us send it with you.

"My," Mary efforted, thinking how she'd always imagined wearing that dreamed-of fur coat on the road. "It will keep me warm wherever I am. Many thanks." Stretching her eyes to the mountains, she asked, "Do you know that the Reverend said we're not allowed to see each other? And that I'm not allowed to visit the mission?"

"That would be difficult to enforce, wouldn't it?" Amadeus raised an eyebrow.

"It's not only about us," Mary said, "it's hurtful to the girls, especially Annie and Nancy."

"Yes, I realize that. I'll do my best to comfort them, but I know better than to think I could substitute your place in their hearts. We'll have to manage visits. The sisters and I will see you in town, but the girls—that will be difficult."

"We'll arrange it though?"

"Yes, we will."

"All right then."

"I have a little money in petty cash—that will get you a room in town, help you get by until the end of the season."

"I'll stir up some laundry jobs. Won't have a wagon to make freight deliveries—that will be hard to get used to—the loss of freedom on the road." Horse flies appeared and nipped at corners of bare skin. They swatted the annoying creatures. "Kinda like having reverends in charge, isn't it?" Mary said, anticipating the chuckle that shook the chest of her kindred friend.

"I'll miss you," Mary Amadeus said, still smiling. "Shall we?"

In order to delay inevitable spikes of sorrow, Mary buckled down to details. What about the hennery, she worried, the medicinals and my tactics to populate higher vegetable yields that as of yet, have not been bequeathed to anyone but Annie? She would talk to Mary Amadeus about the making of lists and notations.

The girls: this required real will power. How would she cloak her heartbreak? How could she delay tears until after she had parted? She gave directives: if I feel like wallowing, I'll pirouette and prance. Yes. I'll spin sad thoughts into golden threads that only my loved ones will see—they'll follow the threads to find me again.

Forty-eight hours later, Mary stood in the center of the compound holding her satchel stuffed with clothes and personal items. It was the same satchel she had arrived with—her first purchase from wages earned at the Toledo convent, where Mary Amadeus had been elected Head Superior and had hired her, ignoring criticisms from the Cleveland Motherhouse.

She embraced the view: Saint Angela's Academy, the Opera House, the barn and hen house, Jesuit buildings in the distance. She listened to the music of hen clucks, cawing crows, cricket chirps and iron skillets clanging. It was a summer day that sounded like any other, nine years of them.

She flinched when the buggy reeled round the corner, Lightning harnessed at the helm, Sister Catherine gripping a whip that wasn't necessary. The kitchen's screen door slammed. Mary recognized the footsteps coming near. She swallowed hard and stroked Lightning, arousing more feelings. Annie flung herself around Mary's waist. Mary lifted the slight girl and couldn't restrain the tears. They squeezed tight.

"You can't leave!"

"You know I have to. If I had the choice I wouldn't."

"I want to come with you."

"You get a little older first."

She set Annie down, got in the buggy and didn't look back. She couldn't. Sister Catherine snapped the whip, wheels spun and hoof-powered dust clouds shielded Mary from further goodbyes. Seconds later she had vanished, the way wind shoveled clouds across the Birdtail without apology.

Saint Angela's had changed. Everyone could feel it.

Annie inhaled dirt and wished she could disappear. Her broken heart raged: my Ucsote White Crow is taken. Everyone important is gone. I hate the horrible white men who steal and murder and kidnap. White Crow was free. Freer than any other woman—and look what happened. I might never see her again!

Mother's heart skipped a beat when she saw a folded paper on her desk. She opened it and read: You'll be wanting to pass on a few things that the Hennery Keeper and gardeners should know.

Poultry and Garden Tips by Mary Fields

Some folks preserve eggs with lye or varnish. I think that might be dangerous. I use salt and bran—half the weight of bran to salt. Mix well. Pour mixture into box or bin deep enough to cover. Place eggs small end down with a finger width between each egg. Put in a cool spot but don't let it freeze. Eggs should keep three or four months until the hens start laying again.

A Scot lady once told me that they dip fresh eggs in boiling water for two minutes and the whites coagulate in the shell, but I have not tried it.

Right now the rows and hills are heaped with compost—half chicken and half cow manure—straw on top to keep the moisture in the earth and the weeds down. Teepee poles are tied over the tomato plants, so tomatoes are lifted and less bugs will share the harvest.

I planted beans and squash next to the corn, so they'll be winding up the corn stalk to keep off the ground. They like each other. You can couple them together in a different spot each year, so the ground has a rest from one kind of plant to another. Might want to move the potatoes around too. Strawberries should be pruned the last of August. Mulch with old hay after the ground freezes. Leave on until danger of frost is over in spring. If anyone has questions, you'll find me in Cascade, I think.

Mary Fields

Mary Amadeus re-folded the letter and locked it in the secret compartment of her desk, as though it were a lover's poem. Her resentment of Brondel's interference had escalated into silent wrath that festered, the way anaerobic bacteria spawned Mary's compost.

She was not ready to speak to his Lordship, but she would. She had to find a way to circumvent the Bishop's control. Then Mary Fields could return. The realization that it was going to take more than prayer and cooperation to gain rightful autonomy over her own Ursuline establishments, burned. How was she going to do it?

PERSEVERANCE

SUMMER 1894

*B*ishop Brondel summoned the Mother Superior to Helena without explanation.

Mary Amadeus assumed that the termination of Mary Fields would be the topic of discussion—it was definitely the prominent subject of her agenda. She decided not to point out the disrespectful method by which he, the first ordained Catholic Bishop of Montana, had executed the unwarranted, slanderous and quasi-legal termination within her domain. Instead, she would act as need be to get Mary reinstated at the mission.

Amadeus envisioned herself employing grace and reason while casually citing Mary's history of contributions—including the fact that without her, the Ursuline Sisters at Saint Peter's would not have survived the winter of 1885. She knew that John Brondel had a pragmatic side—if only she could navigate through his personal biases, reach operative ethics interested in organizational development. He simply needed to realize that Mary Fields was not the problem.

Once arrived in fast-paced Helena, Mother Mary took shelter in a boarding house near diocese headquarters, hoping to rest before the appointed meeting.

The following morning after congenial greetings were exchanged, John Baptist Brondel escorted Mother Mary Amadeus to his study. He lowered his protruding midriff into the worn leather chair behind his walnut desk.

"Firstly," he announced, "I want you to know that I am aware that you coerced the sisters into paying Mary Fields a salary last December: ten dollars a month plus room, board and clothing. Is that what prompted you to declare the need for Local Chapter Ursuline Meetings, thereby usurping my authority?"

The aggressive opening statement surprised Mary Amadeus. Immediately, she positioned a neutral countenance, relaxing the musculature of her face and pushing emotions downward. With practiced patience and years of mediation prowess, she clasped hands palm to palm under sanctified sleeves and tapped fingers to the beat of "Joy to the World" as she conjured reverie that swiftly delivered the wisdom to disregard Brondel's baited prelude.

She noted a bead of sweat poised upon his upper lip.

Assuming Mother's silence to be an admission of wrongdoing, John Baptist supplemented his allegation. "I furthermore have heard testimony that Fields engaged in acts of violence. She attacked the hired help at gunpoint and, on another occasion, threw stones with intent to kill. And it wasn't the first time. She has been a problem for years."

He reached for one of his Cuban cigars while Mary Amadeus concluded that it was more likely that the problem stemmed from the Bishop's inability to interact with a proud and capable African American woman. And women in general.

John Baptist's mind skipped to thoughts regarding the finale of a eulogy he was scheduled to deliver that afternoon. He twitched and rubbed his nose. Once again Mary Fields was disturbing his peace, preventing him from finding the appropriate testament to embody his message. Time was running out.

He threw a hasty glance and exhorted, "She is blasphemous and fosters a multitude of sins, and she will not be allowed to return to Saint Peter's. Nor will you or the sisters have any future association with her whatsoever. My directive is clear, is it not?"

Mary stared at the elm tree outside, its fluttering leaves twisting in shadows of morning light. His voice receded, dismissed by her preoccupied mind. She answered, "Yes, quite clear, Bishop."

"We won't address it further unless you are inclined to disobey my orders."

Having already decided to ignore his orders, Mother Mary creased her emotions and perched them upon the grandmother elm's largest limb. Her lips parted, and closed.

"One more thing before the matter is adjudicated," his voice persisted. "If you thought that listing Fields as "Laundress" in your 1892 June, September and December Quarterly Reports to the Indian Bureau would secure her a long-term position, you were sorely misguided. I noticed what you did. Her name didn't belong on those reports—she was not an official employee at the time."

Mother Superior let her non-response dangle. She appraised the

Bishop's presentation as well plotted, intentionally designed to abort discussion, but flawed. Defiantly engaged, she pushed her providence against his: she would prepare, protest and enlist Ursuline and Jesuit hierarchy to fortify a united response as best she could negotiate.

She blinked at notice of his oily cheeks exercising a male symbol of victory; the cigar's coal glowed hot. He pursed and blew from the end of the yellow-banded cylinder. A roll of neck flesh jiggled over a heavily starched collar as he leaned forward to tidy papers.

"That is all, Mother Amadeus," he said, pretending to search for something. "I'm sure you have business to attend to. Thank you for your prompt attention. And compliance." He blinked heavy behind swirls of smoke and nodded, patted the polished surface of his desk.

Mary bid a tidy goodbye and closed the door behind herself. She leaned against it, incensed. If the Bishop wanted callow displays of Ursuline frailty, he would have to cast his dictums elsewhere.

Outside, she welcomed the city's commotion and charged along, oblivious to tribulations and machinations of those around her, newcomers amassed in the hunt for their share of treasure in the state known as such. Her nostrils flared, not from the stench of sewage that drifted from passing wagons, rather, fueled from indignation at John Baptist's presumptuous gall. How dare he butt into Ursuline management, Ursuline business, her business! The growing burn in her thigh muscles felt good.

She looked up, realized that in her roaming she'd become lost. The usual steeples and landmarks were gone from sight, and one cinctured glance told her that she had wandered into districts of poverty and strife. A mass of cumulous clouds delayed knowledge of the hour. She sighed. Perhaps among the children's cries, filth and flesh hanging loose on the bone, she might identify lost souls searching for sanctuary, females seeking spiritual salvation, destined, perhaps, to embrace the Ursuline pledge. A swarthy crew of men in mining hats rolled into view, black coal smeared across bodies it would age and suffocate en masse.

Invoking a spiritual connection with the first Ursulines, Mary intoned their purpose as scribed in the 1535 declaration: to protect, empower and educate women; protect, empower and educate women. Protect. Empower. Educate. A worthwhile purpose. An altruistic aspiration. The sacred canticle of Ursuline rosaries. She stumbled and regained footing in time to ask for directions, aware mid-sentence, that the easiest route to solicit would have been the way to the Bishop's church.

Changing her pace to one that she imagined as nobler—the stride carried by her sect's shepherdess, Saint Ursula, the brave princess who relinquished her title of royalty for vows of religious faith and thus had embarked on a holy crusade guiding eleven women disciples across Europe on a quest visioned and actualized—Sarah Theresa Dunne, Mother Mary Amadeus of the Heart of Jesus, advanced.

Rumors of Mother's failure to change Bishop Brondel's mind stirred further discontent among pupils at Saint Angela's Academy. After Sunday service, Nancy and her clutch of friends huddled outside of earshot, anxious to share their worries. They had banded tighter together in the wake of Mary White Crow's absence, sharing confidences and support, spirited by their banished mentor's example.

Nancy repeated words she had heard Mother report to Sister Gertrude verbatim: "The Reverend was obstinate, had no intention of reconsidering his decision and, further, indicated disapproval of our decision to initiate Ursuline Chapter Meetings, which is routine convent procedure, our right and none of his concern."

Adding that she had never seen Mother Amadeus so upset prompted a high-strung discussion regarding pervasive anomalies that separated the white men and women: how it had come to be that white men had so much more power than white women, unlike centuries-old customs honored in their tribal communities of origin. A girl shared information just learned: not only did most states deny women the right to vote, the government did not allow married women, even white women, to keep their own wages, a shocking fact demanding consideration. The purpose of their schooling was to become "respectable women" like them. Did that mean unmarried? And, or, unpaid?

How can we build a future, they asked each other. Where will we live? What kind of community will we have living separated—each husband and wife confined on a marked solitary section of land? Or will we live alone, become what they call old maids?

Heads leaned in.

A debate ensued as to whether it was worthwhile to learn the White ways at all. Doe-eyed, they joined hands, as though touch and sight could conjure the sacred past. Everyone knew, and agreed again, that it was natural for women to be leaders: the owners of property, they being the nurturers who held respected positions in councils as wise mothers, healers and warriors—the way it had been.

"But what do we do now?" Nadie posed. "It's no wonder that white women choose to be nuns, 'brides of heaven', they call themselves. The problem is, they lose honor and joy without children."

Others chimed: "they change our names—call us names without meaning—don't realize it steals spirit, doesn't guide us to salvation like they think—I miss White Crow—Me, too. Me, too—She made me laugh."

Nadie said, "I'm thinking about transferring to Fort Shaw Industrial, nearer to my mother on the reservation." And nearer to White Crow, she kept to herself.

A chorus of concern ruffled, "You are?"

"We have to make our own way. Just like White Crow. How can we find out what it's really like at the Industrial School?"

"My brother is there," one of the girls said. "Let's try to get word to him."

"We can't use paper."

"I'll ask my mother to visit him—she will tell us."

"We have to get back."

They squeezed hands and separated.

Three years earlier, the United States Bureau of Indian Affairs ordered that extensive renovations to the vacant army fort located north of Cascade be initiated. Designs were assembled, and crew after crew of workmen had been employed to construct the largest government run Indian school in America. The specialized, multi-curricular facility, Fort Shaw Industrial School, had opened its doors on the frigid morning of December 12, 1892.

True to title, this industrial school, like others before it, adhered to programs designed to influence the "rudimentary" minds of Indian youth. They administered toward the legislated goal of cultural transformation: rehabilitate the nomadic savages into compliant laborers, who would then, ideally, reject their tribal history, stay in one place, adopt a Euro-American way of life and conform, contribute to the homogeneous development of the one dominant nation—and do so cognizant and accepting of their restricted rights and demeaned social standing.

Concurrently, federal policy had effected reductions in Indian school subsidies.

Incrementally decreased appropriations had been dispersed and would terminate within months, rendering most religious organizations unable to maintain operation of their schools. As a result, religious proselytism of Indian youth would diminish.

Notification of this finality had arrived at the Saint Angela's Motherhouse months earlier, when Mother Amadeus was in Eastern Montana taking care of business at Saint Labre, another of her missions.

Upon her return she reviewed the correspondence from the Indian Bureau and formulated a plan of action to withstand the loss of support. She had always understood the appropriations to be a temporal gift that inevitably would slip away, like any anomaly.

Quicksand in our pastoral landscape, she correlated, charging toward her desk, pen clasped, ready to inspire others via concentric help from her Maker—compose words that would truly elucidate the benevolent intentions of the Ursuline Missions at work in the American West—reaching in particular, the compassionate few who would listen and donate before it was too late.

That night, standing by the upstairs window of her bedroom, she pressed herself upon its chill, let her shoulders slump and sighed. Faced with the drastic losses of subsidy income for all nine Montana mission schools, she questioned, would the secular industrial school employ harsh discipline, overwork her students and minimize the importance of spiritual practice and scholastic achievement? Would the instructors take advantage of the pupil's fortitude and physical strength? Force them to labor unremittingly, conscripted to perform trades that they were obligated to master as participants enrolled in the industrial system?

Trades to be taught included: blacksmith, cobbler, carpenter, stone mason, farmer, rancher, brick maker, saddle maker, lace maker, seamstress, housekeeper, cook, laundress, bookkeeper, secretary—skills that would provide if exploited, substantial income for the facility cloaked under auspicious classifications of training, tutelage?

How would Indian athletes solicited throughout the state be treated? And the gifted musicians? Would federal public relations expropriate their academic progress? Would they disregard true assimilation efforts and parade their metamorphosed pupils in exhibitions headlined as Redskin Orchestras and Redskin Basketball Players?

Ultimately, would the innocent graduates be flung into a society that would neither embrace nor accept them—educated and industrially trained or not? Would her precious rising stars find themselves returned to reservations?

Without faith and a rudimentary understanding of religion, art and philosophy, would the rehabilitated graduates sustain the will to persevere?

In truth, could she and her sisters guarantee more? If only her pupils could remain protected under Ursuline jurisdiction indefinitely—an inane notion—unless they were to join the Ursuline or Jesuit community. Have our visions of advanced levels of achievement in academics, philosophy, the arts and devotional faith handicapped Indian assimilation and the individual's ability to cope? Will society advance quickly enough to meet these intelligent, well-educated persons halfway? Have I widened the abyss? Will I have caused fragile hearts additional suffering, unnecessarily? How will sophisticated levels of performance in classical instrumentation and dramatics, fluency in Latin, French and English—overtures from St. Lucia and the cantata from the Last of the Mohicans—genuinely save their lives? That is what I came to do, is it not? Help them to save themselves, bequeath knowledge and enlightened devotion—the very means with which to endure, assimilate, flourish?

The letter that arrived from the Bureau included the "last year" disbursement tables and suggested that she select her most gifted Indians, those in particular who excelled in academics, music and sports and submit their admission applications to Fort Shaw Industrial School, immediately. Unable to choose arbitrarily, she resigned her authority, and asked her savior to indicate who should go and who should stay.

Aware that word of the Industrial School's pursuit for students had already leaked to her student body, she fitted herself in her robes and guimpe and veil the following morning, and stood erect, embracing faith in order to accept the incomprehensible mysteries of God's Will as she introduced the educational option to her young women, students who would exceed the farthest-reaching qualifications, she was quite certain. She did however, delay encouragement to attend.

After weeks of waiting for Catholic contributions earmarked for the Montana Ursuline missions, Mother recounted the total received thus far: ninety-seven dollars and ten cents. Recognizing the time had come, she spoke to her girls again regarding the rapid and inevitable ending of federal allocations for private schools. Alleging that enrollment at Fort Shaw Industrial School represented an opportunity for her protégées, she praised the school's superintendent, Dr. Winslow, and emphasized the versatile opportunities: scholastic excellence, the learning of trades, musical venues and competitive sportsmanship. She advised interested parties to see her in her office. "Rise up, rise up," she said in conclusion, "we must be brave."

Her heart languished. What will happen to the dear youngsters, she worried.

Two days after the following month's full moon, answers arrived via a brief visit from the Blackfeet girl's mother who had spoken with her son, a pupil at Fort Shaw Industrial. Keme Machk (Thunder Bear), George to the white people, had been told to apprentice with a blacksmith, she reported, adding that he had already learned to shape metal into horseshoes.

The question of why horses need shoes was set aside in favor of the advice. The mother reported, "If you mind their rules and work hard, George

Keme Machk had said, then they treat you well enough. Unless you try to leave. There is a man whose work is to track and punish runaways. Members of the marching band are students who wear red uniforms and metal buttons. They travel to Great Falls and Helena, further maybe, and so does the school's orchestra. There are many pupils and sad stories about the tribes. Music class and basketball training is fun. This, George's mother summarized, was all he would say, other than to send his faithful love to his sister.

Nancy volunteered an interest in traveling to those cities. When questioned, she would not say why, only that she was not going back to the Blackfeet reservation.

The day Mary arrived in Cascade both hotels were full up. With no other place to go, she knocked on the door that housed the only minorities living in Cascade.

The Chong family understood her situation, invited her to stay and graciously insisted that she bunk in the washroom of the adjoined home enterprise, The Hong Chong Laundry. Grateful, Mary accepted. After several days of banquet-style dinners, she felt sure that her host's meals were usually far less extravagant. Fearing that she would deplete their hard-earned profits, perhaps even their savings, she declined the generous invitation to stay longer, thanked them profusely and relocated.

After checking into Cascade's Warner Hotel, she did as instructed—located her room upstairs in the back. Trudging up the narrow stairway, she was glad to find privacy where she could clear her mind. Setting her satchel, the vessel that contained all of her belongings, on a sagging bed headed by brass posts, she looked around. The room was bare and smelled of cheap perfume.

"Don't fall for feeling settled," she warned, "because it can change like lightning." Sparked images of lightning bolts led to thoughts of her beloved steed in horse heaven—to memories of training him as a colt—to years of watching his fine mane flow in the foreground of her view as he charged across the Birdtail, helping her lead the team and pull the freight.

Flinching from a chill that traveled up her spine, she returned to the present. Hands on, then off her hips, she sighed again and unpacked her clothing.

Some nights she wished for winter so she could snuggle under covers and satisfy an urge to sleep until an unknown date in the future when things would magically be like they used to be.

Acquiring laundry work proved easy enough. Town mistresses whose husbands had gained some success were eager to hire a laundress who met the expectations of Ursulines. It made a lady's life less burdensome and provided a step-up on the social ladder.

Having no laundry facilities, Mary bartered an arrangement with Mrs. Warner, the recently widowed owner of the establishment. Mary agreed to wash three hundred pounds of dirty hotel laundry per month in exchange for her rent and use of the washroom for her own laundry accounts. New business income would provide money for food, perhaps a few extras, like tobacco and soap.

Sought-after sleep became elusive. Noise from the dining hall reverberated, reminded her of the quintessential peace and quiet she had enjoyed in her little Birdtail cabin. Dishes clanked, laughter clucked, balls on pool tables knocked incessantly. Shoveling through worries and feelings most nights, peppered by hot and cold flashes and ever-present images of Annie and Nancy and Gertrude and Mother Mary and herb gardens and hens and all things uncertain, exhaustion coalesced into brief lapses of sleep.

Contrarily, she had since moving to town, dreamed a pleasant dream. Not once but twice, and curiously, each time, coinciding with the rising of a full moon. It was an adventurous dream, set in a world of water. There were wide and flowing rivers—ripples that folded into currents and moved through Montana landscapes embracing women from Saint Peter's who jumped and paddled into linked channels, splashing carefree. She remembered feeling happy that her birth mother was in the water with her. Both mornings Mary awoke wishing the dream could come true.

Town life gushed with gossip and caused her bouts of nerve-racked irritation, though she had to admit that occasionally, restrung mutterings came in handy. Smoking a cigar outside a Cascade saloon one evening, she overheard men instructors from the Industrial School comparing salaries.

A sharp twang seized her elbow when she came to know that the school's white laundress earned an annual salary of five hundred dollars! Taking into consideration that a white woman normally received two or three times the pay of a colored woman, this disparity scaled pinnacle-sized heights of disproportion. The federal employee earned four to five times more than Mary would be able to acquire.

It's a government run school, she suggested to her ire: salaries set by the federal or state legislature. That makes it all the more sickening, she countered, a wrong example—legal, public discrimination. Seems that the government endorses carnivorous appetites of white supremacy, she posed. Bet they pay colored people about the same as I can make on my own—like slavery, just about. Wonder what they'd do if I apply? That washerwoman's got it made. She bit her lip and searched apron pockets for tobacco.

Still upset after a smoke and a brisk walk around the cemetery northwest of town, she reduced her assessment of appropriate reactions—eliminated the first two ideas: blowing up the fort or leaving for Seattle—and chewed over prudent options left: stoic resignation, offended outrage, petitions—none of which felt exactly right, considering that offenders wouldn't appreciate hearing about African American plights even if she were to orchestrate an effable protest. She'd get herself killed.

"Shssh. Stop wallowing," she admonished, bringing the altercation to conclusion. "Do the best you can, like you tell your girls."

"Yeah, but five hundred dollars. Could squirrel money away for Annie and Nancy."

After hanging wet laundry on hemp ropes behind the hotel, Mary spent afternoons wandering, shoving complaints aside while she studied the symmetry of each building—the structure, place and position—the pros and cons of construction and design—the landscaped correlations in town that might, in some way, improve her footing.

Cutting imagination loose, she asked how she might discover ways to become part of this community that had no colored people in it, except herself. It was a hazardous jig. Considering present levels of violence as well as potential services she could provide to the locals, she weighed against it, the importance of her personal dignity. She did not care to be employed—such a thing felt like eating crow. She would have to create an occupation respectable enough for her and the town residents, both.

Scrubbing white folk's laundry, the most commonplace service provided by non-whites, seemed the obvious solution. The longer she wrestled the realities of it—Mary Fields in a Cascade future, washing and ironing day in and out, alone, her and the laundry and bleeding knuckles—the more depressed she became.

After a week of this she concluded that starting a laundry business was not the answer. She was tired of laundering (she had begun the trade as a child) and had been wrestling with herself, guilty for having become a competitor to the Chongs during her transition. She wanted something new—a solution that promised challenge and satisfaction.

Repeatedly, she stared into the dusty window of a small tired building that used to house the local café, now abandoned. She remembered the quip she'd made to Mary Amadeus weeks earlier on the top of the mountain: You know I'm the best cook in the world.

She had said it to break tension at the time and wasn't really serious, but why not open a restaurant? The old café's cuisine had been grit to gullet, she knew firsthand, having eaten there herself when weather waylaid her freighting timetable.

She figured she would cook superior meals, blindfolded even—but the question was, could or would the community frequent such a place, seeing as earlier attempts had failed. Décor would be easy to gussy up, she thought smiling, since there wasn't any. Probably could lease the place for next to nothing, she supposed. Nobody else wants it, and the weather will destroy it, left vacant. When I gather a few more coins …

It was pioneer procedure to toss rubbish that wouldn't rot onto rocks and cover it with more rocks. Cascade's community rock pile was located at the south end of town, near the river that supplied stones the size of ostrich eggs. Mary scavenged the heap of rocks daily, searching for pots, pans, anything useful for a cafe. Carefully, she rolled one smooth stone off the curve of the other, sometimes from a height that equaled a second-story.

Time spent flirting with these hefty orbs lifted her mood. It was possible to find treasure, and not knowing the stakes or the rewards was all right—something precious could be waiting beneath her fingertips.

She began to address the river stones as her friends and discussed subjects of interest saved up from years of watching and pondering on the sidelines. One afternoon she recalled something Mary Amadeus had said, and told her audience, "I imagine there are enough of you to build one of those burial tombs, 'cairns' I think she calls them: helmet-shaped domes built to last forever, tributes to Irish Clan leaders." She scratched her head. "Hope they buried those fellas in the ground before they put the rocks on top."

A short time later she exclaimed, "Huzzah! Thank you, rocks! Just what I was hoping for!" She resurrected the best prize yet, even better than her first find, a blue enamel coffee pot in pristine condition. A rusty wire had piqued her attention; its barbs had hooked onto a rough, weathered plank buried near the bottom of the mound. After struggling with the object for an hour, she saw the treasure in its entirety: a broad, thick plank as long as she was tall. After brief examination, she stood it on its end, tipped the heavy weight of it onto her back and hefted it to the hotel's washroom. Satisfied, she placed it into a corner and attached a note: "Property of Mary Fields."

Filing for hours with an old rasp, she eventually shaped the jagged rectangle into an oval. During the following week she chiseled a recessed background around each penciled letter that she had carefully sketched: M-A-R-Y'-S C-A-F-E.

She gave the rock pile daily progress reports about her sign, along with whatever news her Cascade sleuthing had turned up. She confided, "I'm at the Y in Mary now, and guess what? Seventy-five percent of the business licenses in Cascade are for saloons. Can you believe there are ten saloon licenses for this dinky spot of a place? Simple arithmetic says they can't all succeed. But food—all people need to eat!"

After painting the textured background green, the smooth raised letters and an edged border bright yellow, she claimed, "It's a beauty, if I don't say so myself! November isn't the best time to open, but yellow is happy and eye catching. I think it's going to work out!" She imagined the stones applauding her success.

Mary passed the evenings enjoying a new ritual—strumming the four horse-haired strings of her banjo. She played old favorites, beginning with the comforting comrade song, "Follow the Drinking Gourd." Summoning her successful escape from the South—on the run with countless numbers of other brave souls also privy to secret directives compassed in the lyrics and the position of the Big Dipper Constellation, the sacred gourd, she played the first chord and sang softly:

When the sun comes back,
And the first Quail calls,
Follow the drinking gourd,
For the old man is waiting
For to carry you to freedom
If you follow the drinking gourd

The riverbank will make a very good road,
The dead trees show you the way,
Left foot, peg foot, traveling on,
Follow the drinking gourd ...

For the old man is waiting
For to carry you to freedom...
If you follow the drinking gourd
The river ends between two hills,
Follow the drinking gourd,
There's another river on the other side,
Follow the drinking gourd...

"Maybe I'll get some store-bought strings for my banjo when my café is going strong," she whispered as her head hit the pillow.

At Saint Peter's Mission, Mother Amadeus took action to block further Motherhouse information leaks to the Bishop and deliver justice to the person guilty of supplying distorted testimony instrumental to Mary Fields' dismissal and subsequent absence.

She finalized hired hand John Mosney's accounts, issued a bank-note dated October 12,1894 in the amount of four dollars and informed him that his services were no longer needed, wishing she could see Mary's face when she learned of the termination.

Exhilarated, Mother Mary freed herself from her duties the following morning, a crisp autumn day that promised sightings of brilliant color. Sharp angles of light reached long across the valley, illuminated vibrant compositions of bark, branches and leaves in particular, tantalizing shades of gold spread into arcs and coveys and stands of distinction, chromatic change that launched signals and mobilized activity. Mary Amadeus felt the impetus to make haste—get to town and keep her promise. She ignored the Ursuline mandate that required a two-adult minimum for travel; there were times for exception, and this was one of them.

She located Nancy in the hennery and told her to get her coat, find her friend Annie and meet her at the buggy in five minutes. Nancy noticed an impish spark in the Superior's eye, similar to the look Annie had when her brainstorms came on—she wondered if the Mother of Jesus had seen fit to answer her prayer, dropped the tin-can scooper into the sack of corn and ran.

Rather than inform the sisters of her agenda, Mother rushed through the kitchen, grabbed three apples and turned to say, "I'll return later today. Don't worry. I'm taking Nancy Burd and Annie Saint Germain with me. Carry on."

As the screen door slammed behind her, Gertrude shot a wink to Catherine. "Wish I was going to visit Mary Fields, too. Maybe you and I should go fishing?"

The girls huddled by the nun's newly acquired buggy, Mother's vehicle of choice. Amadeus appeared and hoisted Annie up onto the black leather seat made soft padded with horsehair. While Annie wondered how the tufted cushion had been fashioned, Nancy tossed coats onto her lap and squeezed in, pushing her friend next to the Mother Superior. Annie's mind sparked to memories of the blizzard night when she and Mother Amadeus had stared through the icy window. She bundled her wool coat, held it close to her chest and set sight on the distant mountain peaks.

Nancy leaned across her and braved, "Mother Amadeus, Annie and I have been longing to go to Cascade." She examined the nun's expression.

"To see Mary Fields. We would be honored to help you with anything you like." There, she had confessed. Now Mother Amadeus knew, and it was up to her whether she would grant their wish.

Mother said, "Don't worry. You'll get to see her. She misses you, too."

Annie squealed, "Thank you, Mother Amadeus!"

"You're quite welcome, Annie." Mother gave a nod. "You've both shown great progress and you deserve a treat."

Neither girl had heard the word "treat" since it was spoken by Mary Fields on the May Day picnic. Grinning to each other, Annie clasped Nancy's hand and held on tight. Three hours later, Mother pulled into the Cascade livery stable and instructed the man who greeted them, to have the rig ready when they returned mid-afternoon. Mother gathered folds of her skirt and stepped down onto fresh-cut straw. Annie and Nancy followed her example and waited, watching dust motes float in streams of light. The air smelled sweet.

Taking the girls in hand, Mother Superior set a vigorous pace. They soon arrived at the train depot, a remodeled railway car extended by a small wooden platform. She released her grip, opened the door, waved them ahead and asked the stationmaster, who was attending to the telegraph behind a latticed divider, if he would be kind enough to watch her girls while she completed an errand, assuring him that the pair would invoke no trouble.

She pivoted, her black skirt inflating.

Annie ogled the shape, like that of cupped petals turned over, she thought as she watched black cotton spin with pleated precision, closing as it crossed the threshold, gone in a blink. The pair edged back onto a thick wooden bench as directed, laced fingers and remained silent. It was intimidating to be an Indian girl left alone in a white man's town, even if she were brave. Annie was thirsty but dared not ask for water. She could tell that Nancy was nervous, though she acted otherwise.

Moments later, Mother burst back in, noise screeching as the bell above the door jerked and labored an incessant trill. Annie's heart skipped. The swishing skirt moved closer and Mother's voice, now panting, said, "I'm sorry, I forgot to tell you. In awhile, I will return with Mary Fields and we'll sit outside. When I wave, you may both come out. Don't let Mary see you—it's our surprise."

The girls nodded and watched as their headmistress made haste, this time reassured by the knowledge of a plan underway. Annie heaved an exhale and squeaked, "Nancy, we get to see White Crow!"

On her way to Warner's Hotel, Mother diverted from the direct route in order to glance through windows of saloons, supposing that Mary might be enjoying a smoke where the audacity of a woman engaged in such an activity could be overlooked. No Mary. She entered the Warner's lobby and asked the mistress if she might gain access to the hotel washroom in search of Mary Fields. Mrs. Warner waved permission, adding that she had been there awhile ago.

The small room, humid from three large kettles of water steaming on the iron stove, was empty. Mother leaned across a wide shelf littered with soap, lye and brushes—balanced on one foot to peer through the window behind. The washing had been hung.

Retreating back through the lobby, she spotted Mary Fields seated near the window, teacup in hand, the sleeves of her blouse pushed up past elbows, as usual. Her gaze caught the attention of the tired washerwoman who heaved up clanking cup to saucer, exclaiming as only *she* could, "Mother Mary! Such a pleasure to see you!"

The women headed toward each other. Uninhibited and carefree, they gushed heartfelt expletives and lunged into a mutually enthusiastic hug. Customers eventually swung their neck-twisted gawks back into positions of etiquette, but glances persisted. Seated together at the window table, the couple chatted vigorously; it had been two months since they had seen each other. Mother Amadeus reached into her beaded deer skin bag, a gift from Blackfeet Chief Machk (Bear), and handed Mary Fields a piece of paper.

Mary squeezed her eyes to focus. "Oh, my Lord!" she cried, "Thank you!" She squinted a second time to make sure she had gotten the numbers right, numerals neatly scribed in Mother's identifiable hand. "This is more than I imagined," she yelped, fanning her blushing face with the crisp bank draft.

Mother grinned, satisfied.

The roomful of shocked onlookers gaped.

Discreetly, Amadeus surveyed the room and suggested, "Shall we go?"

Mary stood up, gripped her friend in a boisterous bear hug and swung her off her feet, heralding before she could think, "Two hundred and forty dollars!"

Feeling suddenly giddy, Mother kept hold of Mary's shoulders, tickled and relieved by her friend's gratitude. Mary Fields gasped, realizing that she had not only read the dollar amount—she had spoken it out loud. Panic wrenched while her mind fumbled to assess—had damage occurred? Had she divulged something that would come back to bite either of them? What would strangers surmise? They wouldn't seriously believe the money was for her, would they? Could she alter the course of their assumptions? Yes, maybe. She handed the paper back to Mary Amadeus and winked. Mother understood and slipped the draft into her bag.

She followed Amadeus' lead out of the hotel and down the newly installed wooden sidewalk. She leaned into Mary's guimpe and said, "Did I fix my colossal faux pas? God only knows what they'll—"

"I don't care what they say—it will all be hearsay and conjecture. Besides, they saw you return the draft—they have no details." Mary Amadeus appeared to have lost ten years. She glowed.

"They won't hear any details from me," Mary chuckled.

Mother Mary stopped in order to gain Mary Fields' full attention. She wanted to speak the words she had been rehearsing. "Mary, you deserve far more than $240. This is all I can do for now, but I credited you $300 in my accounts. So you have a balance of $60 coming." She pulled the draft from her bag. "I hope this makes up for some of the harm we've inflicted upon you. I also fired Mr. Mosney."

"You fired Mosney? Good!" She squeezed Mary's hand and shook it, feeling exonerated. "The salary you've reimbursed—like I said, you've always done the best you can by me, Mary. It's more than I expected. You're a sharpshooter!"

"As are you, Mary Fields. Let's go to the train depot. We can sit on the bench and visit."

A short time later, Mary Fields exclaimed above the sound of her boots clomping, "Halleluiah!" Halting, she said, "I just realized. You've rescued me from a lifetime of laundry!"

Amadeus laughed. "You must have plans. I heard you were making inquiries about the old café building."

"Of course you did." Mary tugged the bill of her cap. "I leased the place. Comes with the counter and half dozen tables and chairs—and the stove. I've been excavating in the town rock pile and found some useful equipment. Found a perfect enameled coffee pot that will get a lot of use."

"So you're starting your own café?"

"Yep. 'Mary's Café' is the name."

"That's wonderful, Mary. I think we may have some extra chairs."

"Thanks. Now I can buy the rest of the important things, like a potbelly for my customers." While she gabbed on about pretty little salt and pepper shakers and the difficulties of obtaining reasonably priced flatware, she suddenly realized the implications of Mary Amadeus' act.

"Mary Amadeus Dunne! You've surely put yourself in harm's way by writing a draft note, and we both know who 'harm' is. All he has to do is check your records to prove you disobeyed his orders! You could be defrocked or something terrible! Why did you do that?"

"You were under Ursuline jurisdiction. I chose to make a stand. Besides, he didn't precisely indicate that—"

"Semantics, and you know it."

"It was the right thing to do, and you know it."

"Fair enough. Just hope he doesn't get his fat hands on your books."

They strolled in silence for a distance until Mother Amadeus said, "How is it, lodging at the hotel?"

"I'm noticing that you're changing the subject," Mary Fields replied. "Just don't get in serious trouble, Mary. All right? The hotel is fine enough." She crumpled an orange leaf she'd picked up earlier. "One thing's for sure about living in town…"

"What's that?"

"Well, I'll tell ya," she said deadpan, "I'd rather be called *Superior Mary* than *Nigger Mary* every other minute."

The side of Mother's mouth lifted. "You'd make an interesting Superior," she rallied, locking eyes. "I assure you, the title is misleading. It would fit you better than those terrible, cruel—I'm sorry you must tolerate ignorance so often."

"Just wanted to get if off my chest. Irritating, like little gnats. I got used to the absence of the salutation, being at the mission for so long. That's all. There are a few Cascade women who would like to see me turn tail. They'll boycott me—hopefully just me, not my café. But I'll succeed despite the nicks and gnats!"

"Nicks?"

"Yes, as in nicks, nicknames, nicks in the road—"

"Oh. Of course you'll succeed …"

The absence of her friend's chuckle piqued Mary's attention; it was apparent that Mother had become distracted—the nun's jaw had squared, and her bottom lip was in a twist. "So spit it out, Mary Superior."

"You reminded me when you said nicks in the road."

"Really?" Mary laughed, "I just made it up. Reminded you of—?"

Amadeus slowed. "I've been attempting to get permission—you can relate to that—to go to the Alaskan frontier. Thus far, I've had no response from my request. I see it in my mind—it's critical and imminent. Now that I've set up nine missions in Montana and they are running satisfactorily, I'm ready."

"Who has to grant you permission?"

"Bishop Brondel."

"Oh." Mary Fields shook her head and patted her friend on the shoulder. "Sorry."

"Would you like to come to Alaska?"

A moment passed, and Mary Fields felt her gut spasm, dismayed by the thought that Mary had made those important plans without any mention to her at all. Of course she didn't have to, but, still … "Ask me later, when you have two of everything on board," she said, forcing a parted smile. "My present aspirations are far smaller, Mary Superior. I'd settle for the welcome sound of 'Howdy' or 'Thank you, Mary Fields. Like to order another helping.'"

They arrived at the station and settled onto the bench in the sun. Mary Fields closed her eyes to calm her feelings. Nancy and Annie spotted the pair and eased toward the door, careful to stay in the shadows as they waited for Mother Superior's signal.

Mother waved her hand above her head and said, "Maybe I can help." The bell jingled. Mary turned in time to see two Indian girls dressed in Saint Angela uniforms burst toward her at a run. Her mouth dropped. She swung herself toward them. Annie squealed as she jumped into her Ucsote's lap. Nancy knelt to clutch the pair, kissed Mary on the cheek.

Mary's heart quaked. She turned to meet the gaze of Mary Amadeus and mutely mouthed the words, "Thank you."

The following morning, Mary Fields eagerly waited for Mr. Flinn to open the doors to the mercantile. She cashed her note and placed orders for the rest of the café equipment. After details were arranged, she folded the receipts carefully, slipped them into her apron pocket and said, "Mr. Flinn, would you pass the word? Tell everybody that 'Mary's Café' opens on Monday, November 26th at 7a.m. Best meals this side of the *Missouri*."

Mr. Flinn nodded and finalized notations in his ledger, still shocked at the large sum of money he had just forked over to Mary Fields. Two-hundred and forty dollars. He wondered if Black Mary had ever held that much cash in hand before. He could hardly find reason to object to a draft written by the Mother Superior and consoled himself by noting that a large portion of the sum had already been returned to his hands, deposits for café supplies.

Mary squirreled the remaining wad of bills into a pocket-size tobacco can she had extracted from the rock pile and headed toward her favorite granite boulder, a mile or so northwest of town. After making sure no one was about, she buried her fortune, careful to leave no trace. She patted the large rock inlaid with tiny pink crystals spiking above its coarse surface and spoke to it, as if it were paying apt attention, "Boulders like you are more reliable than banks, and besides, Cascade doesn't have one. Thanks for guarding my loot. Don't go anywhere!"

Part Two

CHANGE

FALL 1894

Knowing she would be tired from standing at a grill day after day, Mary prepared a window sign to her liking. Instead of the conventional posting, "Closed for the Sabbath" or "Closed Sunday" she used the last of her green paint to print on her placard, "Closed Today, Open Tomorrow". Pleased with her optional hours of business, though likely to concede to the norm, barring emergency, she prepared menus and decorated. As per her announcement, Mary's Café celebrated its grand opening on November 26th.

It was the men who swung through the threshold and eventually declared it their meeting place, where they elbowed up for coffee, checkers, a good breakfast and story swapping. Numbers of shortening winter days ticked by before the clique allowed personal biases toward their hostess to dissipate—attitudes accumulated indirectly, for over a decade.

Perhaps appetites for good cooking helped to encourage acceptance of Mary's remodeled persona—the away-from-home-maker who served delicious meals and accommodated personal requests without complaint. Biscuits, flapjacks, fritters, apple pie and vegetable beef stew satisfied in ways nothing else could.

Postmaster Joseph Kauffman, who went by Joe K., was first to arrive each morning—his greeting, predictable. "Nigger Mary, could I get a cup of coffee?" After settling into his favorite straight-back nearest the potbelly, his gruff tone warmed as he parleyed short tidings he considered to be humorous: "Yours just don't taste like my wife's—and that's good. You won't be telling Clara Belle now will ya, Nigger Mary? Great Gods of Norse—that wind is wicked as a witch's twitch," and so on.

She slid ham and eggs-over-easy under his nose, slung puckered retorts and refilled his coffee mug. They bantered until his cronies arrived, when weather predictions and calamities would be addressed at length. One morning his friends were late, so she asked, "Seen any interesting mail lately, Joe K.?"

"Nah," he said, "just circulars. But there will be lots to sort through today, when the train comes in." He removed his gray derby, set it to his right and rubbed his balding head. "There's some piano music that Mrs. Mortag ordered. The wrapping was ripped, that's how I know. Can you read sheet music for your banjo, Nigger Mary?"

"Yes, Mr. Kauffman. That I can."

"Well, if you happen to be over at the post office later, I could give you a peek."

"Thank you, sir," she said with no intention of breaching any propriety. "Maybe I'll do that."

The door banged and four bodies weighed heavy with overcoats, pushed in. "Good morning, gentlemen," Mary jangled, "Find your places, and I'll get the coffee."

They hung their coats on pegs and shuffled, single file, until each chair at the "regulars" round table was occupied. Scents of tobacco and witch hazel mingled with aromas of coffee beans and cornbread. The day would begin shaping into character as the forum branded their opinions upon local goings on, substantiated and rumored.

Thanks to Mary, the clutch became known as the C.C.C. (Cascade Coffee Council). By mid-morning they had finished eating, pushed chairs back and rubbed bellies while they jawed over the not-yet-announced cost of spring seed.

The café bell jingled and a stranger entered their pocket of warmth. He was a tall man, muscular and light-stepped, his ethnicity difficult to decipher. A thick fur hood framed his clean-shaven angular face; sepia eyes darted stealthfully, like those of wild predators. His lips were full and relaxed. As the cloak slid from his broad shoulders, she noted that his tailored wool vest and jacket were store-bought and of fine quality. The lower half of his body was fitted with contrasted attire that raised eyebrows: leather leggings and knee-high moccasins that hugged impressive brawn: *redskin trousers*. Mary looked closer to identify designs or markings that could reveal a tribe of origin.

Finely quilled leather bags were draped across his left shoulder, as was a long tubular case that several of the C.C.C. assumed to be a container for lethal flint arrows, though the man was not carrying a bow. The same question dominated everyone's curiosity: which ethnic origin of his clothing was native to him: top or bottom?

One of the cronies, a local saloon owner, crooked his neck and tipped his chair, straining to identify weapons, deciding whether he should appropriate Mary's authority and enforce his own establishment's policy: *No Indians Allowed.* Scowling, he leaned forward.

Joe K. hiccupped and grabbed a glass of water.

Mary caught the dark-haired stranger's attention and said, "Come on in and get yourself warm. Have a seat at the counter, here, if you like."

"Thank you, madam," the stranger said as he shifted his gaze from the hostess to the locals, arched his arm and extended a slight bow, portraying manner and dictum of the upper class. "Good morning to you, gentlemen."

He prolonged a steady look at the assembly. His boldness, albeit respectful and sincere in appearance, unnerved some of the men. Suspicions grew. Who was he, to greet them with unbid familiarity? They struggled to assess, unsure how to judge his behavior. The verdict could only be rendered by knowledge of his race. He was after all, in *their* café and should therefore be subject to examination.

C.C.C. members rattled utensils and cups and shot looks back and forth, each hoping that the other would take the bull by the horns and insist on answers to shrewd questions pressed to interrogate, obtain relevant information for the protection of their town.

Attempts to formulate those clever queries failed however; neurons misfired and dissipated. Finally, J.C. Marcum asked, "Where do you call home, sir?"

A lively voice replied, "I find that the whole world is my oyster, there are so many fascinating destinations."

Marcum tapped his foot and signaled John Sheppard to take a stab at it.

The stranger, intentionally perched on a stool to position sight of the men and of the woman, was familiar with the endeavor underway.

He exuded a manner of confidence Mary found to be pleasing. "My name's Mary Fields, of Mary's Café," she said, and extended her hand across the counter.

He reached hers with a forthright grip. "Delighted to meet you, Mary Fields of Mary's Café. My name is Michael MacKenzie."

She smiled. "What can I get you?"

"The special, please."

Michael MacKenzie ran fingers through his hair, flushing the chill out. Shortly thereafter, Mary noticed that his lips had gained color and supposed that he looked like the main character from *Battle of the Grizzlies,* her current novella of choice that featured a mountain man who slid across avalanches to rescue waylaid pioneers, unnerved by ferocious grizzlies chasing at his heels. She formulated her own wager with regard to his racial identity and education: part Indian, Blackfeet maybe, definitely part White—European or Canadian; inherited social standing, upper-class; private boarding schools, university, English or American; speaks with poetic cadence; a trapper, a supervisor for the Hudson's Bay Company or North West Company, maybe? Definitely not from here—probably not from Montana. She noticed a reddish lustre in his dark, wavy shoulder-length mane and decided to add him to her fanciful list of heroes that comprised her mind's eye of the western kaleidoscope—a multi-race American choosing to cross borders. But which borders, exactly?

Joe K. cleared his throat and stood up. "Gotta get back to the post office. Got letters to sort."

Marcum tried again, attempting to disguise sarcasm. "Mr. MacKenzie, is our town one of your many destinations, or are you passing through?"

"I haven't as of yet made that determination. What lodging would you recommend, sir? I'm sorry, I didn't get your name?"

Overall consensus coagulated after failure to obtain pertinent data. Clearly, the situation did not warrant immediate action; they would leave Mary Fields to navigate the diminished dilemma. The sun came out, a good reason to mobilize a C.C.C. exodus, and members took their individual attentions elsewhere, excepting John Sheppard, an immigrant from Scotland, who lingered, then moseyed toward the door and tipped his hat toward the stranger. "Top of the morning to you, Mr. Mac-Kenzie," he greeted, aware that they could be distantly related to folk from isles across the Atlantic. "Come to the store if there's something you'll be needing."

"Aye, thank you, sir."

MacKenzie nodded and remained, chewing small bites of food and sipping coffee sparingly, glad for the opportunity to speak with the adroit entrepreneur alone. While Mary scrubbed dishes in a tiny sink behind the counter, he scanned the room again and noticed that the fire had died down. He slid the bags off his shoulder, grabbed wood from the metal bucket by the stove and cross-stacked the logs.

"Where do you come from, if you don't mind me asking?" she said, watching him move with the grace of a cougar.

"Many places. Recently from Quebec. I am a translator, guide and trapper, most of the time." His eyes rested on a red stool under the counter, recently painted.

"Are you with the government, then?" Mary asked, wondering if he had been sent to investigate local Catholic ties to the deceased Métis leader, Louis Riel, who had taught at Saint Peter's Jesuit School a decade past. If so, he would get no information from her.

"Which one?" He laughed. "No, I represent no government. I am independent."

"So are you American? Canadian? Citizen of …?"

"Officially, I am Métis; my mother is Ho-de-no-sau-nee—Onondaga, and my father is, was, a Scot—his parents immigrated to Nova Scotia. Since my father settled in northeastern America and my mother is Iroquois, I propose that I am an American, with cultural influences from Scotland, Canada, France and the Five Nations." He smiled, noticing the scars and calluses on Mary's hands. "Is this acceptable pedigree to you, Miss or Mrs., is it, Fields?"

Mary grinned, happy to meet someone she liked. "Yes, your pedigree is more than acceptable. And it's Miss." She paused. "What tribe is Ho-de-no-sau-nee?"

"Whites call us Iroquois. You know: The Five Nations, League of the Iroquois Confederacy, from country that is presently called New York State. I am Onondaga—People of the Hills."

Her heart spiked. Annie had claimed to be from People of the Hills. She set the dishrag down. "I didn't know People of the Hills was the name of a tribe—thought it was a place. I have a dear little friend who is a member of your tribe, then. Her name is Annie."

"All the way out here?"

"Yes. She was near to six when she arrived a year ago—scared as a trapped rabbit—talked about being shuttled across landscape for long periods of time in trains and wagons. She says her name was Onatah before it was changed to Annie. Does that sound right?" Goosebumps flared.

"Yes, Onatah. It means, 'of the earth.'"

He thought of his parents and glanced over his shoulder. His father, Liam MacKenzie, recruited by the North West Company, had lived an isolated life. He trapped for many winters before he joined the Ho-de-no-sau-nee, People of the Long House, comforted by mutual congeniality and a fervent commitment to family. After a time, the story went, a beautiful Onondaga woman accepted his proposal, and they married; the following spring, the couple was blessed with the birth of a son. Michael.

He leaned back, remembering his father say that Ho-de-no-sau-nee legends were similar to those of early Celt Clans—remembering, that as he prepared for his sacred Onondaga initiation into manhood, his father made the decision to leave—took him and his mother West, where they trapped for pelts in one pristine wilderness after another—remembered his shock when his father abruptly sent him to a Catholic university in Montreal, and the sincere request his father had asked of him as they embraced at the train depot: *Help the Ho-de-no-sau-nee weather future hardship—family is everything.*

He was glad his mother had returned to the Ho-de-no-sau-nee Onondaga reservation after his father's death (an unexpected event months later) and proud that she had helped the Iroquois Confederacy establish schools on the reservation; she had encouraged her people to allocate ten times the amount of funding that the U.S. government spent on their own schools and the proposal had passed. *The Iroquois will prosper, regardless,* she had written to him.

"So she is Onondaga and Ho-de-no-sau-*kee*?" Mary asked.

Michael turned, faced the woman who had roused his private memories.

"Almost. It's Ho-de-no-sau-*nee*. I hope that someday Onatah will find her family. If they are alive, they are missing her."

Mary refilled his coffee cup, glanced at the foliage arranged in the little vases set on her tables, and crossed her arms. "She says her grandmother is a medicine woman." Excitement surged—maybe Annie could return to her tribe—she had her whole life ahead of her. Would it be better or worse on an Iroquois reservation?

"Ho-de-no-sau-nee have five clan-tribes, all related, who come together as one nation. Onondaga, People of the Hills, is one of the clans. Women are respected and honored. They guide us with wise hearts." He thought of his mother's enduring patience. "Even my father could not fully grasp why Iroquois tradition upholds maternal lineage, and why belongings are owned by the women."

"Things would be a lot more peaceful without the paternal thrust for ownership," Mary said.

They nodded in agreement.

"Speaking of," she commented thoughtfully, "seems like the government wants the entire population of Métis to disappear. Am I right?"

Michael nodded again, keeping eye contact.

Mary said, "What did they think would happen when they sent explorers and fur traders out to map the country and collect Indian information, anyway? I think y'all hold inherited family culture from both worlds. Stands to reason such persons would lend a bigger perspective, both bloods mingling inside. Government could learn a thing or two if they watched how you folks do things with no help from anybody."

"You have my vote," Michael chuckled.

"Is it true that you're not eligible for reservation land or appropriations as an Indian? And at the same time, you're denied homestead claims if you apply as a white immigrant or native-born?"

"That is it in a nutshell, my dear lady. Once in awhile a clerk slips up and follows the law, the one that entitles us, and we get homestead land in spite of opposing efforts. Once in awhile."

"Well, that's not enough," Mary huffed and tossed her potholders on the counter. "Did you know that the majority of girls and boys at Saint Peter's Indian Schools are Métis? But you never heard that from me, cause the Ursuline Mothers and Jesuit Fathers have to get the subsidies. They claim to the government inspectors that the children are full-blood American-born Cree and Piegan as opposed to Canadian-born—they have to, to get the funds. As if there's a big red line at the U.S.-Canadian border dividing land that tribes have been traveling on, living on, for generations. Here I go again—Anyway, the girls that happen to be Métis are some of the smartest ever—in academics and art and in the trades, too. If educated folks were really educated, they'd realize race doesn't dictate greatness. We could all be great if we all had support."

She bit into the thick slice of bread she'd been holding in her hand and chewed. "What a different world that would be."

"Amen. A different world, indeed."

She grabbed a plate, warm from the stack on the stove, sawed three slices from the loaf before her, placed dollops of butter and jam on the side and slid it to Michael. "Fact is, some of the girls in the *White* Ursuline Academy are Métis. So, proves my point. The other Métis girls are in the Indian school, like I said. Bet you can guess the reason for the inequity?"

"Let me try—the ones in the white school have white fathers who are supportive of the mission in some way?"

"Yep. In fact, two of them built the original white girl's school cabin."

Michael bowed his head, spread a length of jam.

Mary said, "Sorry, it's my dream for a just world. I don't fit in most places, and most Colored folk don't care much for Indians, either. Sure you know that, too." She wiped the counter for the third time.

"You must have labored in slavery for a lifetime?"

"Yep. Born into it. Rubbed me wrong from the start."

She watched him smile, took off her apron and folded it.

"What bothered me most was, well, a lot of things."

She sat on her stool behind the counter. "All the slaves in the world couldn't satisfy the lust for more."

Left to interpret her meaning, he thought: Lust for more slaves, certainly—along with a myriad of inequities, exploitations likely taken. She chooses not to, doesn't need to anymore, I suppose, enumerate or divulge the brutalities she has experienced, and concluded: she is remarkable.

"Perhaps the next generation can make progress," he said. "It will be interesting to see what nature of continental culture develops—what virtues evolve to be recognized as American."

"Yes, and whether all races will be included in the assemblage."

After swapping tales for an hour or two longer, they both agreed that Cascade's racial-tolerance pendulum currently tipped against the presence of Métis and that it would be best if Michael moved on, the sooner the better. Corners of the Birdtail had been particularly inflammatory of late—there had been several vigilante murders, and the victims were Indian, Chinese and Métis—guilty only of becoming targets for hatred.

Mary gave Michael directions to the Jesuit Mission because he did, as it turned out, have a message for Father J. Rebmann, Superior at the Jesuit School: information to do with Riel's cause.

She was anxious to share her good news about the People of the Hills with Annie-Onatah, and didn't want to see her new comrade go. As Michael tossed his cloak over his shoulder and headed toward the door, she prolonged their time together when she asked, "Wait, Michael. Is it true that the Iroquois, I mean the Ho-de-no-sau-*nee*, were the first Indians to use steel traps for beaver? I've done some trapping in my day—taught by a Nanticoke man long time ago—showed me the best blend for tobacco, too. Anyway, do trappers still get paid well for pelts?"

"Yes, to the steel traps and no, for pay. Wouldn't recommend that you start a career in trapping. Best regards, Miss Mary Fields. I hope to see you again."

The café bell trumpeted his departure. Mary watched the intriguing man cross the street and swing up onto a pinto horse.

"Guess I'll axe my backup plan to join the fur trade," she mumbled.

When the café bell jingled again, Mary, broomstick in hand, looked up expectantly, hoping her friend Michael MacKenzie had forgotten something. Patrick Dowlen, one of her occasional customers, stepped into her territory and after commenting on the cold, asked for an extra-large serving of the Special.

Mary set a bowl of hearty beef stew sided with thick slices of bread and butter beneath his ragged whiskers and returned to her kitchen, instructing him to holler if he needed anything. Minutes later, Patrick, a short and thick fellow with narrow points of view, carried his empty bowl, licked clean, to the counter and showered Mary with scullery compliments followed by the request to add the total to his tab, promising to pay as soon as his flock of sheep had been sheared in spring and offered a bonus—a pup from Molly, his herding collie.

She acquiesced, unable to turn hunger away, but extracted a verbal promise that he best not forget. Mary had begun requesting such assurances to be voiced aloud, with the hope that she would gain a better ratio of return. A growing number of her customers had been asking for credit, and payments on her own accounts had fallen behind.

She could barely wait to tell Onatah "Of the Earth" her news: the People of the Hills, Onondaga, Ho-de-no-sau-nee! How would she visit Annie without the Reverend Brondel finding out? She'd write to Mother Mary after she got tomorrow's special—lamb roast—simmering.

While she peeled carrots and onions, she reviewed her visit with Michael MacKenzie. He had attended the same university as Louis Riel, The College of Montreal, and had joined Riel's following to fight for Métis rights. She wished that she had lived at Saint Peter's when the Fathers employed that dynamic Métis statesman, Louis Riel, as an instructor. Meeting him had been a near miss; Riel had been extradited to Canada just months before her arrival.

Firming her jaw, she recalled newspaper accounts from the late 70's and early 80's that had kept herself and the nuns in Toledo updated. Mr. Riel was a hero: the first Métis politician to fight against the Canadian government in order to manifest his vision: free, respectable communities of Métis, living on land *that had been theirs* for thousands of years.

Her indignation purged a snort of contempt. She turned to see if anyone had heard. There was only Patrick, hunched behind his newspaper, and he couldn't hear well, anyway.

She completed her silent soliloquy, provoked at the many transgressions: disgusting how they call Métis *half-breeds* and *breeds* when most of them were begot by white men taking pleasure unbid, forcing themselves; *mulattos* being no title of respect, either. Should have their—I'm not gonna say it.

She dried her dishes vigorously and readied the café for the next day, though it was only five minutes later than the last time she'd looked at the clock set on the bookshelf: 3:25 p.m.

She forced her thoughts back to Riel, unwilling to feel rage without a place to put it. Wonder how the Jesuits got a famous man like him to teach at their school. Oh yeah, he was hiding out by then, after he'd established the Red River Republic—or rather the rebellion to create the Republic that almost succeeded, with a constitution and everything. His time in Montana provided him a wife and children at least, some happiness before he got captured, taken to Canada and hung for nothing. What a shame, what a tragedy. If the American government would have stood behind him after granting him citizenship, maybe he'd be alive today—but they took it back, stole his American citizenship! He could have lived his whole life *White* in Canada and America if he hadn't chosen to mention that he was one-quarter Indian. But he wanted to make the world a better place—had more faith in humanity than the rest of us—gave his life for the cause. Now that takes guts.

Patrick hollered, "Black Mary, coffee if 'n you don't mind, please—" Mary strolled over to the potbelly and lifted the pot that had simmered for hours. She poured the thick black liquid into the innocent sheepherder's mug and returned to her kitchen, ticked off and ready to close for the day.

Feeling confined and frustrated, she summarized her point of view: White immigrants from all over the world only have to file a paper and hocus pocus, free land. Potatoes rolled off the chopping block. The door slammed. Patrick had left.

Riel's Republic was going to recognize the Catholic Church as the one true religion. Wonder if that was genuine belief or a political compromise— maybe that's how he knew the Jesuits at Saint Peter's. *What a mess.* She scrubbed pots and pans until she noticed blood running from the cracks of her dry hands, patted them with a towel, promised to make herself some plantain salve, tossed her shawl across her back, locked up and stomped through dirty street slosh, back to the hotel where she went upstairs without being seen. She was not in the mood for company and wasn't sure why she felt so out of control.

That evening, tucked into the lumpy hotel bed wearing two pair of wool socks, she turned to the page tagged by her bookmark in *Battle of the Grizzlies*. After reading the same paragraph three times, she looked up and landed her gaze on a small tear in the yellowed muslin curtain. So what was it, she confronted the nagging tick that rattled her peace of mind. She stared and waited.

Michael had asked, "When they fired you without cause, why didn't you write to the Bureau of Catholic Indian Missions in Washington D.C. or ask the newspaper editor you met to write an article reporting your plight?"

Why didn't I? Was it really just cause I knew it wouldn't get me anything but trouble? Or was I chickening out, hiding behind Ursuline apron strings of safety, somehow? Did I do the right thing staying here, or should I have taken the $300 and moved to Seattle or Great Falls? Did I stay because I'm afraid? I can't tolerate decisions based on fear. So which is it, Fields?

9

CRUELTY

SPRING 1895

*M*arch, April and May were wrought with the same inclement arctic weather that had begun in November. Snow levels increased to staggering heights, and a growing number of upside-down ice spires dangled from rooftops, blocking anticipated sightings of green.

Moods dripped and plummeted like the icicles, making it increasingly more difficult to model Christian temperance and perseverance. Mother Amadeus frowned, fighting personal tribulation that flared concurrently with the burials of children fallen under her watch. This time it was diphtheria and dropsy that had stolen her girls, and she grieved to have acquired such familiarity with messengers of death that perpetually hungered for the young innocents.

Annie trotted upstairs to the top floor of Saint Angela's, brush and bucket in tow, prepared to complete the morning's work assignment: scrub the white girls' dormitory. Her attempts to wash windows with a rag and tepid soapy water ceased as the cloth hardened and fixed itself to the frigid glass. Thankful that her duty was indoors and that she had, now, an excuse to dawdle, she perched upon on a wide sill, arms around knees, and gently tugged at the washcloth until it released, then tossed it into the bucket and steadied a distant gaze from the grand fortress—south, the direction that remained unblemished by man-made structures.

Dismissing footsteps heard below, she played a game she had created the day before; she searched outdoors for all items not white and decided their fate. If they pleased her, she would place them in an imaginary basket and create a story that included each of the gathered objects. This morning, the landscape presented little to toy with. Everything was white—earth, sky, mountains, trees, the bramble bushes on the perimeter where she hid on summer afternoons—all blanketed, weighted by stockpiles of elemental cold.

Only white, she mused, like living inside an egg, waiting to be hatched. I don't like learning to be someone I'm not. I want to go home.

A dark object lumbered into view, and she perked. It was a boy with an army blanket draped across his shoulders—a poor substitute for the uniformed coat normally allocated. Selecting him for her basket, she began composing a story and looked closer, observed him as he struggled to carry a large milking can, apparently full. The plummeted cold had sealed his bared hands to the metal cylinder. He grappled.

She ached, knowing that layers of his skin would rip.

Resolve summoned, the boy yanked. The bulk of him winced as he dropped to his knees.

Annie squeezed her ribs as stared at droplets of blood on the ice. The boy tucked his torn fingers beneath armpits and stood up, stoic, eyes empty. No, she decided, red blood would not stain her basket. When he moved closer, she recognized him. It was Raymond Thunder, *Pajackok* in Nancy's Piegan tongue. Pajackok is his *real* name, she protested futilely. They had met on May Day, and he had kind to her.

Seething, she fumed: why do the nuns make us wear Bible names? Rubbing her head, she compared such acts to other violations—saddles cinched around the bellies of horses, metal forced into their mouths. Visioning a mustang bound in harness and blinders as it hauled a wagon of bricks, she inserted herself into the fantasy, rescued the wild beauty and proclaimed to a throng of nuns and army men: *my name is Onatah, and you can't change me or my friend Nadie, no matter what you do*!

"Annie," Nancy called from below, "you're late for mass!" Spotted by one of the nuns, she was forced to leave without her friend.

Annie glanced outside. Pajackok-Raymond was gone. She realized then, that the footsteps she heard earlier belonged to the white boarders rushing to chapel. She sprinted down the stairs, across the iced compound and inside unnoticed—except by Sister Gertrude, who threw her a disapproving look.

She ducked into position at the end of the choir's first row. The small organ groaned a G-major chord, cuing the Indian choir to sing the processional. Purposefully, Annie diverted her thoughts to streams of autumn light that flickered through oak canopies and onto palettes of crisp texture—the forest floor of her birthplace carpeted by colorful leaves strewn deep—beautiful and more sacred than anything she could imagine, excepting her family. She held her kindled memories and piped, "Alleluia, alleluia, alleluia, Christ our Lord in Heaven this day," wondering if anyone had ever escaped and arrived home safely.

Later, in line for mid-day dinner, Nancy startled her with a nudge, placed an egg into her palm and whispered, "What are you going to do with it?"

Annie edged out of view to peak. Returned, she slipped the stolen object into Nancy's pocket. "Not this kind," she complained, "it's white."

"What? Why not?"

"It's for my dolly's face. I want a brown one."

Nancy sighed. "Next time, tell me ahead."

"Sorry. I'll make you a dolly, too, if you want."

"No, but thank you. I'm too old."

Annie tugged on Nancy's skirt and begged, "Could you bring me a scrap of gingham cloth from your sewing class, if you can?"

"That will be harder. I'll try. You'll have to wait."

"Thank you."

"Annie, if you like to sew, practice your penmanship so that next year you can take Embroidery."

Annie wrinkled her nose, looked up and thanked Sister Gertrude for the generous helping of meatloaf weighting her tin plate. The idea of stitching bright colors pleased her until she recalled the subject matter displayed on most embroidery projects—the English words, filling again, what should, to her mind, be pictures of landscape.

Hours after the bedtime bell had rung its course, Nancy lay awake in the Opera House dormitory, twisting side-to-back-to-side on rough cotton sheets as she listened to comrades toss and wheeze. Wind slapped against the wood walls, whisking channels of turbulence into haunting echoes. Nancy wished the wolves would join in—howl their ancient secrets of clan brother wisdom.

She imagined they knew of her plight and were waiting for the right moment to lead her away—to a medicine place that would help solve her troubles—like what to do when school finished. She wanted the life from her past that began with treasured memories: riding upon a travois pulled by a big black dog, watching women pound dried strips of buffalo, singing by the fire, lying under the safety of stars. She yearned for family, and for a life *with* nature, rather than laying claim to it, cutting it into pieces. Her heart smoldered. What good are memories now, she beleaguered. What if they force us to stay on reservations without buffalo? Will they ration us like cattle—will they watch us starve?

In the morning, eating breakfast, Nancy and her classmates couldn't help but overhear the nuns' voices wafting from their close-knit huddle nearby: "Mother's right, I wish the girls could exercise outside—April 3rd, still no sign of spring—blizzards without pause since Christmas—homesick—my skin has turned to powder." Clanking and footsteps over-sounded more words, then audible, "… shouldn't risk breaking anymore wagon wheels—front is coming—maybe the girls should—"

Nancy leaned to her friends and whispered, "Have you noticed? When each *calendar month* begins the same thing happens without fail—complaints of winter, a natural season. Surely the *educated* should know that snowfall lasts until the earth has rested—longer than one or two of their allotted months!" The girls giggled, glanced sideways. Nancy continued, "They are impatient, the whole of them. So impatient they decide to cut *everything* into pieces: land, stories, even time. I don't—" The bell rang and everyone scattered.

She grabbed her composition book and marched upstairs to Advanced English class, wondering, as she stared at feet bound in thick stiff cowhide with wedged heels, whether every single person at Saint Peter's was wishing they were somewhere else. It seemed like it to her.

Advanced English for Indian girls was taught by Mother Catherine. Students had hoped that the highest-level class might provide lessons less regimented, having worked hard to achieve a competent command of the language. They quickly learned that Mother Catherine's pleasant countenance diminished when it came to elocution and execution of the written word.

Their teacher began class by tapping her ruler against her desk until every pupil was seated. This day, she instructed her class to compose an essay titled, *My Future Plans*, in one hour's time. Without thinking, Nancy raised her hand and blurted, "What's more important, Mother—to know a million words or to know a million feelings?"

Mother Catherine, momentarily stumped, pretended not to be. "Education is the key to unlock countless opportunities in the world, Miss Nancy. If you educate yourself your life will be successful. More so, if you remain religious and attend Mass."

Nancy responded as though it were customary to engage. "I agree that I need to become academically equipped—but only for the purpose of navigating through the altered landscape that has taken our country."

Realizing that her insolence merited discipline, she looked down but found that she could not stop herself. "You say countless opportunities, but by the nature of our place in your world, opportunities are counted and restricted by faceless men we do not see. I appreciate knowing about the Holy Jesus and the Lord God, but I think I would rather have a million feelings than a million words."

Classmates shuffled papers, signaling her to stop. She heard them, knew they were right, and kept talking. "To me, feelings are like the way the God paints the sky, or the way my heart beats when I see loving eyes already knowing my feelings, or hearing a rush of wings flapping to lift above water—knowing where to migrate. The knowing, the feeling."

Mother Catherine paced, agitated by the unexpected outburst that didn't seem deliberately dissident—that actually made some sense. She raised a forefinger to an untamed eyebrow and stroked, debating whether to judge the pupil's words as irreverent or illuminated. She cleared her throat and said, "Your assignment is an essay, not a speech, dear. It seems you have copious words. Write them down."

Nancy muted her voice but raved on inwardly: why should I *want* to think the white way, let alone learn to write essays? English words are like the wind, flying fickle. I must have a plan that gives me freedom, freedom for a good life. Then I might appreciate "education." Yes, that's what I mean—education is a tool, not the answer! I sound like Mother Superior, she thought, feeling dizzy.

Mary Fields compassed her way as Cascade's new minority: the one and only African American, a trial-candidate-resident seeking acceptability, founding a yet-to-be-established premise that coloreds were allowed to settle in Cascade and any other place in the United States—the necessity for which seemed lost to white people. She knew that the novel idea of cohabitation required careful negotiation and she had operated her café for three months without problems, in part, because she had forced herself to "eat crow" more than once. Aware that violence was a light sleeper, she had decided for the time being, not to challenge, even when justified. The plan to acquire resident acceptance by metaphorically keeping one foot *in,* firmly planted in Cascade's pivotal center of male congress, and the other *out,* remaining a transitory lodger at the hotel, seemed to be working. She had also learned that it was necessary to monitor her own level of tolerance; when she noticed herself daydreaming about where to best place a stick of dynamite, she knew she had kept her mouth shut for too long and intervened with recreation—a walk, a borrowed mount to ride, target practice.

She paid regular visits to the Chong household on Sunday mornings, when most of the population was occupied at church and she could cloak her whereabouts, figuring that it was wise to remain exceedingly cautious until she had mapped local loyalties as accurately as possible.

She introduced her specialty, Tennessee fried chicken, to the Chong family. In return, Olive Chong served Mary one of their family favorites— Char Sui Bao, steamed rice buns filled with spicy pork, mushrooms and onions. Mary claimed the novel bun cakes delicious, a perfect meal for travel: meat and bread together in a fist-sized package. She routinely flattered Olive by requesting one-for-the-road (the short stint to Warner's Hotel) which meant she'd have something good to eat for a mid-night snack.

It was the last Sunday in March when Mary rushed to the Hong Chong Laundry with a newspaper tucked under her arm. She entered, uttering cheerful greetings, as usual, opened the paper and pointed to a small headline at the bottom of the front page. Gaining the Chongs' full attention, she announced, "This is terrible news. Listen." She read the two-week-old article aloud: "March 5, 1895: *Territorial*. There are 654 Chinamen in Butte. The Chinamen were given until today to leave Butte."

The message was obvious: leave or die. The couple's small parlor, delicately decorated with folds of red fabric and carved knick-knacks, suddenly felt claustrophobic. Mary rubbed her brow and said, "That's it. No more details." She leaned in. "You moved here from Butte, didn't you?"

Hong nodded, visibly agitated by the violent dictum. He was frightened for his mining team in Butte, his friends. He turned to Olive whose crazed stare met his.

"We knew it coming," Hong said flatly. "Chinese first workers hire to dynamite mines, make tunnels. They hire us, we know how and work less money. We are, what the word, dispensable. After two, three years," he made a confusing figurative gesture, "more Irish and other men come—then they no want us." He looked to his wife and reached for her hand. "We leave when neighbors murdered after miners' drunk New Year party."

"Hong one of best—explosive," Olive shared proudly.

"Really?" Mary arched her eyebrow, "I bet you know all kinds of things you don't let on about. Do you have many close friends there? I'm sorry to bring bad news."

"Gold and silver bring out worst. Washing laundry better. Stay alive, even money less," Hong said, his skin turned clammy. He wondered whether the Butte ultimatum would reach Cascade and if so, how soon. What could he do to prepare?

Olive asked Hong in English, out of respect for Mary Fields, "Where do you think they go?"

Hong shrugged, "Seattle, San Francisco, enough money. I hope."

"I can visit another time," Mary offered.

The Chongs insisted that she stay. Mutual concern over race hate had formed a bond, and it was understood that their friendship would remain concealed. Mary was aware of her advantage, since whites generally spewed more violence on Orientals than Coloreds. She would be careful not to do anything to cause harm for the kind, hardworking couple.

Mary increased her social sphere with caution. Knowledge of Birdtail activities helped to determine whether she should lie low or challenge imposed limitations. Though it was understood that respectable women did not smoke or drink in public, or in private for that matter—a restriction responsible for increased sales of "medicinal tonics" that utilized alcohol as the primary ingredient—she decided it was time to test whether her status as café trivia-secret-keeper might grant an exception to saloon proprieties.

On an ordinary weekday afternoon, she strolled into the Q & L, the saloon managed by H.W. Ludwig, one of the C.C.C., without asking permission and proceeded past the drinkers lined up at the bar to a table at the back of the narrow room. The space reminded her of a varmint tunnel dug for hiding—a low flat ceiling and only one window, south-faced, that supplied indirect afternoon light. She sat for an hour, read the paper twice. When no objections were made, she continued her patronage. After two weeks, she boldly lit a cigar and discretely puffed behind her newspaper.

Eventually, one of the ranchers, Mr. D.W. Monroe, invited her to have a drink, and Mary complied. She sipped a small glass of local draft and felt dizzy from the alcohol and her success. Aware that her acuity had been compromised, however slight, she, on the spot, mandated a personal policy that she would diligently adhere to for the rest of her life: one cigar, one drink—no matter what—and the drink was going to be water. Staying alert and on guard was paramount. She didn't care for the taste of beer, anyway. Those elusive belles of the night could do the drinking, if they wanted to take the risk.

Oddly enough, her presence at the Q & L became routine. Saloon goers forgot to be bothered with her, and she cultivated her original goal that became a long-term ritual: eavesdropping for useful information. At times, Mary was included in local banter, and as winter weeks rolled along, she endeared herself with clever puns and tales of close calls. Still, she knew that admittance to the men's hangout could be revoked at any time, so she kept interactions short and retreated to what became known as "Black Mary's table." When the atmosphere felt comfortable, she celebrated by playing a few rounds of solitaire.

She reported to Olive Chong that jawing with the fellas was far more pleasant than her alternate plan—approval by seeking permission to join the women's clubs or societies. Olive nodded, understanding that such an undertaking would cost a lot of pride with little chance of results. Mary began to feel hopeful, and by mid-April she had negotiated a deal to rent a small dwelling in the south end of town. Though it wasn't much more than a shack, it was to be her home, and she was thrilled.

On her next visit to the Q & L, she enjoyed a celebratory glass of ice water, a cigar and several games of solitaire. It was her habit to smoke a thimble's length of the stogie, then extinguish the coal and save the rest for later, pacifying her desire for more by reciting the commonplace saying: too much of a good thing will come back to bite you.

Tired and content, she started home, detouring to the café to grab the makings of a house-warming feast: slices of baked ham, a generous scoop of potato salad and a big piece of apple pie that she would heat on the potbelly in her new digs. She balanced the bounty in bowls and plates and walked cautiously along dark streets littered with blobs of snow, the surface of which had melted and refrozen, constituting unpredictable drops as weight broke through crust. Snow pies, Mary called them.

Rushing to keep the clay-ware from slipping, she gave her door a casual thrust of the hip and stepped in, shook her feet free from the heavy galoshes. A shoulder nudge closed the latch, and she shifted through darkness, appetite rising as she slid the dishes onto the table. She reached for the lantern.

Force grabbed her from behind, pinned her arm against her back and twisted. Dishes crashed. Rope dropped over her face. The loop was yanked, aborting her scream; an effective noose, it tightened, choked. Adroit skill tied and slip-locked her wrist into the lasso, rendered her tethered. He, she knew it was a he by his bulk and scent, flung his height and weight onto her, flattening her front to the table.

She swung her unbound fist and hit bone; his face, she thought. He grabbed it, torqued her arm backward and up, hitched it to the other. Intent on roping her middle, he tipped her downward, and as he did, she landed a furious number of heel kicks.

Coils of rope cut into ribs beneath her breasts. Ankles were hobbled. Wrenching, she flailed where she could, afraid of what would come next.

More rope snapped and whizzed above, slid across the log beam overhead, and whooshed down. Knowing its purpose, visions of escape diminished. He trussed, looped and knotted the fibrous cordage to the torso casing—a harness complete.

Heavy breath quickened. He hoisted her upward, secured the lever, heaved a satisfied grunt. Again, she attempted to scream, a guttural shriek until her mouth was stuffed with cloth and bridled—a strip of leather pulled between lips, buckled to the back of her skull. Pleased with his progress, he felt for two damp cowhide strips in his pocket, took one and pushed the piece around one calf, laced a rope through the grommets he had hammered in special, and repeated the exercise with her other leg.

Drool dripped. He cut the coil at her ankles and slid the shank bindings down, yanked them taut and knotted the attached roping to keep her pegged, each of her legs firmly bound to opposing table legs, limbs splayed open. Standing, he took a breath, positioned his leg and thrust a knee upward. Again. And again. Until she moaned.

He smiled, sliced her underpants with a bowie. She tossed her bulk from side to side. Bindings pulled tighter. A buckle unclasped. His. Present and past collided. She thrust herself all directions.

Her struggle only proved to arouse him.

From behind, he lifted her skirt, fondled her buttocks, slid fingers along the curves and explored the hidden crevices. Satisfied, he pulled out, smelled his hand and wiped it on her petticoat. Stepping back, he rocked his weight on creaky floorboards. She hardened, contracted muscle into itself.

Lurching forward, he grabbed her breasts and squeezed, spooned against her, began to pant. One grip released. Knuckles rubbed against the inside of her thigh pumping fast, faster. She dared not thrust for fear of worse. After a prolonged egregious moan, he smeared wet leavings onto her. Her throat convulsed.

He put his mouth to her ear and poked a curled wet tongue into it, longing to free the parts of her, rope her again, suck those black breasts, shove himself in, hard, as far as he could poke. Maybe he would, if he caught her out of town. But he wouldn't do it now. Because he was respected. A respected leader. And he would never really suckle a darkie, even though he had the right to. He bit her ear, lingered to taste the salt.

Quaked, he shook her and rasped, "You think you're so high and mighty. Coming in the Q & L like you're what? One of us? You're trash. To be used and thrown away. As we please. Any of us."

Putrid breath sickened. Raw, she squinted, scanned for weapons. Get my gun, she demanded, knowing it was twenty feet away and under her mattress. Should have got a lock before I moved in. If he cuts the rope, I'll grab a shard, cut him.

"You're just like them rodents under the rock pile. I seen you digging, scavenger. Nothing here belongs to you, not even our trash. I'm telling you, darkie." He grabbed, twisted her nipple. "Leave town now before you make me stack them stones on top 'a you." He bore a thumbnail into her breast. "Trust me. I will." Releasing, he kicked her with his boot.

She convulsed.

"Ain't gabbing now with them stupid stories, are ya?"

Stay alive, she charged. It's the only thing that matters. Act meek. Say what he wants, when I can.

"Answer me, nigger. Or I'll lighten the devil's load." A voice inside her argued that she was too young to die. She felt muscles spasm. His or hers? He was too close, again.

He pulled the strap from her head, yanked the gag from her mouth, slapped her face.

She murmured, "Whatever you say. I'll leave town. Whatever you—" She glimpsed a spark of light reflected. Her bound body crashed to the floor. She felt for a shard. Crackling steps paused. A pistol butt smacked the back of her head. She lay unconscious.

He poked at the limp bulk sprawled beneath him. Waited. Swung a violent kick to make sure. Nothing moved. He untied the noose, then the casing. As he yanked up, rope uncoiled around her midriff and she rolled, lifeless. Suddenly frightened, heat shot through his spine. Knife and lasso in hand, he bolted, slammed the front door and ran.

One thought lashed upon another. He headed for the alleys, avoiding light from the rising moon. Had he been reckless not to wear a mask? Had she gotten a look? He darted into shadows to hide from hooves approaching, a wagon. Had she recognized his voice? He'd left the leather bridle strap. Would she take it to the sheriff? Was she alive? He'd been sure the rest of his buddies would support his warning. Wouldn't they? He'd tell them after she left Cascade. She'd better leave. Then he would claim credit. He'd be a hero.

Mary didn't comprehend why she was on the floor when she woke hours later. Stars sparkled in the wrong place. When she pushed to rise, her body convulsed, and she sobbed from the knowing. Eventually, she sputtered, "I'm alive," and felt for damage. Her skin was ice-cold, sticky and wet. Fumbling to stand, she pulled herself to the table's end, dizzy, disarranged. She flinched, suddenly frightened, jerked to check behind. Fisting scraped knuckles, she waited for spasms to release.

Turning slowly, she probed, unable to separate his smell from sticky remnants of food and broken dishes, her new home contaminated, unsafe. She advised herself to suck air into her lungs. Pain stabbed at the attempt. She blinked twice at the water basin. It was full and unbroken. Carefully, she splashed the chilled elixir onto aggrieved skin. Wiping with her shirtsleeve, she stared past window glass to constellations, until her knees went weak and she succumbed. The wooden floor felt punitive. Extracting herself from the clinging evidence, she dragged her hurt body to the edge of her bed and covered herself.

In morning light she examined the injuries. Satisfied that all of them, excepting the cut on her lip, could be hidden, she wrapped the cut on her arm. If bruises from the blows to her face ripened, she would create an explanation. She bandaged her ribs with strips of cotton, sure that two or three had cracked or broke. Her ankles were bruised and swollen, her breasts sore from the abuse, yet she forced herself to move. First, she built a fire, heated leftover coffee. Positioned, at last, on the pillow she had placed on the kitchen chair, she listened to chickadees fill the Sabbath quiet while she fought a strong urge to vomit. She poured hot water from the kettle, added enough soap to boil a full pot of laundry and scoured herself, intent on eliminating every remnant of the man's touch.

She limped outside, tossed the dirty water over her property line and whispered, "Rise above, drink your coffee and snap to." Returned to her house, she sat in her rocker, summoned detective skills and gave the debased stricken parts of herself permission to curl into a sheltered corner of her heart while she pushed forward, allowed stoic resolve to examine the event. It would be difficult to stop past lesions from contaminating the specifics of a new brutality, but she had to. Her right hand trembled.

Find the observations you must have acquired, conscious or not, she demanded as she conjured the reenactment and scrutinized, watching two shadows wrestle on the stage of her mind's eye, retaining the choice to stop, circle, measure or contemplate the scene, at will.

Useful data was extracted. He is tall, she confirmed, extraordinarily strong. Wide chested, a bony chin. His boots had thick heels, she added to her tally, the kind that clop. And pointed toes. Fine hair, medium length. He lives in town or visits with regularity, has been in my company and knows details about me—unless someone relayed those details and he parroted.

But I know everyone, she interrupted. *Evidently not,* her cool examiner corrected: you didn't recognize his voice. She closed her eyes. He wears a ring—that's how I got this cut on my lip. Wait, I'm not sure about that. It's true I didn't recognize his voice; he claims that Cascade is his town, but he could have come up the *Missouri* by steamboat, a mercenary or random wanderer passing through. *But he speaks as though Cascade is his town.* He could be from the industrial school, a hired hand or teacher. The disciplinarian? That would be the headmaster's assistant. I don't know him. She gasped as spasms quaked her ribs.

Can I risk telling what happened? Would it be stupid?

Would bring too much attention to me—might encourage more. Do I know anyone who'd help me threaten the attacker—someone who believes in the law—someone invested in the town's reputation? *I still don't know who he is.*

As the day progressed, she thanked God it was Sunday. It gave her time to decide what action to take, if any—come up with plans that included more than justified rage. She wished for a miracle: *he could simply disappear, and that would be that.* She told herself to rest and not to think about it. It was no use. She did manage to silence self-criticism like, "That's what happens when you take your gun out of your pocket," knowing it did no good.

She directed her attention toward primary matters. Told herself to state the *important truth* out loud. Though her throat was sore and bruised, she uttered hoarsely, "I'm alive. I have the right to live. I'm vulnerable. I need allies. Don't know if the ties I've made here are strong enough."

She dismissed the notion to post a "gone fishing" notice on the café door and stay home for a few days. She would open Mary's Café as usual and act as though nothing had happened. She spent the rest of daylight scrubbing, slowly, where blood and food had splattered on the floor, her table and the walls.

When darkness came, she realized, abruptly, that she had forgotten her birthday. March had come and gone, and she had had no party. She sighed, causing more discomfort, and in the process, forgave her oversight, which led her to imagine a cheerful birthday party attended by all of those who did, and would, love her.

Mary's circle of friends included a small number young people who attended Fort Shaw Industrial School. It was a rare pleasure to see any of them, as Indians and Métis were not welcome in Cascade. On occasion, serendipity prevailed, as on an uneventful April evening when a series of sharp raps rattled the back door of her Café. On edge after the recent attack, she bid the caller to identity him, or her, self. One word sounded. "Jack."

She recognized the voice. Jack had attended the Jesuit school at Saint Peter's. Years earlier, his time had been volunteered to assist her on a hunting trip when mission supplies had run low. She and Jack had snow shoed south to the Dearborn River where seasonal runoff had been diverted by clever beaver residents who had built a log-stacked communal lodge concealed by thickets of cottonwood, currants and box elder. The two trappers came to admire each other's expertise and had returned to the mission with two hundred pounds of dark succulent meat and a newly kindled friendship.

Mary cracked the door ajar, jerked him in like a granddaddy trout and growled, "Jack, you can't come here, you know. If they find out, they'll tar and feather both of us." She gave him a quick hug and rested her hand on his shoulder. "You're cold and wet. What am I going to do with you?" They looked at each other and grinned.

It was long past closing time. Mary had marinated three chickens for the Thursday special and had set the price at two bits, same as the competition. The vibrant youth's arrival lifted her spirits and distracted her from the discomfort that peaked around this time each day, pain from injuries begging recovery time.

The unreformed student had escaped—bribed a guard dog with jerky while he jumped from a window and over the fence. Thankful to have a friend he could rely on, Jack needed food to last three days. Then he would break his run and stop to hunt—maybe risk a small fire.

"This is the third time," Mary charged emphatically, as if her friend didn't know. "They'll throw you back on the reservation. Or worse, jail."

"I don't care," Jack said, undaunted, his chopped black hair, thick and coarse, bent up into a bundle and tied with leather lacing. Mary thought he looked exactly like the brutish "wild heathen" sketched in periodicals and at the same time, to her, dignified and comely. Jack was *Apsaalooka*—Crow to the whites, and detested being held captive in a government school. School officers judged him as incorrigible, the epitome of "native." To Mary's thinking, that was a compliment.

"I'm going back to my family," he said.

"Where?"

"South and east past the sulphur springs—near Billings on the Yellowstone, we call it Elk, River: *E-chee-dick-karsh-ah-shay.*"

"That's a long way not to get caught. Are you traveling nights?"

"Yes'm," his charm contagious.

"And no fires?"

"Yes'm. I waited for the full moon this time—can make better time."

Mary set a plate of sumptuous roast beef, corn and mashed potatoes on the chopping table in front of him. He lifted the plate with one hand and scooped spoonfuls into his mouth, wearing an expression of ravenous appreciation, savoring the taste.

"Mary, you're the best cook there is—except for my mother, of course."

"Of course. Thank you, sir." She set the heavy bowl of chicken into the cooler, grabbed a package of cold cuts and latched the tin shut.

"Yee Lee, the superintendent's cook, doesn't come anywhere close to shining a candle next to your home cooking, Mary."

"You mean his cooking doesn't hold a candle to mine?"

"Yes, that too." He winked as he watched her open the jar of beef jerky taken from the counter.

"When you're finished, young man, we need to get you out of here." She wrapped the meat in cloth. "When I leave, wait a couple minutes. Then take off through the alley."

"All right, Mary."

"One more thing," she said as she reached under the counter to retrieve her cigar box. Its wooden lid was decorated with a lithographic print of an oil painting titled "King of Homers, Longest and Fastest in the World." *Red Whizzer*, the prize-winning homing pigeon featured, had flown nine hundred and thirty-five miles from Florida to Philadelphia in less than twenty-four hours. The champion's picture had struck Mary's fancy, which was how she had come to make it her container for precious possessions, temporarily on loan as the café cash register. She flipped the lid open, grabbed five silver dollars and tucked them into Jack's bundle along with enough bread, meat, jerky and apples to last three or four days.

"No, Mary," he objected, "I don't need money—you've helped me more than enough."

"We both know you need some coin to get all that way. You have to eat, cross the Missouri and buy favors, maybe. If you've got any left, give it to that good cook mother of yours." She wiped her hands on her apron, hung it on the empty peg, and snatched her coat and cap from the same rack, a café addition she had honed from discards.

Jack licked mashed potatoes from his fingers and gulped the last of Mary's mint tea.

"Just set the dishes in the sink."

"No, I'll wash them and put them away—no sign out of the ordinary."

"Good idea. I'll be leaving now," she said. "Be careful, will you? The McKee's live near Townsend if you need a safe place. Danny and Caroline. Caroline was a student at Saint Peter's. When you're safe, send me word somehow. I want to know that you're all right."

She leaned against the door, rested her hand on the latch and asked, "How do you plan on supporting yourself, Mr. Jack?"

"I can blacksmith and make shoes. Want to take care of my mother and uncle and auntie. They are old, and I know they are suffering. Not enough food and—"

"Yeah, I know it's terrible."

"Someday, I could farm if there's a way. There are rumors of places."

"Good man. You have thought-out plans. You'll do well." She gave him an affectionate pat on his shoulder and said, "Goodnight, and God bless you, Jack, who I never saw this night."

He squeezed her hand. "Thank you, White Crow. I'll lock the door."

She set off at a mindful pace, nimble and alert, using wide-angle vision to watch for men lurking in shadows. She wondered how Michael McKenzie was doing. He told her about a place called Spring Creek, where a group of Métis had banded together and built a school, taught English academics and applied for land under both the Homestead Act and the Preemption Act. Maybe Jack could find a place like that. She made a wish on the brightest star.

Mother Amadeus locked her office door and sat in the seldom-used birdseye maple rocking chair. A ray of late morning sunlight shifted, cut through pocketed rain clouds that had assembled in pageant formation. Looks like they're ready to let go, she mused. We need the rain, but not today. Not on May Day.

She thought of Mary Fields, aware that for herself, there would never be another May Day without heartfelt recognition of her friend, an emotional tribute for all the joy and laughter Mary had brought to the mission—to her, to the sisters and the pupils. Mary's May Day picnics had been an annual mission event anticipated and enjoyed—now consigned to cherished memories.

"Sad and unjust," she whispered as she fingered the cross around her neck. The indisputable fact that she had not been able to get Reverend Brondel to retract the order for Mary's dismissal irritated her no end. There was no reason and you had no right, she began to contest in her mind's eye. "Don't get started," she warned herself.

That same May Day morning, Mary Fields' waking thoughts protested the cruelty of a May Day without flocks of children to love. Harangued with melancholy and annoying pain that had revoked her plans for a personal May Day jaunt, she spent most of the morning rubbing salve of plantain and arnica onto bruises. She reminisced over past May Day expeditions when she and the children picnicked in the hills, hunted for wildflowers; what joy she had felt, instigating frolic in the wide open. She wondered if they missed her as much as she missed them, the children, supposed they must be aching to stretch their legs and hearts. "Me, too," she said, "have to get out of this house, least for awhile." And it's time to face the facts, she directed. Whether I, or anyone else likes it or not —I live in town now, and I need to start new traditions. I could give flowers to the town children—could ask their mothers if they could go for a little walk. No. Mothers aren't that fond of me yet. Mostly, they think I am less than, being colored, uneducated and probably disgusting since I like to smoke cigars and frequent the saloon—with their men. Maybe they're jealous. They'd appreciate good company and a smoke if they'd been out working on the prairie, like me. Sooner or later they'll ask me to baby-sit. What else can I do for May Day?

"Maybe the altar," she spoke.

Months before, the Reverend Brondel had initiated a fundraising campaign to build a Catholic Church in Cascade. Given the limited resources of Catholics in the area, an altar, a smidgen larger than a breadbox, had been erected on four planed posts to stand as a reminder in the interim: contribute and behave with moral piety: your house of worship will come. Mary was of the opinion that the petite statue of Jesus' Mother squeezed into an open-box, even if it did have an arch, looked lost and forlorn.

As she slammed the door to her house and locked it, she made a decision. I'll put flowers on that lonely shrine every week—wild ones and homegrown ones, both. It will make the sisters happy, and it'll be my in-the-meantime, May Day—a Mary Fields' town tradition. I'll make myself a garden on my own grounds, grow pretty flowers. "Yes." I'll plant flower seeds, and I'm not leaving town unless I decide to.

She inched along with bruised appendages and a walking stick, to a field out of view. Keeping her back erect, she bent her knees gingerly, pulled some vines and weeds with leaves of varied shapes and contrasting colors:

sweet pea, salsify, yellow dock and mallow. "So pretty you are," she told them affectionately, "even without your blooms. Long winter, this one." She stroked the textured leaves with swollen muddy fingers and squeezed the stalks into a bouquet, gently binding with vine tendrils. Tired, she limped to the Catholic marker and placed the first signs of spring at the feet of the crudely carved Virgin Mary. She stepped back and rested, hand on hip. "Good," she said approvingly. I promise to bring flowers every week through the season, in hopes that it will lift hearts. Including mine."

May Day afternoon, Mother Amadeus excused herself to the privacy of her room, the object of anticipation safe in her pocket. She stood for a moment, watching cloud shadows darken mission homestead acreage that would soon, thanks to the boys next door, become wheat and barley crops that glistened on long summer evenings when light lingered past student bedtime. She looked forward to the long hours of light.

She pulled the letter from her pocket and fondled the textured weave of superior quality, familiar from pre-convent life. It was from her eldest brother, Edmund. She had been savoring the parcel since yesterday's mail delivery and pressed it, now, to her chest—a private reward for prayers said and recorded on rosary beads. She sat down.

I barely remember what he looks like. He must have more memories of me, being nine years my senior. I can't help but wonder, with his immense fortune, why he hasn't contributed to my Montana missions after voicing much concern. Is it because I appear capable? Does he assume I don't need assistance?

Sarah-Mary unfastened the envelope, not with her sterling silver blade and a practiced turn of the wrist, but with an enthusiastic plunge, her forefinger tearing the flap ragged.

The page was dated, Palm Sunday, April 7, 1895. Polite solicitations followed:

My dear Sarah,

> *... I am anxious to hear how the government has treated your schools in the matter of the appropriations. From the little I saw in the paper, I inferred that your appropriation for the school had been cut off. If so, that is going to cause you great anxiety and trouble I fear, though I suppose of course that you have learned to look on the problem of life as merely a question of making the best one can under the*

circumstances, though we always feel that it is so much more satisfactory
if we can carry out our own plans as we have made them ourselves. At
least that is the way I feel …

Mother Mary tensed. Yes, of course the financial crisis worried her.
The end of the Bureau's financial support for Religious Indian Contract
Boarding Schools neared. Previously pledged to continue through
1900 with reductions of twenty percent each year, the funding had
been reallocated and would cease completely at any moment. Indian
appropriations often disappeared without warning. She put the letter on her
night table and paced.

Clatter tapped at her door. She opened it, surprised that someone
would interrupt her private time—saw no one for her trouble. She glanced
down. "Ah, flowers! Thank you!" Her surprise was genuine; she had
forgotten about posies, having moved forward to the next day in her mind.
Sounds of nearby giggles comforted. She called, "Splendid flowers! Happy
May Day!"

Concurrently, Mary Fields leaned against the decorated altar and faced
west. She admired the blushed afterglow of light above the Rockies—layers
of plum and tangerine streaked in diagonal twists lit luminous by fiery sun
sinking behind the range. "Be a clear night for stargazing," she said, her
voice small in the solitude. She thanked the white-tipped glaciers, hoping
they could hear. "Your heights of glory humble me … I wish I were keeping
company with you, there in your crags and crevices, looking out to infinity."

She recalled her first glimpse of the Great Divide, in detail: *I peered*
through frosted windows on the Northern Pacific. *How can earth be that*
high, I cried out, awed by the wall of magnificent spikes. *Teeth of giants,*
visible in the dark. Looks like a stairway to heaven for giants. Soon after,
the train screeched a slow halt and we, the two sisters and I, arrived in
Helena, the Montana Territory. Stepping off, I got smacked by a new
acquaintance—the arctic wind whipping fierce. I looked around and
understood what those posters back east meant by "vast frontier".

Took my breath away, literally. Snow, everywhere. Colder than Ohio
times two. Made the pores in my skin twist and snap. Never knew such a
place really did exist. I was dazzled, except for the town itself. A propped-up
idea of city: wood buildings slapped together, piano music ringing from
what locals called "watering holes," and it was early morning. Helena looked

like a difficult wager, situated in nowhere for no good possible reason, except for the universal dream to get rich from gold and silver and such.

I just wanted to get to Mother Mary. We were escorted to the Grand Hotel, which was the grandest building in Helena at the time. I stayed outside to wait for the stage to Dearborn, our next way station, and there he was again. I first spotted that renegade in the game car when we boarded *The Northern*; he was spouting malarkey fast as he threw dice, pompous as a peacock. Kept my distance until I got stuck with him in front of the Grand Hotel.

He wasn't scary or dangerous, just annoying—the kind you can't trust far as spitting distance. He was short and chubby, like tumbleweed I saw drifting across the street for the first time. Claimed to be a miner. Wore mismatched attire torn and dirty—tried to convey airs of a gentleman but betrayed himself with coarse gestures and cruder personal hygiene. A real charmer—he thought so, anyway. So I entertained myself.

I asked why he came to Montana, and he rambled on about his developed nose for riches—expounded on a tirade, as if I were a fool born yesterday. Said, "I make it my business to strike it rich, when the time is right, when the 'iron is hot,' as they say. In my line of business, that means before the other fella gets there!" He laughed too loud. Even the bellman edged away.

Looks like all kinds of scoundrels are congregating on the frontier— that's what I thought to myself.

When I asked what he was mining for, he answered, "Well, as I always say: silver if you're lucky, gold if you strike it rich, and sapphires and rubies if all else fails. That's why I take heed of myself and figure on hirin' a John to blast out my mine so as I can do the prospectin' on my own. That's how it's done in Cal-e-forn-e-a, and they say that this place has a thousand times more gold—enough to live long at the end of the rainbow. Yes sir, I mean, ma'am."

I turned to roll my eyes. Then I said, *I have a 'red hot iron' observation for you. Have you ever seen so many deep rutted tracks?* I pointed to the ice-covered avenue before us: hard pack, cut into tunnel troughs by metal on sleigh runners and wagon wheels traversing back and forth. *Those grooves are shaped perfect for railroad track,* I said, *Upside-down molds ready to cast iron. Can you imagine how much money you'd make if you could pour molten iron into them? You'd be set for life."* His mouth hung open, eyes blank as a slate board. I told him, *See, the ice ruts are the molds, straight and perfect.*

"For what?" he said.

For railroad track, I repeated. Cogs began to turn. Saliva dripped. *You're a businessman, sir,* I said. *Think of all the money you'd make if you could produce railroad track that doesn't have to be transported from back East. You'll be a millionaire, right here, right now. Just have to pour the red-hot molten iron. Right there. No hard work digging a mine.*

He looked at the ruts again. I could see the lust for wealth clouding the obvious flaw. Then he got it—realized I'd been pulling his leg and barked, "Why are you wasting my time talking about stupid ideas?"

Duped by a colored woman. Ha! Could dish it out, but couldn't take it. Saved my belly laugh for later. Can still remember the exact thought that came to me while I tapped my foot: If I was making *real* tracks, not hanging around here whittling idea-power building imaginary tracks—I'd be there already. I was in a hurry.

"Time to eat," Mary said out loud, "that's the answer." She hobbled home, satisfied to have come back to herself.

"Nancy!" Annie cheered as she jumped, sounding a thud on Nancy's bed minutes before the 5:00 a.m. wake-up bell. "I have a great idea!"

"What, Annie? Did you do your schoolwork?"

"Yes. Will you check it for me? Mother Thomas says I shouldn't have the slate in my room, but she let me because I was late for a good reason. It's my spelling. See?"

Annie held the small-framed slate board in front of Nancy's face.

"Oh," Nancy giggled, sitting up.

"What?"

"You wrote scared for sacred."

"Let me see." She examined closely. "Those are the right letters. It's right!"

"No, look. The 'a' and 'c' are mixed around. It's supposed to be 'sac' not 'sca'." She wrote s-a-c-r-e-d next to Annie's s-c-a-r-e-d and wondered why the words were made with twin letters.

"Oh. Thanks. That reminds me, did you get the gingham for my dolly's dress, and I need something else that I can't ask for."

"Yes." Nancy rubbed her eyes. "What do you need?" She put herself at risk to support Annie's undertakings, but it was worth the trouble just to see what she would come up with. Besides, Annie was her best friend.

"Some black string or yarn and watercolor paint, like you get to have in Advanced Art class, and a brush to paint with."

"You haven't painted before, have you?"

"No, but I know I can."

"All right."

"Thank you, Owl Sister!" She leapt across the mattress to give Nancy a tight squeeze.

"Owl Sister?"

"Yes. You're my wise owl." No further explanation was given. "Nancy, are you going to stay here this summer, or will you go home like some of the other girls?"

"The nuns wouldn't let my mother take me home. She came here to visit once, and they told her that she couldn't take me, even for the summer. I don't know why they were so mean."

"Did you get to talk to your mother?" Annie wished she had a mother to talk to.

"No, that's why I was upset. They showed her a paper and told her that by the authority of United States law, she was not allowed to take me anywhere. And they pointed to the words on the paper, and of course my mother couldn't read it. They wouldn't let me see the paper, either. We only had time to hug and say goodbye. I haven't seen her since."

She threw the covers back, got out of bed. "I think she's afraid to come back—she might think that they will hurt me if she comes here. And it's far away for her, with no horse. I know in my heart she wants to see me."

"That's terrible!" Annie cried, her slate board slipping from her grip. "Have you asked Mother to change her mind? Maybe that was before and now it's better?"

"No. I don't want to get in trouble. I want to be in the advanced classes, and I don't know if Mother will let me stay if I make trouble."

"Maybe Mary Fields could help."

"I don't see how—" Maybe White Crow *could* help, Nancy considered. She might be traveling to the Blackfeet reservation sometime—or might know someone who would send word to her mother.

"Want to see what I made to hide my project in?"

Before her owl sister could reply, Annie lifted her skirt, revealing a small cloth sack with long drawstrings, knotted tightly underneath the mandatory long dress. "Isn't it smart?" She slipped the piece of chalk inside.

"Yes, it is," Nancy laughed. "That's your best idea yet! A bag to hide forbidden doll materials and other unauthorized treasures—they stay with you and won't be found in the dormitory. Good thinking, Annie!"

10

PLANS

SPRING 1895

*B*eing a practical frontier woman, Mary Fields dressed in layers. She set her cup of coffee down and thumbed through a stack of freshly laundered clothes. "Let's see. Want to look nice," she uttered. "Heavy wool trousers, my store-bought skirt with a pistol pocket, and my apron." She pulled the trousers out. "No. No apron today. I'll wear my special ruffled blouse—will match my skirt, topped with my fur coat, boots and my favorite cap."

Minutes later, she checked twice to see that she had locked her door and headed to the café to make sure the "Closed Today, Open Tomorrow" sign rested on the windowsill before beginning the trek on Birdtail Mission Road.

She could have asked the mail carrier for a ride but didn't want to hear the answer she had gotten in the past: "The U.S. Postal Service can't be giving free rides to coloreds: federal policy, ya know."

"Don't believe there is any such policy," she grumbled. "Happy to walk—better company anyway. Wind feels fickle. Did I remember the candies?" She dug into her pocket.

Pacing up the incline, she came to the bend that opened onto a wide vista. In the foreground, large granite boulders, including the guardian of her loot, stood perched in an open field incongruently, as if drunken Grecian Gods had pitched uncut discus stones in a holiday toss. A stretch of Rockies gleaned in the distance. Shaking off worries that had recently shrouded her optimism, she decided to enjoy the day, regardless.

"Treasures everywhere when I remember to look," she said, tickled to spot violets risen through half-thawed soil. Along a meadow's edge she discovered shiny native buttercups that fought for space beneath rogue grasses come to the Birdtail on pioneer wagon wheels rolling west. "Spring is officially here!" she declared, "Love walking the road alone. I feel free when I'm between one place and another." She scaled her voice to replicate birdcalls, attempting to coax hawks or osprey into the open for the fun of it.

An enthusiastic pace had already covered seven of seventeen miles. Stopping at the broadest meadow, she inserted a candy into her mouth and surveyed the area. No other persons in sight for hundreds of miles, she imagined.

Hands on hips, she pounced, foxlike, and lunged into three buoyant strides, as if she were invincible, herself reclaimed. Carefree, she poised effortless balance elevated on tiptoes, arms out—swept her right arm upward as she pivoted and announced, "Introducing Mary White Crow F. Fields: freighter, frontier woman and café entrepreneur. Woman who does lots of things just fine, but nothing perfect. I leave perfect for God and angels. Yes. It's me!"

Silence reposed. She faced her touchstone peak. "Bet you can't guess what the 'F' stands for! Faith, Fern, Farrah, Frances, Felicia?" Reaching up, she invited her beloved panorama to respond. "No?" She lowered her arms, rocked heel to toe and confided, "I've only signed the initial of my middle name a few times—on official papers like my pay contract with the sisters in Toledo. No one knows what the 'F' stands for, except me. You'll like it. It's—"

A high-pitched bawl interrupted, a nearby prairie dog who had popped his head out of a hole.

Nodding, Mary said, "So you have a middle name, too? Glad to hear it. Some folks call you a pika. Which are you, prairie dog or pika?"

The furry whiskered rodent continued cheeping.

"You tell'm, mister. Time for me to get."

The moment lost, she charged into a brisk pace, her thoughts wrestling an issue she had not yet resolved. Three miles passed without notice before she slowed to confront her quandary. "So, Mary," she challenged, "what are you going to do about the café? It's been six months since you opened." She heavy stepped another quarter mile and accused, "You have no profits to show cause you give all your profits away, giving meals to hungry folks who don't have money to pay." She sucked her upper lip, stepped across a length of puddles. "Well?"

Marching straight ahead, she kept going until she had formed a rebuttal. "Nothing, I'm going to do nothing about getting angry at myself.

Can't help feeding hungry people. It's my nature. So I guess I'm not a good business woman, if it means letting folks go hungry." She squinted, roused by a lone crane flying overhead. "But I can't keep on like this. I'm working for free, and my windfall is the only reason I've lasted this long." She kicked a small stone. "So what am I going to do?"

After a few half-hearted steps, she tarried to declare her decree. "Hate to say it but have to close up. Odds are against the sheepherders paying, and even if they do, it would be a couple months from now. Cash season is too short to make ends meet, and there aren't enough dinner customers."

She spun a quarter turn and accelerated. Three bends later, as she angled over a ditch of icy run-off, a piercing thought provoked. "Glory! Mary Moran may have been right about Frank Haley taking his retirement; I didn't pay her any mind. Should have read the ad before I shoved it into my pocket. Do I still have it?" Pebbles rolled as she halted, lifted her skirt to search for the newsprint clipping in her trouser pocket. "Yes!" she cried, positioning her back to the sun. She flattened the crinkles and read carefully:

Mail Routes. The advertisement of the post office department inviting proposals for carrying the mails from July 1, 1895 to June 30, 1899, is out. Proposals will be received up to 4 p.m. May 21st, and the decisions will be announced on or before June 10, 1895. Following are routes for which contracts will be let, in which Sun River and northern Montana are interested.

Cascade to Saint Peter's Mission, every day except Sunday, 17 miles. Fort Shaw, by Florence and Augusta, to Cecil, 43 miles, three times weekly. Sun River to Choteau, 30 miles, three times a week.

"It *is* this route, Cascade to Saint Peter's. She was right. It's up for grabs! I could do it. Been doing it for years already! Rather be out in the open than cooking and scrubbing in town. Would solve the café problem too. All the times Frank's been in my café and he never spoke a word about it! Maybe he's ashamed of giving up. Elements are mighty harsh.

Six days a week, she considered. Doesn't leave much time for laundry service I might have to take on to make ends meet. Would get me away from … I'd be flying on the wings of Pegasus again, on the move and harder to find."

Breaking into a brisk pace, she contemplated the position in earnest, and speculated: What's supposed to be in a proposal—proposed pay, for sure, but what else? Who would know how much Frank gets paid? One of his cronies at The Mint Saloon? Wonder if Monroe would tell me, if he knows.

Perspiring, she unbuttoned her beaver coat, slowed her stride. Good thing I've been reading *The Rising Sun* all these years—keeping tabs on driver notices. Stage lines come and go like grasshoppers. For good reason. She noticed a covey of quail dash into the brush. "I'd be a good 'stage driver'. Tell all snobs to ride in the 'freight' section on top—tell 'em to shovel manure whenever I say so. Ha, ha." She adjusted her cap. "The mail wagon is as close to a stage as it's going to get around here." I know this stretch of prairie better than anybody. Question is whether they can bring themselves to hire a woman, a colored woman. Who does the hiring? The post office department of the United States? Guess that would be federal. Am I up for four years on the road?

She glanced to her touchstone.

"I'd get to see the children! Regular!"

She approached the last stretch of her trek. Admiring a new row of budding lilacs branches that a young postulant had planted years earlier, she noted that the mission acreage would soon be ready to plow. Turning up the drive, she stopped at the steps of Saint Angela's Academy, spied windows cracked open and shouted, "Here I am! Good day, everybody!"

Glances darted. A bell rang. Girls dashed down stairwells and swarmed in her direction, Annie and Nancy leading the pack. Mary's grin stretched so wide it hurt.

"My girls, my girls," she cheered. Gushing giggles rippled. Sister Gertrude opened the kitchen door to identify the source of ruckus. Mother Amadeus, distracted from a spelling bee, glanced from her classroom and waved. Bending rules of protocol for her namesake, she excused her pupils and followed them downstairs, enjoying the falderal from the doorway.

Annie leapt, squealing, "I missed you, White Crow!" Mary held her tight and gazed at the flock of human ducklings that encircled her—reaching, jabbering, vying to shower affections—just as she'd hoped.

The bell rang and soon after, a voice unfamiliar to her barked, "Girls, return to class! What in the daylights?" Most dallied until Mother assured them that they could visit Mary when lessons had been completed.

Nancy returned to sewing class. Annie hid in the henhouse.

Mary decided to visit the poultry, check to see if the hens and ducks remembered her. She stooped into the hutch and called, "Howdy, baby hens—cluck, cluck, giddy-up—come see your Mary, little ducklings, too—haven't forgotten me, have you?" She grabbed a handful of cracked corn and flung it into the run.

Hinges squeaked. Annie burst from behind the door, wrapped both arms around the warmth she remembered, and pressed her head at Mary's waist.

"Annie," Mary crooned.

Gertrude entered, setting off a new round of poultry commotion. Sprite as ever, she called, "Welcome home, Mary," squeezed her friend in a hearty hug and leaned back for a good look.

"Well, thank you, Sister G. Mighty good to see you. And my old cluckers, here. How many ladies now? Looks like a few got the hatchet?"

Mary patted Annie's head, took her hand and winked.

"Yes, quite a few," Gertrude agreed, straightening her apron. "No elk donations. About three hundred hens left, I think. It was a long winter. I take good care of them, Mary. I read your 'Poultry Notes'."

"How many went to polecats? Remember that year, '87, wasn't it?" She tossed more corn on dirt cluttered with soft down.

"What's a polecat?" Annie asked.

"A striped terror; a skunk," Mary scoffed.

Sister Gertrude turned to Annie, "Did Mary ever tell you about the time she fought the skunk who killed forty-two of her hens and how she carried the stinky, smelly creature three miles, just to show us that she got him?"

"No."

"Well, I think you just about told her."

"You're a mystery, Mary Fields." Gertrude shook her head, mentioned there were cookies cooling in the kitchen.

They exited the hennery, carefully stepping over the extra-high doorsill crusted with years of manure.

"White Crow!" Nancy called as she trotted in their direction, risking punishment for having snuck out of class. "Before Mother finds you, I need to talk to you!"

"Sister Gertrude," Mary said, "Looks like we have an escapee here, for good reason, sounds like. Can we take a walk? Will you cover?"

"Not my jurisdiction but go ahead. I'll plead her case, but only for you, this once. No guarantees."

"Thanks. Save me a cookie?"

"Just get back by dinner."

"Yes, Ma'am. Wouldn't miss it."

The trio headed for the aspen grove, the stand that leafed first each year, past the garden and over what Mother Mary called a knoll. Mary touched the tender leaves unfolding. "Hello, tambourine shakers. Will you play us a tune?"

Annie laughed and squeezed a handful of her Ucsote's skirt, the way she used to.

Directly above, an unusual rock formation jutted from the top of an old ravine. Glowing in the manner one does at sight of an old friend, Mary pointed. "You know that was one of the first spots I explored, first spring after I arrived. Couldn't wait to see what the snow was hiding in those sharp crags. Nice spot, don't you think?"

Annie noticed that Nancy wasn't paying attention.

Nancy slipped her hand into Mary's and said, "White Crow, did you know that Theresa Lewis died? Two months ago, in February. It was terrible. She was fifteen—one year older than me. You've known her all her life, haven't you?"

"Her mother is Piegan," Annie said, "I saw her. She is beautiful. White Crow, why do the Lewis girls get to go to the White school and all the other Métis go to the Indian school?"

Annoyed, Nancy stepped between Annie and Mary. Annie's questions were endless, it seemed, and she needed to be heard. She raised her voice. "White Crow, remember when you and I went to the Fort Shaw School Performance—when I came to Cascade the first week in February—when Mr. and Mrs. Moran drove us in their buggy?"

Mary nodded. Annie leaned against her Ucsote and frowned.

"I'm wondering, could you get this letter to the Blackfeet Reservation for me? It's to my family. I heard that the storekeep makes deliveries there sometimes."

"You know I will."

"It's important."

"I can see that." Mary eased her arm around Nancy's shoulder. "That reminds me—I brought you a cut-out from the newspaper. She pulled it from her skirt pocket and handed it over. "It's about that same concert. Been saving it for you. They had another one in town, couple weeks ago."

Nancy took the folded clipping and held it. Stared at the leaves.

"What's going on?" Mary said.

"I'm asking them if they'll visit me, if I attend Fort Shaw Industrial."

"As a student?"

"What?" Annie blurted, "You can't leave!" Mary shushed her with a look.

"What do you think Fort Shaw will have that the sisters don't already give you here? You like to write … Bet you that school isn't up to par with Saint Angela's." She grew anxious, recalling Jack's accounts.

"You're probably right. But I want to see my family."

"Can't argue with that." She gave Nancy a squeeze. "It's a big decision. I'm glad you're taking your time with it."

Annie bellowed, "You aren't really going to Fort Shaw School, are you? I knew you were thinking about it, I knew you were. Other girls are talking about it, too, White Crow." She shrunk, then uttered, "Sorry, Nancy, I know you want your family."

"Nothing is decided, Annie. I'm just investigating—the way you investigate when you have an idea to make things."

Annie sniffled and rubbed her eyes.

"What things would that be?" Mary asked, diverting emotions.

Annie gazed off, retreating to silence. Mary gave her a nudge and a kiss on the forehead. "What things are you making, Onatah?" she asked, thinking that calling her by her real name might soothe.

Visioning the doll she'd been crafting for White Crow, Annie thought about making a second doll—one to keep herself company if Nancy was really going to abandon her.

"It's a secret," she said, turning a shoulder.

Mary dangled, "You two want to hear some good news?"

"Yes," Nancy answered, slipping the newsprint into her pocket.

She considered relaying the information she'd learned about the Onondagan, Annie's people, and shared instead, "I got myself a nice little house in town. Nothing fancy, but now I don't have to stay in a hotel room."

"Where?" Nancy asked.

Unable to maintain her protest, Annie spouted, "What does it look like? Does it have windows?"

"Does it heat with a fireplace or a wood stove?" Nancy quizzed.

"Can we come see it?" they asked in unison.

Gertrude served chicken pot pies and applesauce. Afterwards, Mary gathered both the white and Indian girls and shared stories about café customers who had come to town from faraway places—fantastical adventures enhanced by the teller.

When afternoon classes resumed, Mary pulled Mother Amadeus aside and posed, "Friend Mother Mary, ready for a stroll up Mount Angela?"

"Yes, yes," she murmured, "soon as I get Gertrude started on sulfuring the upper floors. Just be a minute."

"Got pests again, do ya?"

"I suppose it's inevitable."

As the two hoofed it up the mountain. Mother said, "I hear that you have a home of your own. How splendid!"

"To say word gets around fast at Saint Angela's would be an understatement." Mary provided details. "I leased a sweet little place—near the Methodist church—the unpainted flat board house on the corner, couple blocks up from Central Avenue. Know where I mean? It's been abandoned for a year or so. Needs some work."

"Yes, I think I do. You'll make it ship shape. I'm glad you have a place of your own.

Mary raised an eyebrow, surprised to hear slang from the Mother. "Yep. If it floods, it'll slide right into the Missouri, and I'll be seaworthy."

Amadeus slid a smile, wiped perspiration from her forehead. "What is the family charging you?"

"Mr. Herman Wolf owns it. Twenty-five dollars a month. I know, it's high. Aren't a lot of options at the moment."

"That's a great deal of cooking and laundry."

"Yep. Sure is hot, today," Mary skirted, noticing that her frocked friend had become overheated under the guimpe and headdress. "Let's rest for a minute." She leaned against a granddaddy yellow pine, prompting Mary, draped in lengths of black yardage, as usual, to follow into the shade. "I have an idea I'd like your opinion on."

Mother shouldered the neighboring pine, took a long breath and looked up when Mary broached, "I think you realize I can't turn hungry folks away from the café. Just can't."

Aware of concern in her friend's voice, she replied, "Yes, to your credit."

"Well, unfortunately, credit is what I get paid for meals more often than not. Mr. Shepherd won't give me an account, so I can't get supplies without hard cash."

"Will you be able to earn enough profit to pay rent for both the café and your house?"

"Unlikely. Been using my savings that are about gone."

Squeezing her earlobe, Mary pursued, "*The Rising Sun* has an advertisement running. For a mail carrier, and it's your route. Did you know that Frank Haley is retiring at the end of June?"

"No, I didn't know." Mother fanned her face with her hand. "Would you want to be the mail carrier?"

"Well, I'm thinking there isn't anyone more qualified than me. I've been driving this route since 1885."

"And in every horrendous condition that the wilds have thrown at you."

"I'm thinking I'll let the café go if I can get the job as the mail carrier. There's just one thing—"

"What's that?"

"I'm not sure if coloreds are eligible, let alone women. I remember colored women delivering post in Cleveland, but Montana might have different regulations." She recalled her exchange with the Helena sheriff.

"Maybe I can find out, Mother said. Our new telephone line has just been connected—such a help it's going to be. I can call the City Clerk in Helena. It would be marvelous to see you more often—as long as you feel up to it, physically. You know it can be grueling, Mary. And dangerous."

"You know me, strongest woman alive, except maybe for you." They grinned. "You know the best part?" Mary Fields posed.

"What?"

"Can't you just picture R. R., Right Reverend Brondel's face when he finds out?" She slapped her knee, and they broke into laughter. "Come on, sister, let's go up to the boulder."

Blotting corners of her eyes with her hankie, Mother, tired from the exertion, fell in behind Mary's relaxed pace, aware of blisters forming, caused by her ill-suited button-up shoes. She pushed the strength of her voice to say, "I suspect that both postmasters will be part of the approval process. That would be Mr. Flinn in town, of course, and Father McDonnell, next door. As long as no one alerts the Reverend Brondel, there shouldn't be a problem. Maybe Father knows the current postal stipulations in regard to hiring. I'll ask him."

Mary turned back. "Says to write a proposal to the Post Office Department, and there's no address. Guess that means to give it to the newspaper office. They ask applicants to submit a bid for wages. What do you think I should propose?"

"I have no idea. I'll see if I can get any inside information."

"Applications close in two weeks."

"I'll let you know as soon as possible. I'll send you a note with Frank."

"Thanks, Mary." She rounded the last turn. "Ah, here we are, boulders with a big picture view."

They perched themselves in the shade, next to dinosaur-sized granite outcrops, watched chattering chickadees jump from one needled pine branch to another.

Believing Mary's venture to be a grand idea, Mother said, "You still have a balance of $60 on our ledger, and you'll have to purchase a wagon and team if you get the job. Shall I write you a draft?"

"Maybe for $30. I want something left for emergencies. Have a little saved up, too. Thanks." She checked the sun's position and said, "I'm starting a garden at my new place."

"Glorious! Those town folk don't know how lucky they are. I have packets of seeds in the root cellar—take whatever you'd like. I miss your gardens."

"I'm planning on putting flowers in the Catholic memorial once they're grown."

"How very generous of you. I think I'll have to mention that to Reverend Brondel." She tapped her foot. "Did you see the article about our missions in the *Rising Sun*? The one that reported the status of contract school funding? Or rather, soon-to-be-absence of it, I should say."

"No. Is that some kind of double-cross to force you into giving your pupils to Fort Industrial?"

"Hadn't thought of it quite that way, but the federal bureau has been reducing stipends for awhile, and all funds will cease, eventually. We don't have enough money to keep everyone. A tragedy." She watched a large beetle navigate jagged tree bark. "The principal at Fort Shaw knows he has the advantage. He's telling us which students he'll accept!" Lines on her forehead deepened. "Of course, he wants the brightest achievers and our accomplished musicians. For the boys, the strongest and hardest working."

"I didn't know it was that bad, Mary. What will you do?"
"I've been forced to select a number of girls to transfer, and I fear that I will have to add to the list." She swallowed. "I'm hoping that Katharine Drexel will come through again, but she's devoted to The Holy Family Mission project on the Blackfeet reservation, near Two Medicine Lakes. Remember?"

Mary gave a nod. "What about the Fort Shaw academics?" she asked, Nancy's welfare on her mind. "Are they close to yours?"

"Dr. Winslow assures me that his academic program is excellent, but one wonders whether that is possible when a student's schedule includes an excess of mandatory hours spent in trade instruction and work duties." Included in her recollection was the doctor's ostentatious remark: *The Industrial curriculum has been customized for appropriate societal roles—we train our females for their place as wives and mothers.* Mary Amadeus did not mention this to Mary Fields.

Mary imagined Saint Angela transferees sewing countless numbers of Fort Shaw student uniforms, eyes red, fingers crimped and pinpricked. "Did they give you a tour? Show you how and where the girls are to labor? Give you a list of classes?"
"No."
"So we don't really know anything."
"Correctly stated, my friend." Mother sighed, "Other than hearsay."

As they trekked down Mount Angela's switchbacks, Mary said to the Mother, "Saw your new ad in the *Rising Sun*: $10 monthly for boarders, $5 extra for music. You haven't changed your rates for ten years, Mary."
"I know. Didn't seem the prudent time to raise tuition."

"Yeah, see your point. Well, I hope you get an onslaught of paying customers soon—more than I have at the café."

They cut through the pasture, propelled by the sun's departure.

Shortly after Mary Fields had taken her leave the following morning, Mother delivered the weekly lot of bread to the Jesuit sector in person. She sought out Father McDonnell, Saint Peter's postmaster, intending to engage in purposeful chitchat.

They had maintained a respectful relationship during their tenured association, though Mother thought Father McDonnell was too strict with the boys and Father objected to Mother Amadeus's academic curriculum because it invariably exceeded church and state protocol. A mutual love for music had helped them to settle occasional ripples in Jesuit-Ursuline relations.

She located him in his office and handed him a plate of warm yeast bread, butter melting upon thick slices. "Father McDonnell," she began, "You've been Saint Peter's Postmaster forever …"

He looked at her and scratched his balding head. "Hardly forever, but I have been sorting the post since 1889. Seems like forever, some days. Bread smells delicious. Thank you."

"Yes. Well, long enough to know the regulations, certainly. What are the employment requirements for our mail carrier?"

Odd, he thought. She's never been interested in our post unless she's waiting for something specific. He took a bite of bread, leaned against his desk as he savored the flavor, then cited the necessary skills. "A master horseman, equipment repairman, negotiator in unexpected hostile situations, survivalist in cruel weather …" He paused, watched butter drip to the plate, and appraised further, "Of course he should possess stringent moral behavior, including reliability, honesty and punctuality. And good humor." He could feel her eyes. "Sounds like a disciple's job, eh?" He winked. "Is this about the advertisement?"

She stepped closer, leaned against a bookshelf filled with canonical volumes, a body's length from him. "Are there any racial, gender specifications?" she asked, one eyebrow raised.

He set the plate down, crossed his arms. "I just happen to know that. From 1805 until 1859, the law stated that all delivery persons must be white. Now eligibility has been modernized to state: 'No gender exclusion—twenty-one years or older—citizens of any color can apply.' I checked on the regulations after I read an article about the amendments in *The Montana Plaindealer* a few months ago."

Plaindealer, she thought, impressed. "Apply and be hired, or just apply?" She watched him as he bit into crust. "I suppose it's up to us. The Postal Service usually asks for postmaster recommendations—mine and Mr. Flinn's. Oh, wait. Now that I think about it, you're talking about a contractual mail carrier. Not a U.S. Postal employee."

He ran it through in his mind, believing accuracy to be pivotal in all matters. He cleared his throat. "The position available is called a 'star route carrier,' not a 'rural delivery carrier.'"

"What does that mean?"

"A *star route carrier* is technically a carrier who sub-contracts, with someone who has purchased the contract, or with the applicable postmasters, the postmasters of the stations concerned. Such is the case here. We negotiate the pay and choose who we believe to be the best applicant. In the case of a rural delivery carrier, that carrier is an employee of the U.S. government, same as postmasters or postmistresses. They deliver mail on a route that starts and ends at the same official post office, and their salary is set by the government."

"That doesn't make much sense; they are delivering mail on a route, just the same."

"I agree. But those are the current postal regulations."

Mother prompted, "We both know the most experienced and reliable freight carrier in these parts."

The Jesuit Father couldn't place who she meant.

"*She* just might be applying for the position."

Mother knew he'd gotten her gist when a moment later his eyes widened. "Mary?"

She nodded, helped herself to the last slice of bread.

Father McDonnell appraised the proposition—measured potential discord with the Bishop Brondel against the more important matter of staying in touch with the rest of the world. He eliminated personal bias (though he liked Mary, she confused him periodically) and formed an objective opinion for the greater good of the community.

"Hmm," he said, "You have no argument from me. There is clearly no one more reliable and experienced." He was glad to please Mary Amadeus. Perhaps she would grace him with one of those beguiling smiles famous for calming heathen indignation.

"Then I'm sure you'll do your best to negotiate well for Mary Fields, won't you, Father McDonnell?" She smiled.

"I take it this means we have an applicant. Yes, I'll do my best." He allowed himself a moment to adjust, relieved that a solution of such importance had been so easy to agree upon. It made perfect sense. Thinking about the next step, he said, "Flinn's not going to want to pay her much, Mother. You know how people are. And we must consider other applicants, to be fair."

"I'll tell Mary Fields to go ahead and send in her proposal, as per the advertisement's instruction. How much do you think she should propose for salary?"

"Yearly salary for a man is around $500. Advise her to solicit $400, and then we'll haggle. I can't guarantee anything, but I'll try."

As Mother started for the door, he said, having just realized, "Goodness, that means Mary's Café will be closed. Lots of folks will be disappointed. Including Mr. Flinn."

The mail carrier application deadline passed. Two applicants had filed proposals: Mary Fields and a Mr. Sargent, an immigrant from Poland, just arrived.

Father McDonnell drove the mission buggy to town to complete the star route business and answer questions that Mr. Flinn, Cascade's new postmaster who had succeeded Joseph Kauffman, might have. The men shook hands and made themselves comfortable in Flinn's office at the back of the mercantile.

"Frank Haley should have known better than to have recommended that Pol for the job," Flinn griped to the Father, before he explained. "The man was familiar with driving horses, all right, but only from the back of a plow. He told me so himself. Second, when he heard that redskins had been sighted—no big deal, if he were an experienced wrangler—he withdrew."

"Poor fellow is probably desperate for work," Father said, aware that the withdrawal made the task at hand much easier than he'd had reason to expect.

"Ludwig says a friend of his considered applying but changed his mind once he rode the route. Decided the terrain was too treacherous."

"Well, we both know that anyone familiar with our on-again off-again road and the duration of it, is smart to withdraw."

Flinn knew it to be so. He'd had to fill in for Frank on occasion. A driver spent hours patching gullies or pushing rock or timber out of the way, in addition to the usual problems with snow and ice—the precise reason Frank Haley wasn't interested in renewing.

"That leaves us with one item of mail carrier business, then," Father said. "The rate of Mary's compensation."

Flinn leaned back. "Last year, Black Mary made the trip to Helena with the wife and me—when she got fired from your place."

Father blinked, clasped his hands.

"I thought she was brave to confront the Reverend. No offense, Father. She has standards—gumption, for sure. Always pays her accounts prompt here, too. Even so, a woman has never—"

"We already agreed that she's the best freighter for the job, even if we had a handful of applicants. A fair and honest wage is all we need to consummate. Don't you agree?"

Flinn shifted, grabbed a pencil, tapped it on his desk. "Speaking plain, Father, Mary's a negro and a woman to boot. Has no right to a man's wage. Are you sure that it's legal for a negress to be hired? I remember reading somewhere that postmasters will be prosecuted if they hire anyone but whites."

Father was prepared. "According to the law she not only has the right to be hired; the 'free white only' regulation was eliminated in 1859. I checked. She also has every right for equal wages, if we are man enough to offer them. You and I both know that she is as good as or better than any man when it comes to hauling and dealing with elements—of any kind."

"That's beside the point. She can't have the same salary as a man. We both know Frank Haley was getting $500 a year. I'm willing to give her $250 and that's generous."

"Mr. Flinn, that is neither generous nor Christian. $400 at least."

"You realize it's coming out of our pocket, Father. I say $300 tops, or we wait to find someone else—a man for example."

"Mary appeared to be more than satisfactory when you hired her to freight supplies from your store—and when you devour her delicious breakfasts at the cafe. Doesn't she do your family's laundry, as well?"

Flinn blushed red above the collar. He was wearing one of the shirts that Mary starched and ironed just right. "All right, $325, and that's more than any colored woman could ever earn anywhere."

Father McDonnell scoffed at the ridiculous claim, tried once more and backed off, believing that Flinn would declare stalemate if more pressure was applied. Disappointed that he could persuade him no further, Father consoled himself, knowing that he had negotiated upward from $250; at least she'd won the job.

"Agreed," he stated, standing up. "Shall I tell her, or should you?" The priest suspected that Flinn might enjoy the bravado of presenting an offer to Mary personally.

"I'll tell her when I see her for breakfast tomorrow. You're right about one thing. I will miss her cooking. She's a downright miracle maker on the grill."

"Whoopee!" Mary shouted from the Café kitchen, sealing the star route deal with a firm handshake.

Flinn stepped back as she leaned across the counter and announced, "See here, boys. You're looking at the Birdtail's new mail carrier!"

Confused that the café cook claimed to be something other than what she was, standing there at the grill—the men stared.

She patted her own shoulder and said, "Boys, I'm the new United States Star Route Carrier!"

"New as in takin' over Frank Haley's route?" someone barked.

"Yep! Now all I need is a wagon and team. Who has a rig and good horses they want to sell, or maybe trade for a going café?"

"You have to be ready to start morning after Independence Day, Black Mary," Flinn said as he tipped his hat and squeezed around the counter corner.

Mary dismantled her café, sold everything she could and vacated by the second week of June. She would miss cooking and feeding folks, the C.C.C in particular, but not the hours standing on sore feet. She was relieved to gain a snippet of time between jobs and planned to enjoy the comforts of home before hitting the road again.

She started by designing her garden, thinking of her parents who had toiled a lifetime in tobacco fields. Seed planting, she believed, was an important undertaking and one of her favorites, along with fishing. She had prepared the soil. She would plant the seeds in the darkness of the new moon—first the corn, then tomatoes and beans, then nasturtiums.

"Planting a seed is like planting a dream," she said aloud as she stepped outside that evening, rolling a seed against her palm. My family planted thousands, maybe millions. On her knees, she patted the right level of soil over each section. "This garden of glory is dedicated to you," she whispered.

11

EXODUS

SPRING - SUMMER 1895

*S*aint Peter's Mission had achieved some success horse breeding, in part due to Mary advising who to breed with whom. The priests and nuns were pleased that the bloodlines, registered or not, exhibited excellent equine conformation and temperaments that did over time, develop a profitable sideline, yielding a new source of income and respect. Western using horses, stock good for harness and for saddle, were desired almost as much as good seats in Heaven. *Superior horses from the Superior*, satisfied owners began to brag.

Mary purchased one of her favorites, a gelding she had trained herself. A colt full of spirit, she had named him "Broad Britches". Now, six-years-old and standing and sixteen hands high, he was a formidable animal, sure-footed and deep through the heart.

"If any horse can push and pull through Birdtail snowpacks, you can," she said, patting his neck as she rode bareback to her Cascade home. Might need a second steed come winter, she considered, but meanwhile, this chestnut with two white socks and plenty of bone will pull the load just fine.

A second helping of good news reached her by post that afternoon: Jack had made it to Crow territory in southeast Montana. He had evaded capture by Fort Shaw Industrial School's assistant headmaster, E. L. Parker, who had engaged in hot pursuit. Jack had heard the assistant headmaster claim that most runaways headed north or east and had planned his route accordingly. Parker, an authorized deputy when tracking runaway students, had begun taking advantage of the latest invention, sporadically installed—telephone lines. For this reason, Jack had not set foot onto the tribe's reservation.

Jack reported that his family was in fairly good health. He would remain camped miles from the reservation's post and its agent, with the hope that Parker would eventually tire of the chase. Mary was relieved, particularly after hearing that Mr. Parker had recently captured three young men and had hauled them back to school, handcuffed.

A homesteader by the name of Walsh posted a "Going Home—Selling Everything" notice on Shepherd & Flinn's message board. He and his wife were headed back to Missouri, where life's unpleasant elements were more predictable and where Mr. Walsh would reclaim his former position at his father-in-law's funeral parlor. As they were to going to travel by train, their springboard wagon was included in the sale. Mary examined the vehicle and decided the dray would do fine once minor improvements had been made. Haggling proceeded. The two settled on a fair price that included lumber to build casings for the bunk. Twenty-five dollars passed from her hands to his.

The new mail carrier reviewed her plans: I'll build sidings and remodel the springboard to make it comfy. I'll put hinges and a latch on the tailgate, repair that one hub. When I'm done it'll be a custom-made farm-bed wagon, strong and sturdy for freighting. Ought to last for years. Need to choose between the two livery stables, then I'll be set. She deliberated: H.D. Hall & Ludwig Livery Stable is already going to profit from the closing of my café, since Dan, H.D.'s brother, runs the only remaining eatery. That leaves Cornell's Livery. James Cornell is a genuine horseman, a good trainer with experience. "And he buried Bigg while I lay unconscious," she said out loud. "I'll talk to him."

After shoving another tamarack log into the potbelly, she returned to her kitchen table, paper in hand. "Let's see now," she administered, taking a seat. After penciling calculations, she summarized, "An annual mail carrier salary of $325 is far from adequate. Rent for my house, at $25 monthly, comes to $300 per year." She circled the figure. "Add $20 per month for the livery, not counting blacksmith costs. I'm in the red before I start." She sipped from her glass of water. "Wonder how much Frank Haley was getting. Is it worth it to go through all of this?" She considered: I could just stay home and do laundry, play the banjo and mouth harp. Not rack my body against a springboard and hard weather, and make more money doing it. "Golly."

A frown took hold and she uttered, "Will have to negotiate up considerable next year or let them deliver their own mail. Only reason I'll accept this under market salary is because I long for the road and the children. $325 is an improvement from the $50 a year salary at the Toledo convent, though." She tapped her pencil end. "Wait. That included room and board." She calculated again. "This wage is still worse." Will have to do laundry to pay for food and comforts. "I'm going backwards in pay."

She listened to the fire snap and consoled herself, thinking that she still had the beaver coat Mother had given to her. "All right, then," she said.

Sister Gertrude held a handful of straw stalks, the ends hidden in her grip. She told the girls to draw one each; the length would determine their outdoor work assignments.

Annie was delighted when she saw that Nancy's stalk was long, like hers; it meant garden duty. She had designed a scheme to make Nancy realize that she simply would not be able to cope without her, should she choose to desert to Fort Shaw Industrial. With her new Ucsote gone and Nancy's foot halfway out the door, the thought of being left behind again was more than Annie could stand.

The girls were told to work under the direction of the new postulant, Sister Hilda, a city girl from Toledo—the place Mother and Mary Fields had lived before they came to Montana. Hilda exposed her ignorance as she tiptoed through ankle-deep mud; everyone knew if you stepped full-footed you'd be less likely to slip. The thin woman peered wide-eyed, as though plants would attack when she got too close.

The girls went about their business, pulling weeds and thinning seedlings. Hilda rutted a path from pacing back and forth; she rubbed her forehead and repeated at regular intervals, "Yes, that's right, girls. Very good. Keep it up." After twenty minutes, the nun-to-be waved her arms and cried, "Girls, I admit I don't a thing about gardening. Will you assist me?"

The gardeners giggled.

Hilda yanked stalks of greenery at her feet, determined to demonstrate competence. "There, another evil weed disarmed!" she declared, a large plant in hand. She gaped at her hands, fearing that the mud packed into her fingernails carried a pathogen. Losing composure, she looked at the tuber's hairy roots. "What is this?"

"Oh, Sister," Annie said, "that's Mother's comfrey. She needs it for her stomach!"

"I killed Mother's medicine?" Hilda swooned.

Nancy caught her fall, propped her up until the novice steadied.

Stricken, the postulant stared at the green crust dried between her fingers, terrified that she would be sent home, a disgrace to the Ursulines, to her Aunt, the Mother Superior Mary Amadeus, and to the entire Dunne family.

She looked at the small girl who tugged on her skirt. "Sister," Annie said, "Don't worry. There's plenty more."

The postulant's eyes widened.

Nancy pushed between the woman and her friend, bearing mind to words spoken by Mother Catherine, "... a crazed person emulates trepidation and fear and has the look of a heretic!" A series of facial tics increased her concern.

"What's your name?" the postulant brayed.

"Nancy."

"You will be my botany guide."

"Yes, Ma'am," Nancy replied, thinking it a fair price for saving Annie from who knew what, had the city-woman set her sights on the one who merely provided an answer to her question.

When work duty concluded, the girls headed to the washroom, as usual. Annie chatted incessantly. "Nancy, can you get me a needle and thread? I forgot to ask, and I'm ready to sew my dolly's dress. I still need the eggs and yarn and paint and brushes too. When can you—"

"Yes, I'll try," Nancy replied, flipping strands of hair from her face. She had stashed the paints and yarn days ago and forgotten about it. She chided herself for over reacting to Hilda the postulant, who may have only been disoriented. Exhausted, Nancy realized that in truth, she was more worried about leaving Annie and Saint Angela's than she had been able to admit.

"Annie," she said, "make sure you don't cause trouble with that postulant. She is Mother's niece."

"All right. But what is a niece? I need to ask you something else about—"

"She is part of Mother Amadeus's family."

The bell rang.

"I'll meet you tonight," Nancy called as she trudged up the stairs.

After supper, some of the older girls slipped outside before the "lights-out" bell tolled, to talk in private and stare at stars for a few stolen minutes. Christine, one of Nancy's roommates, huddled against her and warned, "Nancy, Mother Superior won't let you come back if you leave. You better be sure."

As Nancy turned to reply, she pushed a hand into her pocket, pricked her finger. She groped for the source. It was the needle she had borrowed for Annie.

"I know, Christine," she insisted, "I *am* sure." She sucked the blood. "I've been thinking about it for months. It's a risk, but I'm going to take it. I'm petitioning to leave with the other girls on July 1st. Mother will recommend me to Fort Shaw, I think, because I am a good student and I play the violin."

"I just hope you know what you're in for."

"That's the gamble. I don't know."

"Did you hear from your family?"

"Yes. Agnes Gobert's mother was here last week; she lives on our reservation. She told me that my mother said, 'Yes, I want to see you, we all do.' Isn't that grand?"

Nancy's mother had neglected to mention that Nancy's father and brother spent large periods of time locked in the reservation cell, jailed for disruptive behavior after drinking firewater provided by the reservation agent who had traded whiskey for her family's food rations.

"That's it?" Christine said. "Nothing about whether you can live with them during the summer or whether Fort Shaw School lets them visit?"

Nancy shook her head and defended, "Evaline Poirier has a brother at Fort Shaw, and she thinks that family can visit on Sundays."

"Thinks?"

"It's all I could find out. I couldn't talk to Agnes' mother any longer. Maybe Mother Amadeus will tell us more when our departure is announced."

"I hope so," Christine sighed, "I'll miss you."

"I'll write. Mary Fields will deliver my letters if I can get them to her. Will you watch out for Annie? She's too little to understand ..."

1895 class commencement ceremonies took place on the last Saturday of June with elaborate regency. Entertainment, performed by talented Saint Angela students, included the play *Saint Lucia*, a drama placed in Syria, and musical duets featuring mandolins and piano.

Many undergraduates had just been informed of their impending transfer to Fort Shaw—most had not volunteered to leave. Explanations were vague; government reductions had been referenced. Hearts twisted in fear. What would happen? Would they be captive prisoners, like Mother's songbirds? Fort Shaw was the place where oppressors had stolen the lives of native peoples before. Nerves twinged. Was there another choice? They looked at each other and to the festivities at hand. Suddenly, the opulent display of pageantry hurt.

Nancy positioned her chin onto the violin, lifted her bowing arm and stroked with precision. The players approached the sonata's finale. Her stomach spasmed. It was too late to change her mind. She had volunteered for what might be federal confinement and panicked, questioned whether she had traded friendship and academics for an unlikely chance to visit her family. And what about Annie?

The graduates stood erect and clasped their rolled parchments to their chests, as rehearsed. Mother Superior said, "Christ the infant God draws nigh. Be careful with your choices. Always pray for the Lord to guide your decisions as you go forth in life, assisted now by the benefits of academic knowledge." Concluding the ceremony, she praised, "May you create and follow your Holy Destiny with compassionate religious zeal." Applause filled the parlor auditorium.

Girls without guests were given an hour of free time. Annie headed for the attic where she stitched with deft skill unnoticed. Admiring her dollies' eggshell faces, she thought about the fragileness of life—one squeeze and it was over. She decided to direct her zeal into a plan of action.

Carefully, she stuffed the dolls' muslin body forms with wool hoarded from last year's sheep shearing. She molded their figures to fit the outfits she had sewn, copied from the cover of Mother's sheet music titled, "American Tunes from Scotland." The dolls modeled full-length gingham dresses with fitted bodices and gathered skirts, accented by tiny quartz pebble buttons glued to the fabric. Black boots fashioned from scraps of boiled wool completed the ensemble. She hurried to add the final touch—happy smiles painted with the borrowed watercolors.

"There," she addressed the dolls. To the one on her left, she said, "Your name is Onatah. You belong to Mary White Crow." To the other she instructed, "You will live with Nancy, I mean Nadie. My best friend. Your name is Onatah, too. You both have to get into mischief sometimes, so you remind them of me."

Nancy squeezed through the graduation buffet queue. When out of sight, she sprinted to the aspen grove. Making herself comfortable on the cedar stump near the babbling brook, she slid her hand into her pocket and retrieved the newsprint clipping White Crow had given to her. She smoothed the paper on her thigh and recalled the cold February evening when she and White Crow had locked arms and struggled to walk on ice, in a rush to get to Mary's house after Fort Shaw's first music concert, also the first public concert Nadie had attended. The article from *The Rising Sun* reported:

"The seats in Murray Hall were not sufficient to accommodate to crowd that gathred there to listen to the entertainment given by the Fort Shaw Indian School, Friday night (February 9, 1895). It was the first time the Indian scholars gave an entertainment outside of their own school grounds. The programme was replete with musical parts and the much applauded Indian Band constituted one of the most enjoyable features of the evening. The presentation of Philomel by the band was the effort of the evening and greatly appreciated by the audience. The choir, too, has been spoken of in highest terms. The entertainment was a credit to the participants and adds to the high repuition which the school has heretofore earned by its enjoyable entertainment. The following is the programme that was carried out; Music, Dr. Winslow's March by E.L.Parker (Dr. Winslow's assistant headmaster) leading the band.

Reading, Selected: Jennie Pheme
Recitation, "Be in Earnest": Frank Choat
Song, selected: Mrs. Pool
Autobiography, A Horse: Josephine Mitchell
Reading, Selected: Charles Reavis
Music, Organ & Coronet Duet: Belle Alyers and Lewis Martin
Bullitin: Minnie Reed
Song, Selected: E.L. Parker
Recitation, "America": Elmer Williamson
Music, Guitar & Coronet Duet: Mrs. Patterson and E.L. Parker"

Nancy wondered if the Fort Shaw orchestra would tour and if there was a chamber quartet. Hopes of future travel tendered reassurance. Mary had told her to remember, "Whatever is, already is. Just keep your wits, eyes and ears open." She was glad Mary was coming to drive one of the wagons that would transport many of Saint Angela's students to Fort Shaw. Aware that her last day at the mission was passing quickly, she returned to find Annie.

As she trotted up the academy stairwell, Mother Catherine called her by name and informed her that the Superior had made time for individual goodbyes to each of her transferees. "You will be first," her teacher said, escorting Nancy by the elbow toward Mother's office. Distressed by the detour, Nancy tapped her foot and watched the crowd from a window. Two floors above, Annie wrapped her Onatah dolls with paper scraps rescued from the burn barrel. She had traded a classmate three candies for pink ribbon to make bows, planning to surprise Nancy with her present at bedtime. She would save Mary Fields' gift for a very important moment she would recognize later.

Mother entered her office, waved the pupil to a chair and sat behind her desk. "Nancy, I am sorry to see you leave for Fort Shaw Industrial, but I understand that being near your family is important to you." She opened a drawer, lifted a small red book, and offered sincere wishes as she handed the volume across, "I want you to have this. You have made significant advancements and I know you are fond of poetry."

"Thank you, Mother Amadeus." Nancy had never owned a book and was taken by its beauty—a cover of fine cloth debossed and painted with gilded letters that seemed to glimmer. Recognizing the title, *Anonymous Verse from the Hearts of Éire Land*, she said, "I remember this book, Mother Superior. My favorite poem is *The Blackbird*. She stood and recited, 'What little throat, has framed that note? What gold beak shot it far away? A blackbird on his leafy throne tossed it alone across the bay.'"

Mother warmed at the girl's enthusiasm. "I think you know that my family is from the Eire Land, where long ago they had tribes called clans."

"Yes, Mother." She couldn't imagine Mother in a tribe. "I will treasure it."

"Perhaps you will teach the verses to others."

Nancy put the book into her canvas sack, held it to her chest, excused herself, rushed outside and into the Opera House where she hid her gift beneath her mattress. From the second-story window, she spotted a dust cloud mushrooming at the road's bend. Mary Fields emerged, riding horseback at a full gallop. "Mary!" she called and ran downstairs.

By the time Nancy made her way to the corral, she spotted Mary and Mother Amadeus arm and arm as they disappeared over the knoll, on the path to the brook.

Mary Fields turned to her friend and said, "I've been meaning to ask you, Mary, how did we, I mean you, I guess, do on the crop numbers last summer?"

"I just finished the federal report; our accounts are fiscal, summer to summer. We cultivated one hundred and forty acres and harvested eighty bushels of corn, six hundred bushels of oats, two thousand bushels of potatoes, two hundred of turnips, one hundred and fifty onions, seventy bushels of beans and five hundred bushels of other vegetables." She took a breath. "One hundred tons of hay, one thousand pounds butter and three hundred pumpkins."

"You're an example to your pupils, memorizing figures so easily. They're good numbers—I thought you'd get that much. It was a wet spring and we had fairly good weather through summer."

"Until *you* went, we were doing grand," Mother said. I'd wager we don't do as well with the vegetable crops this year, without you."

"You'd wager... Well, I'll be. Now what kind of trouble have you been getting yourself into while I'm not here to watch out for you?"

"Speaking of trouble," Mother countered, "Mr. Lewis said that there were prospectors planning to run you out of Cascade, or worse. He and Mr. Monroe took care of it, said the scalawags left the area, but I'm worried about outlaws who pass through, thinking they can get away with anything."

Mary opened her mouth, but Mother raised her hand. "You must have heard about the so-called 'chicken thief' that the men at Fort Shaw caught and hung for the sin of being hungry—and then boasted that they would do it again. There was no legal action. That's what worries me, since you'll be on the Mission Road, on a predictable schedule."

"I can just as easy be giving you the same lecture," said Mary Fields. "We're both stubborn about getting things done the way we think it should be, and you know it—even when we are *reasonably careful* in our orchestrations."

"Yes, true." Mother faced the brook. "It's the things we can't control that create the unfortunate variables. There are so many unable to change the hatred in their hearts, as you know all too well."

Mary squirmed, holding her recent attack secret. "I know a lot of folks who are not too thrilled with the proselytizing of religion, and that hasn't stopped you from running around. Guess we just have to say our prayers and take our chances?"

"Have you shut down the café?"

"Yes." Mail delivery starts July 5th. I'll see you then, unless you're traipsing about the country checking on your other missions. How's the Alaska plan coming?"

"Not so well. I've written to Reverend Tosi in Alaska asking permission to come and establish mission schools. I haven't received a reply yet."

"Well, I hope you get to go wherever you want to be going, Mary."

They listened to the water, a drone of percolated rhythm. Mary Fields asked, "Have you heard any more about the Fort Shaw curriculum? I'm worried about Nancy and all the girls leaving. I heard The Industrial staff is heavy with the whip, and I figure they won't be as kind as you and the sisters, since unlike you, they answer solely to the government. Pardon the pun." She tossed a stone.

"I can't answer fairly. I think I mentioned that they claim to have an accomplished academic program. I have yet to witness class in session. Dr. Winslow is out of town, and I was told that my presence requires his, for reasons undisclosed. It's the emphasis on development of trade skills that concerns me. They have acquired thousands of acres that the students will tend."

"That's a lot of cattle ranching and crop plowing." Mary stripped white bark from a fallen aspen twig.

"Precisely. I hope the girls will not be engaged exclusively in domestic service for the male students and faculty without adequate time for academics and the arts."

"That's what I mean: Nancy is excited about poetry and writing stories. I don't want that part of her education to drown in a wash bucket."

"Even if it does, it's only one year for her, and she has already achieved more than most." Mother fingered the cross around her neck.

"I can see you're just as worried as I am, Mary Amadeus." Mary poked dirt with her boot. "And there are huge numbers of students falling to disease and exposure at the Industrial School. That's why they built that big hospital last year. Did they expect to have high casualties?"

"That's a horrible thought. It's out of our hands, isn't it? Except that as our prayers may affect a positive outcome. We will pray for health and safe-keeping."

"Agreed," said Mary, rubbing the back of her head.

Mr. Lewis arrived early the following morning with his six-horse team and an extra-wide hay wagon. The total number of travelers to be transported came to thirty-eight—more than one-third of Saint Angela's Indian school population. Two additional rigs were readied: the Ursulines' and the Jesuits' to be driven by Mary Fields and Reverend Rebmann, respectively. Mary tied Big Too to the back of the nun's hitch wagon and gave him a carrot.

Anxious murmurs swept through academy grounds. Hired hands loaded the girls' bags onto the wagon buckboards, forming bunkered rows for seating. No one noticed Annie swing up into Mary's wagon and throw a tarp over herself. A heavy bag landed on her back, knocking the wind out of her. She curled herself head down and pretended to be an invisible turtle.

The girls squeezed in. Mother praised her transferees, her cultured young ladies who would face change she had been unable to deter.

"Blessings of the Sweet Lord Jesus be upon you," she bid. "We are all so very proud of your achievements."

Nancy's friend, Christine, who had just been informed of her transferee status, whispered, "I'm scared, Nancy. Aren't you?"

"Yes, but you know better than to show it."

"Dr. Winslow could be horrible."

"Don't think about it. Enjoy the scenery." That's what White Crow would say, thought Nancy.

Reins snapped, and wheels creaked. The drivers set the pace at an easy roll, knowing to pace their horses for a long day of tedious travel. The girls fell silent, riffling through familiar feelings. Nancy had made sure she was in the wagon that Mary drove, and though she couldn't sit on the buckboard, she sat as near to her as she could.

Driving the middle vehicle, keenly aware of her passengers' angst, Mary declared, "Singing is the best way to keep worries at bay." She burst into lyrics from May Day repertoires. One by one, voices joined in. "The Green Grass Grew All Around" was first of the medley, followed by "Mary had a Little Lamb" and "The Bear Went Over the Mountain."

> ... And on that limb
> There was a branch
> The prettiest branch
> That you ever did see
> Oh, the branch on the limb,
> And the limb on the tree,
> And the tree in a hole,
> And the hole in the ground
> And the green grass grows all around, all around
> The green grass grows all around.

Moods gradually lifted. As scorching sun tipped toward the west, the travelers took refuge under boughs of weeping willows that graced the banks of a Sun River tributary. There, they consumed the picnic that Sister Gertrude had prepared special and splashed cool water on their heated faces.

By mid-afternoon, the entourage slowed to stop at the Cascade train station. Mr. Lewis jumped off his buckboard and unfolded a list provided by Mother. He told the girls to step forward if their name was called, resulting in ten Indian girls wearing tailored navy blue dresses they had sewn themselves, positioned in line on the depot platform. A duffel bag was placed in front of each pair of black-leather shoes.

One girl dared to ask where they were going. Mr. Lewis informed that there was no longer enough room for everyone at Fort Shaw Industrial School and that Mother had arranged for them to attend the Canadian Ursuline School in a settlement called Saint Ignatius, a short train ride west over the Rockies.

Nancy's friend Christine, one of the ten posted on the depot platform, the advocate for security who had warned her classmates to remain at Saint Peter's, looked to her, crushed. Helpless, Nancy raised her hand as though it would tether a link; she hoped it would somehow.

The remaining twenty-eight travelers, now configured into the rigs of Father Rebmann and Mary Fields, were not allowed to dally. Father ordered that the wagons push ahead, aware that Cascade was not a good place for Indian girls to linger. Many white folks advertised their prejudice, contending that the only place for an Indian was on a designated reservation, mission or government school. Some locals held the opinion that Fort Shaw Industrial was too close at twenty-two miles distance.

Nancy fought a wave of nausea when she realized that she hadn't asked Mary for permission—permission to remain with her during Cascade's July 4th celebration. She had contrived the plot in detail, had been ready to ask that morning before she'd become frantic searching for Annie who was nowhere to be found.

Mary snapped the reins, wiped her face with a damp rag.

Nancy leaned close and whispered, "White Crow, please can I stay at your house until after the 4th of July? Please, I need to hear the Fort Shaw Band before I—I meant to …"

"And you're waiting til now?" Mary quipped, eyes forward and teeth clenched.

"Sorry, I'm sorry."

"Sit down, Miss Nancy," Mary growled, aware that other girls were straining to hear.

Nancy panicked, sick at the thought of missing her opportunity, yet firmly believing, albeit irrationally, that she still had the chance to back out if necessary. Enjoy the landscape, she accused.

The wagon jolted.

Annie's head smacked against the bunk. Biting her lip, she managed to silence a cry. Her legs were numb and her fingers cramped into fists as she fought to ignore pain that shot up her spine. Remember you're a turtle, she bid. A little longer, that's all.

Fort Shaw, originally built to protect settlers against Indian outbreaks, later used to hold Blackfeet on the reservation, had been reclassified when native resistance had been quelled. Furnished with barracks and fenced barriers, it was an ideal location to house a federally run Indian school. The delivery of new students followed protocol as prescribed in advance by Dr. William H. Winslow, who as the school's physician and superintendent, exercised complete autonomy.

When the entourage came to a halt at the back entrance, Matron Miss Mattie Caldwell took charge. Transferees gripped their duffels and shuffled into line. Annie implored a mute plea: don't move, Nancy, stay on me or I'll be caught. Please, Ha Wen Neyu.

Mary wrapped reins around the brake, turned and shouted at Nancy, "Not so fast, you. Mother Superior says you're to work in town, help setup and takedown at the July 4th—I'm to keep you under my supervision." She could feel the matron's eyes. Shaking her finger at the captive, she threatened "You stay right where you are."

Arranging her face to look measurably trodden, Mary straightened her cap, head down, glanced up to meet the matron's appraisal. "Afternoon, Matron Caldwell. That's everybody except for this one who I'll bring to you directly, on the morning of July 5th, early."

The matron had not heard about this arrangement though it sounded plausible. She decided the exception wasn't worth risking chaos—three days without one girl wouldn't matter—nuns could be trusted and she'd heard that the negress had been with them for years. "Fine. I will expect you then. Your name is?"

"Mary Fields, Ma'am." She snapped the whip for show and barked, "Hold on!" Swirls of dust camouflaged the exodus. Nancy sucked a lungful.

Adamant in the belief that loitering was a sin, Matron Caldwell faced her recruits and barked, "Girls, grab your satchels. Follow me."

Her pear-shaped body jiggled, exaggerated by a slight limp.

"You have twenty minutes to freshen up and clean yourselves. You are to arrive in the dining hall at 6:00 p.m. Promptly. You will address me as Matron Caldwell. You don't do *anything* without my permission. I *will* be watching. The dining hall is that way."

She pointed short misshapen fingers that swelled in the heat, directed the assembly toward the back of the building and up two levels of narrow switch-back stairs. Beds were assigned. The girls had envisioned a group of predecessors to advise them, wondered why no one else lodged in the dormitory.

Mary Fields held her tongue though her mind spun like wagon wheels. Risky enough to house an Indian, no matter how special, she fumed, should have asked me so I could have made plans.

After a mile, she let the horses slow to a pace of their choice. She was irked and decided to let Nancy stew for the full three hours it would take to return to Cascade.

Near to sunset Mary called, "Whoa, now, whoa y'all," and turned her head. "We're here, Nancy. My place."

She set the brake, eased off the wagon and rubbed her knee. "You're to stay inside and wait for me while I get to the stable." She tossed the tarp back and stared. "Well, look who's here," she exclaimed, reaching to the small package of grit, a mission refugee.

Squinting as sunlight blinded, Annie recoiled. She fumbled to present herself, hopes knotted, heart pounding. Shielding her eyes, she searched for Mary's gaze, stretched her lips into her very biggest grin and spoke to the silhouette of her Ucsote: "I love you, White Crow. I just want to be with you."

Mary shook her head. She couldn't help but chuckle. Attempting to sound stern, she huffed, "Well, let's get you into my house before anyone sees you." She lifted Annie over the wagon's splintered edge, certain her baby bird was bruised and dehydrated. "Full summer heat under a tarp, you're as battered as that box you're holding."

Inside, Nancy watched as Mary propped Annie onto her bed, nodded when Mary ordered, "You two stay here, and I'll be back." Avoiding eye contact, Mary marched out, slamming the door for effect.

Her liveryman, Mr. Cornell, waved her, the team and the wagon into the stable, ready to close up.

After giving Bigg Too and the mission horses each a handful of oats, she asked James Cornell if he would mind moving the horses to the field west of town—keep them out of harm's way during the celebration. She also reminded him that she'd need Big Too in town and harnessed before daylight, on the 5th.

He agreed and commended her foresight, addressed her as "lassie" while he unhooked the harness and headed for brushes and water buckets.

Arrived home minutes later, a wave of heat smacked her as she opened the door. "Whew!" she yelped. "Girls, did you light the stove, decide to burn the place down?" She fanned both arms and lurched ahead, looking for a newspaper.

"Would you like some tea, White Crow?" Nancy asked. I made comfrey tea in your pretty teapot. It's warming on the grill." Mary sighed and plunked herself onto the padded straight-back at the head of the table.

"Let me take off your boots, White Crow," Annie offered, springing from the bed.

"All right, you two, all this solicitude won't do you one stitch of good."

Annie scrunched her face.

"You're both in big trouble, you are."

Mary searched for a cigar she had put somewhere, and a glass for water.

"We just want to visit you!" Nancy pleaded.

"We've never been to your house before, White Crow. It's beautiful!" Annie complimented.

"Have you given yourselves a tour yet?" They nodded. "Did you see the cooler in the kitchen?" Heads shook to the negative. "Well let me show you. Look here."

She led them to a cabinet door set into the wall; compact, it measured two feet wide and three feet high. Mary pulled the knob, revealing three shelves like those of a cupboard but set outside, walled with chicken wire and slats to keep critters out. "You see, it's a cooler, for food. In summer I set a block of ice here." She pointed to a tin box below ground level, beneath a wire rack where a loaf-size chunk of ice steamed. "In winter the weather keeps it plenty cold. I should pack some more straw around that ice—another layer of wood around the outside might help, too." She stepped back. "So what do you think?"

"It's marvelous, Mary. Your very own cooler and your very own house!" Nancy exclaimed.

Annie added, "It's so fine!"

The girls moved closer and gave Mary a big hug. In her arms they felt whole again.

Fortified after supper and a bath, Annie shared an epiphany that had come to her while struggling for air beneath the tarp. "White Crow, from now on, when we're together can we call each other by our real names? Nancy is starting over, and so did you. I want a new life, too. We don't have to keep English names anymore, do we? I want to be called Onatah." She looked to Nancy. "Don't you want to be called Nadie?"

"Yes."

Annie crossed her arms. "Do you want to be called Mary White Crow Fields? It's a really long name—"

"Not really sure what my *real* name is," said Mary, "but as for you two, I plum forgot already who Annie and Nancy were." The girls giggled.

"Thank you, White Crow," Nadie said, feeling better.

"I think your real name is White Crow—you are *my* White Crow," Onatah declared.

"Thank you, little Onatah, but it's been Mary for a long time, too. What I meant was, wish I knew what my parents would have called me, if they could have picked—"

"Cause the slave master picked it?" Nadie asked.

"Yes. You girls can call me White Crow or Mary or whatever you'd like."

"White Crow, let's have dessert!" Onatah waited for the grin that she knew would materialize.

"Yes. Special occasions call for dessert!"

"I'll still have to be Nancy at school," Nadie said, turning it in her mind.

"Cornbread or fruit?" Mary asked.

"Wait, White Crow." Onatah screeched. "I have a present for you—you have to open it. Now!"

"A present? That's even better than dessert. How did I get so lucky?" Mary stepped away from the counter and sat in her chair.

Onatah slipped under Mary's bed to retrieve her surprise. She held the squashed package gingerly and soberly presented the precious totem. "For you, Ucsote White Crow."

"What might this be?"

"I made it. Open it, you'll see!"

Nadie grinned as she witnessed Mary in the same position she herself had enjoyed the night prior.

"You made it? Then it must be beautiful!" Mary lifted the crumpled package to her face and sniffed. "Doesn't smell like candy or cookies. Hmm, what could it be?"

"Don't shake it, you'll hurt—I'm not telling! Open it!"

Mary chuckled, paused to give Onatah a grateful smile. She loosened the pink ribbon, undid the bow. "We'll save this for your hair."

Onatah waited anxiously.

Mary navigated through yards of string that the giver had wrapped tightly to fortify the lightweight cardboard, looped over and around, back and forth. "This is the best wrapped package I've ever seen. Don't you think so, Nadie?"

Nadie nodded, still smiling.

The gift giver's rapt attention darted from Mary's hands to Mary's face, transfixed. Sensing importance, Mary prolonged the memorable ceremony. She saved the intricate wrappings and exaggerated her excitement as she lifted the cover, beheld straw. She fingered beneath, carefully, touched a cool, smooth object and pushed the straw aside.

"Oh my word, Onatah. You made this doll? It's so beautiful! You thought of this all by yourself?"

Nadie boasted, "Yes, she did! I can testify. All by herself, and it took her forever!"

"Her name is Onatah, so when I'm not here you will never forget me."

"Who could ever forget you, Onatah Saint Germain? Let me give you a hug."

Nadie gushed, "White Crow, look how Onatah glued the yarn hair, each strand close together, and the face is painted with watercolors, and she never had any lessons from anyone, and Onatah stitched the dress by hand, all by herself, and stuffed it with lambs' wool that she saved from last year's shearing. And she made the boots too! Isn't it incredible?"

"It is amazing and magnificent and stupendous." She squeezed Annie again. "The best doll I've ever seen, and I still don't know how you did it, Onatah. The greatest part is that you figured it all out!"

Onatah, dizzy at hearing such earnest praise, said, "Nadie helped a lot. She got me all the pieces: the egg and the cloth and the black wool for the boots, and the needle and thread." She looked up. "Thank you, Nadie."

Pride emitting from Mary's glowing face convinced Onatah that her Ucsote White Crow truly loved her present. Savoring the moment, she felt her chest swell. Minutes later, she was sound asleep.

When she woke the following morning, a bruised and battered Onatah solemnized the progress of her unorthodox exodus. Showing her gratitude, she thanked Great Turtle, the origin of earth, and decided to let things be for a time, in hopes that arrangements would work out as she desired. She stuffed another of Mary's huckleberry pancakes into her mouth and asked, "White Crow, can we explore town today?"

"Tell you what girls—we're going to hold up in the house. Pretend like we're up in the mountains, camping. The wood stove will be our campfire and we'll tell stories and do whatever you'd like."

"I want to see the candies at the store," Onatah said.

"And the fabric and latest hats, even though I know we aren't allowed to have them. I'd still like to look. Can we, White Crow?" Nadie asked.

Mary, remaining seated at the table, stacked their empty plates and cast her eyes to each of them. "Afraid not, girls. I'm sorry. If it were up to me, I'd take you anywhere and everywhere. Hope you understand. It's just that we can't parade ourselves around the white folk's town without expecting to get trouble for it." She set her napkin on the table.

"Now on July 4th, that's another matter. The town will be full of folks from all over, and the students will be here from Fort Shaw, so we'll fit right in." She forced a bright countenance.

"You mean they don't want any Indians in their town unless they are performing for them," Nadie tackled.

"That's about the long shot of it."

"What's the short shot? Out of curiosity."

Mary fidgeted, hands beneath the table. "No point in discussing it. I'm not taking any risks with the girls I love. Let's just do our best. We haven't played a good game of cards for about forever, anyway."

"I want to play cards!" Onatah chimed. "But I don't know how. Will you teach me?"

"That's one task we can manage." Mary stood up, rubbed her back. "Now, what would your little hearts' desire for supper? I aim to please at White Crow's Special Café."

Nadie bit her lip, resolved to hide disappointment.

The weather provided timely entertainment during their seclusion—afternoon winds from the west delivered a powerful storm front. They crawled into position on Mary's hand-stitched quilts strewn about the floor, listened to winds whipping and clouds bursting and sharp thunderclaps that shook the earth. "This is the best band performance," Onatah said, rolling a pillow under her neck, "I like the thundering drums." She looked to White Crow who had dozed off.

Heavy knocking shook the front door. Mary leapt, signaled the girls to the closet. They jumped inside, shuffled behind clothing, pulled the door shut.

Mary glanced the perimeter for telltale signs of company. She tossed the quilts on the bed and called out, "Evening. Who's there, please?"

"It's me, White Crow," said a man's voice.

"Who would 'me' be?"

"Jack."

She turned the knob, relieved. Waved him in, smiling. "We're having a party," she said deadpan. He tensed, though he knew she would not subject him to harm, glanced for signs, stepped across the threshold. Mary shut the door.

"It's all right," she called, Come on out if you want to meet a good friend. This young man is Mister Jack Willow, escapee from the Fort Shaw Industrial School."

His eyes narrowed, alarmed that she would speak his name to a stranger. "White Crow, I can't stay. Have to leave before holiday preparations get underway—too many eyes. I came to give you this." He pushed coins into her hand: silver dollars, more than she had given freely, and said, "Thank you." Leaning forward to kiss her cheek, he spotted a vision of beauty in the shadows.

Mary felt his body seize; the way fright locks limbs. She pulled back to look, and witnessed the unexpected: courageous Jack, dumbstruck and smitten. "Jack Willow," she said, "Like to introduce you to my good friend, Nadie Burd."

Nadie smiled, distracted by Jack's stunning good looks. She blinked and moved her eyes away, embarrassed—cast her glance along floorboards, his direction—studied his moccasins that were stitched in a pattern she did not recognize—all the while, feeling his stare.

"Very good to meet you, Nadie Burd," he said with an awkward charm. "I hope to see you, again."

He didn't notice the little girl peeking from behind the vision of beauty, nor that Nadie's knee buckled as he spoke her name. He stepped across the threshold backwards, to keep her in sight, held his gaze until the door shut.

The next morning, Mary suggested, "Well, Onatah, now that you've learned to play Hearts and Canasta and whooped both Nadie and me, what do you say we get serious for a spell? Come sit by me." She patted the bed.

Onatah tugged on her own skirt. "White Crow, I'm sorry I hid in the wagon." She pushed up onto the bed, snuggled against Ucsote without looking at her face.

"Why did you hide in the wagon? What were you trying to do?"

Onatah waited for her throat to unleash. "This is the truth, Ucsote. I am hoping that you will let me live with you." She met her gaze, and waited. When Mary did not answer, she added, "I promise not to be any trouble and I'll work hard. I won't eat much and I'll be quiet whenever you say. I'll—"

Mary lifted her hand. "Where will you be going to school in this plan of yours?"

"I'm not sure. At the Cascade schoolhouse, maybe."

"Unfortunately, that school isn't as good as the one you're already in and they don't really want Indian girls. So that, my darling, is not an option. Let's get back to the beginning."

Onatah stopped listening. Her body felt like stone, a burst of tears burned her dreams.

Mary heaved a deep sigh, aware, also, of Nadie's apt attention and mirrored hopes, she suspected. She hugged Onatah and reached out, "You too, Nadie. Come here."

Holding both girls, she comforted, "You both know, I hope, that I love you like my own. To have you live with me as my daughters would make me *so* happy … I won't let myself imagine it." She wiped her nose. "Right here, right now, it is impossible. Cause of the opinions," she paused, "and actions of folks. Maybe if we were out in the mountains, but we're not."

Onatah held her breath and clenched her agile fingers into fists.

"I figure I'm lucky to share company with you whenever the opportunity arises. That's one of the reasons I took this mail carrier job: so that I can visit my girls without raising anyone's dander. And you probably realize that I don't care about whether I raise the dander of some folks. But we do have to be careful. We could disappear as easy as geese heading south. You understand?"

"You mean it's too dangerous for me to live with you." Onatah said, sullen. "But you're the bravest, White Crow. I've seen you!"

"Brave is only a part of what we need. Have to be smart too, little bird." Mary rocked side-to-side, gently stroked the girls' hair. "Most important thing is that you get yourselves educated. Then you'll have more freedom. I'll always be here for you. We just have to be careful."

"I don't care about education. You can teach me all that matters." Onatah insisted.

"Onatah, with my mail carrier job I won't be here most the time, and that wouldn't be good for you, even in a world with perfect neighbors. I know you're lonely at Saint Peter's, but the nuns treat you better than any other place around here. So, I want you to return to the mission and be a good student and learn all you can."

Onatah crumbled. She had allowed herself to believe her fantasy: a home with White Crow. Her dream lay crushed, like dust, like the view from the back of wagons, like what happened to loved ones: they disappeared. She imagined her body flailing in cold water after struggling to stay on Great Turtle's slippery shell and gulped, "Will you come visit me, White Crow?"

"Of course I will. All the time. You know I will, Onatah. And you too, Nadie. Much as I can." They held on, minds apart and together, wishing as tears fell in spurts and waves, for things to be different. The fire crackled.

Nadie extricated herself. "You're wringing wet, White Crow. I never saw you cry like this."

"Sorta looks like you've been under a rain cloud, yourself."

"Me too," cried Onatah, leaning into Mary's warm bosom.

White Crow said, "Let's be like starfish, and stretch."

Ignoring objections that claimed the idea crazy and silly, she stooped down and they followed her lead. Spreading limbs across the floorboards, they linked hands and feet into starfish formation, attaining a collective and personal center of gravity. Nadie and White Crow stared at the ceiling. Onatah imagined herself as an orange echinoderm, her suction cups fixed to a rock while waves of warm water washed over her.

After a time, they looked to each other, and started to giggle. A train whistle tooted in the distance. Nadie said, "Is there anything to eat?"

They spent that day, and the one thereafter, inside White Crow's house playing cards, napping and eating. Onatah insisted that White Crow go out to the garden for the simple reason that she couldn't. "This time, not for food," she said, "can you pick us some flowers?"

Mary gathered poppies, lupine, daises and sunflowers. It was a lively display of summer color that inspired them to prepare more food, effectively filling the hours before Independence Day arrived.

Onatah asked, "How do they make fireworks fly?"

"With gunpowder," said Mary.

"Then I don't like them."

"Wait and see. You might."

White Crow looked at Nadie who appeared to be wrestling gloom. "Nadie, you know what the good thing about you attending the Industrial School is?"

Nadie made the anticipated eye-roll.

"You'll be industrious!" Mary belly laughed.

Nadie reluctantly cracked a grin.

"That's silly, White Crow."

"Made ya smile though."

"I'm hoping I'll get to travel to cities, if I'm in the band. Get to see something other than the reservation and Saint Peter's."

"You could be a famous actress, or musician," said Onatah, who had just recently become aware that there was such a thing as an actress.

"Oh, Onatah," laughed Nadie. "Not me."

"One thing that only Fort Shaw has—" Mary dangled.

"What?" Onatah asked.

"It's very own water and sewer system."

Nadie said, "I read about it. You can turn a handle and water comes out of a pipe into a sink. And you pull a chain to get a shower!"

"Like it's raining?"

"And no more running to the outhouse in the cold, or washing chamber pots," Mary added.

"How?" Onatah demanded.

"You sit on a special ceramic bowl that looks like a giant chamber pot attached to the floor with water inside it. You do your business and then pull a handle and poof, running water washes everything away, down a pipe, gone for good!"

"Are you kidding? I want to see one of those. What do you call them?"

"Toilets," Nadie said.

"They installed fire hydrants, too," Mary reported, "to protect the buildings. But there isn't enough water pressure to make them work. Least not unless they get a bigger pump. They say they're gonna do that, too, just like the big cities."

"Tomorrow is the 4th of July," declared Onatah, wiggling. "What's going to happen, besides fireworks? I have never seen any celebration except at the mission."

"Well, here ya go." She pushed a folded newspaper across the table. "See how important reading is? It's all here in *The Rising Sun*, just arrived this morning." Nadie grabbed it and read aloud, "Celebration!"

"Wait Nadie, let Onatah read at least one line. Then you read it to us."

Onatah orated carefully, "July 4th, 1895. That's the first line. Done!"

Nadie grabbed the paper and narrated: "*Exercises: Horse Races, Foot Races, Clay Pigeon Shoot, Basket Picnic, Baseball, Miscellaneous Amusements and Grand Ball!*"

"Huzzah!" the girls shouted.

"White Crow, there are lots of misspellings in this paper. Even the word, amusement."

"Yes, on a regular basis. See that you sharpen your knowledge of the English language—useful ammunition, medicine-pouch power. But here," she glanced to the wet vegetables dripping in hand, "help me with these greens. Isn't this chard beautiful? Look how rich the color is—it's my special compost recipe: half horse, half chicken, plus other secret ingredients. We'll have some for dinner!"

"Compost or chard?" Nadie joked.

"Ha, ha," Mary chuckled.

Onatah studied the newsprint. "I don't understand, Nadie. Why does it say: 'Horse Races. One-mile race. Free for all, first prize $5. En-ter-anz fee, $1?' How can it be free and cost $1 at the same time?"

"You're right. It is a conundrum or an oxymoron. I can't remember which," Nadie said.

Onatah frowned. "What?"

"Free-for-all just means everybody can be in the race. Everyone who has $1 for the fee, that is."

"Oh. Everyone. Really?"

"Yes."

"They still shouldn't call it free if it isn't!"

"You're right, Onatah. Words don't always say what they mean."

"Huh?"

12

REUNION

*S*unrays fanned across distant tree lines, and glistened upon the surface of smooth streets, broom swept earlier by the Cascade volunteer cleaning committee. Independence Day preparations had been underway for weeks and locals hurried to complete tasks before the anticipated hordes of attendees arrived.

Mary greeted the day as she plucked mustard greens and flowers from her garden. Her favorite good luck crow cruised overhead, his wings whooshing a deep rhythm. "Hello!" she called as she bounced toward the kitchen door in a giddy-up gait.

The girls were dressed and waiting.

She reported, "Folks are pilfering, I mean pilgriming, from all over. You'd think the baby Jesus was celebrating independence!" After changing into her white cotton blouse—the fashionable one with leg of mutton sleeves—Mary braided daisies into the girls' hair. Ready, the threesome locked arms and strolled to Central Avenue where the hoopla was waxing.

Mr. Benjamin Roberts, son-in-law of Cascade's founder, Mr. Thomas Gorham recently deceased, lifted a red enameled megaphone to his lips and shouted celebratory greetings with a distinctive Southern accent—bred from Confederate origins, word had it.

He instructed all contestants in the one-mile horse race to line up. After checking the time, he returned his watch to his chartreuse vest pocket, lifted the start-flag above his head and nodded to his assistant who pointed a cocked revolver skyward. "On your mark, get set—go!" he yelled as he swung downward in unison with the single gunshot.

Fifty riders jockeyed all breeds of horseflesh. A thunderous roar of hooves pummeled twice around the circular course and across the finish line. A spitfire thoroughbred trained by James W. Cornell was flagged first. His elated rider accepted the $5 purse after shaking the hand of Mr. Roberts, who declared the stallion's finish slicker than greased grits. Disgruntled riders begged a rematch.

Record numbers of people treaded upon the town and the adjoining area. Cliques milled about, propelled by curiosity, reciprocated. Rows of kiosks and tables bordered the roped-off "family entertainment" field. Pots and pans rattled; mouth harps scaled. Peddlers clamored, each claiming the finest quality at the lowest price. Children's laughter rippled near the puppet stage. Summer dust thickened. Dogs rolled over, and wives examined other wives' pies, cakes and preserves—entrees in the baked goods competition.

Onatah claimed that the crowd looked like a mass of pestered ants. Nadie said the fanfare resonated pitches and tones like none she had ever heard. Mary was astonished that so many people had come to populate the area, and wondered if frontier days were over.

The 440-yard horse race was won by a feisty little Arabian mare called Flash, owned by George Connors. Mary inspected the racing stock and reckoned that money from the East had infiltrated the Birdtail.

Nadie began to feel better about prospects at the Industrial School as she observed the sport contestants, one in particular—the winner of both the 100 and 200-yard footrace, a tall Blackfeet boy who breezed across the finish line with the ease of a cougar. The announcer identified him as Dan Lone Chief, from Fort Shaw. A cluster of young women pined on the sidelines.

Mary hoisted Onatah onto her shoulders. From her lookout, Onatah imagined herself to be a hawk gliding on thermals above the roving packs of tightly corseted white ladies, one of whom, she noticed, marched swiftly toward the speaker's platform leaving waggling numbers of cohorts behind—dressed up ladies struggling to pull a decorated goat cart loaded with brown-paper bundles.

Mrs. Job Little, chairlady and wife of the Methodist minister, stepped to the podium. She lifted the Sears & Roebuck megaphone to her lips and nervously announced, "Everyone. Courtesy of the Methodist Ladies Aid, we invite you to come forward and claim your delicious picnic meal, free of charge. We invite you to share—" She paled as a number of exuberant young men stampeded toward her, moved behind Mr. Roberts, who tried, unsuccessfully, to hide his amusement.

Onatah patted Mary's cap and asked to sit in the shade. They claimed a spot under the granddaddy elm by Kraus's Sample Room and made themselves comfortable. Pondering the sign painted over the threshold, Onatah envisioned dolls and colorful candies and asked, "What does that place have samples of?"

"Nothing for little girls. Never you mind," Mary said, impressed with the child's reading comprehension.

Nadie crossed her legs, pulled her skirt over her knees and faced the action. She hawk-watched passersby, intrigued by the diversities of race, speech and mannerisms. Spotting a bearded man who wore a shiny top hat and struggled to carry wooden cases and a tripod under his arm, she said, "White Crow, look, a photographer! Do you know what he's going to photograph?"

"He's here to make an image for the soon-to-be first Cascade History Almanac: picture proof of Cascade's first Fourth of July extravaganza."

"Can we be in the photograph, White Crow?"

"I don't see why not."

Mr. Isah Erikson of White Sulphur, Montana, carefully arranged his equipment to face the grand building, recently constructed—the structure identified in his contract as "Murray Hall." Its name had not been sculpted into the façade—the cedar sign above the doorway appeared to have been an afterthought, though carved with skill. The owner's surname had been chiseled onto a replica of a scroll unfolded, horizontally. Isah wondered if the Murray's were scholars or had hoped to be, if they were influential, or if the building was a memorial. He touched his chapped lips and noted that the etching was similar in appearance, to carvings found on fancy mausoleums. Perhaps a local stonecutter had carved what would his backdrop this day.

Isah had reined his horse and single width covered wagon over one hundred and fifty miles to provide professional services to the not-yet-incorporated-town of Cascade. He hoped that the results of his present contract would secure him the house photographer commission for the upcoming first Cascade County fair in October. Such a commission would feed his family and stock through the winter.

He enjoyed long distance employment, as he inevitably discovered new objects to record and escaped his wife's relentless accusations: claims that his infatuation with photographic paraphernalia was the beginning of the end. Your profession is contaminated with evil temptation, divination and alchemy, she had argued, all of which would send Isah, and her by association, to damnation and hell fires. They would be burned at the stake for all time, she had warned.

Isah thought it was she who suffered under the influence: the influence of charismatic preachers filling her head with nonsense. Studying the balance of objects in space, as lit by gradated angles of sourced light, natural or studio, gave him a deep sense of contentment. He labored to capture hue and innuendo, and carefully framed his subjects, unaware that creative passion had claimed his life.

Growing numbers of the Independence Day crowd refreshed themselves with generous swigs of home brew. Voices rose. This worried Isah, as he needed his subjects to remain motionless for long exposure counts; blurry portraits were unacceptable and wasted expensive developers. He offered a well-dressed local boy two nickels to watch his equipment while he searched for Mr. Roberts.

After a brief consult with the photographer, Benjamin Roberts gathered his friends in order of political importance and suavely guided them to the granite steps of Murray Hall. Roberts planted himself at the top, front and center, bidding Dr. Winslow to stand on his right and J.E. Marcum on his left. He directed Miss Fallon, the schoolmistress, to the step beneath them along with his wife, Marcum's wife Ida, and the ministers' wives. He trumpeted through his megaphone in hand, "All townspeople. Attention, everyone. Come to Murray Hall and line up in an orderly fashion. We are to pose for the First Cascade Almanac. A historic remembrance!"

"White Crow, hurry! We have to be in the photograph," Nadie begged. "Onatah, wake up. We're going to be in a photograph!"

"Photograph?" She rubbed her eyes and looked to Mary. "Can I go get your dolly?"

"No child, there is no time. Besides, I have the real Onatah, right here." She pushed against the tree to get up.

There was space to stand on the lower steps of Murray Hall, but Mary chose ground level. She held Onatah on her hip and slowed her breathing, as though such discipline would foster anonymity. Her face flushed, claustrophobic in a sea of bodies. She found a way to comfort herself— imagined a photographic print on the wall in her house where, in the future, she would stare into the eyes of Nadie and Onatah whenever her heart ached lonely.

Isah instructed the assembly to be quiet and remain motionless. It would only be sixty seconds, he told them. During the extended communal silence, while the hooded photographer squeezed a black rubber bulb and the shutter click-clacked, each subject had time to imagine his or her self, recorded for posterity: who would remember, why, and for how long?

A dozen 15x12" glass plates were exposed. Satisfied, Isah dismissed the crowd. He shook Mr. Robert's hand and grew excited as he detailed an inspired daydream: his acceptance of a blue ribbon awarded for his soon-to-be-captured images titled, *A Collection of Revolutionary Fireworks on the Western Frontier.* But he was getting ahead of himself. Those photographs required preparation: night shots, hours from the present moment. Isah hurried to his studio-wagon and devoured the last of his corn cakes.

At sundown, another announcement boomed across the sea of people: "Come one, come all, attend the Grand Ball following the fireworks." Nadie and Mary looked at each other, aware that they had misread the newspaper advertisement. Mary said, "We both thought it was a concert, didn't we?" Nadie nodded, grappling to form an image of herself at a ball.

"Nadie. Sorry honey, but we are not going to any grandiose ball. If it's the quality of music you need to determine, you can hear it just fine from my house."

Nadie tensed; it wasn't only the quality of music that necessitated her presence. By watching the musicians, she could assess potential friends and competitors, observe group dynamics. Suddenly, the obvious became clear: Indians would be denied admittance to a grand ball, in any case. She redressed her disappointment and said, "All right, White Crow."

"Sorry, honey. Maybe you'll be a band member by the time they travel to Great Falls."

"The band is going to Great Falls?"

"I overheard the photographer. For the first Cascade County Fair, he said. In October, I think."

"If that's true, I want to be in the band for certain." Nadie slid her arm around Mary's waist, "Let's find a place to watch the fireworks, White Crow."

Lagging behind, forehead wrinkled, Onatah tugged at her Ucsote's hand until the large body attached, stopped. "White Crow, have you ever thought what it would be like if real life was what you see in the photographer's glass? It's the opposite. Sister Gertrude told me. You would be a white woman, and I would be gray. I guess that means I'm the same, and Nancy too. But the white people would be black."

Engrossed in the proposition, her friends were tongue-tied. Onatah chattered on, "Some of the girls say that it's bad to have your photograph taken because it takes your spirit and keeps it in prison, or freezes it. What do you think, White Crow?"

"What? Oh. I think that worse things can take your spirit—like not standing up for yourself and family—like letting people hurt you because you're afraid."

"Well, I don't think squeezing a bulb makes anything happen to a person. It's science chemistry that makes the picture on the paper. People just think it's magic because they don't understand."

Nadie stared at Onatah, once again engrossed in her friend's thicket of imagination. She considered her own goals, which simply required plotted perseverance and concluded that for her, solace was found in rhythm and melody. She wondered if that was how Onatah's ideas felt to her. Mary contemplated Onatah's role-reversed proposal, and imaged herself as a white lady, a plantation owner's wife. She would set the slaves free. Yes, white slaves. While her husband was out of town. Then what?

Onatah crossed her arms. "I like photographs because it turns a memory into a keepsake—one that your mind can't change when your memories get old. It makes a record of who we are, White Crow. I want today's photograph. I wish I had a photograph of my Onondaga family—to keep forever."

The threesome retired to Mary's house. They carried kitchen chairs and a wash bucket into the garden, the place from which they enjoyed a grand view of fire blasting toward sky and stars—arcs of color, sparks and explosions that streaked the warm starlit evening.

"Glad you were left out of the doings yesterday," Mary said to Bigg Too, who grazed contentedly in the fenced livery field outside of town. She slipped a rope halter over his ears. "Too wild for you, fella. You wouldn't have cared for the fireworks. Maybe you saw them from here. Bet you would have liked to meet a filly or two, though. Bet you heard them, smelled their scents." He nibbled oats from her hand and whinnied affections. "The real day to celebrate is today," Mary said, "Our first day as the official Star Route Mail Carriers. Guess that makes you an official steed!" She haltered the two mission horses and led all three back to town.

Approaching the livery, Mary watched James arrive and unlock the door. He looked up and apologized for not having the horses ready.

"Got to go sooner than planned, Mary said, "Would you give them oats and get these two harnessed for me? Bigg Too can wait 'til I come back."

At home, Mary found the girls stirring mush in a fry pan. She praised, "I'm so proud of you young ladies. You're so capable ..."

"We can take care of you, White Crow!" Onatah insisted.

Acting very perky for one who's going back to where she ran from, Mary mused.

"White Crow, can I cut some flowers? Maybe Mother Superior won't be angry if I bring her flowers."

"Yep. No guarantees, but you can try. Cutters on the table."

Mary's wagon was the first to make tracks out of town. She delivered Nadie to the rear entrance of the Industrial School, as agreed. After hugs and promises, Nadie tossed her bag across her shoulder and marched up the wooden steps to an oversized double-door. She spun around and waved.

"I love you, Nadie," Onatah shouted.

White Crow gave a quick nod and ordered, "Giddy-up! Sun's already shooting rays over the scribble hills." The wagon rolled into motion.

"Scribble hills?"

Mary wiped a tear from her cheekbone and glanced. "Yep, look there, to the east—little mounds, looks like scribble. Hang on!"

Mary didn't slow until she reined the rig into Cornell's Livery.

Onatah's bottom was sore from hours of bouncing. "White Crow," she asked, "did you see all the people sleeping by the river?"

"Yep. Too tuckered out from the Grand Ball, I reckon. Let's make this fast. We're switching horse and wagon at the livery. Got mail to load and a schedule to keep. When we get to the mercantile, Onatah, you get yourself some water, and see that you don't get underfoot."

A short time later, Mary and Onatah returned the mission rig and team to Cornell's livery, transferred to Mary's horse and wagon and drove to the alley behind the merc. Mary told her passenger she'd be back directly and clomped inside, slamming the door behind herself. Mr. Flinn informed her that the *Great Northern* had arrived with an extra-large load—she was to head to the depot and pick up three crates addressed to Father Rebmann while he finished sorting mail by route—he'd give her the Birdtail mail sack upon her return.

Mary followed his instructions, Onatah at her side.

Onatah wished she had eaten the rest of her mush, and soured at the day's reality: she was a package for delivery like the crates. The flowers had begun to wilt. She helped herself to water from a bucket near the trough, wet the stems, put the bouquet under the cross-seat and climbed aboard.

Mary ran her hand over the canvas mail sack stamped with wide capital letters: OFFICIAL UNITED STATES MAIL. She lifted it, estimated the weight. "Near thirty pounds," she uttered. "This duffel is ship-cargo tight—an experienced sailor made these knots."

Mr. Flinn heard, asked how she knew such a thing. "Been up and down the river a few times myself," she said, hefting the sack into the bunk. "Years back, I worked on a steamboat called the *Robert E. Lee* on the *Mississippi.*"

"You're full of surprises." He smiled and pointed, "Nothing to sort, turned out—only mission post today. You got lucky."

Suspecting he was the knot maker, she said, "Yes sir, Captain Flinn, I'll be on my way."

❧

Onatah welcomed the noisy repetition of hooves and wagon wheels that gave her time to organize feelings. An hour out, Mary pulled back on the reins and hollered, "Whoa. Whoa now, boy." Big Too eagerly obeyed, having spotted grass by the spring to his right. Mary gave her passenger a squeeze and jumped onto the damp dirt. "Well, Onatah, what do you think? Want to be a mail carrier when you grow up?"

Onatah looked at the shades of pink and purple under the cross seat, giving herself time to consider Ucsote's question. *No, I do not want to be a mail carrier.* Her heart began to pound, shook by the realization that she would have to "become" something. "What will I be?" popped from her mouth before she'd had time to consider whether any answer other than *yes* would hurt White Crow's feelings.

Mary slipped the bit from Big Too's mouth so he could enjoy his chewing. "I'll take that as a no, then?"

"I'm not as strong as you. I wouldn't last at being a mail carrier. White Crow, can a woman be a photographer? A real professional one, like yesterday?"

"Onatah, I always tell you—you're smart enough to do anything. Of course you can! Bet you'd be a great one, too. You're observant and clever. Can I schedule a portrait appointment, Miss Saint Germain?"

Later, in the heat of afternoon, the Birdtail Star Route Mail Carrier proudly delivered crates and the contents of the mail sack to Father MacDonald, whose ecclesiastic endeavors included post sorting and distribution to both the Jesuit and Ursuline sectors.

Parched, but energized by her new status, Mary directed her horse and wagon to the familiar Ursuline barn and halted at the water trough she had built with her own hands. She removed the harness and brushed Bigg Too's sweaty coat.

Onatah searched the barn for oats and returned with a small heap balanced on her flattened palm. She offered it to the large animal, the way White Crow had taught her. Remembering the bouquet, she backtracked to the wagon, stepped up onto the wheel's hub to reach the flowers she would fluff into a pleasing shape.

Coming from behind, Mary scooped the child into her arms and cried, "Let's deliver the most important package!"

Onatah kissed her Ucsote's cheek. "Call me Onatah, White Crow! I'm going to miss not being called by my *real* name!"

"Yes, I know what you mean, Onatah, Onatah, Onatah!"

Mary's sixty-three year old musculature, stronger after working the route for a few weeks, fortified her physique to the robust condition to which she had been accustomed. She scolded herself for having gotten soft during her Café regime and reveled in her heightened stamina. Still, treks from Cascade to Saint Peter's Mission, thirty-four miles round-trip plus side-routes in and out of homesteads, challenged an aging back—even one held firmly together by strong sinew and grit.

"Love this job," she exclaimed, charging ahead on the dirt road, "as much as town men love to chew fat and tobacco and town women love to organize secret guild meetings. Now they'll be calling me Mail Carrier Mary. Guess that's better than Nigger Mary or Black Mary ... a measure of respect?"

Considering her status again an hour later, she decided that in a world set right, folks would address her as "Mary" or "Miss Fields" without labels attached. For now, she would embrace the advantage gained by this position. Time. More of it spent enjoying her surroundings, less wasted maneuvering opinions.

Though Nadie found the Industrial School harsh and totalitarian, summer passed quickly, and autumn brought her good news. She had gained admittance to the Mandolin Club and was to be featured as the violin soloist at the Cascade County Fair in Great Falls, just as Mary had predicted.

Her aspirations had not prepared her for center stage, however. Facing hoots and jeers as she perspired under spotlights, felt to her, like being chloroformed, a native trinket pinned under glass.

It was the group's third performance. Perhaps it was fortunate that stage lights prevented a clear view of the crowd, which grew louder as more ticket holders pushed their way through the flaps of the canvas tent. Nadie breathed deeply to ease nausea, distressed at having been forced to wear a deerskin dress. Even worse, a deerskin dress manufactured by white people—a holiday uniform identical to those of her comrades decorated with strings of red, white and blue beads. She forced herself to concentrate on tuning.

Unbeknownst to her, support was close by. Mary had gained permission to keep Onatah for the weekend and had lavished her guest with one surprise after another. After breakfast at the Warner Hotel, they proceeded to Great Falls, a distance of sixteen miles, to attend the Cascade County Fair. Mary said, "This will give you a taste of the future, Onatah, and don't forget. You are as important as anyone else."

Onatah had never imagined so many white people in one place. Feeling excited, scared and wary, simultaneously, the way she had felt once when she had come upon a gigantic waterfall that plummeted a massive distance, precipice to bedrock, a roar so loud it hurt. Yet it had lured her close.

The color of dusk comforted, and it was then that she and Mary shouldered their place among people who stiffened their bodies and pushed forward, staked their place in the long line that inched into a huge tent. She tugged Mary's skirt and pointed to a man dressed in strange clothing, watched him climb onto a stack of casket-size crates and make odd gestures. "Look, White Crow. Who, or what is he?"

"A barker, honey."

"Bark like a dog?"

"Come one, come all," the barker on loan from the circus called. His silhouette looked as though he had walked off the page of a fantastical odyssey. Black skin-tight trousers and a gold cummerbund anchored a red satin sequined shirt in place. Multi-colored ribbons with bells tied to the ends dangled from his shoulders, ringing tiny tinker sounds. Ebony shoulder length hair swayed below a sleek ochre turban wound and adorned with cut glass jewels the size of thimbles.

He waved a baton and exercised a liquid chocolate voice. "Don't miss this performance," he called, "Exquisite, entertaining—it will give you a thrill—the music everyone is talking about. It's the Indians from Fort Shaw, playing for us tonight. American hits! A tune for every taste. Three bands, ladies and gentlemen. Hear the brass horns, the mandolins and the banjos, and tonight only, a surprise for classical lovers. Come see the Redskins in their native costumes, playing modern American music! Step right up. Get your tickets, ladies and gentlemen. Redskin musicians, here for your entertainment!"

"White Crow, is Nadie here? We're going to see Nadie?"

Grinning, Mary nodded, pleased as the skunk who had feasted on her hens.

Inside, Nadie turned to the mandolin player seated next to her. "Did you hear that? Redskins in native costumes," she flared, "as if our tribes' clothes weren't, aren't, *real*."

"Keep it down, Miss Burd," the school's conductor snapped.

Nadie closed her eyes. It had been through him, Mr. Arthur Strong, and his love for classical music that she had gained permission to come with the group to Great Falls, the first city she had ever seen. If he hadn't searched the infirmary's attic and discovered an old violin case that to his surprise contained a pristine instrument along with hard to come by, decades-old sheet music, she would not be here.

The treasure had inspired Mr. Strong. Engaging his own persuasion, he had adapted Corelli's Concerti Grossi, Op. 6—Concerto Grosso No. 1 in D Major, written for violins, viola and bass violin, into a score arranged for one violin, three mandolins and a cello. He was convinced that the composition's adaptation would win first place in the fair's Music Competition, if Nadie played well. He had fulfilled his part of their understanding. Now, it was her turn.

She had practiced whenever allowed (there had only been two-weeks) and had used the heat of displaced frustration—not having heard from White Crow, Onatah or her Piegan family—to fuel her perseverance and conquer the concerto's subtleties of timbre, harmonics and vibrato. She had to give an excellent performance; her future at Fort Shaw depended on it. Her left leg began to shake, and she couldn't stop it.

Two women in the crowd outdoors spotted Mary: the wives of Joseph Kauffman and John Shepherd, Cascade businessmen and former members of the C.C.C. Ava Kauffman whispered to Helen Shepherd, "Glory. That's Nigger Mary. What is she doing with that little Indian girl? Do you suppose she's kidnapped her?"

Helen said, "Heaven knows. That woman thinks she can gallivant around, just as she pleases. I saw Mabel in the Homemaking Tent, earlier, and she says that Nigger Mary came here on our train, for goodness sake. I don't know why the *Great Northern* doesn't have a Jim Crow Car. It should."

"Well, what I can't condone," Ada slurred, "is that she parades herself into the saloons with the men, big as you please."

"I hear she smokes cigars on occasion in the saloons. Perhaps we're jealous."

"Helen, that's a sinful thing to say, and you know it."

Helen giggled and took Ada's arm, momentarily distracted by the barker's glance. "You know the music is undeniably good. Let's get our tickets. The men are supposed to meet us inside. They can decide whether to call the authorities."

Mary heard them and nonchalantly placed an arm over Onatah's ear. She leaned down and sighed, "Onatah dear, I want to stand in the back. Is it all right with you if I put you on my shoulders?"

"No, White Crow, I'm too big for that. It's embarrassing." She slung a perturbed look.

"All right then. You stand on the seat in the last row and I'll sit next to you."

"Don't you want to sit in the front so we can see everything good?"

"No, and it's 'well'. Can't see what's coming if we're up front."

Anxiety was warranted, for the performers at least, had they been aware that the majority of Cascade's white males in attendance were there to formulate opinions on the matter of Fort Shaw's Indian assimilation. There had been articles in the newspaper and an invitation from the Federal Bureau of Indian Affairs, a request for citizens to report to their nation's leaders.

What better venue to witness and evaluate the school's progress, Cascade men had agreed. Were the heathens authentically transformed? Were they ready to stay put in their new trades? Would the rehabilitation last? Meanwhile, they and their wives would be entertained—perhaps pick up a tune or two—replicate them on the mouth harp or the piano.

Listening to the barker who continued to chorus his biddings, Nadie pretended to search for something in the violin case under her chair, and said while feigning a smile, "We are perpetuating the conqueror's circus and making them a profit."

Her neighbor retorted, "I heard you had a Minnehaha Club at Saint Peter's. What do you call that?"

Nadie blushed. She had recited Hiawatha at the commencement ceremonies.

"Be proud," the girl said, straightening the fringe of her buckskin dress. She handed Nadie a small lump of lamb's wool. "Stick this in your ears and don't look at them."

Nadie looked before she could stop herself. No, it can't be, she thought. Yes it is. It's White Crow and Onatah!

Mary and Onatah settled into aisle seats in the last row. Onatah shouted over the crowd's chatter, "Nadie, Nadie!" Mary added an ever-distinctive whistle that only she could rip, shrilling an octave-slide through the air. Mr. Strong raised his baton.

Aware of whiplashed looks of scorn directed her way, Mary crossed her arms and considered: we're all straddling some kind of fissure—one foot not knowing how to walk with the other. Bad enough that the true natives of this continent are forced to perform European music to the new-citizen-property-owners, a crazy quilt of Saxons, Germanics and Celts who pretend to be better than the families they left. Baptized themselves modern Americans, a fancy word for immigrants—same as they made us Coloreds into. They're thinking they should be entertained by whomever strikes their fancy—force the ones they kidnapped to do what they want, with no rights. How is that not tantamount to slavery? She sighed, and concentrated instead, on Nadie and her violin.

Nadie relaxed after mastering the opening measures. Her hands knew the music—she had only to let them go. Corelli's concerto required tremendous energy and she played his rhythms with metronomic clarity. The melody pulsed from allegro to adagio, largo and back to a fast-paced allegro: complexity that compelled Nadie's bow to soar up and across strings with deft sensitivity and speed while the mandolin vibrato weaved in and out. A velvet harmony transported hearts during the final transition, as cello and violin modulated in unison.

Arthur Strong was elated. Mary patted tears with her hankie. Onatah bounced as she smacked her palms together. A standing ovation surprised all of the musicians.

"Can we see Nadie, after?" Onatah whispered. Mary nodded.

Banjos were dueling an encore when a man in the audience jumped up and erupted, "Don't you touch her you son-of-a—" followed by another's voice, "I'll show you—"

Bottles crashed, compelling Mary to grab Onatah's arm and exit through the nearest flap. "Sorry, Onatah, it's over anyway. We'll go round the back."

Mr. Strong signaled his players to stop and stepped forward. "Thank you for the opportunity ladies and gentlemen—"

Mary and Onatah waited in the tented alley, a narrow tunnel of slanted canvas walls held taut by staked ropes, crisscrossed—eerie looking when exaggerated shadows from occupants inside, moved. Crisp fall air and a moon nearly full invigorated the companions and they waited, enjoying the privacy.

Soon they heard Nadie's voice, and Mary inched the overlaid tent flap apart.

"White Crow, Onatah, come in!" the star musician called. "I'm so happy you came. I saw you just before we started." Onatah lifted her arms, reaching. Nadie plunged to embrace her, swung her around.

"You were great, Nadie. Knew you would be," Mary cheered.

"You were spec-tac-lar!" Onatah pronounced, repeating the big word she heard a man shout between claps.

"Really?"

"Yes, really. Everyone raved," she said, patting Nadie on the back, aware that others were watching.

Nadie moved close to ask, "How are you getting home?"

"Mr. Cornell is giving us a ride."

"I wish I could come with you."

"Don't think you want to start asking for extras at this point in time, do you?"

"No, but I wish it, just the same." They managed a brief hug. "We'll see you soon," Mary promised, as she and Onatah slipped out of sight. Nadie stepped into the alley to catch a breath of fresh air. Stealing a minute of solitude, she gazed upward, grateful for her friends and her success.

Angry voices shouted. She flinched, squinted to distinguish the dark shapes of men several tents away. There were two who struck at each other, fell, rolled, staggered, jabbed again. Several figures stood behind the fighters, legs apart. Compelled to move nearer, she squealed as light flicked across the brawler's faces. She recognized the man who lost, the one who had kept swinging after he had been bloodied, swinging until he collapsed. She'd known him all her life. Her brother *Kitchi* (brave, in Blackfeet) lay still, a lump in the darkness.

"Kitchi!" She bolted to his side, held his face in her hands and cried, "Kitchi, it's me, Nadie. Kitchi, breathe! Kitchi!" His eyes fluttered. The struggle for consciousness lapsed and his body sunk, as though it had been emptied. She shivered and felt his spirit separate from it, from her. She looked. The others had gone.

A voice she knew, spoke from behind. "Nancy, we're leaving now—" She flinched from the hand that tapped her shoulder, attempted to take her from her brother, her blood, her family. She scrambled to the other side of the body. "Kitchi," she cried again. "Wake up!" She held her fingers on this neck, waited for pulse, watched blood ooze from a gash above his eye. "He's alive," she yelled, "Help! Someone, please, help!"

A man arrived and kneeled over her Kitchi. He put his ear to her brother's chest and looked to her. "I'm trained in medicine," his words said. "He'll survive. I know him. I'll bandage him and take him home. Who are you?"

"I'm his sister, Nadie. Are you sure?"

Mr. Strong tapped her shoulder once more and insisted, "Nancy, I'm sorry, but we're leaving. You must come."

"He'll be all right," said the stranger. "I promise, I'll take care of him."

"What's your name?" she demanded.

"George Thunder Bear."

"Nitsíniiyi'taki, Keme Machk." (Thank you, Thunder Bear.)

She staggered to a white man's wagon that would take her from her family once more.

13

LOYALTIES

*G*et to the point, Mary itched as Mary Ann Moran rattled on, stretching mundane chit-chat to the mail carrier's limits. Mary glanced to the homemaker's delicate hands and counted seconds thinking: I know she's leading up to something—can you bring me such and such, Black Mary—and ask Mr. or Mrs. So-and-so if—

Mary Ann drew another breath and labored, "… and the second crop of beans is still coming, enough ears of corn to build a barge, so I asked Mr. Moran if we could hire help, since the girls are gone to their grandparents, but he never did answer me, and he jawed on about the harvest, the need for more hired hands to help him. Look at my hands, Black Mary, they're cracked."

When the chatter did not cease, Mary blurted, "You know I'll bring you whatever it is you need. Just ask." She winked, attempting to ease the effect of her boldness. "Sorry, Mary Ann, but I need to get to the mission. There's an extra-large batch of mail in the bunk. See," she motioned. "Sisters do all the sorting since the Jesuits left. Need to get back by dark."

Sure enough, Mary Ann's hurt feelings slid across her face like split cream—thick and sticky. Mary watched the distraught farmer's wife squeeze her embroidered handkerchief and sniffle, struggling to concentrate. "No, Black Mary, you're quite right. I look forward to your visits, that's all." She turned away, knowing full well that mail delivery did not constitute a visit.

"Do you need more canning jars?"

"Yes. Five or six dozen, but that has nothing to do with our talks." She reached to give Mary, who had mounted back onto the wagon's springboard and held both sets of reins in one hand, her list. "Thank you, Black Mary."

"Yes, Ma'am. I'll tell Mr. Shepherd."

Scooting to the center, Mary chirked to her team. A wave of dust comforted as the wagon gained speed. "Who needs a telephone line when they've got me?" she mumbled. "Truth be told, I like a measure of chitchat—about a cup."

She scowled, bothered that Mother wanted an answer by Thursday, as to whether she, Mary, intended to apply for the next four-year star route contract. "If I don't deliver the Birdtail route," she muttered, "it'll mean full-time laundry in town." After making a mental note to tell John Shepherd about the canning jars, she traversed memories from the past three-plus years and suddenly felt empty. Sweat dripped. She'd miss friendships forged with Birdtail women if she didn't contract again, and that included Mary Ann Moran, Sycowastakapi Lewis (Syco, for short), Mrs. Herman Wolf and Joseph Bickett's mail order bride, Jessie, delivered from the Cascade depot last year by the mail carrier herself. A pull on the reins persuaded Bigg Too to slow to an easy trot. On the other hand, she considered, there were star route drawbacks to remember: snow too deep for sleigh runners, walking waist deep in it, run-ins with Brondel, like last month when she delivered Lizzie and ran into him.

She drove past the lilac hedge and toward the mission barn where she unhitched Bigg Too from the wagon and paused to watch him slosh in the water trough. After removing his bridle and harness, she ushered him into the guest corral, tossed the mail sack over her shoulder and walked directly to the closet in the foyer, recently converted and designated as The Post Room.

She stacked the parcels on the table, placed letters in a finely woven basket, latched the door and caught sight of Lizzie in the garden. Charging outside, she eased a gentle hug around the slender girl and led her away from the others. After a brief exchange, Mary marched into Saint Angela's, where she found Mother in her office. She shut the door and sat in the chair that faced the desk.

Amadeus looked up and smiled.

"Afraid I have some bad news, Mother Superior. It's about Lizzie."

Mother raised her pen from the page and straightened.

She relayed the girl's burdensome story: how Lizzie had suffered through unsolicited sexual violations forced upon her repeatedly during the fortnight before her return to school. How finally, Lizzie had confided the terrible assaults after much coaxing. Mary watched for a just response—dismay and indignation followed by outrage and action—and added details. "Lizzie was shattered by the knowing that adults engage in such acts and, worse, having them inflicted upon her own virginal body. She was sure that you, the Church, I mean, would judge her as evil and sinful. She's afraid that she's going to burn in hell forever, and also afraid she'll be punished here. I assured her that you would never do such a thing."

"Who was it?"

"Her father."

"Why didn't you tell me at once?"

"Was waiting to see the full extent of damages, if you know what I mean."

Mother leaned forward, blinking her blue eyes. "And?"

"She's missed her monthly and has all the symptoms."

Mother looked as though the devil himself had slithered into her quarters.

"When I brought her back to school," Mary said, "I could see something wasn't right. She's drowning in shame, Mary. She's a good girl."

"Yes. To lose her chastity this way is criminal."

Mary watched Mother's reaction rise—empathy and evangelical fury held in check by pragmatic discipline. She hoped that somehow Mother's plan would match her own, though she suspected it wouldn't.

"We'll have to send the girl away, of course. As soon as possible." Mother Amadeus locked eyes with Mary. "I thought you were going to tell me it was Mr. Burns. Two of the girls recently reported inappropriate behavior on his part."

Mary hardened. She swore a muted vow that she'd find him after she'd gotten details. Right now, Lizzie was the wronged innocent, and a plan had to be made.

"Did she tell her mother?"

"Her mother was gone, nursing a family friend. That's how he got the opportunity. She's not back yet. But I don't think Lizzie would have told her—too terrified—raped and defiled, like she was." She couldn't help remembering herself hogtied and hoisted, montaged with imaginings of Lizzie's horrible experience.

"I understand," Mother said. "Let's ask Mrs. Lewis to take a look, make sure she is in the family way and attend to damages. Would you? Explain to her?"

"Yes. We ought to get rid of it. At least, give Lizzie the choice of whether to ruin her life or not."

Mother's jaw dropped. "Mary Fields, that very thought is an abomination against everything holy." She pressed her temple, stood up and looked out the window.

"You might feel different if it was you or your daughter."

Silence increased the distance between them. Mary added, "Sorry, Mary, but surely you know—dim witted babies come from two of the same seed."

"That's not the point. They are still God's children."

"Keep in mind, Mother, I'm just the messenger. She needs our help."

Mary Amadeus took a deep breath. "Noted. I could send her to the Drexel Institute in Philadelphia."

"Don't you have to get her father's permission?"

"I'll speak to him. Promise me you won't speak to the girl about alternatives."

"You've got to get him to agree. Did Burns molest those girls?"

"No, but he was about to. He'd been drinking. I fired him a few days ago."

"Why didn't you tell me?"

The lines on Mother's face grew deeper. "Perhaps the same reason you waited to tell me about Lizzie. Are we in agreement?"

"What would happen to the baby?"

Mother was irked at Mary's refusal to promise and irritated that she'd need to worry about that, too. "She will be well cared for. We'll talk later."

"You mean, in an orphanage?"

"I have business downstairs, Mary. Thank you for telling me. We'll talk again soon." She hurried to the door, notebook and spectacles in hand.

Mary returned to Lizzie and suggested a walk to the aspen grove. Once arrived, they faced each other awkwardly—tensions eased somewhat by the fluttering chorus of golden leaves above. Touching the girl's shoulder, she said, "Lizzie, I told Mother Amadeus. Don't you worry. She's real good at straightening things out."

"What does that mean, Mary? White Crow?"

Warmed at the girl's effort to show respect by calling her White Crow, she said, "I want you to have choices in a bad situation."

"I have choices?"

"Some. I want you to think like a grown woman, Lizzie. Like a mother." She sat on a boulder. "The choices are: one, you stay here, have the baby."

Lizzie paled and waited for a different choice.

"Number two: Mother sends you somewhere far from here, with Ursuline nuns. You have the baby. They put it in an orphanage, the place where babes and children without parents go, to wait for married couples to come looking to adopt."

Lizzie knew what an orphanage was but didn't interrupt.

"If your babe doesn't get picked, it'll stay there until it's as old as you— or older." Aware that Lizzie's mother was a Methodist, Mary added, "And the child will be raised Catholic." She had spared one piece of information: that some couples adopted solely to obtain free labor.

"I don't want to have a child, Mary. I can't believe there's a real baby inside me. I wish it would just disappear and it never happened." She plopped to the ground.

"Number three: that life inside of you, it wasn't made by your choice, right?"

Lizzie's glazed expression answered.

"Up to you to decide whether it's gonna be born or not." The girl's knitted eyebrows told Mary she needed to explain. "There's ways of getting rid of it, when it's tiny, like now."

Lizzie's pink lips parted.

An "Innocent Sparrow" no more, Mary thought. "Choice number four: you keep the baby and raise it, somehow."

"When do I get to go home and see my mother?" she moaned.

"Child, look at me." She gave her a moment, held her hands. "Course you don't want to be stuck in this spot. But too bad, you are." She quivered from the need to sound harsh. "Pay attention. You're going to carry this choice the rest of your life, so take charge. Be brave and make the best one— the one your heart tells you. Gotta think years ahead. It takes courage."

"All right." Lizzie hung her head and watched a long line of ants marching. "I don't want to kill it, but I'm not going to be its Mama. Not ever."

"All right. That's two decisions. That's real good." Mary sighed.

The dinner bell rang. They'd have to hurry. Mother would notice.

"I'm too scared to stay here. I think my Papa will kill me."

"All right." Mary patted Lizzie's shoulder. "See, you just grew up a few years. Three decisions you made already. You'll let the child live, give birth somewhere other than here, and someone other than you will raise it. That's a big start. We need to keep our talk secret, Lizzie. Can you do that? Even from Mother?"

"Yes, Mary White Crow. You're helping me. That's why you have the name, White Crow. I won't tell."

"Good girl. After we eat, we'll go see Mrs. Lewis to make sure you're healthy down there, not inflamed or anything. Make sure you're in good shape. Mother asked me to take you."

Two hours later, Mary returned Lizzie, who was, according to Syco, physically fit and with child, back to St. Angela's. She didn't stay for supper though Gertrude had asked, and left for Cascade without goodbyes. She couldn't get Burns and Lizzie's father out of her mind; anger smoldered; her head throbbed. "Scum," she cursed, pulling the bill of her cap. "And a hot tiff with Mary, to boot."

The journey home provided more than enough time to bemoan the perilous course of being female—the many transgressions that women endured, from childhood and ever onward, it seemed to her, gauging in particular, the pros and cons of boarding school. "I know boarding at the mission protects the girls from rape," she told herself. "Until summertime, anyway. Never thought of summers off as a drawback for the white girls. Every Star Route needs a woman mail carrier to help women who are attacked, abused or molested. Happens every day probably, everywhere— Men who rape women should be hanged by the appendage that caused the injury. I'll make sure Lizzie gets away safe—make sure she has the choice whether she wants that bastard child."

Resting her eyes on Birdtail Rock, she decided to stop at Bickett's—see if Jessie had found her goat. What a tizzy the new bride had spun earlier, scared that Joseph would find out she'd lost their only source of milk for the third time. "Should bring her a chain to tether that nanny goat," Mary uttered before she declared, "I know a few other people I'd like to hook to a ball and chain."

Stumbling to reach the circle of bright light above, resisting the urge to steady himself as it would require touching the dank belly of earth that encased him on all sides—a hand-hewn mining tunnel from which Burns hankered to emerge—he grabbed the pickaxe blade shouldered by his buddy, up front, flung his weight upon it and propelled himself, upward and out. Sun blinded.

He leaned over to exhale, sucked outdoor light and imagined his lungs resuscitated. Pulling his hat off, he wiped sweat from one side of an aging brow to the other. "Never knew it was so hot in a silver mine, Mosney. I thought shafts was supposed to be cool."

"As you can see," Mosney replied, irritated, "don't have much of a tunnel yet. We have to pick down deeper. Then it's cool."

"We? Haven't decided yet," Burns slurred. "Ain't seen no silver at all."

"Ya only been here a week. Silver comes in streaks. Ya have to stick with it."

"Who'd you buy this mine from?"

"A stout little feller," said Mosney. "His mama was dying in California. That's the only reason he parted with a working silver mine that made him six hundred dollars already. He said to make sure I hire johns to the blastin', but I don't have the cash yet."

"Umm. What's to eat?" Burns hooked Mosney's saddlebag with the tip of his boot, pulled it close and peered inside finding only hard biscuits and jerky wrapped in old newsprint. "We can't eat this unless we're planning on get'n some of those new-fangled false teeth."

Mosney ignored him and sat down on the split log he had placed beneath a pine tree at the edge of the cliff—strategically convenient for viewing the Birdtail-Mission Road in both directions.

"Is this all you got?" Burns persisted. He dug further, pulled out a small corked bottle and guzzled the last of Mosney's whiskey. "Let's go to town. We need supplies."

"Kinda hard, with only the one mule between us."

Town was close enough by foot, but Mosney didn't want to make the effort. He spat, inserted more snuff under his lower lip. Clouds moved in and shadowed their camp. Mosney looked up. A chill slid down his spine and his belly churned.

Restless, he glowered at the road below, said with a tone of entitlement, "We could get a ride." He pointed. "Look there, Burns, see that dust cloud? It's comin' our way."

"That's Black Mary, and you know it. Don't think she'd be likely to give us a ride."

"Well, maybe I'll just make her."

"Don't think that's a good idea, Mosney. If you wanna stay in the Birdtail, anyway."

"I knows lots a people who'd give me a medal for gettin' rid of that varmint."

He stood up, gripped his rifle and settled the scope to lock sight on the negress who had caused him to get fired four years ago—caused him to be out of work since then, he claimed, seeing as no one would hire him without a reference from his previous employer, the Mother Superior. He closed one eye and took his time, enjoying bloodthirsty ideas while he pressed a grubby finger against the big-fifty's trigger. "Burns, get yourself on down there to catch her horse. Don't worry, just givin' the nigger a scare. Get." He smirked, titillated to be the one giving orders.

"John," Burns warned, "Maybe it ain't—"

"What the hell?" Joseph Bickett muttered as he looked up from coyote tracks that had led him to the crest. From the girth of his horse, he identified movement on the south ridge—a man aiming a rifle at the wagon passing below. Dust clouds cleared during the time it took to slide a cartridge into his rifle chamber. He identified the shooter's target—Mary Fields—and cursed as he cocked, steadied sight and squeezed the trigger. A deafening blast reverberated.

Eyes riveted on the wagon, Mosney expected to see his target fall. Irritated by something tickling his arm, he glanced, ready to swat. Blood oozed through his flannel shirt. He sniffed the rifle barrel to make sure. "Yep—made the shot," he growled as his vision went blurry and he slumped against the tree.

It took Burns, who had dropped, spread eagle, a moment to realize that two shots had fired simultaneously: the bullet that had whirred past his face and Mosney's. He looked over, saw his buddy hit dirt. "John, you all right?"

"Yeah. Who the hell?"

"Hang on." Burns scrambled for better cover.

Mosney snaked to the cliff's edge. The horse was on the run—wagon tipped, driver at the helm—standing. He couldn't tell if she was hit but she was alive; he had a bullet hole in his arm. Suspicion pricked his craze, and he looked to Burns. "Did you?"

"Did I what? Shoot you? Mighta deserved it, but no. Stay down."

Joseph could tell that he'd winged the criminal, looked closer and saw who it was, patted his horse, spat, inserted cartridges and hurried down an out-of-sight gulley that merged onto the Cascade-Mission road. He'd witnessed the bad blood between Fields and Mosney: heard how Mosney had baited the bishop, started what ended in Nigger Mary's dismissal. Here he was again, the liar, shooting at her like a tin can. "Should be sheep-dipped," Joseph uttered, worried that Mary may have been hit. He kicked his horse into a run.

Bigg Too had hurled into flight. Mary did her best to slow him down while she scanned for the shooter. A wide curve came up fast. She rose, pulled back with the weight of her body and balanced, reins in hands, shouting assurances.

She saw a woman's body, face down, directly in their path. A wave of fear flushed her strength. Bigg Too swerved. The wagon slid sideways. She threw her torso across the buckboard edge, attempting to divert the wheels from flattening the poor soul. "Whoa boy—"

The rig scraped against the road's shoulder. Mary threw the harness straps free, jumped off and ran. The bad feeling in her gut proved true. It was Jessie. She dropped to her side and called, "Jessie! What happened?" Easing the silent slender body over, she felt for a pulse.

Charging his horse to run full speed, Joseph searched for Mary— instead, spotted a red-haired woman on the ground. "Jessie!" he screamed over hooves sliding on gravel. He leapt from his saddle and ran. "Oh my God, what have I done?"

"Joseph," Mary shouted, reaching across his wife's body. "She's alive. We have to get her home."

"Blood," he said, touching the stickiness on her scalp. His courage expired and he stared, limp and forlorn.

"She's grazed, that's all. She'll be fine."

Motionless, he continued to gape, his heart annihilated. "I did this."

"You're talking gibberish." Acknowledging the presence of shock, she barked, "Joseph! " She placed her hand on his shoulder, squeezed. "We need to get her in the wagon. I'll go get it. You stay here, stay with Jessie."

Joseph blinked, cocked his head and obeyed. When Mary returned minutes later, he lifted Jessie as though she were antique china, eased her up into the wagon. He jumped aboard, held his bride steady and prayed for her to wake. Mary slammed the tailgate shut, climbed aboard, clucked a signal to her steed and added, "Take her easy, boy, real easy."

For Joseph, nothing existed save the moment, a moment with no end. He fixed his mind on Jessie, noting as a tracker would, every detail: the pulse in the vein of her neck, her luscious ivory skin, her scent mingled with homestead dirt. He tried to think. Why she was there on the road? Mosney's bullet must have ricocheted—one chance in a million. She was his one in a million. He stared at her shiny eyelashes—auburn—the curve of each one symmetrical to the other. Sounds of Mary's horse single-footing, soothed. He stretched to see if they were home yet, thinking Jessie would wake on the bed he had built for her, open her stunning green eyes and smile into his. If I had been even one second faster on the draw, he accused, this would not be happening.

Mary's thoughts organized. She would stay the night, take care of Jessie and Joseph, do whatever was needed. She could see that Joseph was sullied in anguish. He had to snap out of it before she could leave. She wondered whether explaining why Jessie was on the road would help.

They laid her in the marriage bed, covered her with the quilt she had stitched as a girl. Mary heated water and searched for bandages, leaving Joseph to speak soft words to his wife. Touched that such a thing as a loving husband existed, Mary felt glad that Jessie had answered that advertisement, taken the risk and traveled to the frontier. The young bride had bundled her hopes and dreams into a satchel and a trunk. It couldn't end now.

Mary spoke as though Joseph were a boy, because he wore that look of time-stopped-eternal. She had seen it before and had worn it herself. "Joseph, I'm going to wash Jessie's head. The horses need tending. Will you take care of the horses, Joseph?"

He looked past her and shuffled toward the door.

She hummed a lullaby as she washed the blood and examined the wound. "Come on back to us, Jessie," she urged. "Your husband Joseph loves you; we all love you, and we need you to wake up, Jessie." She held the young woman's soft hands that hadn't, as of yet, had time to get cracked and calloused from the desolate high country dry. "Jessie, wake up now, wake up, Jessie."

Joseph returned, waited with Mary. Fearful, he noted that Jessie's color, her rosy pink cheeks, had paled. "I love you," he said, desperate and not afraid to say so in the presence of company.

Faint movement twitched below closed lids.

Mary moved from the bedside chair. Joseph pushed it away and sat on the bed—stroked his wife's forehead, called her name, hoped for one of those miracles she always talked about.

When the clock chimed, Jessie opened her eyes. A serene gaze latched onto Joseph. She seemed to embrace him, though her body did not move. "Joseph," she whispered.

Joseph and Mary agreed to take turns on watch, make sure Jessie stayed awake whether she wanted to or not—at least until sunrise, when the risk of drifting off for good had subsided.

At dawn, Mary served the tired husband a mug of freshly steeped coffee and told him she'd be back shortly, after she picked up the star route mail.

He thanked her and said, "Would you ask the doc to come out and take a look, just to be sure?"

"Of course. Anything else?"

"I can't think."

"Would it be all right if I charge a few things Jessie might need on your account at the merc?"

He nodded and thanked her. Scowling, he arched his back and said, "Nigger Mary, I don't think you know. That shot was meant to hit you."

She reached for the sideboard. "How do you know that?"

"I shot him, but I wasn't fast enough. His rifle went off too, same time—off the mark—must have ricocheted."

"So this is my fault," Mary said.

"Don't' be stupid, woman. Not your fault if some rogue takes a shot at you, hiding like a roach in the rocks."

"Who?"

"It don't matter right now. I'll tell you later, promise. Please come back to help me with Jessie."

Her stomach turned sour. She ran through candidates in her mind. "Joseph, I need to know now."

"No, you don't. Just keep a look out."

"Joseph—"

If he had looked, he would have seen gloved hands fisted and fire in her eyes. He didn't, for good reason. Joseph knew the anima response, knew that if he told her now when she was exhausted and distraught, she was likely to retaliate unprepared, get herself killed. She'd simmer down, he reckoned. He'd tell her later, when she would calculate wise.

It occurred to Mary that Joseph had made the effort to inform her of the shooter because the culprit might be waiting, ready to try again. She took a breath. "Joseph, Jessie was out looking for the nanny goat. "She, the goat," Mary paused, "ate through the rope again, and Jessie didn't want you to know."

Joseph smacked his palm to his forehead.

In town, the doc assured the mail carrier that he would leave immediately. While waiting for Mr. Shepherd to gather items she'd requested for Jessie, Mary posted a two bits reward to any youngster who could catch and deliver Bickett's nanny goat safe and sound.

An hour later, mail and packages sorted in her wagon, she began the daily route. Relieved that the Bickett's crisis seemed to be under control, she took time to identify the thorn that had pricked her craw since yesterday: Mary Amadeus had taken the news well enough, at first, she reviewed. But then she snapped at me, tried to put me in my place. That stung—more than being shot at, even. Mary blinked to deter sentimental emotion. Perhaps she was distracted with other mission business and her Alaska dreams—a poor excuse, regardless. I delivered the news well thought out, presented the facts, the options … To say, *we'll talk later* and dismiss me like a hired hand or a slave … She shook her head and watched prairie dogs run as the wagon rattled near.

Before I start getting all righteously indignant myself, she sighed, to be fair, there was me—twenty-plus years ago—knocking on the convent door in Toledo, wearing desperation and dirt-soaked rags … She took a chance herself, taking me on, having just been elected the new Mother Superior. Maybe I'm getting my dander up for not.

She paused to scan nearby hills for renegades and returned to her thinking. I loved that Jacob Tucker, I did, but he wouldn't listen. Told him I'd marry him if we moved off the plantation land, but no, he wouldn't hear of it, said we'd save money, staying put. Me, I was more interested in saving my soul—getting myself far away from the lecherous master's son who forced his personal ownership rights into *my* innocence.

Miss him sometimes, still, Jacob … Wonder what our life would have … Enough. Couldn't tell my parents, either. How can I help Lizzie? And stop that cockroach, whoever he is, from shooting me? Should be enough to worry about—stop dredging the past.

Ravens, squatting high in a large cottonwood that shaded the road, squawked and took flight.

Mary forced herself to address Lizzie's situation. She wagered Mother would be talking to Lizzie's father, today, and decided that she'd have to act just as fast. Each consequence needed serious thought—for Lizzie and Lizzie's baby. And herself. If she veered too far from the Ursuline way of thinking, longtime friendships would end.

Pulling into Bickett's place, she was surprised to see the nanny goat tied to a pole. She knocked, let herself in and raised a hand to Hattie Monroe, a town wife who stood at Lizzie's stove stirring something in a cast iron pot, as though it were natural for her to be there. After she'd identified the scent, chicken soup, Mary looked to Joseph and asked, "What did the doc have to say?"

He waved her to the chair by Jessie's sickbed. "Doc said she'll be fine, as long as she stays put for a week, maybe two."

Mary sat and studied Jessie for herself, felt her forehead. Satisfied, she said, "How are you doing, Mr. Bickett?"

"Fine, Nigger Mary, much better. How about you?" He gave her a pointed look, handed her a cigar from his shirt pocket and excused himself, claiming chores were waiting in the barn.

Unaware that the shooter had missed his target, Hattie asked Mary why Mr. Bickett was so concerned for her welfare when it was Jessie whose life had been compromised.

In order to distract the curious town lady, Mary slipped the stogie into her apron pocket, shrugged and fussed over Jessie as she checked the bandages and complimented Hattie on the delicious aroma rising, asked her for the recipe.

"The patient is fragile," Hattie reported, "but she sipped some broth and appears to be clear-headed."

Jessie opened her eyes and stared toward the far corner of the cabin, then looked at Mary and Hattie. Comforted by the presence of women, she said, "You know what really frightened me?"

They shook their heads.

"Not this." She touched her head and began to sob.

Mary and Hattie shared a glance.

"I … I was scared that something happened … and I couldn't have a baby."

"Are you with child, Jessie?" Hattie asked.

"No," she sniffled. "No, but I want one so badly."

Mary got up, took Jessie's soup bowl to the washbasin and stirred the chicken soup.

Jessie gushed, "My mother died in childbirth when she birthed my sister Harriet, who's younger than me. Harriet lives in Nebraska with her husband. They tried to have children for years and years. Miscarriages three times, and finally the doctor told her: don't get pregnant, or you'll die. She's broken-hearted for a child, and I worry that I'm like her or my mother."

"What happened to her doesn't mean you can't have healthy babes," Hattie said. "I'm sure of it. Isn't that right, Mary Fields?"

Mary frowned.

Nigger Mary, what on earth is wrong?" Hattie demanded.

The door burst open and a wild-eyed youngster ran across the room and whined, "Mama, can we go yet?"

Mary leaned down to ask, "Are you the cowhand who wrestled Lizzie's little goat home?"

He nodded.

She dug into her pocket and flipped a quarter his way. He caught the coin and grinned, proud of himself. "I'm Lester," he said.

"Go on outside and stack some wood for Mrs. Bickett, Lester. And what do you say?"

"Thank you, Nigger Mary."

Mary nodded, turned to the patient. Footsteps sounded and the door slammed. "Jessie, are you sure that your sister wants a child real bad?" She rubbed her neck, deciding whether it was safe to tell.

"Of course I'm sure, Nigger Mary. She'd die to have a child of her own."

"Would she want someone else's baby, just born? Be the babe's mama?" Hattie dropped her knitting sticks.

Mary glanced to each woman. "Both of you, promise you never heard this. Promise on your lives."

Jessie crossed her heart, and Hattie replied, "All right, I promise, Nigger Mary."

"There's an innocent victim: a white girl, with child. A solution has to be found right quick. She can't stay home. The sisters will probably send her back East if she's lucky. But I figure, that way, the baby will end up in an orphanage for who knows how long. Would be better if the girl had a choice." Including whether she wants to go through with having it at all, she kept to herself.

"Why can't she stay home?" Hattie asked. "Is the young man unacceptable? Oh. Is he married?"

Jessie's mind raced. Would Clifford, Harriet's husband, allow such a thing? Would he be the father, love the child, adopt it? She was sure Harriet would jump at the chance. She surprised herself with a bold notion: if they didn't want the baby, maybe she would take it. Would she? Would Joseph let her have it? Her head began to pound.

"Now before you get excited," Mary warned as she sat in the chair by Jessie's bed, "I should tell you the whole story. This girl, she's a good girl, goes to school at Saint Angela's, known her for years." She took Jessie's hand and gave her a serious look. "The truth is, Jessie, her father had his way with her. He's the Pappy."

Jessie squeaked and covered her lips with both hands. Embers collapsed during the silence that followed. "I'm thinking," she said in a small voice.

Hattie, long-time member of the Catholic Ladies Guild, spoke, "That baby is a child of God no matter what and needs a home like everyone else. Would they tell interested couples who come looking at the orphanage, those kind of details you just shared, Nigger Mary?"

"Don't know. Probably not."

"It doesn't matter," Jessie insisted. "Harriet wants a child more than life itself, and if she doesn't take the child, I will." Her mild demeanor rushed to catch up.

Hattie held her breath, studied the young woman's valor.

"I mean it," she insisted.

"This is the situation," Mary laid out. "Mother Amadeus is going to get the girl's father's permission to send her away—any minute. Maybe she's done it, already." The atmosphere tensed.

Hattie propped pillows behind Jessie's back.

"And then," Mary said keeping eye contact, "she'll put the girl on a train, pronto. I don't know if there's enough time to do anything different. If we do this, we'll take the chance of getting the nuns very upset; interfering, in their minds, anyway."

"Wouldn't Mother Amadeus be happy if we found a home for the child?" Jessie asked.

"I can't say for certain. Catholics generally like Catholics to raise their orphans—least from what I've seen." Mary glanced at Hattie. "I want to give the girl as many choices as possible. She's the one who's got to live with it, rest of her life. I talked to her already. She says she will not raise the baby, but she wants the best. What do you think, Hattie?"

Hattie's thoughts spun. She twisted her wedding band. "What if the sisters don't know? I mean, what if the girl just, ah, disappears?" She stood, yarn in hand, stepped back, stepped forward. "I think Mother Mary will be happy if the girl's baby finds a good life—regardless of the parent's faith—but Mother must adhere to Ursuline protocol, of course, and that would stop her from approving what we're talking about, I think."

Jessie twisted a long strand of hair. "So we would be doing her a favor. Both the girl and the Mother Amadeus."

"Possibly," Hattie answered.

"Absolutely," Mary said, pleased that a solution that did not require her to take charge on her own was underway, one that, thankfully, avoided the issue of abortion.

"Where in the world is the girl's mother?" Hattie thought to ask.

"Went to take care of someone—a friend, I think. Isn't back yet."

Hattie racked her brain, and it came to her—which mother was out of the area. While in the mercantile last week, she had noticed bruises on the daughter's arm. "Oh," she said, saddened, "we need to act immediately." She looked to Jessie. "Are you absolutely sure? Shall we get Joseph?"

The women relayed every detail to Joseph. Overwhelmed at first, he came to the same conclusion after he'd latched onto a broader scope of implications for all concerned. This done, he went outside, whittled at his personal feelings until he reached the core. If that's what his Jessie wanted, it was fine, he told them. All of it. He could use the company of a child, if it came to pass. And more children of their own would follow. He felt energized and surprisingly committed to the idea.

Jessie's gratitude gushed. Her Joseph was amenable, and her love for him bounded.

A unanimous agreement tied the conspirators to lifetime secrecy. They would act on faith.

Joseph summarized, "It's too risky to send Harriet and Clifford a telegram. Mary will present our plan to the girl. If the girl agrees, if it is truly her wish," he turned to Mary, "then tell her I will pick her up by the boulders in the nun's aspen grove. Tonight."

Jessie clasped her hands.

He stroked his beard, planning. "The creek's on the back side of the Opera house. Lucky it's a quarter moon—enough to see, not too bright. Tell her to wear dark clothes."

Mary nodded, well aware of the necessity.

"I'll get her to Helena by morning. In time for the train."

"And no one will ever know." Jessie cried.

"Is this kidnapping, her being fifteen?" Hattie asked, beginning to wonder if she was colluding in a criminal act.

"There's one last problem," Mary summoned. "That sweet girl loves her mother like a bear cub. When I tell her she can't write to her mama, like we all agreed—I'm a bit worried. She might bolt. Or she could write home when she's near due and by then she'll have lost the protection of the Ursulines. And the law."

"That's up to the girl," Jessie said.

"And out of our hands," said Joseph.

"She'll agree," Hattie said, "Tell her, Nigger Mary, to act like her mother would. And tell her she can write after the baby's born. Time will go by fast." She reddened, recalling how unfortunate events had hogtied her own dreams, how her heart had ached in silence once, for what had felt like a millennium.

"We're agreed then," Mary said, hands on hips. "I don't want anyone wondering why I'm late. Better get." She lumbered toward the hat rack.

"Wait," Jessie cried. "What's her name?"

Mary scanned the group. "Lizzie. Short for Elizabeth."

"I think her mother's got the hardest part," Hattie lamented. "Her daughter gone—she'll be tormented with worry."

"Hattie," Mary snapped, "would you simmer a decoction of yarrow? It's growing out back. To wash Jessie's wound."

"She's gone to St. Labre's Mission, Mary," Mother Sebastian replied in response to her request of the whereabouts of Lizzie or the Mother Superior. "Left this morning. Says she'll be there six months or more, depending."

"You mean, Mother?"

"Of course, I mean Mother. Come in out of the sun."

"Did she take the buggy somewhere, yesterday?"

"I don't know. Maybe Sister Catherine does. Why does it matter? You look tired. You'd better come in and have some tea. She left me in charge of the mail if that's what you're worried about. I know what to do."

The dinner bell rang, and Mary excused herself after having sorted through the post with Sebastian. Relieved, she spotted Lizzie at the end of the queue and shuffled her, unnoticed, to the barn. "I have good news," she whispered. Noticing Lizzie's bloodshot eyes, she asked, "Are you feeling all right, Lizzie?"

"What's the good news?"

"Are you still of the same mind? About giving the baby to good parents, I mean?"

Lizzie nodded, clearly distressed, pressing her hands on her stomach. The small effort seemed to tire her. She looked at Mary.

"Queasy?" Mary solicited.

"Mother Superior said I'm to leave on the train from Cascade tomorrow, to the Drexel School. She said the sisters have taken care of," her voice cracked, "girls like me before."

"Did she say if she talked to your father yet?"

"Mother says he told her I should go to further my education. That doesn't sound like him, but she showed me a paper with his mark."

Mary lifted an eyebrow. Won't be seeing his daughter anytime soon, she thought to herself, pleased.

"Mama isn't home yet. She'll be real upset. What's the good news, White Crow?"

"Remember we were talking about the orphanage yesterday? How it could be years until a child finds a home?"

Lizzie made a face and squeezed her legs together. "How can I worry about that? I want to see my mother before—" She slid onto a dirty crate.

"Listen honey, this is good. I found a God-fearing white couple who live in a nice city. They want a baby more than anything, can't have children themselves."

"They want this?" Lizzie whispered, pressing her belly again. A flock of pigeons flapped, and she flinched.

Mary patted the girl's shoulder. "Shish. They'll be giving you a home, too. You can live with them while you're carrying, and they'll keep the baby when it's born."

"How did you—?"

"Doesn't matter child, it's all arranged, if that's what you want. Or, you can go to the Drexel School, up to you: the school and orphanage or the husband and wife and home for the baby. You have to decide right now. No time left." She pulled Lizzie up. "Easier choice than yesterday."

"No, it's not. I want my Mama," she cried, "I might never see her—"

"Lizzie, stop it. Right now you are the mama, and, sorry, I can't give you more time. If you say yes—well—what do you say? You stand here and think on it 'til you're ready. I'll be standing at the—"

"No, don't go. How can I leave without being seen? Can you take me?"

"No. My friend will—better rider. You'll have to travel through the night. He'll get you there safe and quick—to the train. The couple will pick you up at their train station and take care of you."

"All right. I choose the couple. I'll give them the baby. Are you sure they are nice?"

"Yes."

"What do I do?"

"Wait at least two hours after the bedtime bell. Don't tell anyone else. Not your friends, no one. Go real slow, quiet as a cat. Slip out of the Academy, and around the Opera House, the side with no windows, and get yourself to the aspen grove. Don't take anything with you, except the clothes you're going to wear—dark clothes. We'll take care of the rest."

"Thank you, Mary White Crow," Lizzie cried as she leaned against Mary's shoulder. Mary watched the wet sparkle of tears outline the plump curve of Lizzie's face.

"Lizzie, I promise, I'll find a way to tell your mama you're safe, and how brave you are. You *cannot* contact her until after you give the baby away. It could put you, and all of us, in danger." She pulled away, lifted the girl's chin. "You must keep two promises: give the baby up, even if you change your mind, and don't contact your mama until after you've done that. Do you promise, Lizzie Tully?"

"Yes, I promise. I swear."

"All right." She squeezed her hand. "We've got to get to the dining hall. Don't let anybody tell you that you don't have rights. Let's go."

They walked across the courtyard to the back door of the academy, where Mary nudged Lizzie across the threshold and hurried to her wagon. Two hours later, she reported the news to the Bicketts, effectively passing the weight of responsibility to Joseph. She drove home, dog-tired and hopeful.

What seemed like minutes later, Sunday morning air sifted through Mary's windowsill. Her day off, she treated herself to a leisurely breakfast before dawn, and imagined Lizzie safe on the train, headed east to a new life. She thanked the Lord and thanked her friends, including Mother Mary and Saint Ursula, and considered how appropriate it was that "Ursula" meant "She Bear" (Mother had told her once). Everything had conspired for the best, she felt sure. "For me, too," she added, patting herself on the shoulder. Takes a long time to change. Circumstance and habits cut so deep—like habits built from slavery, doing what other people want. I'm not who I used to be. And I have every right to be respected. I earned it. And it's a good day to celebrate. Gonna wash up and head out to Bickett's, check on Jessie and wait for Joseph to get back, hear the rest of the story. It's a glorious day!

She pulled her boots on and slung the door shut, forgetting her cap. She watched misty light rise as she marched to the pasture where Bigg Too would be expecting her. Scarlet highlights streaked across a forget-me-not-colored sky, marking summits that seemed close. "The Birdtail has a special freedom," she uttered. "Untainted wildness. Gives me more freedom than I ever had, and the chance to work on my own. And time to think."

She felt in her pocket. Gripping the red apple, she called, "Come and get it, Bigg Too. We're going on an adventure!"

14

LOVE

*S*tanding on Cascade's railway platform, Mary tapped her boot on planks iced by the night freeze, intently joined to the furious beat of "Yankee Doodle" as it clipped through her mind. Her ankle cramped and she muttered, "Must have sprained it. Better make a poultice of comfrey, add some valerian, Saint John's wort. How many times have I come here to pick up guests for Saint Peter's or the Birdtail families? Can't even count."

She felt the rumble and turned to welcome a familiar sight: the *Great Northern's* locomotive engine, pumping steam—opaque puffs of white curling into, seeming to be swallowed by, pewter light rising from the dawn. She gave her leg a shake and watched the railway cars slow to a stop at the edge of the landing. Metal screeched. She shot a hopeful glance to each pair of shod feet stepping off the train. At last, a voice called, "White Crow!" Her heart leapt.

"Glorious flower!" She wrapped her arms around Nadie, the way a mother does. "You're all grown up!" She stepped back to look closely, noticed a sallow complexion and dark circles under her darling's eyes.

"White Crow!" Nadie kissed her cheek. "It's been far too long."

She took Nadie's case from her ungloved hand. "Let's get going. Lots warmer at my house."

Aromas of orange and apple peels greeted the pair as they kicked off their boots and set them near the stove.

"It's good to be back. Back to you, I mean. How do you get fruit this time of year?" She rubbed her hands over the stove.

"Mr. Mortag, at the Cascade Mercantile—the new store in town. He saves me fruit because he knows I make gifts of it to the children. And the candies, you remember. Spend most of my babysitting pay on treats. I love the smell of oranges."

"You haven't changed. I missed you, White Crow."

"White Crow. Nice to hear that name again. Let's have ourselves an orange, and I'll get some coffee on. Would you like a cookie? Baked them this morning."

"Yes, thank you." Nadie noticed that her elder, known for her strength and endurance, had a limp and moved slower, with deliberate attention. "I'll peel it, if you like."

They sat at Mary's small table, rough from scars from the many tasks that fell upon it, including the regulars: butchering game, boiling laundry, kneading dough. It had history, like the women who faced each other. Young innocent Nadie had matured into a woman, and there was something heavy pressing on her mind. Mary decided not to pry; she'd let patience invite the burden forward.

"It's good to be here," Nadie repeated, "Good to be with someone who loves me." She hardened her jaw, straining to present a casual calm.

"It's all right, child. You're here with me now. You're safe. Safe and sound."

"Do people ever *really* change?" she blurted, her thumb lodged between peel and membrane. "Inside, I mean. I know behavior can change—look how the Whites changed our lives." Her eyes narrowed. "I don't think a person can change their innermost nature, unless something shattering makes them able to."

Mary reached across, took her hand.

Sniffling, Nadie pulled strands of hair from her face. "Even then, I'm not sure it can be true." She looked directly. "I need to know whether it's my heart or my soul that's crying. It makes a difference."

That's a riddle, Mary thought. Don't see the difference—tears are tears. Sermons must have made her think that way. She ached and felt helpless.

"White Crow, remember how happy we were, Jack and I, when we got married? I thought my life was laid out to be a wife and mother, forever."

Mary nodded. So that was the problem. She remembered how they ran off together when Nadie graduated from the Industrial School. She had been glad for them, given them her blessing.

"I thought my mother would forgive me for marrying into the Apsaalooka, once we had a baby. But we didn't, so now she blames me. And Jack has been cruel. I can't take it anymore. The drink has destroyed him, and his rage is frightening. I can't fix it ..."

"What's happened?"

Nadie gasped. More tears gushed, slid eventually, toward a quiet interval. "He was in the mountains, riding through a pass. A cougar leapt onto the trail and his horse reared, threw him off the cliff. He fell a hundred feet onto rock."

Mary moved to the edge of her chair.

"Mounds of shale fell on top of him. It took hours to get him out. I was there, calling to him, to keep him conscious." She paled as she revisited the memory, the life-changing day that would never leave Jack and Nadie. "We were lucky to have found him."

"And?" Mary encouraged.

"He fell on his back, and it was broken," Nadie reported, wishing she didn't have to, wishing she could tell a different story and it would be true. She looked to Mary and swayed.

"My Lord, I'm so sorry," Mary said. "How long has it been?"

"Four years ago."

Nadie looked to the ceiling, closed her eyes. "It took over a year before he could walk, with a crutch." She looked to Mary, who was no longer able to curb her dismay. "He has to twist and pull his left leg—it has no feeling—his dead limb, he calls it."

Mary sighed, pulled a hankie from each pocket, handed one to Nadie and wiped her eyes with the other, trying to maintain strength for Nadie's sake.

"That's when he started the drinking—and how he got hooked—all the pain. I'm so sorry for his suffering, White Crow, but it changed him. He's changed." She tightened her lips, swallowed, and swallowed again.

Mary's chest throbbed. She had always loved Jack and his contagious vitality.

"You know Jack, Nadie said. "He's so proud—he would not accept help—or charity. He made sure that he lost all of his friends. I stayed. But his rage, the look in his eyes … One time after he was hooked on firewater—it was terrible—he ordered me to sleep with a soldier to get him money. I almost did it."

Mary closed her eyes, sipped water from the glass in her hand. She looked at Nadie, the good-hearted one who had always empathized, cared for those younger, like Onatah, since the time she was a child herself. The whole thing was too awful. She'd had such high hopes for the two of them—and they had been so well matched. But bad luck had got them, and here was Nadie, bleeding from the inside out.

"You have to protect your life, Nadie, or you'll have nothing to give. Doesn't matter who blames you for what. You know that—"

"I still love him. It makes me angry that I do." She gulped to stop more tears.

"I'm sorry, Nadie. So sorry."

"And Na'a still blames me for leaving the reservation even though she was the one who sent me to Saint Peter's. Now she says I'm not taking care of her."

"Maybe your mother's scared to be alone."

"I can't go back there. It would be suicide. Just like it is, was, with our marriage."

"You don't have to go anywhere. You stay here, long as you want."

"I hope I don't die in sin, like the church says I will, for leaving."

"I'm proud of you for leaving, Nadie—for believing that you don't have to endure violence. So many women live tortured lives, indentured to cruelty. Let's do something right now."

"Now?"

"Yes. How long has it been since you rode a horse?"

"Forever." She patted her face with the hankie, sniffled, set it on the table.

"Would you like to? It's the Sabbath, so my steed just happens to be available to best friends of White Crow. I'll saddle her up, and you can take a jaunt. Come on, don't think about it."

Nadie was grateful that White Crow had not inquired about Cricket, the pinto she'd given her and Jack for a wedding gift. She felt ashamed that she'd failed to get the mare back; Jack had lost her in a poker game.

She slipped into Bigg Too's saddle, anxious and distracted, paced the huge gelding at a slow trot and headed up the familiar mission road, where she could enjoy the sight of Birdtail Rock, the buttes and mountains in the distance, clinging to her deepest yearning: to be free.

Hours later, she returned to Cascade, purged and exhausted. Mary lit candles, her special tapered ones, and served a nutritious supper—thick beef stew with carrots, turnips and watercress.

"You'll get to see Onatah while you're here, if you like," Mary said nonchalantly.

"Onatah! Is she at the Industrial School or at Saint Peter's?"

"She got sent to Fort Shaw, I mean the Industrial School, the year after you graduated. The government stopped paying churches for their schools, and Saint Peter's had to reduce the numbers of pupils—girls and boys, both. Onatah was one of them. Upsets me to this day, but she's done well. Top of her class," Mary boasted. "Remember her interest in photography?"

"Yes."

"Well, now she is Mr. Erikson's assistant in his portrait studio, here in town."

"The photographer who photographed us on the Fourth of July?"

"Yes. Look. I got a portrait made: me and my dog, J.T. See there?" She pointed to the wall.

Nadie stepped across the room to examine. "It's lovely, White Crow! So regal and gracious. You're beautiful, you know. It's so in character—you with your Star Route rifle." She turned. "What do the initials J.T. stand for?"

Mary grinned. "Never mind. Got to have some secrets, don't I? Onatah will be at the studio tomorrow afternoon. Should we surprise her?"

"Yes. I'd like that. Let's pretend that you're bringing a friend for a portrait. She'll be dizzy!"

Mary leaned into her rocking chair, relieved that Nadie hadn't asked what happened to J.T., her loyal collie killed by the man who had broken into her home. "Sounds like a good plan." She grabbed her Red Whizzer Homing Pigeon cigar box, now serving its original purpose and not that of a cash register. Removing a half-smoked stogie, she lit up. "Ah, this is good after a full meal. Don't you start smoking, Nadie. Not lady-like."

"That's funny, White Crow. Just call me Lady Nadie, my true title." They giggled and stared at the potbelly fire, visible through its opened door.

Nadie asked, "How are you faring, delivering the mail? Must be hard on you traveling back and forth in brutal winter. Do you think you should keep doing such strenuous, and dangerous work?"

"Well, my four-year contract ends this June. Will be eight years since I started as the mail route carrier, to be exact. You know how I love to be out in the wide open. But I admit, winters are awfully harsh. Specially when I can't get through with horse or wagon and I snowshoe."

"You walk miles and miles through snow drifts. And what else? Howling, blinding blizzards? Is that why you have a limp now?"

Mary composed a jingle on the spot and sang: "*Through every weather God creates, Mary Fields will not be late. Star Route mail is safe with me—I'm the best freighter hereabouts, says me.*"

Nadie refused the distraction. "That's too much labor, White Crow. You know what you always tell me: take care of myself or—"

"Yes, Lady Nadie. That's exactly why I'm not renewing my contract. I figure I'll stick to home and run the laundry business for awhile."

"Glad to hear it. Laundry is plenty for an elder who's worked hard all her life. That's cute, your ditty."

"Thanks. Least I'll be able to keep up on town gossip."

They grinned, acquainted with the fact that Mary was not included in women's social circles—that she might, on occasion, join the men's banter, though discourse tended to be random and mercurial. "Good thing I can read," she goaded. "Would never know what's going on in the world if I listened to local accounts. Let's get some shuteye."

After breakfast the following morning, both women tipped their chairs back from the table and exclaimed distress after having gorged themselves on the banquet Mary had fried in celebration of Nadie's return. "I think the last time I had steak and eggs was with you," Nadie bawled, holding her swollen belly.

"Got to get some weight on you, gal. Nadie?"

"Yes."

"Did you hear the recent news about Mother Amadeus? About the train?"

"What?" She lowered the chair legs to the floor.

"Well, you know how she is always traveling around Montana to her other Ursuline missions?"

Nadie flinched, preparing for an accident story, like Jack's.

"Well, in October she was traveling to Saint Labre's, the Cheyenne reservation. You know, in the southeast part of the state. She was on the train when it crashed. Thrown across the car." Mary's throat spasmed and she gasped for air.

"White Crow, are you all right?"

"I'm fine, fine," she forced between coughs. She'd never spoken of the event. Bloody images appeared each time she'd thought about it—insinuated, to her mind, that she could have somehow, prevented the collision. She knew it was irrational—an accident was an accident. She couldn't change things now or then.

"That's horrible. Is Mother all right? I didn't hear anything about it."

Mary swallowed and said, "Her leg or legs, not sure which, were broken and she was all bashed up. They took her to the hospital in Billings, where she's been ever since, to my knowledge. Sister Gertrude says they didn't know how to fix her, so they tried traction or something. She wasn't real clear."

"Oh, my word." Nadie couldn't think what else to say. She made a personal promise to pray for Mother Superior, recalling moments of kindness and the book of poems she kept among her handful of special possessions. She looked to Mary, whose gaze oozed heartache. "You two were close. I'm sorry you haven't been able to see her. Is there no more news?"

"Afraid not."

Mary clutched another sorrow: disappointment at the absence of correspondence from the nun. She worried whether Mother Mary had remained cross about the Lizzie incident. We were close friends for years, she assured herself ... Maybe she is too injured to write and the letters that came from her for the sisters, hand delivered by me, were written *for* her. The scrawl on the envelope was not her hand. She should have answered me. Wish I knew more ... Hope someone mentioned her weak stomach compromised after the lead poisoning in Ohio.

"White Crow? You're far away. What are you thinking?"

"Oh, nothing. Just wish I could do something. Would like to see her with my own eyes."

Nadie thought of Jack's convalescence and sat motionless, in mental traction.

Mary poured herself another cup of coffee. "Did you know Mother Amadeus isn't just the Mother Superior of Montana anymore?"

"No. What do you mean?" Nadie strained to pay attention.

"I am personally proud of her for figuring a way to get free from the Catholic priest control; that would be Right Reverend Brondel in this neck of the woods. Well, wait. I have to backtrack. You know how Mother Mary was trying so hard to get to Alaska, to build missions and schools up there for the Eskimos?"

"No, don't think I remember that."

"Well, she was trying to get permission to go there since about the time you started attending the Industrial. First, she asked Father Tosi, up in Alaska. When that didn't work, she asked Father Rene, the new Prefect Apostolic of Alaska. He said, 'Yes, come. We want you.' Then, my favorite N.R.R." her face puckered, "because he's too chicken to face the Mother, he said in a note: 'I regret that I must deny you permission to leave for Alaska.' That was in '97."

"Oh. Then what? Wait. What's N.R.R.?

"*Not*-Right-Reverend, of course." Mary laughed, glad to see Nadie crack a smile. "Then Mother waited three whole years, and her prayers were answered!" Her voice slid up a notch. "A bulletin arrived from Rome, inviting all American Ursulines to join the Roman Union."

Nadie interrupted, "Which is?"

"A society of Ursulines in Europe. They govern themselves from Rome and the Pope, instead of through Catholic priests in separate countries. See, if the Montana Ursulines voted to join the Roman Union, then N.R.R. would no longer have authority over them, and Mother could travel to Alaska, as long as she got permission from the Roman Union. So guess what she did?"

"What?"

"She sent copies of Rome's invitation to all of the Ursuline missions here in Montana, with a letter explaining why she thought it would be a smart change, and then she traveled to Ohio, Pennsylvania and New York, rallying for Roman Union votes and doing her usual fund-raising campaign."

"That must have gotten his goat."

"Yep. Didn't mind too terribly, myself." She winked. "And he couldn't get the sisters to stop fraternizing with me either, since I'm the mail carrier and mission transport. He tried, though. Sent another mandate forbidding them to talk to me and all." She wiped her forehead, suddenly flushed. "Anyway, then Mother, determined as she is, made sure it would happen— joining the Roman Union. She wrapped up one of her prize Indian girls and took her to Italy, to cinch the deal."

Nadie's jaw dropped. "Who?"

"Angela Pretty Eagle. Remember her?"

"No, she probably wasn't at Saint Angela's when I was."

"Oh. Well, in October, two years ago. I remember the date cause they stayed in town overnight, waiting for the *Great Northern* to take them to New York. They sailed to Europe on a ship called *Aquitaine*. Mother dressed Pretty Eagle in buckskin clothing that Pretty Eagle had never worn in her whole young life—so that she'd be a sensation to the folks in Rome. Make an impression. Which I'm sure, they did."

"I know about the buckskin regalia from being in the band. Remember?"

"Right. So, you get my drift. Mother arrived in Rome to cast the assembled votes, as designated, from America, and her plan succeeded! She's no longer under the thumb of Catholic men reverends. Hooray!"

Nadie chuckled. "So was she elected to some office?"

"Yes. As I started out to say, Mother was elected to be the *Provincial of the Ursuline Province of the North of the United States*."

"That's vague. Does that mean she got permission to go to Alaska?"

"Yes and no. She got permission to go to Alaska and build missions, but she's not allowed to start schools until the Union votes again, I think. It's confusing. And she's still the *President of the Ursuline Convent of the Holy Family*, in charge of her Montana missions. As it should be."

"What a story. I'm not so sure Alaskan Indians need anyone to muck up their lives, though, White Crow. Did that all happen before she got hurt in the train accident?

"Yes. And things didn't fare well for Angela Pretty Eagle. They didn't return until spring of 1901, and Pretty Eagle was very ill. She passed away three months later, in June. From consumption, they said."

"Probably caught a disease from the Europeans."

"I suspect so. She was buried at Saint Peter's. The sisters changed her name again."

"What? They already added 'Angela' to the translation, 'Pretty Eagle,' from her *original* name. So that would have been the *third* change," Nadie accused.

"The name on the headstone is Mary Flathead."

"What! Her descendants will never find her! We should carve the headstones with their real names—to help descendants find their ancestors." Nadie reeled toward the depression she had arrived with. Nostrils flared.

"They said her soul was saved because the Pope gave her his blessing. She was twelve."

Nadie calculated. "That means she was just a couple years younger than Onatah." Neither spoke, grateful that Onatah had not been chosen.

Mary felt compelled to add one more thing while it was on her mind. "Remember little Watzinitha, one of the first Indian girls at Saint Peter's? She died six months after Pretty Eagle—right after she took her vows to be an Ursuline sister. She was the only one of you who joined the cloth, and she passed over within a fortnight of being professed. Don't know the meaning of that, if there is one. Sorrowful tragedy. I liked her."

"White Crow, this is morbid. Let's take a walk before we see Onatah."

"You're right. We have to deliver the mail—that is, if you want to come with me. Tell ya what. When we're done, let's go to the school and pick up Onatah ourselves, if weather allows."

"Yes, let's!"

Later that day, as they headed to Fort Shaw Industrial, glacial crosswinds whipped their bare faces. It felt good to withstand a diluted measure of pain in reverence to the milieu of suffering. Unencumbered vastness presented a broader scope; both women knew the exhilarating magic of this phenomenon and welcomed its medicine.

"I love the Sun River," Nadie said as they traveled north approaching familiar banks. The thought of seeing Onatah, coupled with the realization that she had won her freedom for the first time, ticked raw exhilaration.

Peering down at what was in summer, a slow moving mineral filled river—presently a frozen mass with ice crystals and layers of swirls cast by successive freezes and thaws—she proposed, "White Crow, you know how most rivers begin from a steep, precipitous place like a mountain, and rush, by twists and turns over boulders and crevices, slowing finally, to glide through foothills and valleys?

Mary raised an eyebrow. "Yes …"

"It's so interesting that this river isn't like that. She's almost empty of rocks and stones and pebbles, unlike her mountain-river sisters. She moves slowly—winding, locating gravity in no particular hurry. It's the only river I have ever seen do that. The Yellowstone River in Apsaalooka country is like the rivers in the Rockies, running fast, gushing over families of rock. This one meanders casually, below a carpeted bank of earth, and sculpts her own story. Don't you think so, White Crow? She's a gentle river, Sun River. My people named her for her healing properties."

"You are a natural storyteller, if ever I heard one, Miss Nadie Burd. A poet."

"She almost looks handmade," Nadie said, "like a plowed ditch, extra wide, with a fistful of stones thrown in for effect. Maybe the valley was originally irrigated by a huge dinosaur who dragged his enormous foot through the earth, plowing a watercourse to create his own personal drinking pool."

"That's uncanny! I always pictured dinosaurs living around here. I saw pictures of a skeleton exhibit once."

"That's splendid, White Crow! Let's proclaim that irrigation was not a white man's invention, after all—that dinosaurs were doing it long ago! Ha ha!"

Mary pulled the wagon round to the freight dock behind the school, where Mr. Mortag, hunched on the platform, stacked empty wooden crates. After cordial greetings were exchanged, Mary offered to transport the Indian girl, save him some time, if he liked. Herman, anxious to get to the Warner Hotel, wiped his sweaty brow and thanked her. A player piano, the newest invention in music, had been delivered from New York that morning, and he wanted to see it, hear the complimentary, locals only, performance at three o'clock. Squeezing into his rig, he waved a riding crop and took off.

Onatah, dismissed from the school office, rushed to her dormitory to take off her uniform and slip into her only other dress, a blue and white checkered frock that sported rows of ruffles and a high collar. She had sewn it herself after purchasing fabric from Mortag's store, The Cascade Mercantile. Eager to practice her new photographic skills (Mr. Erickson had demonstrated touch-up techniques using tiny brushes and dye to conceal flaws in the prints, she rushed to the back door and turned the knob.

She saw a horse and wagon—though not the right one, waiting below at the loading dock—and shaded her eyes to reduce the blinding glare from sun upon snow. The driver's shape looked familiar. "White Crow?" Two heads turned. "Who's with—?"

She rushed down the steps, slid into the space next to Mary and screeched, "It *is* you!" The friends reached for each other, across Mary, clinging—thrilled to see their best friend from Saint Angela's, at last. Nadie kissed Onatah, who cried out, "How? When did you get here? I can't believe it!"

"I came to visit White Crow and you!"

"Hang on," Mary hollered, "Here we go."

Details of life absent from the other were consumed with voracious enthusiasm. Only Mary noticed the temperature dip below freezing; she pulled another blanket over their shoulders. Nadie talked about people, places and the music she'd learned—everything but the painful chasms that had pushed her marriage to its brink. She asked, "How did you get work in town? I'm surprised people allowed it."

"Didn't White Crow tell you? Mr. Erikson told her he was looking for help; she probably put him up to it." Onatah laughed and elbowed Mary, who recalled a condition he had made: "Deliver her 'round back, out of eyesight."

"I love working with the cameras and the developing," she gushed. "It's thrilling, making an ordinary image, beautiful. So many details: the exposure, the chemistry, the composition. I want to be a photographer."

Mary had weighed the pros and cons before telling Onatah about the job: it was imperative for young women to gain a vocation—the girl wouldn't be seen in the dark room and thus would remain out of harm's way—on the other hand, a dark room could invite unsolicited advances. Mary had decided to trust Mr. Erikson, though after Lizzie's attack she had worried herself sick, lamenting over whether she'd done the right thing.

The rig rattled across a bumpy section of road. It was difficult to hear, so Nadie leaned across Mary to ask, "Onatah, how long has the studio been in town? When did you start working there?"

"About a year. Mr. Erikson's wife left him for a farmer who stayed put. She didn't like her husband leaving home to take stranger's portraits. He moved here when Cascade advertised for a photographer in their list of 'Professions Desired.' Remember those beautiful fireworks photographs he took, when White Crow let us stay with her on Independence Day?"

Nadie began to feel protective, the way she had when they were little. "I never saw them. Does he pay you?"

"No, but I don't care, because I'm learning the trade. Someday I'm going to buy my own camera."

"Onatah, I didn't know you were at the Industrial all this time. I hope it's better than when I was there."

"It's not so bad. I've met girls from all over Montana." She pulled the blanket around her shoulder. "School is easy. I finished the prescribed curriculum, so Mr. Campbell, the new superintendent, lets me work in town. I'm his student assistant. I help fill out the federal forms."

"Why would you help him do that?"

"Payback for letting me off grounds. It's good because I think I can increase the possible success of a homestead filing for us—being familiar with styles of language used in official reports. I hope it will help."

"Us? There's an us? Who is he? You're not married, are you?"

Onatah blushed.

"Tell all!"

"He's wonderful!"

"And?"

"I met him at school two years ago. We got to know each other after church service on grounds, Sunday afternoons. Remember those?"

Nadie tossed her head, determined to forget. She hadn't minded the rituals so much while in school, but, once released, resentment had awakened. Dictated religion had, in retrospect, separated her from close elemental relationships, wise communal guidance. She decided to hold onto the connection she had formed with the Holy Mother Mary, however, and often included her in prayers along with Na'pi, Old Man Creator.

"He's from Sun River. His father, who is French, tutored him at home until he decided school could teach the subjects he didn't know. His mother is Piegan, like you. He is handsome and kind and thoughtful. And clever. He has dark wavy hair—when the sun shines right, there are glimmers of red. And he has green eyes. Can you imagine? He makes me laugh, and he's patient. He's going to help run his father's trading post, and we'll farm on his parent's homestead until we get our own. After we're married, that is—"
Onatah let her announcement dangle and eyed Nadie anxiously.

Nadie didn't pounce with shouts of glee, as anticipated. She considered ramifications of marrying a Métis—whether it would give Onatah an easier life or not. She asked softly, "When are you getting married, Onatah?"

Mary cut in. "Yes. When *are* the nuptials happening? You haven't given me a date yet. Don't worry, Nadie. You'll like Edward. That's his name, Edward Bruneau."

"Yes, Edward. The wedding is in July. We're having our own custom ceremony in Saypo where his parents live."

"What do you mean, your own ceremony? Without a priest?" Nadie, startled to hear accusing words fly from her mouth, immediately confronted: why should I object to Onatah's adaptations of church covenants? They damaged our lives, after all. Jack would say "shattered." She looked up to meet the stare that could pare and slice with unnerving ease, but Onatah was not angry.

"We want to have a ceremony that honors everyone. I've learned things about my family: the Onondagas, members of the Iroquois Confederacy. Their government works better than the United States government." Onatah crossed her arms to warm fingers under her armpits. "Tell me more about you and Jack. Are you hoping for children? What is he doing?"

Nadie, embarrassed and agitated at her defense of Christian protocol, replied, "I came here to get away from him. He had to quit blacksmithing after an accident that left him crippled, years ago already. He started liquoring—he's angry and violent. I couldn't bear it any longer. So, I came to see White Crow."

Onatah kneaded her hands.

Nadie stiffened, feeling raw and exposed. "Jack was, is, a good man. He's not himself."

The horse's gait slowed.

"Ladies, sorry to interrupt, but we're here. Whoa, Bigg Too. Whoa there, boy."

"Will you come in, Nadie? I'll introduce you to Mr. Erik—"

"Not right now. Maybe later."

Mary said, "Onatah, why don't you spend the night? You gals can talk, and I'll get you back early tomorrow. Mr. Campbell won't mind, I don't think. I'll ask Mr. Mortag to telephone for us."

"Would you, White Crow? I'll come over, soon as I'm done." Onatah squeezed Nadie's hand, gave a look that only a sister could. "I'll meet you at White Crow's, just like the old days."

Mary entered the mercantile, unwound the scarf from her neck. Before she could convey her request, Herman Mortag said, "Black Mary, I have a telegraph for you."

"You do? What?" She grabbed the folded sheet of paper he pushed across the display case and read: *I'm on my way. Please keep her there for me. Jack.*

She pulled on the bill of her cap. He knows better than to put us in jeopardy, she riled. Nadie will bolt. Darn it, Jack. Love you, and I'm sorry, but no! No way are you two going to lock horns under my watch. She crumbled the telegram, shoved it up her sleeve, made arrangements for Onatah's overnight pass and started home.

Mary clomped through the doorway, wiping beads of perspiration from her face that dripped, despite temperatures below zero. It was obvious to Nadie that her mentor was ticked about something. She busied herself with supper preparations.

When Onatah arrived, the trio devoured ham and eggs and applesauce. Mary yawned and announced that it was time for her to retire to the hearth. Tugging her shawl tight, she slumped into her rocker by the potbelly. For her, rocking was the best way to figure things out, so as not to fly off the handle and do something stupid. She puckered a succulent inhale on the butt of her last stogie and blew smoke rings, thinking: where can Nadie go? Can't live in town, can't get work around here. Maybe at the mission? No, sisters are broke, anyway. She's in danger.

Onatah carried a large kettle of hot water from the potbelly, poured it into two enamel basins that Nadie had placed on the counter and whispered, "Nadie, tell me what's happened. Has Jack hurt you?"

"It's been ugly for a long time." Nadie put a hand on her hip and looked at Onatah who was no longer the little girl she remembered. "You wouldn't recognize him. He's lame, wild eyed, like he's thirsty for blood. He bates me until I get angry—says terrible things—then turns crazy mean. The next day he doesn't remember, and pleads—"

"Has he hit you?"

Nadie's silence answered the question.

Onatah latched onto her big sister's arm. "You're right to leave. I'm so sad for what's happened—to both of you. I know you, Nadie. I'm sure you tried everything."

Nadie stopped stacking dirty dishes.

Onatah leaned against her gently. "It must have been terrifying."

"It was." She swallowed hard, slid her arm around Onatah's shoulder. "I thought he would kill me. That's when I left." Sap on a burning log, popped. Nadie flinched. "I'll wash," she said, easing her hands into the water.

"Where will you go?"

"I don't know yet." Pressing the dishrag in circular motions, she said, "Tell me more about your sweetheart Edward."

Onatah tossed the dishtowel onto her shoulder and detailed the virtuous qualities of her beau. She tried to restrain her excitement, conscious of Nadie's pain, and cut the chronicle short as she asked, "It would mean so much, if you could come, Nadie. Don't answer yet. The wedding is Saturday, July 18th."

Nadie agreed to attend if she could. "So tell me about your ceremony," she said with an adjusted perspective. "What kind is it?"

"It's an expression of new tradition. We don't want to exchange sacred vows inside an institution supported by a government that denies our right to exist, denies us a place to live. We are caught in the middle of a legal loophole they created, with no rights to anything. Métis are denied rations, are pushed off reservations, and it's against the law to hunt on private land *or* reservation land! They treat us like we don't exist and hope we'll starve to death."

"You aren't Métis, Onatah."

"No, but I as might as well be. Can't prove I'm Iroquois, either, and that's just as bad. Wait until you see the reservation. Your people aren't getting food or supplies, half the time. If and when a day comes when it would serve a purpose for us to be 'legal' married by white law, then we'll have a courthouse ceremony."

Nadie's parents lived on the reservation. She'd need to witness the conditions for herself. "Yes, that's reasonable. Back to your ceremony?"

"You know how it was before: simple: vows made between a man and a woman, blessed by the tribe. We want to honor all of our relations. It became a ceremony to design because of the three nations: Piegan and Onondaga and French. We'll have music from all three and weave customs and words from each—together, in our pledge of love."

"You've always been an original, Onatah—made things your own way. Remember your dolls and the nicknames you gave us?" She passed the bride-to-be a wet dish and watched her smile.

"That reminds me. The Iroquois Council is made of several tribes (in English they say gens or clans), mine being the Onondaga. Each tribe has a special purpose and a name like the ones I used to make up: Turtle, Bear, Wolf, Deer, Snipe or descriptive, like On-the-Watch. Isn't that grand, Nadie?"

"Yes, it's very grand. You're dripping."

Onatah flipped the dishtowel. "The Iroquois tribes have always lived peacefully on large territories of land. The 'white fathers' copied some of our practices to make their United States Constitution. And I learned that the Iroquois: the Onondaga, Seneca, Oneidas, Cayuga and Mohawk tribes— they believed from the very beginning that all the white people should go away. They were not tricked like other tribes. It feels good to know more about my family. Remember how sad it used to make me?"

Nadie squeezed Onatah's shoulder. "You must have felt council tradition in your heart, Onatah. You were gifting us with ceremonial names without knowing it. Who was I again? Deer?"

"No, you were Owl because you watched out for us and knew more."

Nadie hugged her little sister. She had forgotten how much she loved her. "You deserve the best, Onatah."

They returned to their task. Soothing sounds of water splashed, and dishes clunked. Nadie's jaw began to tremble; she forced herself to share, "Remember the Methodist Reverend Van Orsdel's favorite song, the one he started Sunday congregations with? It went: *Throw out the lifeline, someone is drifting away—throw out the lifeline, someone is sinking today*. That's how

I am, Onatah. I don't know how to start over. I don't want to go to the reservation, but where can I go? How will I survive? I'm sorry I'm a dark cloud raining on our time together, but I'm not the wise one anymore."

"Nadie, you're the best of us. You're the heart that gives us strength!"

"You just think so because you were little and I was there for you at the mission. That was a lifetime ago. The church says it's a sin to leave your husband, and I'm scared—"

"What did your *Nation* say, Nadie? When a man hurt his wife, she put his things outside the teepee, and it was over. You told me that, remember?"

In the background, Mary squirmed, deciding whether to tell Nadie that Jack was on his way.

"All I know is, my heart is black with sickness. I tried everything, and it wasn't enough."

The women climbed into the frost-laden buggy long before sun cracked across the prairie. Mary decided to drive the team around the town's perimeter (she had Indians in her company), carefully selecting words that might appeal to Jack's heart. Was he really on his way? She hoped he would get distracted or change his mind. But that was not his nature, she thought. Nadie and Onatah didn't notice her silence; they were engrossed in the exchange of final confidences, uncertain of when or where they might meet again.

"It feels strange riding to the Industrial School with you, Onatah. The last time I saw you was when you and White Crow dropped me off years ago."

"No, it wasn't. We were at your concert, at the fair. Remember?"

"Oh, that's right. Yes. That was a bad time."

"What are you talking about? It was your great debut. You were sublime!"

"My brother Kitchi died that night. After you and White Crow left. He was beaten in the alley behind the tents. I was there. He was covered in blood." She looked away, looked back. "There was a man who helped—his name was George Brave Bear. He was sure Kitchi would be all right; he tried to save him. Days later, I heard that my brother had died at sunrise. So useless, his death. I'll never know what the fight was about. "

"How horrible, Nadie. I had no idea."

"When I finally saw my Mother, she blamed me for that, too."

"Did she ever come to see you at school?"

"Never. After graduation, I went to see her. I wanted her to know that I'd finished school and had agreed to marry Jack, hoping for her blessing. She disapproved of him because he is Apsaalooka. I should have known better. She told me if I married outside of the Siksika, her daughter would no longer exist.

"You can't change her, Nadie. She wanted the old ways back."

"Yes, so now she doesn't have a daughter, because I don't exist."

"You don't mean that."

"I know—"

"I'm sorry that you lost your brother."

Nadie closed her eyes.

"Why don't you come to live in Saypo? Edward says it's a good place, a community."

Nadie rubbed her arms and looked at her friend—the friend who had always tried to make her happy. "Thanks, Onatah, but what would I do there? And I'm not Métis. They might not want a Piegan."

Onatah hesitated, realizing she didn't know. Edward's mother was Piegan, but she was married to a white man. If someone like Nadie wasn't welcome, the Métis community was also prejudiced.

Mary drew the reins, directed Bigg Too to slow and stop at the Industrial School's delivery dock. While the women said their goodbyes, the horse helped himself to water thawed by the Industrial's state-of-the-art hot water tank; a pipe connected the tank and concrete water trough, dosed a steady drip that raised the basin's temperature above freezing.

Onatah hurried indoors to change clothes and get to work before the bell rang. Mary got down to stretch. She had decided to invent a reason for Nadie to remain at Saint Peter's while she dealt with Jack, upset to be sandwiched between two people she loved.

Nadie probed an emerging sense of resolution. She admired Onatah for having learned a trade, and she vowed that she would do the same. But what?

Miles later, Mary shouted above sounds of ice crackling beneath wagon wheels, "Nadie, how about giving yourself a new name, in honor of the courage it took to start a new life. What do you think? Your Nation has a knack for it. I should know!"

While Nadie appreciated the well-intended compliment, it was, after all, a whole people, the family united, that chose a member's new name when significant events had occurred—not one individual, deciding. "Thank you, White Crow, but I'll stick with Nadie." Noticing that the pressure in her chest had lessened, she reconsidered the frightful dramatics between Jack and herself and came to a realization: fear had propelled and assisted her escape: it hadn't been something to avoid—it had served her. When she had embraced her dignity and made a stand, she had rescued her body and spirit—symbolically, she had reclaimed her heritage. She envisioned herself wearing the moccasins of a warrior, a Niitsitapi warrior. There was no going back.

She massaged the stubborn crimp between her shoulders, posture that had squeezed her chest into a concaved, submissive position. She arched her back and stretched her ribs open. She took a full breath and imagined her toes wiggling in soil that nurtured tree roots while her hands wound through branches and touched the sun, close to Old Man Na'pi.

White Crow and Nadie agreed: Nadie needed to gather white people recommendations, no matter what plan of action she chose. She needed a diploma or a certificate if at all possible. Was there any college or vocational school that would allow an Indian with academic merit into its institute of higher learning? Dr. Winslow, the first Fort Shaw Industrial superintendent, had given her a letter of achievement, but it was years old.

Mary mentally filed through her list of friends who might help.

Soon thereafter, Mary Amadeus was surprised to receive a telephone call from Gertrude, who had deemed such an extravagant non-Ursuline expense necessary because Mary Fields had been so adamant and stubborn, refusing to hand over the mail until Gertrude promised to relay her request. Such a thing had never happened before.

Mother Superior, who was convalescing in California, instructed Gertrude to tell Mary Fields that she would compose a recommendation immediately. Feeling guilty for not answering her letters after the train crash, Mother hoped that prompt assistance to Mary's present cause would make up for, at least in part, her inconsiderate behavior. Nancy Burd deserved a glowing introduction, regardless.

Nadie had refused Mary's bidding to lodge at the mission temporarily. Jack never arrived in Cascade. Mary was glad she hadn't told Nadie about the telegram, hoped that Jack had aborted the chase for good, hoped that he was safe.

A seasonal migration of cranes flying north reminded Cascade women that it was time to fulfill their responsibility and organize one of the two annual events entrusted to Catholics who were, or had been, affiliated with Saint Peter's. These traditions—Black Mary's birthday party and the May Day expedition—had moved to town with her. The March birthday celebration had been hosted at the schoolhouse for six years thus far.

Cascade's school board, originally comprised of town founders and homesteaders, found themselves at present, outnumbered by new constituents. Traditions regarding the Negress Mary became a subject of contention, an item of business. Old-timers soon learned that most newcomers embraced mainstream racial prejudices. This was not unusual, in itself. The seasoned board members unanimously agreed that the difference, in this instance, was simply that newcomers had no history with Black Mary. If they had, there would be no reason to waste time holding a vote.

Newly elected board members could not fathom why a negress had been allowed to step foot in a public school after hours, tradition or not. The fact that their Cascade facility had been used for a negress's personal gratification and, worse, that the negress had, heretofore, achieved some kind of glorification, honored as the belle of a party, further proved that their modern administrative expertise was long overdue.

Heated debates pursued. Wives argued that Mary was, in fact, an illustrious contributor to Cascade. Not only was she heavily relied upon for childcare, laundry and cooking, they insisted, she was instrumental in blazing the rutted trail that had put Cascade on the map. Besides, they needed her help to sustain an improved lifestyle.

In the end, the new board members, all of whom were husbands, acceded to the tradition that had proved itself beyond their control—this time. They cast their votes in favor of continued allowance of Mary's party—irritated, not only by having to eat crow, but by the burdensome fact that once a vote had been recorded, it was policy—official school board policy.

On the afternoon of March 12th, lesson plans were set aside and twenty-six pupils helped to arrange party decorations, as directed by their teacher, Miss Lewis, the Métis daughter of Ed and Sycowastakapi Lewis, and several mothers, including Mrs. Moran, Mrs. Bickett and Mrs. Monroe.

At home, Mary primped, accessorizing her original self-tailored dress, a Christmas-red floral shift accessorized by a wide black-corded belt and a red felt hat that she had adorned with scarlet crocheted flowers. She pressed a long pin into and out of the artful arrangement, tucking renegade hairs, most of which had turned white, underneath. Placing a harmonica in the case alongside her banjo, she shut the lid and held it, along with her purse, pausing to appraise herself in the small mirror by the door. "Well, I'll be darned," she said with a smile. "Look like one of those leisurely wives." She turned for a profile. "Nah, better!" Leaving, she slammed the door and kicked ice crust clear with her exclusive footwear, a worn-out pair of work boots. She proceeded to the soiree in quarter-beat time.

The merry gaggle of small guests clustered around the birthday legend when she arrived, anxious to wrangle attention. Mary had volunteered Onatah to accompany on the fiddle. This caused further agitation, Onatah being an Indian, but objections had been silenced by Hattie and Jessie. Eager children engaged in sing-a-longs, musical chairs and pin-the-tail-on-the-donkey while Mary grinned and presented little homemade prizes for the winners.

Mrs. Lewis had provided the lace tablecloth. Mary Ann Moran centered her contribution, a large chocolate sheet cake, on the table's center and placed gifts from the children to the left, a cut-glass punch bowl on the right. Mary was delighted by the tiny, never-seen-before pink candles that decorated its surface, an embellishment provided by Mrs. Mills, the new postmaster's wife who had planned ahead and ordered the novelties from New York City. Mary winked at her audience while able hands lit the spiraled miniatures.

Rounds of "Happy Birthday to You" sprang forth, singers inspired by lifelong affections. Repetitions from the boisterous chorus escaped windows latched tight and drifted downtown.

"Mary, make a wish!" the youngsters cheered. She paused to memorize the occasion, scanned the assembly of innocent little people who would soon be taking their parents' places. She closed her eyes to think. *I wish for good health, the right to vote and … the happiest marriage for Onatah and Edward … for Mary's recovery and Jack's … And Nadie's safety, wherever she is.*

She felt a tug on her sleeve and opened her eyes, startled to see candles blazing. Like wildfire crossing the prairie, she thought, about to scourge her chocolate frosting. She sucked a lungful of air, and memories tumbled: acrid scents of red leaves located her childhood-self draped over a tree branch, and nearby, her mother's face, smiling. She twitched and blew with ample might, combusting elements of air and fire into dark carbon, swirling. To be loved in innocence, she mused.

Later, Mary and Onatah performed tunes together, children's favorites on request: "London Bridge is Falling Down," "Follow the Piper" (for this ditty, Mary played the harmonica), "Skip to my Lou," "Eensy Weensy Spider" and "She'll Be Comin' Round the Mountain," to name a few.

Dimming light prompted satisfied guests to search for coats and slickers. Mary posted herself by the door where a haphazard line took shape. She dutifully performed the ceremonial conclusion of her party, placing three hard candies in each right palm, whispering a personal sentiment and cheering, "Thank you for coming," before maneuvering a bear hug or a polite kiss, depending.

The classroom emptied, Mary and Onatah started for Mary's house. Launching off the concrete schoolhouse steps, their ankles dipped into thick mist that had made its way up from the riverbank. Lit by flickering lamps, the town glowed tawny, surreal.

"How does it feel to be seventy-one, White Crow? You're a model of health. I don't know how you do it." She knew her praise pleased her Ucsote, and she worried that White Crow would be lonely when she left for Saypo in three months time.

"Never thought I'd be old. Tried to make good choices. Working makes the body strong, especially if it's a medley of tasks. Three more months of mail delivery and I'll retire to full-time laundress. See what I mean?" She slipped an arm through Onatah's.

Safe inside the little plank house, Onatah lit a rusty lantern that Mary had rescued from the rock pile.

"Look," the birthday girl cried, having identified an object on her table, "another cake!"

Onatah reached for the note tucked under its platter. Mary motioned for her to read, and she obliged: "To our dearest Mary, with thoughts of appreciation and best wishes for a blessed year ahead. From the Sisters."

"How sweet of them. Wonder how they got it into town."

Onatah giggled, "They're almost as industrious as you, White Crow. Shall we have a piece?"

"You betcha!"

Part Three

15

THE UNEXPECTED

FALL 1903

"Retiring from the Star Route was the right thing to do, Bigg Too. Been three months already. I can tell you're enjoying life in the pasture, and I've got plenty of dirty laundry to wash and iron."

She stroked his face, gave his velvety ears a squeeze. "Our Birdtail families will manage," she told him, "They have that telephone line, some of them. Remember Lizzie? She sent a photograph. She's a clerk in a dry goods store. Found herself a husband, too. How about that?"

The horse sniffed her skirt pockets and swung his head about.

"Remember Nadie? She's probably somewhere living a better life, like Lizzie. Takes courage to run, a woman on her own."

Bigg Too pawed the earth, damp from morning frost.

"Hold your horses, B.T." Mary doled the sought-after apple, a Montana Macintosh, and watched her star route companion gobble and mash with his long teeth. She stroked his neck and told him what a good horse he was, before adding, "Mother Mary is gonna make it to Alaska, after all. She's got the Roman Union behind her. Least that's what I heard."

Bigg Too slobbered on her arm.

"She's been recuperating in California, soaking up sunshine after the train wreck." She glimpsed someone coming and stopped talking, fussed with Bigg Too's mane awhile longer. "If you behave yourself, I'll bring you some oats tomorrow. All right? Good boy." She walked around him, noting his mud-caked coat, dirty from rolling on his back. "Edward's coming to get you this week, and I don't want any crying and whimpering." Her voice began to crack. "You're their wedding gift from me, and you'll have a good life in Saypo, yes you will. I love you, Bigg Too. You can bring Onatah back to me once in awhile, and you and I will visit." She wiped her eye, patted his rump and let herself out, squeezed between barbed wire fence lines.

Crossing her arms over her chest, she walked back to town, thinking how different things were already: a full-time view of the world from foot, not wagon, and only one panoramic vista of the Rockies. Mary looked at her hands, stained from lye, swollen from scraping the washboard. I'll get used to it, she comforted. I've got friends here, and lots of children to babysit—much as I want. Ignoring a bellyache cramp, she spoke, "I'll eat later."

While she waited for the morning laundry to dry (a half dozen orders pinned on the clotheslines behind her house) she walked over to Cornell's Sample Room, claimed her spot toward the back corner and browsed through an old issue of *The Rising Sun*, the rag from Sun River. Positioning to feel waves of afternoon air supplied by the ceiling fan that squeaked, she thought how odd it was to see James Cornell behind a bar instead of on a horse. "Afternoon, Miss Mary," he called. "Can I get ya something?"

"If you've got any spare water, I'd be obliged." She scooted the chair back, ready to fetch it.

"No, you sit," James said, "I don't get much exercise in here." She watched her old friend, the best liveryman ever, limp toward her. He had gotten kicked in the hip by a testy mare: half-Arabian, half-Mustang. No longer able to shoe horses or handle heavy lifting, he'd bought the saloon. A melancholy mood slipped over her, and she wondered where Nadie was, why she hadn't sent word.

The double-action spring-hinged door swung open. A handful of regulars glanced from upright positions at the polished mahogany bar. "Howdy, D.W.," one called.

"Afternoon, Herman, everyone," D.W. replied to murmurs and hats tipped his direction. "Hot enough to fry eggs on a rock out there."

Mary chuckled. "I know where you got that idea, D.W."

"Yeah, little Alfred's become famous for that prank, all right."

Those Sampson kids are, bar-none, the most incorrigible—I should know, being their babysitter.

"I'm sure ya do, Nigger Mary," he winked. "How about you—staying out of trouble?"

Placing hand to hip, she countered, "Couldn't find none—what kind have you got yourself into?"

He took his hat off, wiped sweat from his forehead onto his sleeve, grinning. "I'll leave it those little people you're so fond of ..."

"Can fill your day, all right. Had to scrub pine pitch off the Sampson's outhouse seat. Another of little Alfred's shenanigans."

D.W. shook his head. "Sounds like the boy's got potential. A regular Ben Franklin."

"Are you the real Stagecoach Mary?" a stranger interrupted.

"Who wants to know?" D.W. answered, inspecting the dark haired man wearing overalls at the end of the bar.

"Name's Grange. Working at the Moran Place. Heard stories about the Stagecoach Mary all the way east 'a Fort Benton." He turned a hopeful, sun leathered face toward Mary's table and squinted, as though she were out of focus. "So are you?"

"Used to be. Name's Mary Fields." She gave a nod and placed her eyes back on the newsprint, hesitant to engage.

Herman Wolf, a former mail route recipient bragged, "She's the best freighter west of the Missouri."

"And sharpshooter," Grange addressed the negress. "I heard you delivered tinhorns over the prairie in one 'a them fancy Wells Fargo Stagecoaches—and train rustlers tried to steal a payroll box full 'a gold from you—but you shot all three dead for their trouble. Single-handed."

The roomful of laughter left him bewildered.

Mary spoke first. "My, my. Wish I had that reward, be buying y'all drinks."

"That leather cushion stagecoach seat with a half dozen horses would be dandy, too," said Wolf.

"Yep."

"Well, part of the story's true," said D.W. swabbing Grange's disappointment. "She is one of our best sharpshooters. We're thinking of electing her sheriff, soon as Cascade's incorporated." He kept a straight face. Mr. Grange did the same, not wanting to be the butt of any more hoodwinking. More laughter peaked and rolled.

"My fancy stagecoach was a regular old ranch buckboard, customized with sides, a tailgate and a springboard seat. Carried a crazy patchwork of passengers, it did." Mary rubbed her shoulder. "Freight and all manner of supplies, the post and an occasional bishop and mother superior—operated by me and one special horse."

"Stagecoach Mary kept us current," Wolf added turning to the man called Grange. "She delivered news, and gossip, too."

"She's also the best laundress west of the Missouri," D.W. claimed, rousing Grange's suspicions once again. "No really, she is—isn't that right, Cornell?"

Mary took a sip of water and added, "One time, Flinn, our former postmaster, got a telegram that requested two first-class tickets on my Wells Fargo Stagecoach." She chortled at the recollection. "Wells Fargo was a local operation way back, in the sixties—pulled up stakes cause of Indian attacks." She glanced Grange's way, her expression sobering. "A stagecoach in these parts wouldn't be practical. I hauled freight and supplies more often than not." She turned to the fellas. "Couldn't you just see me hosting a tenderfoot tour serving up flapjacks and tea on the way to some hot spring resort?"

"They'd have to mind their P's and Q's," D.W. said.

"Mary's wagon suited us just fine," Wolf bravadoed, "No fancy stage needed hereabouts. Road ends at the mission anyway. You must have noticed—Moran's ranch is next to it." He swung a look to the newcomer who nodded, engrossed.

"Want to hear something funny?" Mary asked, *The Rising Sun* in hand. "Says here, and I quote, 'The Fort Shaw and Augusta Stage Line runs semi-weekly from Sun River. Passengers must prepare for extended waits if they plan to return.' Now that's a wild west adventure for tenderfoots—wonder if it's a coach or wagon—might be something to write home about."

"Or send them packing," Glover laughed.

"Or bore them to tears, stuck in nowhere," added Glover.

"Well, I'm proud to meet you, Mary Fields. You're the first famous person I ever met." The hired hand clomped across the floorboards, his hand extended, "Abel Grange, mighty proud." Mary shook his hand and he retreated to one of the empty tables—pulled his hat, a battered old derby, low on his brow.

"What did you do with your horse and wagon, Stagecoach Mary?" Wolf asked.

"Gave it to friends of mine."

"Must be special friends."

"Yep."

"Maybe you could use one of those dog carts, have your dog deliver the laundry."

"D.W., that's the best idea I've ever heard out of you! Except, he's not with me anymore, my dog. Maybe I'll get those clever sons of yours to build me a cart. Keep them busy."

Saloon conversation turned to food and where to find it. Wolf wanted dinner before the long ride home. Cornell and Monroe agreed that there wasn't much to choose from. Mary piped in, "Meals at the Warner Hotel aren't up to par now that Mrs. Warner sold out to Miss Ella Williams. I'd offer her cooking lessons, if I didn't think she'd have a stroke at the thought of a colored woman giving her culinary tips."

Her friends guffawed. "Rep, I agree with you, Nigger Mary," said D.W., "Someone needs to build a new hotel or open a good full meal restaurant."

"How about you, D.W.?" Mary arched an eyebrow. "Or you, Mr. Glover," meeting his glance. "You're new to town."

"I seem to remember someone else who cooked mighty fine meals for us Cascadians," D.W. quipped with a measure of praise.

"Well," Mary straightened, pleased at the acknowledgment, "that person is retired from the business. Need to find someone else to feed us hungry citizens. A hotel with good meals might be able to make it here, now that Cascade's getting bigger."

"Still hungry, fellas," Wolf said, patting his belly.

"I'll make you a sandwich if you want," Mary offered.

"That's all right, Mary. I'll take my chances with Miss Ella. Maybe things are improved."

"Let us know," said Cornell.

"Speaking of improving, when's our next target practice?" Mary scanned the lineup at the bar.

D.W. said, "Same time, same place. Two o'clock, Saturday."

"Can I come? Just to watch?" Abel Grange petitioned. Eyes shifted to Mary, who had initiated the activity.

"Just this once." She said. "Whizzer cigar for the winner?"

Mary arrived at target practice early. Wearing a heavy cotton skirt and a loose-fitting blouse, as usual, she rested on the rock pile and listened to red-winged blackbirds trill. She was an attractive woman, but few noticed, and those who did kept quiet, assuming one thing or another. She dusted her dove-gray skirt, and placed a total of ten cans and bottles along the length of an old tamarack log riddled with holes from beetles and bullets.

Five more shooters arrived on the south side of the clearing, having taken the longer route through the cottonwood grove: D.W., Cornell, Wolf, Glover, Two-Dog Jim, and the greenhorn, Abel Grange. They drew straws. Cornell got first. Though the purpose of target practice was to sharpen firearm skills, the fellows often clowned around, piece-milling random snippets into yarns for later use. Wolf, Cornell and Fields were fine shooters, unlike the rest of the town residents whose skills were average at best. Mary's motivation for promoting the club had hinged from specific intent—she needed to keep her legendary sharpshooter reputation on the lips of those who traveled, encountered the highest number of strangers. In her opinion, shooting was for killing game, not for dares, showdowns and shootouts where she might be killed before her time.

"Why not put them cans on the rock pile?" Grange asked, pulling a packet of chew from his pocket.

"Ever heard of a ricochet? What kind of a cowboy did you say you was?" sawed Two-Dog Jim with a snort. "Don't know 'bout you, but I don't care to be the bulls-eye."

Grange retreated, parked himself on the rocks.

Mary won the first two rounds. Wolf hollered, "You haven't lost your touch living in town, Black Mary."

"Could ya show us some mercy, Stagecoach Mary, like you do for those tinhorns you transport?" Cornell teased.

"Nah, you fellas are just going easy on me."

Cornell unbuttoned his vest and winked to his cohorts, "Yeah, we gentlemen are letting you win—need to keep our town negress happy." Heads bobbed. "Hand me the flask, D.W."

The high-pitched voice belonging to Abel claimed, "I was the State of Missouri Rifle Champion, 1880."

"1880 is long past," Two-Dog pounced. "Maybe you'd best bring you and your rifle next Saturday, that is, if we let you put your money where your mouth is." He glanced around. "What do you say, bulls-eye members?"

"And I caught the biggest catfish in the *Shenandoah*, 1872," Abel chatted, excited for the attention. "Night crawlers—that was my secret. Those fat suckers just love em."

Mary laughed, thinking Abel could do with some story coaching from her tomfoolery friends; night crawlers—hardly original. She pressed memory to identify the best malarkey artists she'd come across: the saxophone player in Cleveland or that dandy riverboat gambler. Quickened by an involuntary twinge, she lifted her Winchester and blasted each one of the six targets from the opposite direction: right to left.

D.W., in charge of keeping track, reported, "So far we got Cornell winning one round, Wolf, one, Two-Dog Jim, zero. Grange, zero. Me, zero. Nigger Mary, seven. One round left. Let's give her some grief boys, so she doesn't go home with her head in the clouds."

Mary missed three shots on her last round, maintaining her number one status and leaving male egos intact. She shined a sweeping smile and called, "Thank you, gentlemen. Best get back to drying herbs. Never know when one of you's gonna cry from a winter bellyache, need a Mary Fields' remedy."

They laughed, knowing they might very well be sending their wives over for some kind of herbal concoction of her making.

"Got one for sharp shooting?" a gruff voice belonging to the grittiest among them dangled.

"I'll be bringing you that tonic, Two-Dog. Bye now."

Nadie strapped the bundle of belongings onto her back and started walking. Leaving the reservation was a relief. It had been a depressing visit with her parents—her father delirious with fever and her mother desperate, frightened. People were hungry and few buffalo were left. Rations had not been distributed as promised. She would not give up. If able to find work, she would help her parents. Now, three people depended on whatever earnings she might muster.

She assembled courage by thinking of her friends. White Crow—any other colored woman living alone in the Birdtail would be dead. How did she survive? Nadie wondered what she didn't know about White Crow's life. Had she been married, did she have children? White Crow could be slippery, changing the subject when she chose not to answer. And Onatah, her best friend, always a veritable source of industry. I need to be like I was that day in class, Nadie pledged—speaking my truth, unafraid to say *a million feelings, that's what's better.*

Hours passed slowly. Nadie's thin-soled shoes, too small and poorly constructed, had ripped at the seams, allowing mud to seep inside. Blisters burned and she shivered from damp that reached above the *Missouri* banks, the watercourse that compassed her journey. By the second day, she wished she had accepted the moccasins her mother had offered.

From behind, she heard hooves and wheels cut mud. Moving to the side of the road, she tucked her long braid inside her coat and quickened her pace. A bearded man seated on the farm wagon behind her, noticed, felt sorry to see a woman walking alone, even if she was an Indian. He offered her a ride.

Appraising him as they exchanged greetings, Nadie accepted. She watched him open the wagon's tailgate; he was tired with age but strong. Keeping her promise to dare when necessary, she allowed his calloused hand to assist her into the bunk stacked high with a harvest she did not recognize—green stems branched into small round leaves with cones of purple flowers—dried, yet fragrant still.

The farmer talked as he drove his steadied team. He told her he was on his way to Helena, to deliver his experimental crop called alfalfa, how the government-sanctioned-produce brought a higher price than hay. His rounded shoulders, dense muscles and beat up cowboy boots substantiated his story. Nadie explained that she needed to get to the hospital in Helena as soon as possible. He, being a devout Catholic, decided it was his duty to deliver her, fearing the worst.

Leaning into the alfalfa, Nadie reached for happy memories. She recalled an autumn when she and her classmates had snuck into the Jesuit fields, climbed to the top of haystacks and took turns falling backwards into the softness. Now, she inhaled the pleasant fragrance, rubbed her sore feet and wiggled down to stay out of sight; more wagons had come onto the road. Frowning, she thought about the matron at the Great Falls hospital— she had laughed when Nadie sought employment. Helena was the only other city within her reach and it had two hospitals. She had decided to apply at the Catholic facility first.

Hours later, she stared at stacks of distant buildings that piped steam into the sky. Vehicles—wagons, carriages and automobiles—advanced toward what the newspaper called "Montana's metropolis," the state capital perched upon the continental divide. As they came closer, she identified a prominent brick building on a hilltop, a white cross crowning at its apex, as described by White Crow's friend, Mr. Cornell. She scooted to the front of the wagon's bunk, pointed and asked, "Sir, do you know if that building with the white cross is Saint John's Hospital?"

"Yes, young lady, that's Saint John's. Should be there in an hour's time."

Having noted his concern earlier, she said, "I'll think I'll rest now."

He positioned the end of a long alfalfa stem between his teeth and she returned to her nest in the stack and looked to the pale sky above. She gripped the handle of her satchel, a gift from White Crow, and prayed for a miracle—to be hired, learn nursing skills that would support herself and her parents. Repeatedly pressing wrinkles in her skirt, she promised to work hard without complaint, prove her dedication. She figured it couldn't be any harder than the last three years with Jack. I am fortunate, she assured the hunger pains in her belly. She glanced at the sun, two or three hours past its peak, and rehearsed words of introduction she would recite to the person who might save her from begging on the streets. Would the woman administrator grant her employment, allow her to acquire nursing skills, certificate or not? High hopes were attached to the name "Sister Murphy" written on a paper scrap tucked deep in her pocket, along with the last of her money, one silver dollar.

The farmer stopped near the hospital entrance and helped her from the wagon. Brushing alfalfa from her clothes, she thanked him for his kindness. He wished her well and went on his way.

Inside Saint John's, Nadie gave her name to the clerk seated behind a polished granite counter and waited, listened to peculiar echoes that bounced between stone floors and high ceilings. The pungent smell of disinfectant made her feel dizzy.

The tidy looking clerk walked away and returned donning a look of surprise. He explained that protocol required an appointment, yet for some reason, an exception had been granted. She followed his instructions, walked down a long corridor and knocked on the door with an opaque-glass window. Entering a large sunlit office, she curtsied to the pleasant looking blue-eyed Catholic seated behind a massive desk.

The administrator wore a habit unfamiliar to Nadie. The nun's headwear, a white starched accordion-pleated cornette, left her neck bare, unlike Ursulines who wore white guimpes and caps with black veils covering from head to shoulder. The wide-eyed applicant swallowed her fear, pushed her shoulders back and spoke, "Sister Murphy, please allow me to introduce myself. I am Nadie Burd. I apologize for arriving without an appointment or letter of recommendation."

"Quite the contrary," the nun's crisp voice rang, "Your recommendation arrived this morning, brimming with high praise from an indisputable source."

"How—" she uttered, her mind racing. She knew that Mary had asked Mother Amadeus for a letter of introduction. It hadn't arrived, so she had written to Mother Superior, asked her to send the reference directly to the reservation—yet nothing had come, so she had assumed—had she mentioned her intent to apply at Saint John's?

She heard her satchel drop. "I'm sorry," she apologized. Leaning to retrieve it, her eyes locked on her mud-caked shoes. Embarrassed, she pretended they were polished and asked, "Was it from Mother Amadeus, Sister Murphy?"

"Yes, dear. The famous Mother Superior Mary Amadeus of the Heart of Jesus appears to support your cause." She tapped her pencil. "Before you get your hopes up, I must tell you, little lassie, women of your race are not allowed in our nursing program, though I debated against the charter, being a suffragette and Indian advocate myself. Please, sit down, Miss Nadie Burd."

Nadie sat on the edge of the high-back chair and wondered if a nun married to Jesus could really be a suffragist and Indian advocate, and if so, wondered if it would help her, somehow. Sister Murphy's English rolled in a brogue she guessed to be Irish. The administrator explained the community's reliance upon the sisters' medical services—particularly emergency care. Listening attentively, Nadie examined the woman's facial lines and decided that most had been furrowed by smiling. When she noticed four calico kittens playing on a pink satin cushion near the nun's feet, balls of yarn strewn under the desk, she relaxed.

Sister Murphy slipped her spectacles on and studied papers spread across her desk blotter. She looked at Nadie's hands and leaned forward. "Are you willing to work hard?"

"Yes, Sister Murphy," Nadie replied, "I will work *very* hard."

It was difficult to interpret the nun's expression. Nadie wondered why she had asked so few questions, supposed that rejection loomed near.

"I can hire you as a wash woman and kitchen assistant, if that is agreeable to you. Our previous worker left us last Thursday." Sister Murphy observed the applicant's response closely; if she sensed disappointment she would withdraw the offer.

"I am honored. Thank you, Sister Murphy." Nadie laced her fingers and squeezed, hesitant to say more. Heartbeats pulsed.

The five-foot tall administrator rose from her seat and stepped forward, hand extended. Nadie did the same. The last person Nadie had touched in this white-custom way was Mother Amadeus, the day she had left the mission to attend Fort Shaw Industrial. She gushed, "You are the answer to my prayer, Sister Murphy."

This pleased the nun and she said, "I think you will do well here, Miss Nadie Burd. In addition to your tasks, you will give an overwhelming number of male patients a reason to recover, as they pine at your beauty."

She struggled to respond.

The administrator led her new employee to the door, stating, "Lung disease and gunshot wounds come to us in epidemic numbers. Do you have lodging?" Nadie shook her head. Knowing the girl's forthcoming wage would not be ample, she offered, "There is a small storage room in the basement. It's full of rubbish in need of disposal. "If you don't mind knuckling down, our janitor will help you clear the space. It's tiny and you may need to share, but it's yours to use and you'll be safe."

She gasped, "Thank you, Mother, I mean, Sister. How generous. I am—"

The nun interrupted, "Return in an hour, and the two of you will get started."

Nadie leaped down the hospital's front steps, quaking from the shock of receiving more than she had dared to expect. She whispered, "That letter from Mother Amadeus must have tipped the scale. It *has* to be White Crow's doing. I'll write to her, soon as I'm settled. I bet there were white women who wanted this job."

Diverse assemblies of people and sound fueled her exhilaration; her gait bounced to the rhythm of hooves that clapped on the cobblestone streets. Metal clanked, babies cried, dogs barked. From a distance, overtones of bells announced trains, trolleys and church services. Delicious aromas wafted from small kiosks, bringing her attention to the task at hand—something to eat. She hurried downwind, wondering why her predecessor at Saint John's Hospital had left, hoping the reason had been positive; perhaps she'd joined the ranks of nursing professionals, like she would someday. She stopped to ask for directions.

A man had been waiting for Nadie outside Saint John's, maintaining anonymity as he leaned against an elm tree thirty paces away, his face concealed by a pamphlet he had plucked from a soapbox proselytizer. He had come from backcountry, where he had squatted in a deserted log cabin on a remote peak, comforted by the company of wild creatures. After watching bighorn sheep mate the previous spring, he had decided that he would take a wife to keep him warm, share in the wilderness work. When aspen leaves and tamarack needles turned color he buried his food and special possessions in an underground cache and set off.

The non-descript dark haired immigrant had trekked downhill for three days, dropped onto the main road after spying the brown-skinned beauty alone in the back of a wagon. To him, she appeared cushioned, contained in wrappings readymade and ripe for market. He followed her to town and watched her go into and out of an enormous brick building with a cross on its steeple. Unable to read English, he assumed it was a church and imagined her paying penance with shiny objects, making herself ready for him.

His lips puckered when she leaped down the steps; he clutched his wrist and followed in her wake. She was strong, agile, vibrant. The dark haired, average looking loner trotted after her, out of view. "She will be mine," he uttered from beneath his thick mustache greased with beeswax. "This is my lucky day. And hers." Releasing his wrist, he pressed a sweaty palm against his good luck charm, a copper-tipped bullet he had found, smooth and warm when fingered long enough. He crouched and watched her heart-shaped lips speak to the man who stood, to his thinking, too close to her—a vendor pointing and talking. Pretending to search for something on the ground, he willed her to step away, remain pure for him.

The intruder touched her elbow and said, "Up there, cut across the alley on your right, then left at the next street."

Fueled by passion, the stalker bolted, mumbling the clerk's words as he raced, agilely concealing his presence from the beauty as he cut through crowds of shoppers and located the turn before she did.

Afternoon thunder rolled in the distance. The alley, paved with the same brown brick as tall buildings to each side, stunk of mold and decay. Overfilled bins littered the narrow passageway. He pushed his back against a dank wall. Clouds split apart and rain fell, casting black shadows. He pulled a split barrel that oozed of rotten discards, close, to conceal his presence. Minding an unprompted memory of the woman who would have been his widow had they married, he muttered, "She was delicious, she liked it when I made it clear I was in charge, told her what to do ..." This one will, too. I'll stroke her and tell her she's beautiful ..." He fingered the bullet again.

Nadie held her hand to her chest, savored one more breath of steam generated by the medley of showers that had raised complex scents and tantalized her imagination. Goose bumps scurried up her arms and she raised her face to a churning sky. "Thank you," she whispered. Raindrops pattered faster and harder. They're drumming, dancing, she thought. I must go, I can't return to work wet and ragged. She dashed around the corner, anticipating the taste of bread and cheese, and paused to let her eyes adjust to the darkness of the alley. Winding her way through barrels and heaps of trash, stench turned her stomach and she gagged, firing an opinion that the invisible enemy of disease lurked in putrid messes such as these.

"Good afternoon, my lady," a hoarse voice called from the shadows.

Nadie slowed. In a moment she identified the source: a man standing, blanketed under a hide. He wavered slightly. She willed her vision for details but could only see his chin.

"Good afternoon," he repeated.

She stepped back.

His head looked small in the oversized hat, a wide brim. She hesitated, warned herself to be quick and decide, friend or foe? Heartbeats pumped hard, but she exercised the teachings of Jesus—shouldn't I share kindness with the needy? I would be in the same position, if not for today's good fortune—but it might be a trick.

"Will you help me?" he asked, testing her instincts.

The rain beat heavy; it seemed to hold her captive. A rat rushed out from behind a garbage pile. Startled, she glanced to the alley's end, then toward the voice. The figure, now hunched, wheezed and reached a gloved hand toward his mouth. She stared. *The glove, it's new, expensive.* Glimpsing deviant lust before he blinked to feign virtue, she realized, then, that he had inched closer, close enough to grab her. *Don't move yet, she ordered legs ready to sprint. Pretend. Look for a weapon.* She saw rusted metal strips on barrels but they were nailed tight.

"Sir, you don't look well," she said with postured intent.

The man inched closer and slung an arm forward, hand cupped. Wielding a convincing plea, he begged, "Please, don't leave. I'm hungry. Come, help me up."

Maybe he is, Nadie despaired. *No. Don't.* Forcing herself to appear calm, she disguised the heat of adrenaline pumping her limbs. "I'll be right back, I'll get you food."

She bolted.

A cold clench seized her ankle and she dropped. Rough mortar scraped her face and knees. He pounced and flipped her over, met her eyes and squeezed her throat with one hand. With the other he grabbed her breast and pushed his weight upon her, locked his hips and thighs into position and rode with animus hunger. Unable to breathe, she twisted and yanked her unfettered arm from beneath her back, scratched his neck and when he turned, poked his eyes with forked fingers.

He jerked. She thrust her knee into his groin.

Contorted, he managed to keep his gloved hand fixed on her neck. Angry, he knuckled her face. She's perfect, he thirsted—she is a fighter. "Settle down woman, testing our fit is all, listen—"

She flailed, smacked her spine on the overturned barrel. Again he loomed above, her wrists pinned. She curled her torso upward, butted her head from beneath, hit bone to bone. His head torqued; his hold weakened. Wrenching, she spun out from under and lunged.

He hurled himself beneath her, grabbed her shoulders and rolled her over. Restraining his female once more, he gave pause for her to come to her wits and be grateful while he stroked the full length of her, assessing bone, muscle and sinew.

Instead, she screamed.

Indignation hurled. He slapped her face, gripped her jaw and roared, "You savage bitch!" "Look what you did! I was going to make you my wife."

Peering through bloody hair, Nadie shook. *He's the devil,* a thought hammered. Transfixed, the leering monster panted vile fire-breath into hers. Drool spewed.

The grip on her neck tightened. Consciousness slipped, eyelids fluttered, her arms could not move. She heard herself gag. Crazed, she invoked revenge: he would drown and she would be cleansed, set free. Her heart called to the Creator. *Na'pi!*

Eyelids jerked open when he pushed the tip of his knife into her navel. He carved upward, slowly. *I can still escape.* She watched her legs twitch. She was late for work, for her new life. Agonizing pain sent screams outside; she heard them. He cut deeper. Her body convulsed and her eyes closed.

Warm liquid gushed across her skin. *I can't die now.*

He looked at her, his prize, sucked wet air and held it, waited for the pulse to stop. Releasing his hands, he stared. He checked his pocket for the lucky bullet. Satisfied, he inserted his knife blade at the pubic bone and sliced upward, to the first incision. His beauty, fully gutted. Too bad, he thought, temporarily saddened.

He thrust his hand inside and squeezed for the pleasure of holding what was dead but still warm, submissive to his will. He clenched hard until membranes burst. "You should have listened," he snarled.

Why is everything silent, Nadie's spirit asked, floating above the alley. A man in dark shadows, crouched over a sliced body. She watched him move long black hair off the face of the dead woman and recognized her. *Nadie is dead and I am her soul. Wait. I want to be alive. I want to go back.* She saw her brother Kitchi standing in the blood and then Kitchi was with her, holding her.

The predator kicked Nadie's flesh, rotated her face toward the barrel, suddenly repelled by the entrails he had caressed. She watched him twitch, toss the fur pelt onto his shoulder, wipe his hands with what had been her blouse. He reached for his gloves and his hat. She understood then. It was too late. Her body lay mangled, torn. Blood pooled. Her vitalness expelled into rivulets, doused by more outbursts of rain.

As the spirit of Nadie rose higher, she recognized the patterns. Rivers flowed like veins of blood coursing through body earth, flowing to nurture the sacred planet, her beloved *stah-koomi-tapii-akii*, a globe of blue and green alive in a vast galactic womb. Clouds embraced the curvatures; a rounded horizon; a sphere, she realized.

Entering the company of stars, she sparked.

16

MOVING FORWARD

FALL 1908 - SUMMER 1909

*M*ary's knees went weak when she opened her door. Not much caught her by surprise, but sight of her old friend Mary Amadeus on her doorstep, did. Emotions somersaulted and she struggled to remember the unfinished business between them. "Mary Amadeus," she cried, waving her namesake forward, "come in."

Without reply, the Sister's black walking stick propelled over the threshold followed by a pronounced limp. As Mother cast a quick glance about Mary's quarters, she felt as though she had stepped backward in time.

Mary closed the door. "Please, have a seat."

Amadeus remained standing, rested her eyes upon her old friend. "It's good to see you, Mary." She advanced, arms open. Mary reciprocated. They held a polite embrace for some moments, each unsure of the other's feelings and of their own, now that they were face-to-face. Released, Mother lowered her good hip onto the straight-back at the table's side, hooked the handle of her cane to its back. The room's humidity, sourced by rising steam from laundry tubs, was uniquely pleasant in the otherwise dry Montana air.

"Would you like some tea?"

"That would be lovely, thank you. How long has it been?"

"Eight years."

"Really?"

Mary poured hot water into her teapot and transferred a handful of cookies from the crock to a scallop-edged dessert plate, all the while observing changes in the Mother Superior's appearance: though her characteristic sparkle remained, age spots dappled the ivory complexion, shadows circled her blue eyes and new wrinkles indicated hardships; chronicles unknown. As Mary carried refreshments to the table, she wondered what degrees of injury were concealed under the guimpe and veil and skirts.

"I see you've kept your laundry concern going. Does it provide well enough?"

"Has to. Been five years since my route." she shrugged. "Locals come to me. Hotel laundry goes elsewhere." She thought of the Chongs, who had remained loyal friends.

"You've become a Cascade local."

"Long time now, thirteen years," Mary replied, thinking that her friend should be well aware. "It's all right, for the most part. Life was simpler before, when we were all struggling at the mission. But that is history, isn't it?" She wasn't sure if her guest would detect the edge in her voice, or if she would notice that the tea she had served, was special, imported oolong. "Still like your tea plain?"

Mother nodded, calculating how much time she'd need to drive the horse and buggy to Saint Peter's. She lifted her teacup, blew and put it down. Ready to release the albatross that had weighed heavy on her heart for quite some time, she came to the point. "Mary, I'm sorry that I didn't write to you after the train accident. I was grateful for your concern. You've always had a good heart. I have no excuse. I was consumed with recovery initially, and once I received permission for the Alaskan missions, well … you know how wrapped up I get."

"I know how you used to be." She broke a molasses cookie in two. "I worried about you—for a long time. When you were here in Cascade a couple years ago to resign from your Montana post, I thought sure you'd make time to visit. And you didn't." She squared her shoulders and attempted to lock onto those blue eyes for a heart-to-heart, but the Sister blinked and turned her head the other direction, as if for good reason. Mary had seen the nun use this tactic during negotiations and believed the glassy contrivance to be a trespass upon honesty, at least, today.

"I had the Roman Union Mother General Superior from Italy with me, Saint Julien."

Mary stared at the tablecloth, wrestled the credence of right and wrong.

"I'm truly sorry, Mary. I should have made time."

"Yes," Mary said, as she headed for the cooler, warning herself not to wear hurt on her sleeve. She returned to her chair, placed the creamer between them, gnawed on the first half of her cookie. As moments passed, she realized that Mary Amadeus was done addressing the lapse of contact that had broken their closeness. Two little sorrys, she fumed, polite and sincere. It didn't feel like enough. She simmered like her laundry, weighing pride against forgiveness. "Must have been hard on you too, Mary," she offered, "The pain, I mean."

"It had its moments," the nun said, choosing to think of her recovery rather than the cataclysmic event and intense physical suffering endured afterwards, adhering to the belief that such piety forged a blessed path toward redemption and did not require her understanding. At present, however, she misunderstood two things: she had missed the moment to share a tragic personal experience, exchange a heart-to-heart with a kindred spirit the way she used to, and she had forfeited an opportunity to embrace the spiritual calling of her religious middle name, *Heart of Jesus*—to empathize with someone who cared for her and was in need of well-deserved acknowledgment. "Mary, these cookies are delicious."

Veering from the norm, Mary said, "Thanks." She didn't explain that Hattie had baked them. She would have, before. "By the way, belated congratulations on becoming the Roman Union Alaska Boss. Sorry, don't know your full title."

Mother Mary stroked the napkin on her lap. "Thank you. I'm so grateful; you know how long I waited, worked on it. My title is a mouthful: *The First Provincial of the North of the United States.* I am in fact, on my way to Alaska right now." She smiled, expecting Mary to ask for details.

Mary knew the Mother had sent a cadre of Ursulines to build a mission in Alaska two years earlier. "You going with your flock this time?" She pressed front teeth into her lower lip.

"Yes. First we're going to Nome and then we cross the Norton Sound to Saint Michael's, where we will establish Saint Ursula-by-the-Sea, our second mission."

Mary looked out the kitchen window, admitting that while she was pleased to see Mary, the splinter in her heart had a choice: to confront and talk it out until some kind of understanding had been achieved, which was a risk—or suffocate the hurt, knowing that it would be the end of the friendship—for her, anyway. She refilled teacups and restocked the cookie dish. The need for commensurate decorum had not escaped her—it was her turn to apologize for kidnapping Lizzie, though she didn't want to. She compromised, "I'm sorry if I hurt your feelings by taking charge of Lizzie. It was a God-send: hankering parents out of nowhere, hours after you left."

Surprised, the nun considered her answer. "At the time, I thought it underhanded, Mary, but I'm glad you found parents for the child. Would you have told me, if I hadn't already left for Saint Labre Mission?"

"No. You would have been obliged to put a stop to the arrangement."

"So the entire episode must have been divinely guided?"

"I think so," Mary said. She stared through the kitchen window, a view distorted by steam and mineral deposits, watched a crow snatch and hold something in its beak, and thought about efforts—how it took two persons to mend a friendship. She said, "Can I make you a sandwich, Mary?"

Feeling ambivalent, Mother Amadeus answered, "I'd love one."

"While I'm fixing," bid the hostess, "tell me about your travels. You've been everywhere, probably more than I know about: Ireland, Italy, an island in California. Did you get to the place where Saint Germain lived?" She cracked her knuckles, stepped to her counter, opened the breadbox.

"Yes, I did, actually."

"Roast beef all right?"

"Yes. Mary, you would love California. It's warm all year and the beach is sublime: heavenly stretches of warm sand, a vast blue ocean and waves lapping, time to search for seashells. It was a blessing to recuperate in such a peaceful place. The island is called Coronado, Spanish for "crowned." I think you'd love the heat. No blizzards. No snow. Remarkable."

"Sounds like a good place to retire. I'm sure I'd prefer it to Alaska." Relenting, Mary gave Mary Amadeus a small smile.

"And Ireland," Mary Amadeus continued, "so bright and so green. Green that made me want to skip. Artful stonework, rolling fields, brooks, mountains and valleys. Glens, they call them, proportionately smaller than America's. Makes everything feel cozy. The people have such heart and humor, with accents like Mr. Cornell's."

"And good horses, I hear."

"I don't know about that, but I wouldn't be surprised. Speaking of Saint Germain, who surely traveled to court in royal carriages, I rode in one, in Austria. It was exquisitely ornate, inside and out, and the harness hung heavy from tooled silver. Superb."

Mary slid a crate beneath the table. "For your leg," she said responding to the nun's body language.

"Thank you, Mary. We're both getting older aren't we?"

"Yep, we are."

"You were invincible, freighting through sub-zero winters. In Alaska they travel by dog sled, long teams of dogs." A stream of light drew Mother Mary's attention to the far wall where she noticed a framed photograph. "Mary, what a lovely portrait. When did you have it taken?"

"To mark the beginning of my Star Route. Seemed like a good time to document who I was, how strong I was. 1895."

"Do you still have Bigg Too?"

"Gave him to Onatah and Edward, a wedding gift."

"Who's Onatah?"

"Annie. Saint Germain"

"Oh." She chewed on bread and roast beef, recalled that her flock had informed her of prior students reverting to native names. A frown crowded memories.

"How bad is the pain, honestly?" Mary Fields diverted.

"At times I am confined for periods of recovery; I call them retreats. Eventually, things improve, and I can travel again. It's not so bad."

Mary knew that meant it was pretty darn bad. *I know because we were close*, a voice within shouted.

"Are you still the altar's flower donor? I noticed a bouquet on the way here, this morning."

Mary inwardly gagged at the superficial chatter, at her cowardly participation in it. Exhausted, she leaned against her chair and said, "Our words are so shallow."

"What?"

"We sound mundane. We used to delve deeper." She sipped a breath. "I have to say this, Mary, to clear the air. Blood sisters don't act this way. You ignored my concerns for you when you got hurt, and afterwards, you didn't care what happened to me. Years went by. You would have written, found a way if you cared. I delivered your letters to Saint Peter's. It felt like your silence said: I don't need your help, so I don't care. That hurt, felt like you broke your promise, our blood sister promise, and that's neither religious nor friendly."

"What are you talking about, blood sisters?"

"Way back, you asked me to call you Mary, not Mother Superior, a sacred symbol of the bond between us. Said how I saved your life, how we were like sisters. I held that to heart. We used to help each other. Me helping you survive the first years at Saint Peter's, and you helping me when Brondel fired me for not. You gave me back pay, remember? After the train wreck it all stopped, because—"

"Wait, Mary. Calling me Mary wasn't a blood—I never stopped caring—I don't know what to say, other than what I've said already." She grabbed her cane and stood up. "I said I was sorry to lose contact."

"I thought we were blood sisters permanent, not temporary."

A moment of silence lapsed.

Mary Amadeus said, "In my mind, communication doesn't need to be constant. I have hurt you." She asked, "Will you forgive me?" and turned, swallowed tears unbid and turned back.

Mary moved close, met her namesake face-to-face, heart to heart, convinced the apology was in earnest.

A prolonged hug sealed the reconciliation. They shifted to arm's length and shared history, beyond the ordinary. Each of them thought: *this is probably the last time I'll see her, I'm glad we came together, so very glad ...*

Six months later, creek bed saplings twisted wiry roots downward, suckling mud juice and sprouting sinewy orange branches that reached with primal certainty. Sunrays provided heat, urging tightly spun virginal buds to crown and bloom into stands of willow, elms and hawthorns that, once matured, would shade, protect and benefit all manner of prairie life.

With like-minded verve, Onatah and Edward stood together on the twenty-first of June 1909, resolved with purpose in the whitewashed interior of a county office-chapel.

"Do you take this woman to be your lawful wife?" asked Reverend Prescott, minister of the Gospel of the Congregational Church and part-time pastor for Teton County, a sparsely populated region east of the Rockies.

Edward lifted Onatah's hand and vowed, "Yes."

"And do you take this man for your lawfully wedded husband?"

"I do," said Onatah.

Reverend Prescott, a kind man, proceeded through the nuptial vows with zest and reminded the couple, in their case without need, of their obligatory responsibilities to sustain lifelong matrimonial affections.

"Until death do us part," Onatah repeated, believing that such vows lasted longer, through time eternal.

"I now pronounce you man and wife, Mister and Mistress Edward Bruneau. What God has joined together, let no man put asunder. Amen. Congratulations."

Edward gave Onatah a soft kiss.

"Who bears witness to this union?" the reverend asked looking to the back of the chapel.

A compact gray-haired man cleared his throat. "My wife and I bear witness reverend, sir. I am George Dale, and this is Mrs. Annabelle Dale."

He looked them over, suspected they were half-breeds. "Are you both citizens of the United States of America and the State of Montana?"

"Yes," Mr. Dale replied.

"Did you bring citizenship papers?"

"No sir, we didn't know it was necessary."

The reverend could take Mr. Dale at his word, and that would be the end of it, if the information was true. He worried, however; if Mr. Dale and his wife were not citizens, the ceremony would be invalid, and he would not be paid for his services. At least that was what the clerk had told him. He could question the witnesses further, as recently recommended by the circuit judge—attempt to ascertain tribe identity and birthplace—but if he discovered either to have Canadian Cree blood and reported the findings, he would profit with a finder's fee—and they would be deported. It seemed unfair.

What had begun as a simple way to earn extra income while providing vital services to the community had turned into an anxiety-ridden predicament. His brow furrowed. The last thing he wanted to do was interrogate someone who had come to celebrate a marriage. Running fingers through his hair, he made his decision: he would have Mr. Dale sign as a witness (thinking one potential error was better than two and have the woman who accompanied the services on the harmonium, sign in place of Mrs. Dale as the second witness. Furthermore, he would search for another man of God to take his part-time post.

Outside, on the busy streets of Choteau, the Teton County seat, George Dale gazed at the happy couple. "Congratulations again!" he bid, "Liked your first wedding better, though. Seems like yesterday. How many years ago?"

"Six. Thank you, George, and thanks for coming." Edward's tone soured, "I hope it's of some use." Hours upon hours spent deliberating homestead strategy had worn him out.

"Can't do any harm, can it? Seemed to go well enough." George reached for his tobacco pouch.

Onatah removed her bonnet and gave Edward a look. "… vowing to cherish, love, protect …"

"You know what I mean."

"I know. Still …"

George asked the bride, "How does it feel to be Métis instead of full-blood?"

"I'm not sure. Perhaps I shouldn't have created that phantasm. I didn't mean—"

"I'm sure you made the right decision, as for getting married for the record, I mean." George wasn't clear about all of it—the connection between this wedding and the upcoming homestead claim. He hoped that would be the end of it; signing on white-government papers gave him the willies.

Edward put his arm around Onatah. "Like Mother said, scribbles on documents have nothing to do with reality." He took her hand. "Now we can claim our land." She squeezed back.

"Isn't Onatah a lovely bride?" Annabelle prompted.

"Yes, she is. And a lovely woman and the lovely mother of our beautiful baby girl."

Onatah smiled. "Do you have the certificate?"

He patted his jacket pocket. The group climbed into Louis Bruneau's buggy and left for Saypo, a two-hour ride.

"So is the party still on tonight?"

"George," Annabelle scolded.

Edward said, "Next Saturday night. By then we'll know whether to celebrate or not." He glanced at the women in the back seat. "The homestead, I mean." Onatah leaned her head against Annabelle's shoulder and sighed.

"You did a smart thing, protecting yourselves, Annabelle said. "You never know when laws will change."

"You're right," Edward replied, "We are lucky. Just want that same luck at the land office."

"Turned out different than I thought," said Onatah. "I spent years planning how to outsmart the homestead odds: Edward being Métis, and me, full-blood. I eavesdropped on so many conversations between administrators, inspectors and teachers." Her voice cracked, "For two years I worked in Fort Shaw's office, for Mr. Winslow."

"What?" Annabelle asked.

"Father didn't tell us, before." Edward stated.

"Tell you what?" asked George, confused.

"He didn't know we'd planned the whole thing out: two half-breeds applying for a homestead," Onatah explained.

Edward resented all the distress it had caused his wife. And it wasn't over. He turned to George. "Father didn't tell us until recently, that in the first state census, in 1900, the census taker listed my mother as 'half-breed' and me as 'white,' the son of a white French trader-storekeeper."

"Really?"

"So, we didn't need the complicated plan and paper trail to win the homestead clerk's favor, like we thought."

"And worked on forever," Onatah added.

George and Annabelle looked even more confused.

Edward slowed the horses and turned, citing, "You know how Métis have a fifty-fifty chance of getting homesteads, even though the law says anyone over twenty-one, citizen or not, can file for one?"

"Yeah, I guess," George replied, unsure.

"Since before we married the first time—for over six years, Onatah and I thought that's what we were up against. That's why she made the plan to become Métis on paper, hoping it would up our chances when we applied as two Metis. Just because I have a white father doesn't mean our homestead patent application will be approved. They can still deny it—they do it all the time."

"But it's less likely now, because you are 'white' according to the census?" Annabelle asked.

Onatah pulled a shawl around her shoulders. "We didn't have all the facts. I didn't need to—"

"Now we're filing as 'white' and 'half-breed' and yes, it gives us a better chance."

"Isn't it only the man who counts, because the title is only in his name? Isn't that right?" asked Annabelle, "Mrs. Johansen at—"

Edward interrupted. "That's exactly why we, well Father, actually, wanted us to wait until now to file. Father said that if we waited until I'm twenty-one, then as the 'head of household' and 'white,' things would fare better. Both for getting the approval and for the future."

"But he should have told us about the census years ago."

"I thought you could be any age as long as you're the head of household," Dale said.

"Yes. If you're married officially, the white way. We still have three to five years proving up time before we get the land patent title, but that's not what I meant."

"I see what you mean by complicated, Onatah," Annabelle whispered, rubbing her forehead.

"Now that we're married by U.S. law, Onatah is a citizen. The law gives her rights to the homestead if I die before proving up, but her ownership isn't guaranteed. If I die *after* we have the land deed, the title and the homestead are transferred into Onatah's name. Less chance of something going wrong."

"You two think of everything," said Annabelle.

"But if I understand you right," said George, "it isn't a sure thing, and you won't know til you make the application and it's approved at the land office?"

Onatah's anxiety burned. "Yes," she answered, "it all hangs on the clerk's integrity and mood. We're talking about increasing our odds. I suppose that it was still good for us, that I made myself Metis. We want a good future for our children."

"So today's wedding was to make Onatah a citizen, to help get and keep the homestead in your family?" George wanted to make sure he had it right.

"Exactly."

"Wish us luck, George. I'm going to file for a 320-acre tract through the Enlarged Homestead Act. I'll take father with me as a witness."

"Not Onatah?" Annabelle asked.

"You know that European saying, 'Best not wake the snakes'."

Crossing the Bruneau threshold an hour later, Edward squeezed Onatah's waist and cast an impish smile. "Like you to meet my second wife, Mother."

She laughed. "Did they question anything on the papers? The color or family?"

Onatah tossed her handbag on the kitchen table and teased, "Not a thing. The clerk was so smitten with Edward, she couldn't take her eyes off him. That Bruneau charm is our secret weapon."

"Mrs. Bruneau, you know that isn't true," Edward protested, pleased to see his wife's humor return.

"Yes, it is—"

"All right you two, give me details," Father said, looking to his son.

"Nothing to tell. We filled out the papers, did and said as requested, gave them the certified census papers you got from the state to prove my race and citizenship. I just hope the homestead clerk believes I'm white."

"You have those green eyes," Onatah teased.

"And dark skin." Edward countered.

"The land office clerk would have to take issue with the enumerator. That's enough to make him hesitate. I think our odds are good." Louis Bruneau's enthusiasm was reassuring to the couple.

"What's an enumerator?" Isabel Bruneau asked.

"The census taker."

She studied the marriage certificate. "Onatah, you're so clever," she cooed. "You have a new tribe and a new Mother's maiden name, along with that amazing history."

"What did you write down?" asked Father Louis.

"I decided it was best to list a tribe within the state. Raise less questions, if challenged. Salish."

"Oh, right, we talked about that."

"I suppose we'll be the only ones to know," she said, unsure how she felt after changing the little bit of identity she had clung to so fiercely.

"Supper is ready," Isabel said, "and Onatah's got citizenship." She untied her apron. "I wonder if we will ever get to vote, as full-blood women."

Edward had made certain that the land he sought in his petition was government-surveyed land: untilled, uninhabited and "non-irrigable" as required under the new Enlarged Homestead Act. He had contacted the land commissioner's office in Washington D.C. and purchased the *General Land Office's Homestead Booklet* and a township plat for his region. He carefully marked the location of the three hundred and twenty acres he desired on the plat: the median, range, township, section and aliquots thereof, notating section corners and including it as an addendum to form No. 4-003.

In response to the requirement of familiarity with the area, he described the acres as *the piece of earth bordering my father's homestead* and included testimony of the land's characteristics, both from himself, his father and a second witness, William McCrae.

It took three days of wagon travel for Edward, Louis and William McCrae to reach Great Falls, the location of the nearest Montana Land Office. As the door to the land office banged shut, Edward approached the registrar behind the counter, set his leather case down and pulled out a tidy bundle of papers. He arranged them before the drawn-looking bureaucrat, who, after scanning Edward's application, walked to a cabinet at the far end of the office, opened the middle drawer and withdrew a thick folded document.

The clerk unfolded the poster-sized sheet, placed it to face the men before him.

"What is this map?" Edward asked.

"This is the map that will tell us if the land you want is eligible. Hot off the press: a preview to one due to come out in a few months."

"But—"

"I know—you're going to say you were thorough and checked for the requirements. But not all homestead land, even the "non-irrigable" kind, is eligible under the Enlarged Homestead Act. See here, this is a state map, a new one. The sections marked in red designate land available for the Enlarged Claims." The map smelled of ink and the heavy paper was slick to the touch.

Edward scanned the Saypo area. "Oh, no," he muttered, turning to his father, Louis, who cleared his throat and asked the clerk if he was sure.

The clerk tapped on the bold caption in the bottom right corner: "State of Montana, Enlarged Homestead Act." See the color-coded legend? Just north of Choteau there's land available, here." He pointed to a red rectangular square.

Edward said, "I'm sorry, sir, I didn't get your name," giving him time to think.

"John Ellis."

"Mr. Ellis, I've always planned to homestead next to my family."

Ellis shrugged. "Perhaps you can, under the old act, up to 160 acres."

Edward stated the obvious. "I'll lose 160 acres."

Louis Bruneau explained, "My homestead is in Saypo, right here." He placed his index finger an inch or so below the clerk's, as if that would somehow change the unexpected disappointment.

William strummed his fingers on the counter, waiting for the clerk's attention. "I'm witness number two. At least I think you need two for the application, is that right?"

Mr. Ellis nodded.

"William is my name. William McCrae. Mr. Ellis, would you check for us, whether the land Edward has marked is available under the regular homestead?"

"Certainly." He gathered Edwards's application and set it on top of the large state map. "You gentlemen seem to know the area well. That's an important part of the procedure, an accurate description of the area. I see no problem as long as you, Edward," he glanced his way, "set the boundaries within the prescribed parameters: a rectangle, not to exceed a mile and a half wide—up to 160 acres. Did I see additional papers for submission?"

"Yes," Edward said, jarred by the denial of his dream. He pulled the remaining stack of papers from his case, papers that would, in part, dictate the future of his family: census, citizenship and birth documents, the marriage certificate and supplemental photographs depicting the Saypo settlement and Bruneau's Mercantile. "This is probably more than you need. And here's my father's homestead patent. Perhaps it will help to verify the modified adjoining piece I'll apply for now." The registrar took the papers, along with the application, to his desk at the far corner of the room. Edward swallowed the lump in his throat.

The Saypo men huddled. It was easy to reconfigure the plat size, sections being forty acres each, but the location was crucial. The claim had to include essential resources: water placed in the quarter where his house and barn would be built, the balance for working land, crops and grazing. His father assured him that he would share acreage if need be, and they agreed with familial gestures that the adjustment was to be taken in stride.

The clerk examined the Bruneau family documents. Finding everything in order and noting the difference in skin tone between father and son, which was of no import in this case, but necessary when racial detection was relevant, he concluded that approval for the 160-acre homestead was in order. It was a relief to engage with civilized individuals, he mused, after dealing with applicants who clearly wanted something for nothing and who had no intention of proving up, thusly, generating additional work for him when the claim had to be re-processed as stipulated. If he were a betting man, he'd wager this Edward would proceed according to regulations, return in five years with the necessary "proving up" documents and receive his patent, the permanent title certificate. He was curious about one thing only—the young man's style of crossing consonant letters at an angle—a single deviation from his otherwise perfect penmanship.

"I think we're ready," Edward said, "Whenever you are."

"Yes, gentlemen." The clerk returned to the counter and wiped dust from its surface, a habitual quirk.

"Penny for your thoughts?" William McCrae prompted the clerk. "You have the look of tomfoolery, sir."

Surprised, John Ellis stared at the red-cheeked Scotsman. "I was just thinking how easy my job would be if all applicants came prepared like you gentlemen."

William and Louis chuckled, and Edward realized how lucky they'd been to have the office to themselves and lucky that Mr. Ellis was amiable. His confidence welled, but he would not disarm his anxiety until approval was in hand.

The clerk glanced at the clock. "Let's see what you've decided." He examined the new markers and calculated the size to be exactly 160 acres, positioned in accordance to the rules. He checked his patent pending book to verify that boundaries were without conflict and fell into the rehearsed ceremony, the part he enjoyed most. First, he folded the supporting documents and returned them to Edward in a nonchalant manner, then folded the large color-coded map and returned it to its place in the cabinet, leaving only the revised application and regional township map that he took in hand and examined once more, with a pensive scowl. He could feel the applicant holding his breath.

He set the papers on the counter and paused before he opened the drawer beneath, removed a wooden seal and an inkpad, placed them to one side. He returned to his desk and leaned over to peer at a booklet of some kind. Edward cocked his head to see if he could read the stamp's woodcut. The older men exchanged glances. Mr. Ellis returned with an ink well and quill and placed them intentionally, just so, before Edward. "If you would like to sign here." He motioned to the line at the bottom of the document. "And you gentlemen can witness Mr. Bruneau's application, where indicated."

They did so in earnest, after which Mr. Ellis flashed a grin and said, "Congratulations, young man! You are land rich, 'proving poor,' as I like to say."

"Aye, Edward," cheered William, while Louis Bruneau draped an arm around his son and gave a tight squeeze.

Mr. Ellis blew on the ink, authenticating; he had memorized their signatures from provided documents earlier. He inked the stamp efficiently and pressed it upon the application's upper left corner.

Watching closely as the word "approved" branded the transaction, three sets of shoulders let down. Edward shook the registrar's hand and slipped his copy of the patent application into his case.

"Saved yourself twelve dollars," Mr. Ellis added.

They looked at him, bewildered.

"I'm sorry we couldn't process the Enlarged Homestead Act. If that tract you wanted becomes available—and I think there's a good chance it might, since the land looks rocky, not conducive to farming—we could add it to the acreage you have, change the homestead to an enlarged claim as you intended, if that suits you. Here's my card."

"Suits me well. Very well. Thank you, Mr. Ellis. Meanwhile, I'll put that twelve dollars toward the well and get started."

The Bruneau celebration began the afternoon following their return. Louis, a Saypo founder, invited everyone in the area to partake in the festivities. A gathering of adults and children, most of whom were Métis, some white, some full-blood, packed into the cabin's small sitting room and, when that was full, spilled into the kitchen and onto the steps outdoors.

As the sun set, Louis Bruneau stood, raised his arms and waited. When chatter quieted, he announced, "Thank you for sharing our joyful occasion. As you know, my son Edward and his lovely wife Onatah are the proud holders of a 160-acre homestead—land that joins Isabel's and mine." Friends and neighbors clapped and hooted. "Before we feast and dance, I want them to tell you their story. Edward, Onatah, please." He waved them forward and took a seat on a bench next to Isabel.

"How did you do it?" a voice rang.

"It wasn't just Onatah and I," Edward began, "Father had a hand in it too, of course. To start with, in the first census, nine years ago—Father was listed in the United States Census, *not* the Indian Census—as Head of Household, White; his wife, Half-breed; his children, White." As you know, mother is full-blood Blackfeet, and I, the proud descendant of two bloodlines."

Murmurs rippled. Someone asked, "How did that happen?"

"You know how Mother speaks eloquent English and can dress fashionably 'white' when she wants to—" He looked her way. "I know it doesn't make sense, but census takers can put you in any category they please. There's no way to know, but it was lucky for us when applying for land."

"Did you apply as head of household?" George Dale asked.

"Yes. As a 'white' head of household with a 'Métis' wife, we had a better chance. But nothing was certain. He could have denied our claim. Some of you were denied, though you are legally eligible. Onatah, tell them how you created your parents. Now there is a truly, ingenious story."

"What do you mean, Métis wife? Onatah's full-blood," a Blackfeet woman elder called out.

Onatah replied, "Yes, I am. Father and I agreed that somehow, I had to get recorded officially as half-breed. Would you like to know how I did it?" The yeses cheered her on.

"I was born Onatah, of the Iroquois Onondaga tribe, as most of you know. But I was taken when I was little. The Saint Peter's Ursuline School recorded me originally as Iroquois and then as Piegan, and then as half-breed. I think the sisters were simply trying to keep us alive; records of our heritage were not a priority. Also, they were pressured to tell the government that their students were whatever race was eligible for funding. So, I could, if need be, claim that they told me I was half-breed."

"Listen, everyone," Edward interrupted. "First, you have to know that the only surname Onatah remembers, the one she was given by an Army clerk on the way to Saint Peter's, was Saint Germain. Then, Mary White Crow, our friend from Cascade, learned the origin story of Saint Germain and told Onatah."

"Are you going to tell the story, or shall I?" asked Onatah.

"Just giving background, my dear." He blew her a kiss, though he was standing close.

"Go on," she goaded, "tell us who Comte Saint Germain was."

Edward scanned the jovial crowd. "Mother Amadeus, the Ursuline Superior at Saint Peter's, told Mary Fields that the white name-giver may have been referring to a legendary man named Comte Saint Germain who lived about two hundred years ago, in Europe. He was a master shape shifter, a man of mystery, a healer. Because he was able to change rocks into gold and jewels, he was wealthy and had close ties to Kings and Queens. And he was ageless. That is the history of the name, Saint Germain."

Oohs and aahs raised interest.

"Explain *Comte*, Edward," Onatah pushed.

"*Comte* is a French word for *Count*, as you most likely know," he said, aware that European titles of nobility were unfamiliar to many. "A count is a nobleman, like a chief.

"But that man was no relation to Onatah, right?"

"Right."

"I'll go on from here," Onatah said. "I'd gotten to like the name Saint Germain, as much as one can like a foreign name—because my grandmother was a healer—so it felt all right to me, though in a distorted way, I suppose. Anyway, we couldn't go to the Teton County Clerk for the marriage ceremony or to the land office without having every line on the application filled in. I learned that from working in the office at the Industrial School. The only paper-name I had was Annie St. Germain—the nuns had replaced my given name, Onatah, with Annie.

I set out to create my parents' names and the location of my birth for the documents. I knew it would complicate things if I listed a birthplace outside of Montana, because if they hadn't heard of it, they might deny the application by simple ignorance and the inability to obtain a complete list of North American tribes, mine being among the most—"

"Back to the story," Edward prompted.

She caught his meaning. "So, I listed my place of birth as Flathead Valley—not in our land office district, and not far away: a known location. They don't ask for the name of your tribe. They just want to know what color you are, Indian or half-breed, and the names of your parents."

"You got to name your parents?" one of the youngsters asked, intrigued.

"Yes, I did. Since it was the government who stripped us of our names in the first place, I thought, I'll create a secret message with the names I return to them on paper-forms—yet they must be names that appear appropriate and white in every way."

Parents shushed their children in order to hear. "Did you call them Count?" someone shouted, "the story?"

"Oh, instead of Comte ..." a voice in front murmured.

"Well, wait. First, I made my father's last name, Saint Germain, like the one I was given. I wanted an ordinary Euro-white name for his first, and I picked Frederick. So, my 'father' on paper, is '*Frederick St. Germain*.'"

"What did you name your mother?" Annabelle asked, excited that such a plot had worked.

"Did you say she is Salish or Blackfeet?" a neighbor known as Running Elk asked.

"If they inquired, I would have said Salish, because I gave Flathead Valley as my place of birth. But they didn't ask for the tribe—" Murmurs grumbled. The Salish were longtime enemies of the Blackfeet. As if she knew what some were thinking, Onatah clarified, "I didn't claim her to be Blackfeet, because I didn't want them to be able to check records easily."

She looked to Isabel who nodded with encouragement. "I needed a first and last name for my paper-mother—this is where I create my message. The English word for the French words, 'Comte,' or 'Conte,' is 'Count'. The Old French version of 'Count' means a title of nobility or to add up, or to tell a story.

"To tell a story," a clever boy declared.

"Yes. Learning French from the sisters finally came in handy. I woke up one winter morning, thinking 'Pate,' that's it!'"

"What does that mean?" asked one of the children.

"Pate means: paste, pasta, batter or dough. So, joined together, Countpate sounds like a noble French name, yet it can mean...?" She scooped her palms upward and waited.

"The story of dough?" the same boy guessed.

Onatah grinned. "Yes. Anymore?"

"A royal tale pasted with," a woman called.

"Yes," Onatah cheered.

"The noble tale of pasted names!" Annabelle hollered.

"The tale of names which rise and fall!" George shouted.

"Exactly!" Onatah whooped. "*A tale of names that rise and fall like dough*. Then I christened my paper-mother with the name 'Julia.' It's Roman in origin, a name for women saints and martyrs that also means *joyous*. I like to think of 'Julia Countpate' as my mother's voice expressing a message—a response to her death—action taken by the United States government. She says: *'You cannot take our culture. Our ancestors are not gone by the taking of names. We will learn to unite, and we will prosper while you rise and fall like pasty dough, in the complacency of power and illusion. We will live on, make our country home again, for all the peoples.'*"

"I, as her daughter, Onatah, say, thank you for celebrating our homestead success—our small step toward manifesting such a future." Feeling exposed and exhilarated, she scanned faces that had fallen silent.

Two hands clapped, and then more. Louis stood up and called, "To the continued success of our united community!"

Overcome with pride, Edward joined his wife and waved for attention.

"To complete our homestead story," he shouted, "the registrar at the land office did not deny us because we had census papers and our marriage certificate stating that I am white and Onatah is Métis. We have five years to prove up and get our patent title. Then we'll have an even bigger party! Is anyone hungry?"

Foot stomping cheers rocked the cabin. The crowd moved outside while the women set up tables for the food. Musicians unpacked instruments and played passages that promised a spirited evening of dancing.

After everyone had eaten, the players strummed, bowed, beat, blew and sang favorite melodies from Irish, Scottish, French and Blackfeet origins, adapting jigs and reels and rhythms to suit their fancy. Dancers leapt to the sounds of fiddles, pennywhistles, harps, banjos, dulcimers, spoons and drums of every kind and shape, twirling into spins, circles, waves, swings, do-si-does and allemandes for nearly a week.

Mary was on her knees in her garden, stretching under prickly squash leaves to channel irrigation furrows from one plant to another, when she heard the postmaster, Mr. Rowe, holler, "Stagecoach Mary, got a fine look'n letter for you."

She raised her head above the foliage.

"Brought it over cause I think you'll be wanting it."

Clad in an old scarf and ripped galoshes, Mary pushed up and tottered the length of her prized hollyhocks, stroking scarlet pleated petals as she trod to the dusty road where he waited.

"Thanks, Mr. Rowe, mighty nice of you. Didn't have to bring it. Who's it from?"

"A friend of yours. Mary, are you coming to the Sample Room tonight? J.E. Marcum's talking about Cascade's future."

Raising an eyebrow, she feigned interest. "I'll try to make it," she fibbed.

Though she held opinions about each local issue, she needed to be cautious; she didn't trust J.E. or his wife. They wouldn't appreciate comments coming from me, she thought, and I'd likely get peeved and have to squelch myself. Better off making relish. Or maybe I'll pick some currants before it's too late, put up some jelly. She glanced at the letter's return address. Excited that the sender was Mrs. Onatah Bruneau of Saypo, Montana, she slipped the envelope into her apron pocket, excused herself and hurried inside for privacy.

Onatah chronicled thrilling news in detail: success filing a homestead claim, hers and Edward's "white legal" marriage and the unexpected status of her American citizenship. Best of all, the birth of a girl child born last winter, Saturday February 27, 1909—five months old already. Tears gushed when Mary read the last sentence on the page: *"We named her Mary Ahwao (Onondaga for Rose) after you, White Crow."*

A second burst of tears watered her face and the stationery. She turned it over and read anxiously:

> *I'm sorry to have taken so long to write about our little Mary. Edward and I would like you to be her Godmother. Will you accept?*
>
> *Also, I know you want to keep up with state politics, and you mentioned Cascade might be incorporating. During my homestead research, I sent for a copy of the Montana State Constitution, ratified August 17, 1889. I have copied Article IX for you because I thought you would like to have actual proof of Montana women rights. Note in particular, Section 10-12. If only you owned property! It appears that you would have the right to vote in all school, city and county elections. I can find no item that prohibits it. What do you think?"*

Mary White Crow moved to the edge of her chair, reading Sections 10 through 12 three times:

> Sec. 10. Women shall be eligible to hold the office of county superintendent of schools or any school district office and shall have the right to vote at any school district election.
>
> Sec. 11. Any person qualified to vote at general elections and for State officers in the State shall be eligible to any office therein except as otherwise provided in this Constitution, and subject to such additional qualifications as may be prescribed by the Legislative Assembly, for city offices and offices hereafter created.
>
> Sec. 12. Upon all questions submitted to the vote of the taxpayers of the State, or any political division thereof, women who are tax-payers and possessed of the qualifications for the right of suffrage required of men by this Constitution shall equally, with men, have the right to vote.

Onatah had also included Sec. 2, the description of male persons qualified to vote. Mary checked quickly to see if there was a racial exclusion. There was not. She held her breath. Can this be true? Montana women property owners can vote in state elections? Then how come it isn't happening already, or is it? Have they changed the law after 1889? Got to find out. So much news at once!

She replied with haste:

Dear Onatah,

Congratulations for giving birth to your precious baby girl, and I am speechless. You know how powerful big something's got to be for that to happen. You named her Mary, after me! I'm honored. I love her middle name too—Ahwao. Can't wait to meet this little Mary. I'm going to knit her a pair of booties, make them on the large side so she can walk in them next winter. Of course I want to be her Godmother!

A homestead! I'm holding my breath until you get the final deed in your hand! Yippee! You and Edward are so smart sleuthing through complicated government law. I'm so proud! You're going to have a home and land and no one can take it from you! Little Mary won't have to worry where she's going to live.

Yes, I knew that women could vote in the Montana school elections. That was legal in 1889. And I hear you asking, White Crow why didn't you register and vote then, seeing as women's rights are so near and dear?

Wanted to, but didn't want to make things any harder on myself in town, until I was here for awhile anyway. I was hoping we'd have voting rights, at least in Montana, by now, whether we own land or not. I wish all women could be voting in the next presidential election. How can we find out for sure whether women who own property are allowed to vote in city or county or state elections? I want to know. I don't know how come I don't know this.

One of the little boys I baby-sit, Earl Monroe, told me about riding by Fort Shaw—how he was "marveled" to see whites with Indians in the same place. He was plum bug-eyed about it. Things change so slowly.

You'll be interested to know that Fort Shaw Industrial has come to its end. It will be closed after commencement this June. Paper, that's another piece of news! Cascade has its very own newspaper, The Cascade Courier. Hope it does a decent job of getting world news. Anyway, The Courier reports that the school will be shut down along with all Indian government schools to reduce costs—reason being, students can now go to the improved reservation schools. Ha! Makes all the more sense for you all to run your own. I guess you were smart to go to Saypo.

I am excited to register in the census this summer. First time I was in a United States census was 1870, when I lived in Tennessee, and last time, here, ten years ago.

Do you think you'll be listed as half-breed or white? Will it affect your homestead papers?

I'm not sure things in Cascade will get better, incorporated. I worry about one or two men having all the power to do whatever they please. I think there are two men considering running for mayor in the city council vote that follows incorporation: Marcum and Hall. Don't care for either one of them.

Love you all very much,
Mary White Crow

It was Mary's habit to visit a saloon of choice several afternoons each week. On this mid-summer day she strolled toward the Q&L, hoping that banter would contain subjects other than Cascade incorporation. And that reminded her. She needed to make a plan. How was *she* going to get registered for the vote? She had to become a property owner if she wanted to vote on city issues other than school ballots. She wasn't about to homestead out on the prairie alone—too lonely, vulnerable, hard to prove up without help; she had made that decision years back. So how am I gonna do it, she demanded. Can't vote one way or the other about Cascade incorporating—or on anything else. And that's got to change. If I can't come up with something, I'll be just like all the Cascade wives, and that's not acceptable, especially since I don't have the few benefits a husband might provide.

Pushing the saloon doors open, she locked eyes with the nearest customer: J.E. Marcum. She glanced to the men lined up at the bar and thought of milk cows in the barn. But the cows were giving drink, and this menagerie was doing the opposite. She looked away, pretending she had been distracted. She had watched Marcum gossip with the others for years, but not one word had passed between them. He was skilled at persuasion and he had been promoting incorporation. More reason to be suspect, she thought as she drifted back to plans for getting registered, then to the pain in her back that ached from scrubbing large loads of laundry that morning.

When she moved her gaze from the floorboards, she was surprised to see her table occupied by three construction workers—part of the crew who'd come to town, bricklayers mostly, to build what would be the new three-story Cascade School up the street from her house. The large man in her chair had the look of a lumberjack—armature with brawn and bravado. His checkered shirt was splattered with mortar, and he was full of himself, bragging about something. Probably his strength, Mary gaggled to herself. No, he's begging an arm wrestle over the cost of a whiskey, she corrected, as she edged her way to the only empty table. Wishing she'd brought something to read, she looked to the ceiling, studied dust moats flung by the fan's slow propellers, the smallest parts of earth hitching rides on thick smoke that curled, and eventually, plateaued. The room had become stifling. She wondered if she should buy something, seltzer maybe, and considered going to Cornell's instead.

The new barkeep arrived with a glass of water. She ordered seltzer and asked for *The Great Falls Tribune* or, if not available, *The Cascade Courier*. He said he'd look and went behind the bar. A stranger leaned against the rail, slugging shots in a hurry: his fourth, if the empty glass-count was accurate. He hawked a wad of phlegm and tobacco chew and the mass launched toward the spittoon, a lambs-quarter distance. When the spew splat upon the floor, Mary turned away.

He thrust a slicing glare, arched an evil eye and shouted, "I'll be sure to put the word out—that Cascade's a coon lovin' town." When he'd gotten everyone's attention, he cast a venomous grimace toward Mary and threatened, "Even if you *are* the only one, Cascade's sinful secret. You don't belong here."

Ludwig, Marcum and Hall, Cascade men that mattered, sized him up. Ludwig, average in size and steadfast in character, stepped forward, wishing he'd learned how to throw a punch. "Seems to us, you're the one who doesn't belong here. I'm sure you have better things to do elsewhere," he dared.

"And we don't care what you say to anybody," Marcum added. "You're hardly credible."

"Nigger Mary is our rabbit's foot," the barkeep barked.

"And our friend," another voice hollered.

Customers watched the stranger slide a hand beneath his vest. Mary lifted the curtain to see if a non-local horse was tied to the hitch post, concerned that none of the Cascade men present were packing a pistol—that she knew of, in any case. There was a rifle behind the bar, so she kept one eye on the barkeep.

The accuser counted four against him, more nigger lovers than he'd anticipated along the *Missouri*. He gripped his derringer but decided after turbid moments not to push further. Tossing coins with a gloved hand, he flared broad nostrils and snarled, "I'll be finding better company," and exited.

She watched him ride north. If he wanted to hurt her it would be easy enough to locate the Mary Fields Laundry. She hoped that he, like most drifters, was tall on bluffs and short on following through—though she had to admit, the level of racial hostility toward her and the Chongs had been on the rise, from locals, too. Was it the sudden interest in politics that made men believe they had to take sides? Maybe it was suffrage, she considered, men's fear of women holstered with rights.

John Tully stepped away from the bar, crossed his arms and surprised most patrons when he looked Mary's way and accused, "You used to work for that Mother Amadeus."

Showing no emotion, she ignored him, knowing it would add fuel to his fire. She didn't care. Instead, she thought about his daughter Lizzie's new life, proud that she had helped her get away from the monster. If the few friends he has, only knew, she harbored.

He turned to those nearest. "That nun acted like she owned the place— she butt into my family business and put crazy ideas into my girl's head. Good thing she's run away to Alaska, the Mother. Can't be far enough." No one joined in. He swung himself toward Mary. "You were that nun's shadow, doing whatever she told you. God knows what dirty work you and—"

"Shut your mouth, Tully," Marcum warned. Heads raised, surprised to see the banker lose his temper. "She is a sanctified nun, you idiot, a servant to God, and she helped put Cascade on the map. I've never seen you contribute to this community. In fact, you are a disgrace—liquored up all day, every day."

Tully slurred, "I'll show you and your kind."

"Our kind?" Marcum threw glances left and right.

Locals from the bar and tables sidled toward the obnoxious drunkard, ready.

"You'd best leave, Tully, find yourself another town," Hall threatened.

Oblivious, Tully slurred, "You think you're so almighty. Should be ashamed of yourselves, keeping company with that nigger. Some example of town dignity. That man was right."

Mary sipped her seltzer, ready to slug Tully herself if he said one more word.

The door burst open. A short grizzly-looking man entered. When glowers darted his direction, he straightened and moved aside. Heads recoiled to Tully who suddenly staggered and fell, unable to break the force of Hall's calculated shove. "Get out and don't come back," he shouted.

Mary had been so engrossed she had not noticed the newcomer standing by her table. She continued to grip the colt in her skirt pocket as the man with light eyes and bearded stubble asked for permission to sit down. He claimed that they had been acquainted, but she had no such recollection, proffered a blank nod. He sat, thanked her politely. She gripped her gun again when his hand moved to a jacket pocket and he pulled a knotted bundle from it, set it on the table and proceeded to untie the casing, a blue bandana.

She scanned the room, noted that the men had already returned to their drinking and banter, the discussion of her presence, forgotten, it seemed. Relieved that they had defended her, though in part they had been spurred by mention of Mary Amadeus, she sighed and watched the calloused cracked fingers tug the cloth open. A stack of silver dollars shined.

"You may want to put that away," she suggested.

"Now why would I do that when it belongs to you, Miss Mary?"

Her shoulders dropped and she looked closely. "Who are you?"

"You were kind enough to give me many a delicious meal in your café. I asked if you would wait til my sheep had been sheared and you said yes. I never forgot. Thank you for trusting me."

"Patrick, is it you?"

He grinned.

"How good of you—Sorry, there's just been—"

"I gathered."

"It's been so long. Good to see you, and many thanks." Concerned that her windfall might be too tempting for many saloon patrons, she said, "Think I'll get going," and placed the large coins into her other skirt pocket, unlined, returned to the afternoon heat and walked toward home.

Walking along Central, Mary witnessed a strange sight: J.E. Marcum stood in the center of the street, hands on hips, holding a rooster-in-the-coop stance, a self-decreed King of the Beasts pose. She forced herself to call out, "Thanks, Mr. Marcum," and held her hand high. He deserves that much, she figured, for diverting Tully's tirade.

"You're welcome, Nigger Mary."

J.E. was a planner. He had predicted lucrative rewards for his efforts, past, present and future, and had picked the right spot again. In Cascade, things had progressed as planned thus far, and he believed they would continue to do so in accordance with his calculations. Soon, the town would mature into an incorporated city. By that time, his bank would be relocated to the lot he had recently purchased, a new fortress of his own design. He had also purchased the Shepherd and Flinn Mercantile and had increased profit margins, even after having incurred the additional expense of its manager, Mr. Robert Flinn. Incorporation would increase property values and business would prosper. Cascade would get the respect it deserved from nearby cities like Great Falls. Elections would be held. Cascade's first mayor and its council would solicit new entrepreneurs and regulate undesirables.

Most importantly, he and his wife would rise to the apex of social status they deserved. He had spent the last three years befriending the right people, and he was ready for results.

By the time he heard the wagon coming from behind, it was too late. Loose hay from its bunk whirled in its wake leaving him littered with broken bits of chaff. Irritated, he uttered something, fluffed his lapels and marched undaunted, three short blocks to his Craftsman home that overlooked the *Missouri*. Entering the foyer, he removed his hat and vigorously brushed off remaining farm residue before proceeding to his study where he made himself comfortable in his wing chair by the window, all the while thinking he would make an impressive-looking mayor, a gentleman dressed in fine attire. He glanced at his new twenty-four-carat pocket watch and gnashed his teeth as he imagined himself on a decorated podium, the orator of a riveting campaign speech delivered flawlessly to a crowd of enlightened citizens who had been mesmerized by his every word: *I promise you that Cascade will become a cultured utopia in no time!* Crossing the room toward his liquor cabinet, he caught his reflection in the gilded mirror and grinned with satisfaction.

"James," his wife called.

Once I'm mayor I will have sidewalks built, he decreed as he twisted his mustache. My suits will never become soiled when I stroll along Central. I'll spend my free time in the men's club I will have designed and constructed— similar to the one in Helena.

His competent, high-strung wife, Ada, often read her husband's thoughts. She noticed the familiar peacock smirk and said, "First thing you can do when you're mayor is get that vile woman, Nigger Mary, off the streets and out of the saloons."

"What?" J.E. coughed.

"You heard me," she pressed.

"How do you know what I'm thinking?"

"You have that particular zest about you, James, when your mind is campaigning for public office ..." She stroked a finger along his jawline, "... foreseeing our successful future. It is ... rather inviting." She parted her lips flirtatiously, tempting desire with practiced expertise, aware that he was scheduled to chair the Methodist Church Council in five minutes.

17

RECOGNITION

SPRING 1910 - FALL 1910

*M*ary puzzled over the odd seasonal behavior of her customers: why was it, when they wore twice the number of garments, they clung to them longer? As though heaping on layers made grime and sweat disappear. "Just gonna make my job harder when they do bring the crusty—" she uttered as she wiped her brow. Don't have enough money, she grieved, and since I can't hunt for game or haul firewood, let alone chop the dozen cords I need to keep this place warm, I need more. Didn't expect. Sounds dumb, but didn't think I'd get … old. How will I get the mountain plants I need to make my remedies?

She discarded these concerns as temperatures rose. After a brief downpour at dawn, the third according to marks made on her complimentary calendar from Cascade Mill & Elevator, Mary slipped galoshes over her wool socks and tucked rumpled hair into an old straw hat. In a mood for adventure, like the May Day expeditions she'd had to relinquish, she grabbed her walking stick and strolled. As she passed the bare weather-beaten altar at the end of town, she thought of Mother Mary and of Nadie, and picked up speed.

Inviting a lungful of June sunshine to fuel her verve, she came to the familiar creek bed, felt goose bumps rise as she peeked at the lush spread of early clover. She stepped closer, as though a secret beau waited in the shadows. Who says passion crumbles with age, she mused, the young are so naïve. Pivoting around violets that sported brown stripes on crisp yellow petals, she claimed, "These are for me."

Posies in hand, she started home. As she neared the Mint Saloon, she heard voices she recognized. C.C.C. cronies barked, and a rowdy younger gaggle cavorted in turn, excited about something. She paused by the door and listened.

"What progress?"

"Do we have enough?"

"This is gonna be great fun, better than gathering for roll call. We've finally got enough of you strong young men to see it through and I, for one, am in favor."

She elbowed the door ajar. Once acknowledged, she couldn't help but sling a wildcard, "Are you going off to war then, Fred?"

Chuckling, he snorted. "No, but this is one club you can't join. Sorry, Black Mary."

"What club is that?"

"The Cascade Cubs. Our new baseball team."

"Yes!" Mary hailed. "Splendid. Finally!" She set her posies on the bar and crossed her arms, grinning. "Yes," she repeated.

Fred snapped his suspenders. "R.B. says he'll donate the uniforms and equipment if he's captain and we mention the New Cascade Hotel as much as possible."

"That sounds like him," Mary said, joining the laughter.

"Lucky thing is, he also happens to be a great ball player," added a young local named McKay.

"Mary's got to have a place in this, Fred," the hopeful team candidate insisted. "She's been scheming with us, all along."

"A place in what, Jones?" R.B. boomed, slamming the saloon door behind him.

"Howdy, R. B.!" McKay shot. "We're just saying how Stagecoach Mary should have a place on our baseball team, since you and her been scheming it all along."

Fred prodded, "Yeah, we took a vote and made her captain!"

R. B. Glover knew when his leg was being pulled. "Great!" he hollered and ordered beers all around, slid a hand into a hip pocket, pressed his lips and faced Mary who had requested lemonade instead. "I've been thinking, Black Mary, as team manager I'd like to know if you would consider signing on as our team mascot."

Aware that the term "signing on" had been employed to make the offer sound appealing, Glover being the ceaseless promoter that he was, the notion, nevertheless, came as a surprise. When they had talked baseball, the pros and cons of forming a team, he had never mentioned a mascot, and she had not thought about the superfluous addition.

"I don't know," she said, not thinking to ask what expectations he had in mind, exactly. "Let me think about, if you don't mind."

"Of course, Black Mary, you think it through and let me know. Are those your flowers on the bar?"

That afternoon, team manager Glover ordered equipment: bats, balls, a catcher's mitt, uniforms in several colors (each designating a specific team position), bow ties, caps, belts and socks and royal blue above-the-knee socks: the article of color that would identify and represent the team. Having signed an agreement to renovate the Cascade Hotel in May, he had spent most of his savings redecorating the lobby and guest rooms, outfitting the restaurant kitchen and hiring a bare bones staff. Like Marcum, Glover believed that the community of Cascade had matured, and accordingly, would reward those who had prepared to reap from its commerce. He was anxious to retrieve the level of prosperity he had enjoyed once, in Ohio—build a comfortable life tailored by design rather than by laboring at trades typically promoted in the west: mining, cattle ranching and railroading. One more advertising expense, The Cascade Cubs Campaign, wasn't going to make or break him. If the Cubs prospered like the gains he planned to incur after the recent upgrade, he would purchase new shoes for the team next season.

Mary believed that baseball would provide good old-fashioned fun—the reason she had encouraged the locals with free time to organize. She liked the game itself, and had watched professional ball games in Cleveland, thirty years earlier. She considered the position of Mascot. She knew, of course, that there would be recompense—any woman mascot would attract attention. The question was, what kinds of attention? And what would be attached to the official offer, Baseball Team Mascot? Another name, such as, Mascot Mary?

"Yep. They will be calling me Mascot Mary," and I'll have to wear it." her heel tapped. "Notoriety, good and bad, comes with this kind of job. Some mascots get picked due to prestige," she said, as she raised her chin. "In my case, it's notoriety: exaggerated legends, some mutated by warped bias, some not. Will the Cubs do their best to protect me, if fans give me trouble?" Mascoting could be a feather in one's cap, she contemplated. Though she understood the potential of being perceived as an amusing sidekick or an adopted pet, she might, on the other hand, be viewed as the revered star route mail carrier who generously agreed to share her legendary status with Cascade citizens. "Hmm," she sighed as she went outside to her garden, eased onto the old tree stump and watched bumblers scout for pollen, as of yet unavailable.

"I think I'll do it," she announced. She decided soon after, that she'd better get her little Eden planted before Glover organized a practice schedule. She looked at the soil around her. "Come time for official games," she said, "maybe I'll make boutonnières for the Cub players, flowers grown and arranged by me. How about a bouquet for the winning team?"

The following day she tracked Glover down, advised him that she would accept the generous position he had thoughtfully offered, and finalized the agreement with a handshake, extolling, "…normally, I'd be trying out for first base, but I'm tired of running round in circles—know what I mean, R.B? Being your assistant sounds—"

"Sounds fine to me," Glover ballyhooed with a finger snap.

By the time Mary's sunflower seedlings stood a hand high, baseball practice occurred three times a week. "Same number of times I water my garden without the tiresome necessity of carrying heavy buckets," Mary mused, having scheduled garden watering on corresponding days to reduce the number of calendar notations. "There are a few buckets involved laundering the boy's socks and uniforms, however." And oiling the bats and balls isn't what I'd call luxuriating, she thought as she counted crows on her fence line. I don't mind. Watching Glover whip players into shape is lively entertainment and well worth the labor. They're a long way from professional, but they *are* getting better, and they, we, just might have a chance. Maybe us Cubs will beat the odds, take the trophy, win the season, be champions, first place. The upcoming United States census is just in time to record each of our names so future fans can remember who we are, in case they're looking. We're already in the regional circuit. Should I give my middle name?

It was Robert Flinn, shop-keep now retired, who advised Mary that the census taker had arrived. She had been waiting, anxious to see her name recorded on the official document. Leaning against the stone exterior of Marcum's Corner Store, Flinn reported that Glover and Marcum were going to wine and dine the enumerator in hopes he'd spread word that Cascade was the "up and coming" Birdtail-Sun River metropolis; then said he liked the old days when folks were less pushy.

J.E. Marcum made haste to represent Cascade as its self-appointed emissary. He, a genteel representative of the now-civilized West, would be first to welcome the federal representative. Who else could impart pertinent background data, summaries and projections with expertise, he thought. Posting himself at the depot some time before the *Great Northern* was scheduled to arrive, he reviewed profit and loss statements from his bank's previous quarter and contemplated whether to increase interest on property loans.

The train whistled. He inserted the papers into his breast pocket, flicked lint from his trouser leg and strolled forward. Spotting a petite sharp-nosed gentleman with nondescript features, a likewise bowler, spectacles and an extra-wide case clutched to his chest, Marcum decided to time his steps to intersect with those of the bureaucrat.

The census taker debarked down the rough-cut ramp provided. Peering over his case to keep himself steady, he noticed a pair of fancy gentlemen's boots come into view and looked up.

J.E., glad to have had his sable leather buttoned spats polished the day before, parleyed, "Good morning to you, sir. May I assist?"

After confirming that the traveler was indeed the census enumerator, Marcum identified himself as a Cascade businessman at his service. The passenger nodded, introduced himself as Mr. Benton, asked his greeter to help locate his suitcase and accepted Marcum's offer to escort him to The New Cascade Hotel.

In the interim, Mr. Benton pressed the modest, well-kept train station to memory, a particular habit he had engaged to recall each of his census locations, and to acclimate himself before proceeding. Marcum returned, suitcase in hand, and they fell into step, charging uphill.

Marcum launched into a well-rehearsed preamble of regional history highlighted by descriptions of local advancements made since the last census, a decade earlier, beginning with a detailed description of the recently renovated Cascade Depot waiting room, which Mr. Benton might desire to peruse upon his departure, he suggested. He also mentioned that he was the founder of the only bank in town, the J.E. Marcum Bank, and also, the owner of the largest mercantile. Approaching the hotel entrance after the four-block journey, he enthusiastically re-emphasized Cascade's desirable location, accessible by train or riverboat.

Mosquitoes were getting hungry, and it was hot. Marcum noticed that the traveler, who had spent the night on the train, was blinking more often than one should.

Hotel administrator, R.B. Glover, stood by the raised reception desk, waiting for Marcum and his guest. He pressed his spine against the polished edge. His shoulders cast a shadow across the hand-bound guest registry laid open, displayed like himself, in a prominent location. Pivoting his glance from one front window to the other, he tapped his foot to a melody that had sounded in his mind since breakfast.

He spotted Marcum addressing a pale, intelligent looking stranger—the enumerator, he assumed as he lunged forward, opened the lobby's double doors and bid, "Welcome to the New Cascade Hotel. We are honored to have you as our guest, sir, compliments of the Cascade Commercial Club, our local business association." He waved his hand. "Right this way."

Marcum made the introductions, after which Mr. Benton commented, "I didn't realize Cascade had such comfortable lodgings." Wide-eyed, he noted the grand architectural accents: etched glass, palm trees, an abundance of sculpted moldings, columns, corbels, brass fittings and fixtures. Nor was the interior's structure lacking: handsome woods, inlaid and overlaid, floor to ceiling. First class, he assessed. Perhaps he would spend his allotted day off, here. Wafting aromas turned his attention to another doorway from which tableware tinkled. His stomach growled.

Glover formed the opinion that Mr. Benton was not the type of man who dawdled, so he postponed further discussion and graciously offered an amenity he thought would surely please this guest. Sparing commentary he said, "Mr. Benton, I'd like to offer you my private office during your stay." The guest's tired eyes followed Glover's manicured fingers that pointed toward the front of the establishment. "If you'd like, I'll put the word out for folks to come to you, make things convenient."

Mr. Benton spotted the referenced office behind two palm trees anchored on each side of an imported glass door. Light crisscrossed from multiple sources: a row of east-facing double-height panes cased with velvet dressings, a standing lamp next to a well-worn leather chair sided by a table littered with periodicals and painted wooden ducks and, most pleasing, a green glass-hooded reading lamp that capped a radiant glow upon a lengthy foundation—a glorious desk, uncluttered, broad and shiny.

Meeting the eyes of the proprietor, whose barrel-chest measured twice the circumference of his own, Benton replied, "Mr. Glover, sir, generous of you indeed. But the law is specific. I am obliged to physically meet each person I register—in their habitat." He cleared his throat and shifted his weight, daring himself to accept the gratuitous gift. "I would, however, appreciate the use of your study in the evenings, perhaps, to finish ledger entries." His eyes darted toward the polished mahogany surface and back to the Cascade men.

Glover handed Benton a key. "Just lock the doors as you leave."

"Thank you, sir."

Glover raised his arms and snapped his fingers. "Our dining room is open from two to eight o'clock, all meals complimentary to our census taker, of course. The bellhop will see you to the presidential suite."

Benton was anxious to wash, nap and eat, in that order. Tipping the bellboy, he inquired about laundry service and was informed that there were two local establishments, equally good—the Chink's place and Nigger Mary's. Benton placed a second dime in the boy's white gloved hand, along with a bundle of shirts, asking him to take care of it.

Waking after a brief snooze, he remembered the words on the placard by the hotel restaurant door: *The House of the Well Fed.* "Well Fed" made him think of livestock, but thus far, everything seemed to be top-notch. Famished, he slipped his slender profile into cotton casings and trotted down the red-carpeted stairs.

Mary, clad in her Sunday best, gathered coins from her new, second favorite cigar box, "Croaker" the frog, and proceeded to her intended treat—supper at the New Cascade Hotel. She'd listened to Glover brag about the fancy décor and mouth-watering menu for weeks and thought she might run into someone interesting, like the census taker. Taking her place at the back of the establishment, she added the cost of items in her mind before ordering.

Benton, having been ushered to a table topped with white linen and a red rose, scooted himself forward on the tufted brocade chair, adjusted his recently purchased congress shoes to point forward directly below each knee, aligned to form an angle perpendicular to his lower leg, precisely. He opened the menu and perused, his attention drawn to an encased parchment that read: *The House of the Well Fed features four courses in six categories: soup, relishes, meats, vegetables, desserts and pies.* Knowing cost was not a consideration, he smiled.

Glancing across the top of her menu held open with both hands, Mary surveyed the dining room. Six tables were occupied, including hers; only one, other than hers, with less than two people. There, by the window, a thin man fiddling with his napkin, tidy looking; must be him, she concluded. Appears pleasant, if looks be true. I should tell him to check the Courier "local news" section if he's on the lookout for anybody; it's all there: who is where, for how long, the names and dates of hotel guests, social event attendees. No, I'll leave him in peace.

She heard him speak.

"I'll have the cream tomato soup, dill pickles, prime rib of beef au jus, creamed potatoes followed by apple tapioca and the chocolate soufflé, Miss.

Please wait until I'm finished with one course before you bring the next, if you would be so kind."

He waited, mentally reviewing techniques to optimize census interviews, having made it a personal challenge to succeed in the art of obtaining accurate facts from individuals diverse in character and disposition. Religious standards further mandated that he harbor no prejudice in regard to a resident's age, sex, occupation, social standing, or anything else, in order to gather accurate information for the annals of American history. He held the belief that census taking should be entrusted only to persons with moral principles, though he admitted that his motivations were not entirely selfless; a personal objective had urged him, originally—the desire to become less shy.

A full-time watchmaker, his craft had not supplied adequate opportunity to develop social skills he had grown to desire. This is what had prompted him to contract as a federal enumerator ten years previously, during America's 1900 census. This time, his second census, he was feeling less anxious, after having surprised himself the decade before —initial fears had quelled after recording demographics, and on several occasions he had found himself engaged in delightful conversation. Thirsting for more, he had waited for 1910, anxiously resolved. What social junctures might come his way, he continued to wonder, as he set time straight for his customers.

Mary's excitement grew. This census would be her second as a Montana resident. She was pleased that her status, both as a resident and as an American citizen, would be verified, and she appreciated documentation of additional facts, personal details as required on the official form, such as: whether one could read or write, one's present age, occupation, and place of birth, (one's own and one's parents), information that when scribed by the enumerator, was recorded, forever—historical public records, she believed it was called.

As she waited for her meal, a side dish of mashed potatoes and gravy, Mary drummed her fingers on the tablecloth and listened to a pair of women at the next table. They were out-of-towners, average to the eye on all counts.

"…Thank you, Mabel."

"We shouldn't have let the past keep us, you know …"

"Apart. I don't understand politics like you—help me to—so ashamed that I can't read—and you know they will ask."

"Don't worry, Minnie."

"But I feel so ignorant, not knowing. He kept me away—you warned me."

"Never mind. You got away. That's what matters."

"Will you tell me about Lucy, and what's that other one's name, Susan? Did Taft make any new deals, like Mr. Roosevelt?"

Mabel glanced around. Mary nonchalantly turned the other way.

"This time it will be different, don't worry, I'll teach you—"

"When I can read, I'll decide who to vote for, and I'll be ready when Congress passes suffrage. We can cast our votes together, Mabel. Our new life—"

The elder placed a finger to her lips. "Keep your voice down, dear. You never know. We're just—and you never—"

Amen, Mary thought, when congress passes suffrage I'll be right there at the polls with you ladies. Wonder what happened to that poor woman. If men and women had equal rights, I'd be a retired lady of leisure. Wouldn't need the laundry at all. And if I did keep it going, I could employ hired hands to wash and iron—someone like Abel Grange, for example. And I would be soaking in the hot springs at that Helena resort, the Broadwater Hotel Natatorium. Maybe Onatah's Mary Ahwao can do that someday—be in charge.

A dressed-up dishwater-blonde walked across the room to the piano. She sat down, opened the fall and began her recital with an arrangement of "Danny Boy."

While Mr. Benton slowed the speed with which he had ravenously consumed the feast before him, he wondered about the simply dressed, muscular colored woman sitting at a small table toward the back of the room and tried to recall the Christian name attached to "Nigger," the name of the laundress mentioned by the bellboy. Diverted by flat keyboard notes, he tucked a shoulder and returned to his engagement. Ceremoniously, he spooned the last dollop of soufflé into his mouth, pushed a pointed tongue through the creaminess, pressing dark chocolate flavor to his palate's arc, and, savoring the richness, thought about who he might interview first.

Once word about the census taker was out, the Birdtail populous split into frontier factions. Citizens who wanted to be registered and recorded stayed home, anticipating their visit from Mr. Benton, while the remainder who did not wish their names or whereabouts known, took off.

Toward the end of his second, carefully tallied eight-hour day, Benton arrived at a small, flat-board house where a smudged hand printed sign in the window advertised, "Mary Fields' Laundry." Ah, he thought, Mary, that was it, the boy said Nigger Mary's.

His knock was answered by a cheerful voice. "Howdy, Mr. Benton. In the garden, over here."

Wiping sweat with his only monogrammed handkerchief, he walked around the back and located the strong colored woman he had noticed the evening before. He watched her cradle the root balls of small plants as she organized, redressed random emergence into permanent parallel rows. He thought of his wife, an avid gardener.

Touching the rim of his derby, he began, "Good afternoon. Since you know my name, can I assume you know the purpose of my visit?" He squeezed the oversized ledger against his chest and smiled.

"Got a seat for you right here, Mr. Benton." She pointed to a three-legged stool at the edge of her garden. "It's the spot with the best view. Let me just wash my hands."

He sat on the dusty surface, thinking it impolite to brush the dirt off, which led him to consider there was a fifty percent chance she had laundered the shirt he was wearing and a one hundred percent chance she would launder the trousers contacting the stool; he would engage her services before he moved on.

"May I take a few moments of your time to record your information in the United States Montana census?"

Pushing hair into her bandana, she flipped a bucket and sat down. Her stomach was flipping, too, with nervous excitement.

"Yes. My name is Mary F. Fields. I am seventy-eight years old this past March, and I can read and write, and I'm a citizen and the head of my household."

Mr. Benton notated, distracted by her affable manner.

"Can you read and write?"

"Of course, I can," she repeated, "Didn't I just mention that?"

"Oh, yes. Sorry. What is your occupation?"

"I own and operate my enterprise, Mary Fields' Laundry, and have since moving to town some fifteen years ago. Was the Star Route Mail Carrier for eight years, between here and Saint Peter's mission, seventeen miles out, but I retired from that seven years ago." Pride welled up, and she didn't mind one bit.

"So, you are O.A.," Benton uttered.

"O.A.?"

"Yes, working on your own account—one of the census abbreviations. Do you rent or own your home?"

"Rent." She thought of Montana's constitution, the conditional taxpayer property ownership prerequisite for women, and shoved her trowel into the dirt.

"Marital status?"

"Single."

"Where were you born, Miss Fields?"

Mary orated, "I was born in Hickman County, Tennessee."

Years of labor rushed through her mind. She picked up a small stone and squeezed it. Her hand got sweaty.

"Just need the state. Were your parents both born in Tennessee, as far as you know?"

Using her monotone voice to veil emotion, she found herself grafting an edge to it, to keep things right, insist on the civil respect she deserved.

"Well I wasn't born yet to bear witness, but they told me they were birthed in Tennessee, into slavery."

Benton felt her eyes watching his hand on the page.

"Thank you, Ma'am, that's all I need. Oh, wait, I'm obligated to ask if you are a citizen."

"Yes, I am a citizen," she emphasized, "A *free* citizen."

Distressed that he had not performed his task well—how could he have forgotten her first answer in seconds—he shut the ledger and stood up. He feared that he had fueled justified irritation during his last interview of the day. Unintentional or not, there was no excuse. He deserved her ire, but it was strangling hot, and he was tired, and it had been an honest slip up.

"Thank you for your time, Miss Fields. Very nice to meet you. Good—"

Mary interrupted, "You forgot one question, Mr. Benton."

Benton twitched. Had he failed his criteria? Sweat rolled behind his ears. "What question is that, Miss Fields?"

"You didn't ask my race," Mary said, deadpan.

Benton clamped his jaw shut, fearful it would hang open.

She saw his dismay. As he grasped for an appropriate response, she called, "Gotcha!" and grinned. "Never know, though, I could be part something besides Colored. I think you should have asked."

Benton caught his breath. "You are correct. I apologize, Miss Fields. I assumed, and that was neither proper nor correct. What race are you, Miss Fields?"

Mary wet her lips. "Thank you for asking, Mr. Benton. I am a woman of the Negro race, which folks call colored or black nowadays. How is our category named on the census papers?"

"Black, if that's what you mean."

His thoughts turned to iced tea in the hotel dining room.

"You have a good afternoon now. And wait." She bent over, snapped a budding blue blossom, a flax flower, and held it out to him. "A boutonnière for your lapel?"

He returned her gaze and in so doing confirmed what he had known at first sight of her—she was a good natured, astute woman. She was testing my competence and bias and has every right to—she is an American citizen whose data I was hired to record—correctly. Evidently, I passed. He reached for the stem, letting tension drop.

"Thank you, Miss Fields."

"You are very welcome, Mr. Benton. Good of you to travel out here and register all of us settlers."

Wonder if I'll be here next time, she thought, looking for her seeds.

The man who built and retained title of the Cascade Hotel had promised Glover an extended lease after agreed-upon renovations were completed. In September he motored across the Russell Bridge from his residence on the eastern bank of the *Missouri* to sign contracts prepared by his solicitor, finalize the business arrangement.

An hour later, the ten-year lease signed and notarized, he proceeded to his second destination.

As he stepped out of his Model T, two women passing on foot covered their lips to whisper, "Why on earth is a gentleman calling on Nigger Mary?"

When Mary finally heard the persistent knocking sounds, she opened her front door and waited for the stranger to say something.

"Good afternoon to you, Miss Fields," the portly white-haired man greeted.

Miss—second time this summer, Mary thought to herself. "Who might you be?"

"We met years ago, when you were the mail carrier. You worked for the nuns, and you gave me a ride to town—my buggy wheel had broke—name is Burt Stickney."

She cocked her head, willing her vision to focus sharper.

"All right. Are you here to drop off laundry?"

"No, I have business to discuss—a proposition."

"My, don't hear that every day." She backed up. "Come in, Mr. Stickney."

She waved him to the straight-back that cornered hers at the head of her little table and plopped down, tired.

Ignoring the strange smell, supposing it was some kind of laundry additive, Burt Stickney settled into his seat and looked at the woman who had been strong since the beginning, a Birdtail legend—the one who helped the nuns build their mission, the one who forged through impossible elements alone, delivered what everyone needed—the pivotal Birdtail Mail Carrier—the grit that connected everything—until we got so comfortable. Deserves more, she does, much more. He set his hat on the table.

"Miss Mary, I have news that I want to share with you before the whole town knows. I've signed a ten-year lease with Glover for the hotel."

"You won the hotel?"

"No, I own it. Built it back about the time you and I met." He was pleased that he'd decided to present his proposal. She appeared frail, and her voice was changed. We are all different now, his mind rambled.

"That was a long time back, I don't recall—"

"No matter." He looked at her hands, chaffed but agile. "I want to tell you something."

"Shoot."

"You were kind to me, and I'd like to thank you."

"You're welcome."

She wondered how long this stranger would talk. The laundry was waiting, ready to scrub.

"I am leaving soon, for California, to join my son and his wife, retire in the orange groves."

California made Mary think of Mother Mary—she never mentioned oranges, but … She tried to imagine a field of orange trees. Grove is a nice word for a family of trees … She drifted. Must be magical, sweet scented orange globes hanging in green leaves, like Christmas decorations. A crow cawed. Startled, she answered, "I'm glad for you," wondering why he was telling her all this.

"What I want you to know is," he said as he leaned forward in the chair, "I have arranged by legal stipulation in the hotel lease between Mr. Glover and myself that you are to receive meals gratis, whenever you wish, for the rest of your life."

"I used to dry orange peels on my stove. Bought the oranges from Shepherd and Flinns to give the children." She paused for a moment. "You want to give me food, for free?"

"Yes. It is my pleasure. The arrangements have already been made."

"Why would you do that?"

"I don't mean to offend you—I realize that you, of course, do not need financial assistance. You've helped most everyone at some time or another, and I'd like to see that you don't have to make daily efforts to prepare meals, unless you choose to. You still work hard running a business, and I think this town is lucky to have you. You were kind to me. I hope you will accept this small token of my appreciation."

She wondered what he might ask for later. "And you'll be in California?"

"Yes."

"Well if you put it that way, thank you. I accept. I wouldn't mind not having to cook at the end of a long day. This is mighty generous of you. I don't know what to say. Can I do something in return? Free laundry, at least until you leave?"

"No, no. Now you can remove meal preparation from your list of tasks. Whenever you feel like it, go over to the House of the Well Fed and order whatever you want, on the house."

"On the house?" she repeated to make sure.

"On the house, forever. Here is my California address." He slid his calling card toward her. "If there's ever a problem, contact me. I mean it. You'd be doing me a favor—I need someone to check quality control. R.B. is keeping my chef, Charlie Gunther—he'll take good care of you."

He looked at his pocket watch, stood and scooted the chair back, concerned whether the poor woman could see well enough.

"I must be going. The best of everything to you, Miss Mary Fields."

"Have a restful life in the orange groves, sir, and in the sunshine, Mister …"

"Stickney," he said stepping into the crisp air.

Mary closed the door and took a deep breath. "Glory" she said, grateful for the unexpected windfall. "I just might make it now." She swayed and caught herself.

Sometime later that afternoon, Mary shared her news with the locals at the Silver Dollar. Monroe bought the boys a round, ordered Mary a pink lemonade with ice and made a toast to the thoughtful B.F. Stickney and to Nigger Mary in congrats. After her third refill, Mary sauntered home with high hopes, whistling. Food and good company, she thought, essential ingredients to life. I'm lucky.

18

CRUELTIES

FALL 1910 - SPRING 1911

As Mary hung bed sheets belonging to three local families onto her backyard clothesline, she admired bright patches of color in distant mountains, the annual tamarack turn from green to gold to amber. Why do larch lose their coats before winter when their relatives, the pines and firs, don't? Never gave it a thought. Just liked to watch the colors. You'd think they'd get too cold … Why don't the other trees lose their needles? Don't they want to mulch the forest floor? Probably have no control over it, like being colored instead of white … or yellow instead of red.

Thoughts of binding flower-bud boutonnieres for the Cubs, came to mind … how she had enjoyed herself, the best summer for years. Then she compared present fall tasks to those of her past: won't have to be like the squirrels this fall, don't have to go hunting, that's good, too. Or buy food hardly at all. Will make my winter luxurious … never had such a convenience—meals cooked for me, free. I'll catch up on things, listen to radio broadcasts at the Monroe's, spend my babysitting money on skeins of store-bought yarn for Mary Ahwao—crochet her baby blanket, a matching cap and more booties—think I'll order red. Would I choose to be white if I could?

As president of the newly formed Cascade Commercial Club, J.E. Marcum seated himself behind a small table that faced three rows of sparsely occupied chairs in what he called the conference room of the Opera House. Tapping his gavel, he called the October meeting to order and announced the first item of old business: Cascade Incorporation Progress, and the first item of new business: Cascade City Election Planning.

Marcum informed the growing number of associates, a congregation to his thinking, currently numbering seven men which included H.D. Hall and R.B. Glover: "Montana county elections are held every six years. The last election was November of 1906, for the 1907-1912 term."

"But city elections are two-year terms, aren't they?" Glover asked, annoyed by Marcum's proclivity for overviews.

"Yes," Marcum replied, spreading fingers through his hair. "The next statewide city elections are mid-April, but once we're incorporated, we can have our election immediately."

"We want to do that as soon as possible, don't we?" someone asked.

Marcum cleared his throat. "It's best to have our city election as soon as our incorporation papers are approved. We want to get our vision of growth into motion. We will, of course, have another election in April, as mandated by state law. That will be a two-year term that will synchronize with all other Montana incorporated towns and cities."

"Who are we backing for Cascade Mayor?" Monroe asked, aware that new members might not know.

"And how many aldermen?" asked another.

Marcum cleared his throat, again. "This brings us to the second item on this evening's agenda—Cascade City Election Planning. Most of us, I believe, are in favor of proposing H.D. Hall, our respected associate here, for the seat of Cascade Mayor."

Hands clapped. Hall glowed, making no attempt at humility.

"Gentlemen," Marcum asked, "May I see a show of hands? All those in favor of supporting H.D. Hall for Cascade's electoral candidate for Mayor on the Citizens' Ticket, raise your hand."

Who's stupid enough not to vote for our sheriff, thought Harry Ludwig, who had been out of town for a year. He tried to remember how long H.D. had been Cascade's sheriff and wondered if winning the election would mean he'd retire, thinking that he'd always been a lousy shot. He whispered to Monroe, "Who's running for the other party?"

"There is no other party, just the Citizens'."

Marcum's voice boomed, "You understand, of course, this is an informal show of our support, not an official vote for candidacy."

"Of course, we all understand," said Frank Warner, Vice President, sitting in the first row. He looked back. "Don't we, gentlemen?" Heads nodded, and pipes were pulled from pockets. "H.D. is our prize businessman, been here longer than most of us—I don't think he'll give us any surprises—will you H.D.?" He shot a glance to the hopeful candidate and winked.

"Been here since our town was called Dodge," H.D. said proudly.

"I didn't know Cascade was called Dodge." Heads turned to McKay, the newest member, arriving late. Irked at the accusing stares, he defended, "Well, how should I know? I'm young—"

Marcum smacked the gavel. "Gentlemen, back to business, please. Let the record show that the Cascade Commercial Club supports H.D. Hall as candidate for mayor. Frank, would you notify the Courier as such?"

Frank nodded.

"And Frank, invite Hinton to join our club while you're there."

Glover raised his palm, asking, "Who is going to nominate H.D. at the Citizens' Party meeting?"

Heads turned back to Marcum. "It would be my honor. Meeting adjourned."

State documents arrived the first week of 1911. Cascade had been granted the State Seal of Approval. Marcum and Glover spread the exciting news: Cascade was officially incorporated. The city election would be held as soon as possible.

On January 23rd, five dozen men gathered in Cascade's Opera House Theater to formally nominate and elect their candidates to run on the single-party Citizens' Ticket. A unanimous show of hands confirmed Hall as the Citizens' mayoral candidate. Doctor Russell and Misters Rowe, Atkinson, Lemon, Wedsworth and Thompson were chosen to run as aldermen. Election Day was set for February 14, 1911.

Harry Ludwig, browsing in the hardware store for nails and utensils, noticed an election placard leaning against the register and scratched his head, baffled by Cascade's apparent interest in proprietary development. He recalled Cascade's earlier policy of doing things. He hadn't known the meaning of the word "proprietor" back then, when he built his saloon … you just paid the license fee and got on with it, each man to himself.

He asked the cashier, "I suppose this is a dumb question, but doesn't a real election need two parties—or at least two candidates? What's the point of voting if there's only one party and one candidate running for each post?"

Women standing nearby snickered. A murmur slipped, "Men always get their own way." Her companion muttered, "One way or the other."

Ignoring them, Ludwig frowned. "It's just that I've never seen the place so organized," he said with candor, maintaining eye contact with the clean-shaven clerk. "Makes me a little nervous."

"I don't know what to tell ya," answered the young man as he held the prettier lady's change, coins that he would sequentially count in pausal time, pressing each into her cupped palm. "I just do as I'm told." He broke Ludwig's stare to wink at her and purposefully watched her blush before swinging back to Ludwig with a hollow shrug.

On Valentine's Day, women watched droves of men march to the town jail to exercise their constitutional rights. By sundown, the ballot counters announced what everyone expected: all candidates listed on the "Citizens' Ticket" were victorious.

Harvey D. Hall won the mayor's seat in a landslide majority—fifty-one of fifty-two votes, male votes.

The men celebrated at The Mint Saloon. H.D. Hall distributed cigars, and R.B. Glover handed out tickets for fifty cents off Sunday dinner at the New Cascade Hotel. Mary, who normally didn't frequent taverns in the evening, watched them from a table in the back as she played solitaire, listened to boastful accounts and strategies. Hall is pleased as a barn cat herding the ignorant grain-fed rats, she thought as she gripped the pistol under her apron, the one she carried at night. Rats ... wonder if his brother Dan served rat stew at his café. Wasn't hard to compete with him. Wish I could have kept Mary's Café going longer. Knowing it was best to leave before the crowd got looped, she slipped out the back.

Rowdy patrons toasted Hall and each of the aldermen: to winning the first election, to Marcum's vision of incorporation, to victory in general. Tongues loosened as drinkers took turns telling what they'd like to see change in Cascade while Marcum sipped seltzer, recording notables that could be useful for bank policy—interest rates in particular.

Cascade's first City Council meeting was held on February twenty-fourth, in the lodge room of the Opera House. Hall introduced an ordinance he had drafted in advance and put it to the floor for discussion.

"Well, gentlemen, want to say it right off, congratulations once more. Here we are. I'm mighty proud to have you with me. Let's get started." He hammered the gavel again, for emphasis. "All right. We have new business, like to get this voted on tonight, get things rolling. As you know, we have a lot of ordinances to work on—getting water and sidewalks, lights maybe. Those are gonna take some fact finding and more money than we have yet. This one doesn't. I've ironed it out:

City of Cascade. Ordinance Number One. As of this date, no member of the female sex has the right to smoke or drink alcohol in a public place. No woman of any race will be allowed to enter any drinking establishment in Cascade for any purpose, from this time forward.

"On the floor for discussion."

Alderman Rowe responded. "Mayor Hall, why would you want to start with this? Do you want all the women up in arms?"

"No lady would be offended by such measures," Dr. Russell stated.

"Yes, well put," Hall agreed.

Mr. Thompson was concerned. "How can you say that Doc? My wife would be offended to hear that Black Mary was thrown out of her socializing post. She's never caused trouble."

Hall raised his hand. "This ain't about Black Mary, Thompson." He crunched brain cells to remember the words Marcum had helped him rehearse, "Cascade is an incorporated City, and it is our responsibility to clean it up. I'm talking about the prostitutes. We have to get them out of sight, like every big city does." Close enough, he thought.

"We do? I heard that in New York, there's dancing halls that will pop the eyes right out of your head, short red skirts and—"

"This is not the time for stories you cannot verify Char—Mr. Lemon," Hall reprimanded. Charlie Lemon scratched his head and looked at a crack in the table around which they all sat.

"I think we've been very lucky with our prostitutes," Rowe commented. Chuckles tumbled.

"You would," Mr. Wedsworth uttered.

Rowe looked to Hall, and Hall hit the gavel on its block, scowling. "This is a formal meeting, let's behave. Mr. Rowe, please continue."

"Yes. Well, Cascade ladies of the night have always behaved themselves. In fact, none of our saloons would have survived without them, such pretty lures. They have never been lewd, to my knowledge, and always take their business elsewhere."

"That's right, H.D., I mean Mayor Hall," Mr. Atkinson concurred, followed by several voices affirming the same. "The lot of them. Always been good entertainers, singers, dancers ..."

"Just the same," Wedsworth objected, visibly upset, "admiration of flesh is a private matter and should be taken off the streets. A proper city doesn't allow whores to advertise their wares in the open."

"But they're not in the streets," countered Lemon.

Hall scowled and reclaimed the floor. "Gentlemen, we're getting off track. We're not here to talk about the pros and cons of whores. This is a discussion of a proposed measure for city protection. Once passed, all of Cascade's *good* women retain the right to drink or smoke in the privacy of their homes, if you are of a mind to let them, so this measure does not infringe on the rights of God-fearing women. On the contrary, it protects them, honors their codes of decency by removing offensive sinning from Christian eyes."

Everyone knew he meant fornicating and adultery, of which some, including Hall, were guilty.

"You know," added Atkinson, "I have to agree with you, H.D. Moral, God-fearing women—our wives, mothers, sisters who work hard to take care of us and our children—should not be forced to face that which causes offense, heartbreak, even."

The room grew silent.

Wedsworth cleared his throat to calm his nerves. "Of course, we are bound to have differing assessments about the necessity or lack of it for whores—good, bad or indifferent."

Minds rallied.

"As alderman, Wedsworth continued, we need to set our personal predilections aside. We are here to advance the state of our City. I take that to mean it's our obligation to protect the physical and moral health of our population. We're a small City, with several saloons."

"Yes!" Hall slapped his knee. Straightaway embarrassed by his parliamentary error, Hall uttered, "Sorry, Wedsworth."

Wedsworth bowed his head. "As I was saying, the presence of Satan, I mean *satin*: the presence of indecent satin necklines strutting to and fro, to the saloons, exposing our children to sin—children who, by the way, ask uncomfortable questions without tire. Well, I'm—"

"If the prostitutes can't get their customers at the saloons, what do you think they'll do?" Charlie Lemon looked worried. "Leave town?"

"Of course, they won't leave," barked Rowe. "They'll set up their own place."

More than one glance swerved. Lemon moaned. Atkinson elbowed him in the ribs.

"Well, I'm not married," Lemon objected. "Maybe you don't know what you're missing."

"Councilmen!" Hall brayed. "I believe Alderman Wedsworth was saying—"

Dr. Russell interrupted, adamant to share his conclusion. "History shows us that there will always be saloons and whores and objections to them. Let's design an optimal solution for everyone. By passing this ordinance, we'll create additional funding and comfort for the Christian community. In so doing, Cascade will become a beacon for wholesome growth."

"Where will this additional funding come from?" Rowe asked.

"Taxes." Russell took a sip of water, "Every business, even a brothel, has to be taxed. Up 'til now they've not paid."

Lemon sucked on his lip, convinced that the whores had paid somehow.

"Yes," said Wedsworth. "Seems to me, brothels would merit the highest tax."

"That's another issue," said Hall. "We'll take it up at another meeting."

"Wait a minute. If you take the glittery ladies out of the saloons, some of our saloons aren't gonna make it," Charlie Lemon pointed out.

"What about Black Mary?" Thompson persisted, "She's done nothing wrong."

"One nigger can't stand in the way of a whole town's future," Wedsworth advised.

"Even she could see the point in that," said Atkinson.

"Back to the issue at hand, alderman. I think we're ready for a show of hands. All those in favor of Ordinance One, raise your hands."

Six hands lifted high.

"All those opposed, raise your hand."

Mr. Thompson raised his, bound to honor defenseless women who didn't deserve to be thrown out of anywhere without cause.

"The ayes have it. Motion passed." Hall slugged the gavel down. "Meeting adjourned. Excellent work Council. Next meeting in two weeks or so."

"An ordinance divined with morality and money. What could be better?" Dr. Russell felt it necessary to add.

Charlie Lemon's mind lingered on red garters and occasional glimpses.

Not quite ready to fight the cold winds that hammered outdoors, half of the group remained and wandered into the lobby.

Victorious, Hall lit his pipe and reviewed in his mind: whores relocated to the edge of town, easy to control—Nigger Mary, she's out, more angry she gets, the better—might just get herself arrested. I'll make sure to tell the judge to send her as far away as possible.

Thompson worried about telling his wife. Black Mary had babysat his children since birth. He was anxious and beginning to feel angry.

Wedsworth estimated revenues from a future tax base, calculating whether the Council would be able to accrue enough funding for salaries and

City improvements. Allowing a whimsical idea to formulate, he thought: if we collected a quarter from every visit to the whorehouse, taxing both the customer and the service, that precinct would generate the highest cash flow and bestow its aldermen with the most clout—but not without a number of headaches—which led him to the same question Rowe voiced simultaneously:

"Which precinct will the bordello be in?"

"Not ours," Dr. Russell barked.

"Well, that leaves ward two and three," said Rowe.

"Don't be hasty," Wedsworth replied, "They will be working to everyone's advantage, paying their share of our healthy fiscal budget, providing more jobs—"

"What? You're the one who wanted them long gone," said Lemon.

They bade their goodnights and left.

Hall, feeling smug due to the ease with which he had guided and his Council had followed—"orchestrate" was the word Marcum used—decided to stop by and have a brandy, as J.E. had suggested. Hell, he thought, now we can hold City Council meetings in the saloons if we please. No women to mess it up.

Council ordinance news spread, the way the *Missouri* flooded during snowmelt—fast for some, slow for others.

The prostitutes were furious.

Mayor H.D. Hall paid for the first round of whisky at the Silver Dollar Saloon and men from everywhere pushed and shoved to get their share, many having no idea what the celebrating was about until the words "council—victory—election—men only" rang in their ears repeatedly. The boisterous collection of guests celebrated their newly acquired status; now they were voters in city elections, part of the future that had been glorified during campaign speeches, recipients of increased prosperity and innovations they would soon enjoy, like running water.

Men toasted, hooted and hollered for this new, better life. They were ready and they had earned it. They had, after all, built the settlement that became a town that became a City. Lady luck was cheered.

When the saloon was full, H.D. Hall stood at its center to make an announcement. "Welcome citizens of Cascade. We invited y'all here to celebrate Cascade's first Ordinance to make your City bigger and better. As your representatives, we have, excuse the pun, barred women from entering our saloons. This makes our town more desirable to businesses we'll be encouraging to move here."

"All women 'cept the prostitutes you mean, right?"

"Think of it as your private men's club—gentlemen in big cities pay lots of money to get in men's clubs, have to apply and all. You got it for free." A bead of sweat formed on Hall's upper lip.

"The whores ain't allowed in here no more? Why the hell not?"

"We're protecting our citizens, the good women: wives, mothers, sisters."

"That's a back-assed reason if I ever—"

"No offense, but it's a sin to steal satisfaction from a man's loins."

Aldermen Russell and Rowe stepped closer to Hall who shouted over the complaints, "We aren't stealing your sex. It's gonna be relocated, that's all. We made a City law, an ordinance. Says no women allowed in the saloons and they can't drink or smoke in public, that's all."

"That's all?" animus bellows demanded.

"They was beautiful to look at," one voice simpered.

Visions of cleavage incensed outrage: "You can't take our entertainment without asking. You've ruined everything—the dancing, Belle's voice, sweet as—" More customers chipped in. "Yeah, you're deflowering our place, or is it defrock, I forget—"

"You mean they're not just takin the night off?" the one at the end of the daisy chain spattered.

Contrary support diverted a full-fledged attack on Hall and his entourage: "It was an overdue necessity if you ask me—morally on target—women got to learn their place—public temptations of the flesh are blotches on our City's glamorous future."

"So's the Black Mary," a burly bricklayer added, "a big black blotch."

A well-known homesteader objected, "She never did any harm. She's the one who actually listens when a man has a sorrow to get off their chest!" He quivered, remembering his daughter's death.

"Not her chest we want to be see'n," a local without teeth brayed. Suckling sounds came from someone nearby, bent over.

Reasonable minds counted to five, tightened lips as nostrils widened. Drinkers guzzled, spurs rattled. Marcum shook his head.

Monroe couldn't let the offense go. He squeezed through free loaders and their spirits to interrupt the gaggle of aldermen. Squaring himself face-to-face with H.D. Hall, he said, "What's the matter with you? Nigger Mary, an old woman sitting at the back of the room, minding her own business isn't far enough away for you?

Hall swallowed the smirk rising up his throat.

"Answer me, H.D." Monroe threw accusing stares to the medley. "Aren't you all ashamed? She's been here longer than any of you. Cascade's own baseball mascot for God's sake. Throwing her out?"

Hall's years of sheriffing were of benefit to him. He coughed up an impartial voice as though nothing was personal. He was the rule keeper who informed. "The law can't make an exception. You should know that, Monroe. No matter how you feel about her." He let a sour tick of disgust dangle. "She is female, and the ordinance is about commerce. We can't have whores strutting around children. And the law includes all the Cascade women, including yours, and an old black woman." Hall leaned back.

"Whores have the right to be in business, too," yelped Duggan, an upright property owner. "Why wasn't it put to a vote?"

Eyes darted. It was clear that this was no run of the mill wingding.

"No one's stopping them from conducting business," Hall said matter of fact.

"Don't forget your soapbox on the way out," Monroe growled.

"You lambaste yourself sir," Dr. Russell said to Monroe pointedly.

Hall, grateful for Russell's two cents worth, waved a comrade salute grinned to his public and headed toward the bar.

Watching his mayor in action, Charlie Lemon lamented. What have I done, voting the way Hall wanted? It's more than bare flesh that'll be missed. Next time I must think harder, contemplate, he vowed. "There won't be no more dancing," he heard himself blurt. Musing further, he lamented: that sweet scent of rose water on fair skin causes a fella to pucker his lips, even if'n he does nothing about it—standing shoulder to shoulder with cowboys who bathe once a month maybe, cow dung and sweat crusted, whew—to get a moment of relief ya only had to wander over to Black Mary's corner, revive with a whiff of laundry soap, and she always had a smile waiting for ya—That's the Silver Dollar. Now it's lost and gone forever, like Clementine.

Nervous, Alderman Rowe defended the Council and his place in it, "City Ordinances are made for the welfare of our community. If head of household boots are not firmly planted, who knows what ideas will penetrate the frail minds of women; petitioning for temperance or the right to vote for example—things we don't need. You voted for us to represent you and we are acting in your best interest."

Instead of the applause he thought he deserved, customers turned away and asked for refills. An anonymous voice hollered, "Is our incorporated City tax money pay'n for this moonshine you've been hand'n out?"

Odors of grease, hair tonic, saddle soap, sweat and horsehair ripened as the night wore on.

Monroe berated himself: he had been foolish and naive to believe that

Hall held Cascade's best interests at heart. He clenched his hand into a fist, certain that Nigger Mary was the real target of Ordinance Number One, sidled to the bar and ordered another beer.

Seated at a long table near the establishment's center, a crotchety old regular snarled, "Well gents, more important than all that nonsense, I'm rais'n my glass to Mayor H. D. Hall for relieving us of that darkie canker that's darkened our doors like the plague." He swayed, groping for eye-to-eye contact.

Hall raised his right hand in acknowledgment and turned back to his company.

Clinking glass with strangers to his left and right, the insolent codger pushed a chaw of tobacco into his cheek and guzzled. He asked faces he could not identify, "Who decided she could jaw with us men in the first place?"

Braggarts quickly agreed and swapped uncouth vulgarities. Shoulder to shoulder they touted in succession: "Finally, we got the old nigger out of our way," … "We can relax without her ugly mug listening," … "Yeah. Put in her rightful place at last," … "Beneath cracks and floorboards like the cockroach she is," … "Or six-feet under."

Another round-on-the-house was hosted by Marcum.

Hall's brother Dan bellowed, "It's worth paying tax if it means getting rid of Nigger Mary who don't have the right to be in Montana in the first place, along with all them darkies who should still be slaves."

Monroe had had enough. "You hedonist Confederate," he charged as he kicked Dan's stool and watched him grapple to catch himself, "I'll rearrange your point of view." He seized Dan's collar, arched his free arm to strike the troublemaker with a lethal iron punch—the earmark of his short boxing career, pre-marriage.

Jim Cornell, just returned from the outhouse, intervened. He was not going to see his friend locked up for losing his temper. He pulled a Smith & Wesson from his holster and blasted the ceiling, nudged Monroe aside and spewed, "He's not worth it, D.W."

Hours later, when customers had gone, a peculiar boding seemed to groan in the empty tavern—both saloon owners felt it and turned to each other.

"Did you step on a crack?" Porter asked.

"What?"

"Something—" He looked to the shadows and saw nothing.

Wagstaff shrugged, reluctant to say what had occurred to him during stomach spasms sustained throughout the wild evening. A solemn voice confided, "I was so wrapped up in the night's profits, I missed the obvious."

Porter sighed. He knew exactly what his partner meant. "Yeah," he growled, "No more income from the prostitutes. And by the sound of things, plenty of tax."

"We had a good system," said Wagstaff.

"Yeah. Worked for all of us." Porter wiped the last glass clean and set it on the bar. "And we're the ones who kept this little toad hole of a town going all these years," he objected.

Wagstaff pushed his hands into back pockets and caught Porter's glance. "Feels like I'm being dumped for a prettier gal named Money."

Claret, the eldest and more experienced prostitute, having worked in St. Louis, Missouri prior to her narrow escape by riverboat, gathered her associates in the room she rented at Ma's Boarding House. She shut the door, turned the key and faced worry.

"Now don't fret, gals," she assured. "Watch them get a wiggle on over to any place we tell em to go." Her long fingers flicked a fan open, and she fluttered perfume-scented air onto her rosy cheeks. "We'll take our time and be real careful."

"But, Claret," the youngest girl complained, "They're makin' laws to tell us where we can and can't go. What law's protecting us?"

"Have you ever known any?"

"All the saloon owners are gonna be mad at us, losing liquor sales we brung 'em all this time."

"Yeah," another joined in, "and we're losing our cut on those sales."

"Wonder if we can work with the barkeeps somehow," Claret said, thinking aloud. "I'll think of a way."

"Are they gonna make a law against us?"

"I'm scared of Hall."

"Trust me, he doesn't want us gone."

"Nor does his brother."

"Or his father," said the plumpest with the prettiest face.

Laughter felt good. Limbs stretched, shoes and stockings rolled off.

"We'll have to get our own place, have to charge more to cover rent. That's the Council's fault, if anybody complains." Claret paced, hands on her famous voluptuous hips. "Have to find a way to serve liquor without them saying we're operating a saloon. Maybe we can create a package deal: one drink, one poke, one hour. What do you think?"

The clutch of women reckoned.

"Does that mean more pay?" one asked.

"Lust will be levied and we'll reign," Claret charged, raising an arm toward victory, pulling her shawl off with the other. "No free ogling at the dirty old saloons anymore!"

"We can make our place fancy."

"I know how to sew."

"Good, darling. Our customers will pay on entry. This could be, will be, a great thing—all of us coming together into one house—get out of the alley cribs and dark corners, make our business legit."

"Can't wait to see the look on those aldermen faces. We should charge double for them, and three times for the Hall family."

They all laughed.

Claret asked, "Can you think of any empty buildings on an edge of town?"

No replies came forth.

"We'll find one. Maybe old man Duffer will move out of his place, it's big enough."

"Or we could give him free company and meals in trade, maybe."

"Now you're thinking! One thing is very important: we have to keep quiet. Don't say a thing about this." She narrowed a firm look at two of the girls.

"Let's make 'em wait for their pleasures for a few days, at least."

"Yes!" We'll get the upper hand."

"They'll be eager to see things our way, just you wait and see."

"Will you be our Madame?"

Claret, pleased for the sentiment, studied the handsome assembly. "Let's think about that later," she said, considering how it would be to retire from active duty.

"All those in favor, say yes," a vivacious redhead proposed.

Affirmative shouts rang unanimous.

"Guess I better make us a business plan then," Claret declared. "Seriously, we'll share to get by. No more favors—no tricks of any kind until we're all working together. It has to be this way. Agreed?"

"Like the musketeers?"

"More like, royal courtesans, incorporated."

Wives, mothers and daughters were also distressed. Though the new law didn't alter their actual survival (unlike the prostitutes), it did affect freedom. The fight for it. Ordinance Number One segregated them, limited them—implying, if not confirming, a higher degree of ownership that would delay acquisition of equalities such as: the vote, the right to keep their own earnings, and property ownership.

Emergency meetings, religious and secular, were held to redress their loss. Wives of City Aldermen were questioned for inside information. Even if the ordinance took the painted ladies out of drinking holes, so what? They knew how far desire could travel. Some weighed retaliatory measures. Others plotted revenge. Leavened determination was on the rise.

One woman, the inspiration for Ordinance Number One, navigated her outrage alone. The unpainted interior of her small house seemed to impinge, change from walls that protected to boundaries that fenced.

Outside, waist-high snow covered the land. Bitter northern wind forced limbs to its will, whipping Mary's naked lilac branches against the building's exterior. She stoked the fire and paced. Disgusted and angry, she threw shouts of irate indignation against her confined space—the cell that would shackle her lifestyle, thanks to the ordinance. "They planned it for months, the ogres. Black-hearted sinkholes. It's Hall, and Marcum, probably. Like I'm so much of a threat. Damn."

Pacing, she chewed on a leftover piece of corn fritter, then kicked the bucket of kindling. "Why do I pitch optimism? Convince myself it's gonna get better? So foolish. I'll lose my friends now, out of sight. They'll forget about me while I'm stuck in here. Too cold to stand about outside—depot has no heat either. I'm left with mealtime at the hotel. My friends out of reach—me and the laundry, stuck."

It took practiced willpower to stop the foregone conclusion—that her life was sliding backwards to a reconstituted version of slavery surviving overseers who wielded, withheld, stole and punished. If only I could harness a four-horse team, launch onto the wagon's helm and take off, feel flight, catch breath in the wild open like I used to.

Her arthritic thumb twitched. She settled into the chair that headed her table and exhaled, knowing what would come next—the sad heart breaking. She watched memories of other ambushes—tired memories that resurrected themselves without permission. She felt vexed, beleaguered and extinguished, like thin fragments of ash detached from the flame. Kissed. Dismissed. Burned.

The next morning she rubbed her eyes, rolled out of bed and started a new fire. Winds had stilled and temperatures had dropped. Nature had bound the living, made things brittle. Certain to crack, Mary thought, if one chose to fight elemental forces.

Unexpected sunrays lit rime frosted glass, spreading diffused light into nooks and crannies. Pleased for such a gift, opaqued portals providing improved vision and privacy, her mood levered. She felt different, further removed from the situation at-hand—surprisingly buoyant. Sauntering in her solitude, she composed a melody that became a verse and she repeated it, to set her oath: "I'm staying peaceful to myself, behaving like the sun. I'm rising and setting without dramatics. That's all I have to do." She repeated her vow as she combed her hair with her fingers, gazing at her photographic portrait. "That's me, the strong, accomplished Mary Fields. The Star Route Mail Carrier, standing proud."

"I'll know what to do, when it's time," she told the self that worried, "This is nothing new, the hunt and the hunted. Don't spend energy on the ugly. It is, and I am part of it, whether or—And I have enough preserves."

She opened a jar of peaches, grabbed a spoon and ate, gracefully, by the fire.

In the beginning, Mrs. Ada Marcum was pleased, assuming her husband had minded her bidding to rid the town of Nigger Mary. She had heard him discussing the measure with Hall in her parlor immediately after the election.

After initial havoc settled, she evaluated the broader implications. Though James had complied with her demands, exorcizing Mary and the prostitutes men claimed did not exist from the saloons, her own rights, and those of all her friends, had been curtailed in the process. The already slim freedom doled out by husbands, fathers and employers had been buried, legally, and new freedom would be harder to excavate. Worse, it had been, in part, her own doing. It was hard for her to admit that according to the law, she was her husband's property, still.

This was certainly not the intended result of her ultimatum to get rid of Black Mary.

She was not alone. Women wringing hankies with worry called their physicians and reported an increased number of maladies, all of which required laudanum syrups. What would happen next? Would the Council confine the female sex to parlors, kitchens and laundry rooms? Would elixirs containing opium be outlawed? Would women be hauled off to jail, as the breach of each ordinance threatened?

Mary was glad she'd stayed inside. When Hattie knocked on her door, she checked to see who was there, then opened it greeting, "Welcome to Mary's Laundry, otherwise known as House of the Shunned. Come in if you dare."

Hattie stepped across the mudsill. "I see you've managed to keep your humor." She leaned close to give an extra-long hug.

Mary made rose hip tea and Hattie unwrapped the food she'd brought in her basket, their usual ritual.

"Did the Council happen to send humble pie with you? Posies pleading forgiveness?"

Hattie laughed. "Wish I could say yes."

"Well, I'm sure your muffins are far better. No arsenic."

They made themselves comfortable at the table.

Mary said, "Thanks for visiting, Hattie. It's good to see you."

"You too, Mary." A pause ticked by, each wondering where to start. Hattie decided to get to the point. "Mary, you're not going to like this."

"That's all right. Rather hear it from you."

"They had another meeting, passed another ordinance."

Mary raised her eyebrow, reminding herself to act like the sun.

"They're pompous jack-asses," Hattie declared.

"My word!" Mary said, "Hattie Monroe swore."

"Well they are. There's no excuse for this one."

"Go on."

"The schoolhouse is no longer eligible to the public for any reason, other than use as shelter during God-made emergencies—fires, floods, earthquakes and such. No meetings for any members of the community except for pupils and school staff and related administrators—councils, boards and the like. Violators will be fined and put in jail."

"My birthday party."

"Yes."

"That's custom-made, without a doubt." Mary stayed calm until she thought about the children. "Mean enough to me, but the children! The aldermen's children too—denied the party and treats they so look forward to—as if they get so many in this small-minded birdbrained—No, that's insulting the birds. Rodent-brained, town. Talk about childish behavior."

"Earl and Lester are very upset."

"Of course, they are." Mary's wrath gained ground. "This is personal, real personal. No reason to punish the children. Stupid idiots."

Hattie sighed. "And after those debates about it, last year. They know very well how important it is—to their wives and their children and you. It's the one time we all get to appreciate you without hiding it. You have a new dress all sewed, too, don't you?"

"Yeah, purple one, with a hat."

Hattie bit into her frosted oatmeal muffin.

"So now I can't fraternize, sip or puff. Or love my little friends in public? God forbid, what? Someone might catch a glimpse of love? The C.C.C has been replaced by the mongrel C.C.C."

"What?"

"The former, from my Café days. My faithful customers, the Cascade Coffee Council have been replaced by the Cascade City Council. Dark times. That leaves the C.C."

Hattie smiled, waiting.

"The Cascade Cubs. And they can make an ordinance for that, too. No women mascots."

"Glover would put a stop to that."

"Maybe. I don't care."

"How did you hear about the first ordinance anyway?" Hattie asked.

"Note under my door."

Hattie gasped. "You must have been one of the reasons they were in such a hurry to get incorporated," she said, knowing so already.

"Yeah. I'm afraid to think what they'll do next. All people not white, register here, pay all your money, then we'll burn you at the stake."

"We can have your birthday party at our house Mary."

"Thanks, Hattie, but it's not right. They all know my birthday's in a couple weeks. That's why they were in such a hurry. I thought the school board was supposed to regulate school policy. How are they—Oh well— Dang it. Wasn't gonna let myself react. It's the children, Hattie."

"I know, Mary." They all love you, that's for certain. The Council can't change that, ever.

"Unless they get me out of town."

Silence wavered with what felt like enough power to shake teacups.

"Had my birthday party at the school over ten years now."

"Yes, " Hattie nodded, thinking. "I hope this at least gets the rest of the women upset enough to heckle their husbands. Maybe it's possible to change—"

"Don't count on it. It's law already. Nothing they like better, making up laws everybody has to follow." She shook her head.

Hattie poured more tea and placed a second muffin on Mary's plate.

"Has it occurred to anybody besides me," Mary stated, "that some of these lawmakers have ownership in companies such as the Cascade Valley Realty Company? The company that the Council will likely hire for City projects. That's a conflict of interest or a double indemnity. Has it slipped everybody's attention?"

She picked at the cigar butt in the ashtray, then looked to Hattie. "We'll all be getting a tax bill saying our city is buying some land from a realty that will manage its development for a fat fee, plus their profit."

"I'm so sorry, Mary. So sorry." She placed her hand on Mary's and watched her look away … and back.

"And I'm being punished like I'm a criminal. You too, Hattie."

"I know. It's frightening. It's like returning to the dark ages. What are we going to do?"

"I don't know what you're going to do. I'm thinking, better find a way to unincorporate the incorporated greed before it's too late."

"When are you coming out of your house?" Hattie asked.

"Before it's too late," Mary replied.

The ante had been upped. Members of "ladies only" guilds proposed consequences, including abstinence of home-sweet-home desserts, culinary and otherwise. Their children's annual party, a harmless social event if there ever was one, had been cancelled without consideration, conversation or concern for the youngsters.

Irritated mothers once again bore the brunt of their husband's greed for control while endless cries from the children demanded fair play. Why was Mary Fields' birthday party cancelled? This was not about prostitutes; this was about their babysitter, laundress, and occasional confidante: not of their class, but a kind old woman who provided important services.

Ada Marcum thought about women in states to the west—Idaho and Washington. They had gotten the right to vote, even foreigners. Powered by scorn and guilt and the desire to act on her own, she invited Emma Smith DeVoe, a suffragette from Washington, to come give a talk on suffrage and temperance at the Cascade Methodist Church.

What was there to lose, Ada weighed. She'd already lost the potential for motherhood when Marcum was hit by a random musket ball in an unspeakable location. It was about time to take control of her own destiny, she decided. At least speak her mind.

Mary thought of her father's last words: *Pick your battles.* On his deathbed, he had struggled to clarify: *Not a war—a fight for life—wisdom is knowing—* His last breath withered to a silent absence. Seven years old, she'd held him, crying.

She sat in her rocker and contemplated, *when exactly, is it too late?* Coming up with the same answer after studying various future scenarios and facts known to her about each of the council players, she considered her father's words again and got up, washed her hands, packed her satchel, tied the wool blanket she had folded and rolled to suffice as her bedroll and added extra cording to craft a shoulder sling.

Posted outside her house, she waited, listened and watched for wagons coming or going, from town. She was ready and determined to walk to her destination if need be—over a hundred miles.

Hours later, good fortune delivered a colored miner and his wife. She watched them drive a wagon pulled by two big mules—enough horsepower to carry extra body weight. They stopped at the mercantile.

She rushed indoors, shut the stove's damper, grabbed her satchel and bedroll, locked the door and scampered, chin high.

On the way, she ran into D.W. Monroe, explained she was in a hurry and asked if he would keep an eye on her place while she was out of town. He complied without questions, and she arrived at the mercantile as the couple stepped onto the street.

Mary engaged, asked politely, offered to pay. Kind-natured, they welcomed her, glad to accept her offer to care for the mules, take turns with the driving. They asked her to return in fifteen minutes time.

Mary had told no one, not even Hattie, where she was going—or if she might return. It wasn't personal, in Hattie's case, just smart. A week earlier, she'd paid the landlord two months in advance, used most of her savings. She would send more somehow, if she stayed longer, in Saypo, with her beloved Onatah, and Edward, and her Goddaughter Mary Ahwao.

She faced the first part of her self-appointed mission; marched to the Silver Dollar, the establishment that sheltered the majority of Cascade's barflies. Inhaling patience, she idled, waited for the door to open. She was not going to break the ordinance, see herself in jail.

A stranger obliged. She pushed a large stone she had positioned, against the opened door with her foot, and stood sideways, eyes auditing the length of the street, mindful not to touch the building.

"Well," she started, taking a gulp of air, "it's the cavern of the big bully scaredy cats, making laws instead of justice." Her voice grew louder. "Is this how you thank your women, show them your respect, unlike the dozen states that have already passed women's suffrage? In case you don't know what that means, women in those fair-minded states have the right to vote, same as any man in any election—state, county, city and schools."

She glanced to make sure she had their attention. "The first act of your liberated thinking Cascade Council was to ban women from smoking and drinking. Small minds, gentlemen. Half of the women in this town smoke, drink and otherwise medicate themselves, and looking at their husbands' behavior, I sympathize." She squinted, gauging time.

"Why not arrest all the women, put us all in jail? Or might that be inconvenient when your three-square meals per day aren't served? As for being your mascot, find someone else to give Cascade notoriety. And find someone else to baby-sit your children. At least savage whites in the South have the guts to call themselves what they think they are: Masters. And by the way, why do you suppose the first two ordinances didn't get put in the newspapers? Think about it."

She kicked the stone from the doorway and walked even paces, hand on pistol in pocket. Forty seconds brought her to the wagon. She tossed her things into its bunk, asked if she could ride shotgun on the way out and stepped up, settled next to the bearded man who held reins in hand.

Spotting Hall across the street, she hollered, "Nice day to leave town," then put an unlit forbidden stogie between her lips. Matchstick in hand, she struck it against the under-seat spring when they reached City limits. She could feel daggers of anger from behind, burning hot as the cigar coal.

Pumping her cheeks, she pitched clouds of smoke signals in her wake.

19

RESPITE

"Thank you, lucky stars," Mary whispered as she unrolled her blanket and made her bed next to the miner's wagon. "A safe place. Been ages since I slept on earth."

She gazed into Big Dipper's pathway of light until weighted eyelids closed.

The next afternoon, she thanked the kind couple when their route veered from hers, and set off toward her destination, a few miles further. Stepping over puddles, she counted the number of days since she had left Cascade, when she had paraded a victorious exodus.

"It's my birthday," she called out.

A distant train whistle screeched a drawn-out bray followed by tail wind repeats sidled into trills that reeled, resonated and, at last, diffused. A heightened silence swept into place.

"Glad I'm here and not in Cascade," she said to hear herself say it.

Memories of birthday parties in the schoolhouse pricked.

"Drop it," she advised, and she did, thinking of her goddaughter instead. "I'm going to meet her today, on my birthday. Huzzah!"

She entered a grove of western hemlock and noticed smoke rising in tufts beyond. Bracken ferns reached her waist, and she ran her fingers along their shiny fronds that led, eventually, to an open meadow. From there she verified the source of the swirling signals: a small cluster of buildings perched beneath cliffs of rock split in defiant formations—the magnanimous base of the Rockies ringed by evergreen labyrinths of primeval forest.

Excited to compare her imagined view of Saypo to the real one, she treaded to the length of rutted clay sighted beyond budding thickets, allowing hope to warm the ache in her bones. She made up verses for "Over in the Meadow," one of her favorites:

Over in the meadow
where the sky is blue
I'm here to visit Onatah,
and little Mary, too.

Over in the meadow
And everywhere I look
Today is special
It's my birthday,
And look,
Here I am.

Grazing in a not-to-distant patch of green stood Bigg Too, her old horse, head up and ears pointed. "Oh," she squeaked. "He looks good, for his age. Best as I can see from here." She began to hum.

I harnessed him each morning at dawn. Years together, we traversed the Birdtail Cascade Mission Route. We were so strong. So much happened, such great freedom. We were important. It was us bringing everyone's mail to them safe. Delivered letters and supplies, protected personal messages that crossed states, and continents, even.

"Delivered the out-going mail sack, too." She reminisced and thought: I waited at the depot until I saw it locked inside the boxcar. Me, Mary F. Fields, also known as White Crow, and the Birdtail Expressman or Mail Carrier. Eight years I carried that Birdtail mail through Mother Nature's harsh milieu of weather: snow, wind, sleet, hail and heat. You name it, we got through it.

Sometimes, I forget.

"Don't forget," she said, staring at Bigg Too, who was munching fresh spring dandelions.

Onatah will remember what I did. I was important to everybody, whether they remember it or not. Folks don't remember much now, in Cascade—but who cares? Onatah and Edward and Nadie. Nadie, my darling Nadie …

She set her bedroll upon a boulder, suddenly tired. A large well-built cabin with a milled-plank porch and a second structure attached, living quarters, she assumed, stood fifty yards away. Large letters, neatly carved, painted and attached to the building's face, were arranged to display three words: "Saypo General Store."

Just like the letters I carved for Mary's Café except bigger, she mused. And better crafted, I admit. This is it. Onatah's family's trade post, the Bruneau place.

A bell tinkled as the hand-honed door opened and a longhaired man dressed in overalls, a straw hat and moccasins, emerged. He carried a shiny pick and grinned, as though he had found treasure.

Bet he saved a long time for that, she thought.

A man's voice cut the tranquility. "Bye now, George."

Mary's heart bucked a second time—that resounding bass voice was similar to that of her friend, Michael McKenzie.

And he lives here, too, she sparked.

Looking at her soaked boots, she shivered.

The man named George walked behind Saypo General Store and returned a short time later, leading a handsome mule, his pick tied to the back of a handcrafted saddle. They did not see her, the man or the mule. She had positioned herself out of view and watched them amble toward the mountains on a well-worn trail made narrower by greens she noted to be good ingredients for spring tonics.

There were no telephone or telegraph poles and wires; the general store was the place where modern utilities would be attached.

So, she thought, there's no way to contact Saypo residents without arriving in person. Except for post, she corrected herself. Bet they have their own Star Route Mail Carrier. I'll make sure to shake her or his hand. She gauged the time, having waited for clouds to move east, and thanked the sun for returning. Around noon. Guess I better announce myself.

She stepped onto the porch and opened the mercantile door, listened to the little bell and scanned indoor dimness for the owner of that deep voice—or even better, Onatah or Edward.

The broad back of a man faced her. Positioned behind a long, wooden, hinged counter, he stretched to hang leather-tooled harness parts on the log cabin wall. Expecting to see one of the regulars, he greeted as he turned, "Good morning, or is it afternoon?"

"Good day, it is," Mary replied, sure the virile man was Louis Bruneau. He wore a white shirt, collared by narrow lengths of fine cotton—wrapped, looped and tied into a tired bow at the notch of his neck—the body of cloth revealed curves of firm muscle beneath. Wavy gray hair brushed against shoulders that had, according to Edward, hauled countless numbers of hides from the wilderness in earlier days. Perhaps Louie had brought the shirt with him when he migrated from France, she mused, distracted.

He studied her. "You must be White Crow—and Mary Fields?"

"One and the same, sir. Is it Mr. Bruneau?"

"Please, call me Louie, like the rest of the family." He swung the hinged countertop up and came close, cupped her hand with both of his and shook it gently, "I am pleased to meet you. Onatah and Edward will be thrilled." He wondered why she had come now, before the weather warmed. Clearly it was not easy for an old woman to travel alone, there being no stage to Saypo.

Mary blushed from such a warm greeting and the touch of a man's hands. He was not only robust, he seemed kind, liking to Onatah's description. She thought she might even grow to trust him.

"Would you like to come in? Our house is just through the storage room here. My wife, Isabel, is home and she would love to meet you. You can rest, have something to eat. You must be hungry after such a long journey. Cascade, isn't it, where you live?"

"Yes. Thank you."

"Onatah and Edward are out harvesting mushrooms, morels. This way."

He motioned and followed behind her, reached across to open a second door.

Light from an east window flushed the cabin's contents, a large room divided in parts, well organized and clean. Furry black bear hides dressed the planed floor between two comfortable chairs that faced a large river-stone hearth. Inside its arch, an iron hook held a large kettle, indicating a belief that some meals were meant to be cooked over flames directly. The cabin, skillfully chinked and daubed, still held warmth from its morning fire, long after charred wood chunks had fallen through the yard-long grate. It was a cozy place. Mary couldn't help but recall Gertrude's open pit hearth, big enough for pigs and lambs; Gertrude, her mission comrade who had long since transferred to the Ursuline school in Great Falls.

On the far side of this setting was a beautiful beaded hanging—beads sewn onto a soft pliable hide supported on a rod of some kind—an artful image of flowers and leaves and stems that swirled together in shades of green, pink, red, and yellow. Its height was equal to Louie's, six feet, and its width, double that. Countless hours of beadwork had been dedicated to what was truly a magnificent painting, a mural that caught light and shimmered. Mary stood, struck by its beauty.

"Isabel? Are you here?" Louie called.

The beaded flower garden opened at its center and a petite child with wispy dark hair and amber-rose skin waved a small doll in a chubby hand. Sounding a triumphant giggle, she sprang into the room and tottered forward, her bare feet halting at Mary's boots. Gazing upward, her clear brown eyes sparkled—the result of love's covenant, Mary believed. The tiny person bounced and pointed to herself. "Mary," she said, imbibing grace only the very young and old could sense.

Mary knelt. "I am Mary, too." She put her hand out, and the little Mary placed the doll in the open palm.

"You can be my friend," the child offered, matter-of-factly. She sprinted toward the eyes Mary had felt watching from across the room and grabbed the woman's skirt. "Aaáh, look!" Mary pointed to Mary.

"Mary Fields, I am Isabel. Welcome."

Forthright like her words, Isabel's appearance was striking—straight black hair shimmied to the waist of an able physique, more than pretty. Mary saw the bond of love between Mary Ahwao and Isabel and felt pleased.

She watched Isabel, young-looking for a grandmother, move like waves of the sea, rhythm partnered in natural balance as she gathered papers and a stray moccasin and motioned her guest toward the table and chairs Mary had not yet noticed. All the while, the little one, Mary Ahwao, skipped alongside, gripping Isabel's skirt, just as Onatah had done with Ucsote Mary.

Mary eased into a side chair where she could admire the beaded wall hanging and the girth of Mary Ahwao's home. She wondered why she hadn't come earlier; it had been two years since the girl's birth. Meeting this precious goddaughter on her seventy-ninth birthday was better than any party, anywhere.

Isabel placed Mary Ahwao on her hip, thinking as she had for the past two years, that a cradleboard would have been so much more practical. She placed a teapot full of steeped Earl Grey, along with sugar, milk, a plate of biscuits, dainty spoons and hand-painted china onto a silver tray and carried the arrangement easily, with one hand.

Mary supposed the woman inherited this seamless strength, physical and spiritual, from her family. She carried regalness, the kind folks are born with—at least that's how it seemed to her. Mary Fields thought about names. This Blackfeet woman had to have been given an Indian name at birth, she mused. She wondered what it was and what it had meant. She must have been strong to leave her tribe for a Frenchman—be demeaned by whites, taunted as a white man's country wife. Perhaps she had been orphaned early, too, like Onatah.

"Tea?" Isabel asked. "I'm heating some elk stew and fry bread."

"If you truly don't mind me barging in on you like this, I'd love it, to be honest." Mary relaxed and felt her feet swell up beneath her.

"You are not barging. We have been wanting to meet you. Shall I call you Mary or White Crow?"

"White Crow."

Mary smiled, pleased to have reclaimed her Indian name on her seventy-ninth. She listened to Mary Ahwao, who was murmuring baby talk, a tonic for hearts.

Louie joined the women for stew and bread and sweet potato pie. Mary Ahwao maneuvered food fairly well with a spoon carved by her grandfather. He called her his princess and she clamored for his attention, making silly faces and laughing at his.

Afterwards, Isabel insisted that White Crow rest, lie down on their bed while she took little Mary on an errand. Grateful, White Crow fell asleep in seconds.

Hours later, she roused reluctantly, from a dream in which someone stroked her hair and she felt loved. Eyes fluttering, she visioned unfamiliar shapes and recollections of Onatah as a child.

Small eyes peeked from the side of the bed.

"Annie," Mary mumbled, slipping toward slumber again.

"I'm here," said a voice from above.

She looked up. "Onatah!"

And down, rubbing her eyes. "Mary Ahwao!"

Later that evening, Edward, the sweet boy to whom Mary had released her position as Annie's protector, listened attentively, as did the rest of the Bruneaus, while Mary shared news from Cascade: the windfall of free hotel meals and jolly times with the Cascade Cubs—tales of a satisfied life that almost convinced her it was so.

"You're both so grown up now," she repeated, looking from Onatah to Edward, her mind set on recapturing gestures from their youth, in hopes they had not changed much.

Edward asked if the Cubs compensated her for laundering their uniforms, to which she admitted, "They call it my team contribution, and that's fine." She quickly changed the subject.

The proud parents detailed the acquisition of their homestead. Months earlier, they had finished building a small cabin on their land, their 160 acres that adjoined Louie's and Isabel's. It was close by, they said, two pastures over, where she had seen Bigg Too grazing that morning.

The family decided that White Crow would lodge with Louie and Isabel, the quieter of the two cabins. Louie set a cot by the hearth. Isabel cushioned the taut canvas with a cotton casing she had filled with straw and herbs, and insisted that White Crow stay as long as she'd like.

During the following weeks, Mary developed a new routine. She began each day building and tending the morning fire. After breakfast, a carrot in one hand and her goddaughter in the other, she wandered into the open field and called Bigg Too, and he came to the women he knew. They petted him, and teased him until his good-natured patience grew thin and he insisted on receiving his reward.

In the afternoons, after their naps, Aaáh (Grandmother or Godmother) and Issotan (Granddaughter or Goddaughter) played in the field near Onatah and Edward's cabin, under an old cottonwood tree. They covered a patch of earth with hides from an old teepee, added quilts and hats on top, a jug of water to the side. Mary Ahwao wrapped her dolly in the blanket Aaáh Isabel had woven and placed her carefully on the edge, instructing Baby Belle to take her nap.

White Crow had invented a game: she laid down, covered herself with a quilt, and at random intervals moved an arm or leg, that suddenly stopped or jerked. A disguised voice chorused guttural growls and high-pitched scratchy whispers. Then, that hidden someone, or something barked grizzly tongue-twisted squealing sounds and croaked, "Who's there? What's that I hear? Is it a squirrel?"

Wide-eyed, Mary Ahwao scooted back. "No," she uttered.

An underneath limb twitched, and the phantom quizzed in a changed voice, "Are you a fox?"

"No," Ahwao braved.

Escalated huffs challenged, "I know, you must be the beaver who's been gnawing my tree trunks. You smell like a beaver!"

The thing twisted toward her. "No!" Mary Ahwao screeched as she leapt from the quilt, "I am no beaver."

Movements stopped. The child crept closer, holding her breath.

"I know who you are," the creature thundered, "You're a big buffalo, and I'm going to tickle you!"

Fabrics flew. Ahwao screamed as the terrible, funny faces let loose. Buffalo arms grabbed her and held on tight; she was tickled and tickled until teary laughter rippled into pleas for mercy. The pair rolled onto their backs and gasped for breath.

"Do it again," Ahwao petitioned.

Mary often took supper with her three favorites: Onatah and Edward and her namesake goddaughter. Like a regular family, Mary allowed herself to consider, embracing the simplicity of it all. When dishes had been washed, adults took turns storytelling. Familiar characters appeared in various dilemmas and victories; heroes and heroines with strange accents: muskrat, sky woman, buffalo, alchemists and elephants in settings that included mountains, thunder, drums, hunting, cities of gold, potions, riverboats, Africa, teepees and forts that washed away in climatic floods—countless versions of adventure filled with trepidation and laughter, inspired by wishful imaginings and histories and aspirations where ancestors and their deserving descendants danced on, changing the world.

Edward, exhausted from farm labor and his duties at the store where he consolidated orders and made deliveries, admitted one night after putting his daughter to bed, that he found it difficult to fulfill expectations held from contrary cultural beliefs, his parents'. He honored them, yes, but he and Onatah had to determine their family's path. It pained his heart, he divulged teary-eyed, when each of them pulled him aside to share dreams for their granddaughter. It wouldn't be so bad, he explained, if the longings were not anchored in traditions long-gone, unlikely to manifest in America even *if* they, he and Onatah, desired it to be so.

Onatah's stamina spread thin, too. She, along with Louie and many residents, mostly Blackfeet Métis, worked together to create curriculum for the Saypo School they had established.

"In the doing," she explained, "we have to figure out what our children will need most to get ahead. We are responsible, in part, for their success. Our academic choices will help or hinder their success. Which culture do we place as the one to admire and emulate? Are the lives of our native parents and ancestors to be told as history, extinguished? How do we honor our ancestors, and, at the same time, recommend adopting the European way of life that suppresses innate love for nature and community? You can imagine the many points of view, and how difficult it is to reach consensus—at least to finalize the programs for our children. It's so complicated. I often wish we could return to the way it was, before the conquerors came."

Edward, the son of a "conqueror," and one of many racially conflicted first-generation Métis, fidgeted.

"You used to say that when you were little, Onatah—that you wished life could be the way it was," Mary said, releasing a sympathetic sigh. She'd not thought about next steps for the Métis—goals more difficult to achieve than her own in some respects. "Doesn't help to pine over the past, but we all do it. I'm sorry it's so hard. You are both warrior parents plotting a strategy for a future impossible to foresee. But you're all so smart, and you have experience from both worlds. Who better to decide?"

Mary Ahwao woke, crying; Onatah brought her by the fire and rocked her in her arms.

Mary gazed at the beautiful child. "When it's May Day, can we go on a picnic?" she asked.

"Yes. That's a grand idea, Ucsote. We'll take Mary Ahwao and my handsome husband here, if he'll let us?"

Edward grinned. "That's in two weeks. Spring seed to deliver, lots of orders. We'll see."

"And Isabel, if she'd like to come?" Mary added.

"Oh, no!" Onatah squealed, "We forgot your birthday, White Crow. It was about the time you arrived."

"Day of. Best present and party ever, seeing y'all again."

Onatah's mouth gaped.

"Don't fret yourself, Onatah. You don't have to remember everything in the world," she teased.

Mary bade her goodnights and walked across the fields to Isabel and Louie's, gazing at stars and a crisp sky, grateful she didn't have to watch her back, grateful to be outside when she felt like it. Though planting time was coming near and her garden plot called to her, she noticed that of late when she spoke of her Cascade residence, she had begun, inadvertently, to say "going back" or "going to Cascade" instead of "going home."

Squeezing into the cot relocated to the far corner of the cabin when temperatures had warmed, she lay gazing upward. She made a list of all the little things she could do to help, if she lived here in Saypo: feed the stock, pick berries, plant a garden; make healing salves, tinctures, dry the herbs and leaves and roots for poultices and fomentations; collect the eggs … She drifted off.

It was Louie, observant as ever, who finally got it out of her. He purposely waited until the entire family was gathered outside, eating supper around a table he had reclaimed from rafters in the storage room.

"So what's the story, Mary White Crow Fields?" he asked with bravado reserved for family, having waited until mouths were full chewing first greens of the season.

"What story is that?" White Crow slung back, providing a moment to decide whether she would say.

"You've been here for a month without baring your soul. Since Onatah's your soul child, I figure you might want to tell her."

"My, oh my," she said, aware that denial would be useless, simultaneously granting Louie a new level of respect. "It's nothing I can't take care of."

"White Crow, what's going on?" Onatah demanded, shocked something had slipped past her.

"I'm sure you can handle it," said Louie, "but would you tell us, just the same?"

"We are listening," Isabel spoke, concerned. "Please tell us."

"All right, fine. It's not such a big hullabaloo. Just having a showdown of will power, I guess you could say."

"With whom?" Edward asked.

"The town council and their new mayor. Don't know if you remember H.D. Hall, brother of the other café owner, when I had my café."

His blank look spurred her along.

"Anyway, somebody's always got a bee in their bonnet ..."

"And?" Onatah's voice raised a notch.

"H.D. and I never got along—Difference of opinion in the care of horses, for one thing. Anyway, first thing he did after getting elected mayor was to pass two ordinance laws. Him and his aldermen cronies think they're Roman emperors, ruling the world. If each person were a separate kingdom, I'd be Africa and the only thing they'd want from me is slave labor. Not even that, now." She stirred her apple cider. "First Cascade law was made was against women—me in particular. Excludes all women from saloons at any time and denies a woman's right to smoke or drink liquor in public."

"That's your special place, source for—" Onatah bit her lip.

"Yeah. And then, just before my birthday, they made the second ordinance: no more local activities in the schoolhouse."

"Like your party."

"So, I hid out for awhile. Local insanity on the rise. Decided it was a good time to come visit y'all."

"Before you did something you'd regret?"

"Yes. Still thinking about putting itching powder in a few folks' laundry, at least. Irks me plenty—Conquerors with palsied minds."

"It's money and power," Edward said. "Like always."

"Always promised to see myself voting in that town before I die. Been there sixteen years now."

Louie Bruneau had been observing Mary's innuendoes, free for the noticing. She's frightened, he thought. As tough as they come, she's scared. "White Crow," he asked.

"Yes."

"I'd like you to consider something, if I may be so bold."

"Of course."

"There's no winning if you're dead before it happens."

She gave a nod. "That's what I've been thinking on. How high the odds are against me. One never knows for certain. She looked him in the eye. "Variables, you know."

"Yes."

"The thing you're wanting is mighty big," Louie stated.

"Want them to understand the polls are not just for them. And I'll vote as I please. In this case, against Hall."

"Equal rights," Edward said, unsure if it would ever exist for everyone— his mother, for instance.

"Suffrage passed in Idaho and Washington. Why not keep yourself out of danger, move here and wait for Montana suffrage to pass? Should only be a year or two, according to the newspapers," Onatah pleaded. She looked at Mary Ahwao, then to Mary and said, "You'd have all that time to play with your goddaughter."

"Have to pull my weight."

"You always have."

"Might've said yes to that kind offer a few months ago. But this ordinance—it's a slap in the face to all women, not just me. And it really grates ... And I do have to pull my weight. Besides, I'm old, and they can't shove me around like their wives and the prostitutes."

"If one of them hates you or your race in particular, you could easily get a bullet in your head, day or night. You know that. Since you are the only colored resident, it makes it all the easier."

"Father Bruneau," Onatah objected.

"White Crow knows it. Harder to ignore such variables when they're spoke out loud."

Mary looked up. "He's right, Onatah."

Isabel gave her husband a kick under the table.

"That said, I'll speak for us all now, Mary. We will be honored to have you come live here with us, in Saypo," Louie invited as he had been instructed, though he genuinely shared the sentiment. "You'll be a help to us all."

"Yes, White Crow," Isabel added. "That's right. We'll build you a cabin, and you'll be safe here."

"And we'll give you a big birthday party every year. You can have it in the schoolhouse if you want," Edward encouraged.

Mary Ahwao started to cry. Mary wiped a tear from her cheek and got up, insisted that she and her goddaughter needed a walk and headed across the field toward the cottonwoods.

"That's all White Crow needs to know from us," Louie said, turning to Onatah and Edward. "At least you know now, what's been going on." It occurred to him that if any of his Métis and full-blood neighbors refused to welcome a colored woman, he'd need to change their minds.

Holding Ahwao close, Mary wrestled through the Cascade scenario again, this time consciously aware that her option to leave town and live in Saypo, was undisputedly real. The deciding factor was integrally joined to the original issue, she concluded. A colored woman citizen had the right to vote and folks had to learn to accept it. She thought of Michael McKenzie, who, she had learned recently, been faced with a similar issue, and had paid the ultimate price. The bright light of a man she liked so very much had been killed by a sniper's bullet as he rode home from Choteau only three months earlier. It grieved her, deeply. When some locals claimed he should have avoided the volatile situation by stepping down, she understood why he chose not to—no person with high-minded principles would have done so.

Michael had opened a law practice some years earlier and was, at the time, defending a case concerning property rights—his son's. A well-off local had trespassed onto John McKenzie's homestead, discovered a large vein of gold in a deserted mineshaft, backcountry, and claimed the treasure as his. The case had gained statewide attention; Michael had filed three appeals. The petitioner, aware that his claim was false and illegal, had miscalculated and underestimated the McKenzies—which left him with one of two options: admit to his guilt, incur penalties and jail time, or find an alternate method by which to close the case. No one doubted that Michael had died true to his cause, nor that his life had been taken by the white man's greed. Was she ready to take the same kind of risk?

Michael, Mary reminisced, had been so brilliant and kind—an able negotiator and mediator (she had kept track through news accounts) and the one who had gifted her with the meaning of Onatah's name. She had wanted to know him better, learn about law, perhaps, befriend a new family. His wife and two of his three adult children remained in Saypo. Now he was dead.

Sunny days passed rapidly. Mary continued to spend her afternoons frolicking with Mary Ahwao, but she had made up her mind and spent most of her daylight hours strategizing details to accomplish her goal: the vote, in Cascade.

Onatah had skimped to bake an abundance of entrees for the May Day feast she planned in secret. Edward, who had to work after all, borrowed a team and buggy for them to use, suspecting that the women would be happier to spend the day on their own, anyway.

On May 1st, picnic supplies and fishing gear were packed in the buggy's trunk after breakfast. "I'll drive," Onatah said, giving Edward a peck on the cheek, "We'll be home before dark."

"This is luxurious," Isabel cooed, stroking the metal siding. Louie watched in disbelief, never having seen his wife excited over a vehicle.

"Be careful, most beautiful women in the world," Edward called.

"A glorious sight to behold," Louie added.

Onatah had ridden Bigg Too up the mountain, days prior, to make sure the meadow she had in mind, was pristine. Reins snapped against horseflesh, and they were off. "We'll be there in an hour," she said, though no one cared, content to be coasting through warm sunshine, watching for butterflies and robins.

Inspired, Mary decided to serenade, impromptu. She introduced a theme: *"Onatah, of the earth, and Mary Ahwao, of the sky, mountains that stand, wings that fly, birds that sing, wonder why—"* she paused, *"And that is why, Isabel and I are nearby, to sing you a lullaby."*

Onatah pitched back, *"And little Mary and I are here to sing to you, White Crow and Isabel, who we love as much as sky woman—"*

"I love Mama and Aaáhs," Ahwao jangled.

"Aren't we the song singers," White Crow belted above the buggy sounds. "Here goes:

Song for freedom,
song to heal,
song for a lullaby,
song to feel,
songs over water,
songs over hills,
songs for the big picture,
bouquets of flowers and frills.

"In the blue sky!" Mary Ahwao shouted, bouncing next to Isabel in the back seat.

Mary leaned back to tickle her and sang:

Yes, said the froggy,
Yes, said the hen,
we're not done a croaking or a squawking,
until you sing again

We're going to the mountains
singing to the trees,
singing in the forest,
and singing on our knees,

She gulped air for the finale:

Yes, said the froggy,
Yes, said the hen,
we're not done a'croaking or a'squawking,
until you sing again

We'll pick some pretty flowers
And dance and shout and sing
For this is our special picnic May Day
And we love the Spring!

"Did you just make that up White Crow?" Isabel asked.

"I told you, she's May Day magic personified, our own flower bouquet," Onatah laughed. She slowed the team and pulled off the side of the narrow road. Locking the handbrake, she looked to the cheerful grins. "This is it. We're walking from here."

They unhitched the two-horse team, tied knapsacks and fishing poles to lightweight saddles and hiked up an old path, horses behind. As they rounded a sharp turn, they saw falls of water drumming against stone—snowmelt splashed through crevices made narrow by ancient boulders and swollen roots. Patches of fluorescent green moss coated varieties of rock worn slick by wind, rain and time.

"It's so beautiful, Isabel declared, "I've never been here."

"We need to get out more," her daughter-in-law replied.

Ahwao picked up a quartz pebble and handed it to Mary.

"Thank you," her new Aaáh said. This child is so like her mother, she thought, it's like reliving the past.

Ahwao scampered ahead.

"Looks like that small pool might have some trout." Mary pointed. "Campfire trout."

Mary Ahwao turned around. "You're funny, Aaáh. Look. Flowers."

"You found the perfect May Day place—bouquets of posies within reach," Mary praised.

"Without hours of hiking." Onatah beamed. "A-n-d," the May Day scout announced as she took on a barker's tone, "for your pleasure, ladies—a big picture view."

Mary belly-laughed and sat down on the closest boulder. "Mary Ahwao, come here," she called, "I need you to help me find a walking stick."

Isabel watered the team and tied them at the end of the small meadow; horses in view, flies occupied.

Onatah unfolded an old teepee hide and moved it around until she located preferred measures of sun and shade.

Mary Ahwao lunged into the meadow's vibrant growth—knee-high green speckled with white yarrow, yellow glacier lilies and spikes of scarlet fireweed—spring poised on the edge of infinity.

"Ah," Mary sighed.

Having agreed to cast daily routines aside, they unanimously decided to enjoy their picnic feast first.

"Just like the old days, White Crow. Potato salad and my specialty—northern fried rabbit."

Mary hooted. "Kind of like southern fried chicken?"

Onatah grinned, rewarded for her labors.

Mary considered, so this is what it was like to be one of the children—everything arrives without the planning and the making—what a treat. "Yum," she crooned.

Sprawled under dappled shade from a huge mountain ash, sonorous drones of bees buzzed by, inviting daydreams. The four companions stretched their backs and arms and legs upon blanketed ground. Isabel and Mary Ahwao closed their eyes.

Onatah laced her fingers with Mary's, sharing her vitality with the woman she had relied on so completely at Saint Peter's. Respecting Mary's appetite for freedom and free will, she refrained from her desire to ask, *will you come live with us now*, and asked instead, "Are you happy, White Crow?"

"Are you kidding? This is the best." She pointed up and said, "She's a beauty, this grandmother ash." Admiring its age and shape, she added, "Don't usually get this big."

"Bears will love it in the fall, the clumps of red berries," Isabel collaborated, opening her eyes.

"Where I lived in Tennessee," Mary said wistfully, "the most beautiful arched trees you can imagine, grew giant." She painted the arch, waving her hand. "Red Oaks, they're called. Their strong branches twist and curve and rise perfect, like the sun. You know by shivers in your spine, that they're ancient and wise. Seen it all, they have." Transported, she continued, "In the fall, their leaves turn all red—so many shades of red I couldn't count—full of acorns and squirrels collecting their share."

Onatah scratched her head. She had never seen a red tree or acorns, and wondered whether red leaves were an anomaly, an aftereffect of blood spilled. Wasn't it Civil War territory, Tennessee?

"Can you picture that?" Mary's voice toned in sync with the bees, "a gigantic noble tree calling out to you?" She cradled her arms, "Come climb on my branches—I'll hold you—come see the world up here."

She stretched her arms and kicked her boots off. "So I did—I climbed up into that 'ol magic oak. There was a particular branch that curved like a horse's back and neck, a comfortable spot to straddle, way up. That big branch became my fine steed, and I wrapped my arms around its broad upward arc, stroked her bark mane. I named her Lightning, Lightning Pegasus, and I rode that horse many a day, galloping through blue sky, red and gold fluttering when the afternoon breeze picked up. I could see my parents in the fields, in the distance, but I was hid by the leaves …"

"What was gold?" Mary Ahwao asked, opening one eye.

"The acorns."

"So that was your first Lightning?" Onatah asked.

"Yep. Lightning Pegasus and me would travel to places I dreamed about, to lands far away, galloping free, exploring. And when we had to find our way back, I traced the patterns, remembering the scents from other lands. Wings flew beside us, birds telling us secrets. That's what we did, me and my red oak Lightning steed." Her face softened. "When I was little, not much older than you, little Mary."

She talked on, as if by urgency. "I thought no one knew where I was when I was riding Lightning in my tree. Years later, my mother told me she'd wait as long as she could before calling me down—til trouble would be had if we weren't back to our quarters. She said that she could see I was flying free somewhere. I'll always love her for that."

She took her cap off, let her hair be wild. Glad for the soft breeze that had arrived, she lifted and leaned onto her elbow. "Onatah, you always had eyes to the future and eyes to the past. You knew your tribe's history with your heart and soul—least that's what I think. I always thought your mother named you right. *Of the earth.* You are of the earth, and the earth holds all the wisdom we need. Except for when we need to fly," she teased as she reached up, ready to fly again herself.

Surprised to see tears welling on her Ucsote's face, Onatah said, "I wouldn't have survived without you."

A steady stream of shared history, gushed. Mary turned, touched her little bird's cheek and whispered, "Onatah, I thank God you're alive."

"I love you, White Crow."

"I love you, too."

The moment stretched as they listened to chickadees chirp, magpies caw, leaves swish and water splash.

Mary had begun to doze off when Onatah said, "I feel Nadie when I come here. What do you think happened to her?"

Mary rolled to her side, looked at Onatah directly. "I don't know. I was afraid to know for a long time. Imagining can be a jump off the cliff."

"You know she's gone."

"I know." A long sigh melted Mary's resolve to insist otherwise. "She would have written, come to see—one of us, at least. She's free somewhere now—wherever she wants to be, I hope. I send my love to her every day."

"Me, too. I miss her so much. Time doesn't change my feelings."

"She'd be here right now, if she could."

"Yes."

Mary Ahwao, who had succumbed to sleep, woke up sprite and cheery. She kissed Isabel and played with her hair, absorbed in her own thinking. "White Crow," she said seriously, "I saw you and Mama dancing. And your friend was playing the drum."

"Just now?"

Mary Ahwao nodded.

"What friend," Mary asked, sure that it was Nadie, or Nadie's spirit, rather.

"I don't know."

"That's a beautiful dream, darling," Mary said as she glanced to Onatah. "Come here, you—" She opened her arms. "I got ya, tickle, tickle."

Squeals of young delight flooded the woods.

Onatah stood up. "Is anybody ready for chocolate cake?"

"No, not us," Mary clamored as she rocked her goddaughter from side to side. "First, little Mary's gonna catch us some trout," she teased, letting herself be tickled back.

"I am going to pick flowers," Mary Ahwao cried, "*after* I eat cake. White Crow, do you know that Ahwao means Rose in English?"

"That makes sense. You *are* a beautiful flower. Should I pick you for May Day?"

The entire cake was devoured. Crumbs were given to ants. Splendid flowers were picked and bundled; stems set into the edge of the stream.

Later, trout were caught—enough for a big family dinner. Sunlight began to drop below mountain tips.

Onatah announced, "One more surprise." She dug through her duffel and, with care, lifted a brown box.

"It's Mama's special box," Ahwao explained to her new Aaáh.

"All of you, squeeze together. You can stay under the tree."

"Oh, my golly, it's a camera?" Mary bellowed.

Onatah's grin confirmed that she was correct—a manifest reality of her childhood vision.

"Onatah, you have a camera!"

Isabel put her arm around White Crow and Mary Ahwao snuggled between them.

The shutter clicked.

"I wasn't ready," Mary protested.

"Too late. Don't worry."

She held her prize high, turned it as though selling its features. "Mother and Father Bruneau gave it to me. It's the latest: a Number Three Kodak Brownie camera, with rolls of celluloid-covered film." She turned the winding key, readying the next exposure. "Sure is easier than coating glass plates with chemicals and developing them—though I did like the developing. Remember when I worked for Mr. Erikson?"

"Of course I do. You always wanted to be a photographer. I'll never forget that Fourth of July."

"What's a Fourth of July?" little Mary asked.

"I still want to be a photographer, a professional one, with a studio and equipment, someday. Taking portraits and landscapes, both."

"Ah! What a great gift you have given our Onatah, Isabel." Mary squeezed Isabel's hand. "So great."

"We are blessed to have her."

Isabel looked to her daughter-in-law. "Let me," she said. Brownie in hand, Isabel directed, "Get next to White Crow—you too, Issotan, next to White Crow." They squeezed in. "Are you ready? One, two, three." Click. "And again." Click.

"That's good." She explained, "Onatah showed me how, White Crow. It's easy. Click and turn the winder, that's all."

"My Lord, what magic. And the view isn't upside down?" she asked, recalling words spoken during Onatah's epiphany.

"No. It's right side up," Onatah said. "Negative images are still the same, reversed. And it's still a poignant idea, if you know what—"

"Indeed, I do," said Mary, proud of the little Iroquois girl who imagined such big ideas, who did still, and acted on them.

She asked Mary Ahwao, "Help me up, little one?" Solid on her feet again, Mary opened arms wide to the big picture and proclaimed, "This is the best day ever!"

Isabel positioned Ahwao upon a small boulder next to the waterfall. As she was about to turn the camera lever clouds moved and masked the sun. She looked up and frowned.

"It's all right," Onatah said, "this light is better. Really."

Isabel clicked, and helped Ahwao down.

"Looks like you already have your portrait studio associate," Mary declared, as she winked at Isabel who, flattered, nodded. She handed the camera to White Crow. "Will you take one of us?"

Mary looked through the viewfinder, framed her favorite faces close up, hair-to-hair, skin-to-skin, happy. She clicked the lever and handed it back to Isabel, who turned the winding key. "Can't wait to see that on paper," Mary said, "That is the first photograph I made."

"Louie will send the film for processing, Isabel told White Crow. "I promise to send you the best picture."

"Thank you, Isabel. I will cherish it."

"We should start back, "Onatah said, packing leftovers.

"Mary Ahwao, pick some of that grass over there, will you, sweetheart?" Mary asked. "Pack it in this basket, between each fish. Here, I'll show you."

Ahwao helped as prompted, ran back and forth for more grass.

"You're so smart, little one, just like your mama and your aaáh. That's right, a little more."

"It's sticking to my fingers."

"Never mind," Mary comforted, "We'll wash it off over here. Come on." They ambled to the bubbling stream. "Thank you for fixing the fish, Mary Ahwao. Adding grass makes them stay fresh."

"Oh. We are going to surprise my papa and Grandpa Louie with fish and flowers!"

"That's right, honey." She gazed into the youthful eyes, said, "Well put."

The day after, White Crow announced that the time for her departure had come.

Mary Ahwao felt sad and cradled her dolly in the pink blanket, reassuring Baby Belle that Aaáh Ucsote Godmama would come back.

Louie made the arrangements, and Mary thanked him for the gift of the stagecoach ticket over and over, until he would hear of it no more. Little Mary kissed big Mary as did everyone else during the last moments before departure.

Edward drove White Crow to Choteau in the delivery wagon and stayed by her side until the coach was ready: a new coach with windows and soft seats and a driver who didn't insist that coloreds sit up top.

"Guess it's time to shuffle my luck," she told Edward giving him a hug.

He smiled and wondered how long it had taken her to design the clever quip—a goodbye composed to avoid tears. "Come back when you're ready, White Crow. You can vote from here, too, you know. And if it's work you want, we'll give it to you. You're the boss."

She looked him in the eyes. "It may seem like I haven't been listening to all of you, but I have. Tell Onatah not to worry."

She sighed, leaning on soft velvet as she slid to the far window. Why *am I* leaving, she questioned half-heartedly. She tucked her lips and pressed them, fighting a gush of tears as she waved goodbye.

Weather had turned and clouds seemed to be wrestling, too. Ignoring the other passengers, Mary watched the landscape move by. Allowing herself a brief taste of melancholy, she admitted that it had felt extraordinary to be part of family who genuinely cared for her welfare and concluded: if those legislators would just pass Montana suffrage, it would all be so simple.

Part Four

20

PROGRESS

1911 LATE SPRING

It all depends on Herman Wolf, Mary concluded repeatedly, as she listened to the stagecoach wheels whir and rattle, rattle and whir. If he says no, I'll let it be and move to Saypo. If he says yes, I'll forge ahead, see it through, have my victory, and retire to Saypo, later. Either way, I win. A good life. Remember that, Mary Fields. You have nothing to prove anymore. Right now, I am choosing to exercise my free choice for something important. That is that. Then I'll move on, live with a family. Well, Mary and the sisters were family, too. I'll love being an ucsote, aaáh, godmother, elder, whichever name fits—share a life from the beginning with my precious Mary Ahwao.

She eased her head against the small coach window, viewed the landscape turned green and visualized the garden she would plant—which flowers would go where and in what ratio to vegetables, and what varieties of seeds and bulbs would she look for if she bartered babysitting or laundry services with other gardeners—assuming she still had a business upon her return. She wondered which blooms Mary Ahwao would like best and imagined planting a garden with her. The coach changed direction and rays of light warmed her hands. Evoking May Day's big picture, she drifted off.

Hours later the driver called to his team, "Whoa, whoa there."

Mary woke, surprised to have arrived so soon.

"Cascade," the man's voice shouted as he slowed the stage to a halt in front of John Thomas's Corner store, formerly Marcum's.

Remember the plan, she told herself. Don't talk or listen. Get home, unseen if possible, scoot over to Cornell's and get out, avoiding all distractions.

She did exactly that, delaying only to deposit her bedroll and satchel at home and grab a few things. Happy to see her, James Cornell let her borrow his horse and buggy. Within minutes she had completed the first part of her plan and was traveling on the Mission Road by mid-afternoon, refreshed and hopeful.

An hour later, she turned into Wolf's place as she had done hundreds of times before as the mail carrier, stopped at the water trough near the house, took the bit from the good-natured mare's mouth and eased a rope halter over her ears, assuring, "Won't be long, girl." She patted the bay's neck, straightened her own cap.

Mrs. Wolf peeked through the window when she heard Mary's knock, bustled to open the door. "Black Mary, so lovely to see you. What a surprise. Can I take your shawl?"

"No, thank you, Mrs. Wolf. I'm hoping Mr. Wolf is at home. Is he?" Slow down, she told herself.

"Why, yes, he is. Come this way. Do you have any mail for me?"

"No, you remember. It was a long time ago, since I was your mail carrier. Noting her confusion, Mary said, "I remember, Mrs. Wolf, you were often in a hurry to hear from your sister. Ohio, wasn't it?"

"That's right." She buttoned the top button of her blouse. "Yes. How kind of you to remember, Black Mary. Come sit in the parlor. I'll find Mr. Wolf."

"Thank you, Ma'am." Mary sat in the soft chair and closed her eyes, organizing thoughts to present her proposal the way she had planned.

She had known Mr. and Mrs. Wolf over twenty-five years. In the beginning, from a polite distance—they saw her at the mission when they came to church on occasion—then personally, as their mail carrier. During the last year of Mary's star route contract, Mrs. Wolf, Gerlach was her first name, had started to lose track of things, forget what she was doing, revert to her native German tongue. Then she would recover, right as right. Mary was glad to see that Gerlach hadn't gotten real bad, like another Birdtail wife she'd known who had been sent to a sanatorium; crazy, they claimed, just because she couldn't remember. Wasn't it just old age?

Hope Mr. Wolf is really at home, she fretted. Tapping her foot, she decided he was more like a bear than a wolf, always had been. Lumbering steps came into earshot.

Heavy bellied and hardworking, Herman Wolf kept to his ranch most of the time. He had made it a habit to treat Black Mary proper. At first he thought of her as a curiosity, then decided she was like the homesteaders, trying to get by. When he asked for mail delivery favors, to bring or take something extra to town, he'd ask politely, accept a yes or a no. He was special to Mary because he had not hesitated when she'd asked to rent his house in town. He didn't talk much though and was hard to read.

Footsteps stopped. The middle aged, tight-jawed rancher stood centered in the doorway, waited for her to notice. She looked up, and he greeted, "Good day, Black Mary," in a friendly tone peppered by his receding German accent. Mary liked the crisp rhythm of his speech, and it seemed to her that, accent or not, he always made himself clear.

"What brings us this pleasure? Is rifle practice to begin, again?"

"Oh, no sir." Probably an ordinance against it, she thought, as she started to rise.

He shook her hand and said, "No need to get up, unless you are leaving?" The upward twitch of his lip was familiar, signaled his good-natured wit. Mary eased back. The master of his house sat down. Gerlach had disappeared from sight.

"Mr. Wolf,"

"You call me Herman, Black Mary, you know that. You have talked to Gerlach; you might see she is forgetful sometimes. Comes and goes. She is fine, smart as ever."

"Yes sir, I think it started up when I was delivering your mail."

"Oh, yes." He had forgotten the change had begun that long ago.

"Mr. Herman, I'm here because it's very important, to me at least. You know I keep my word and work hard."

Mr. Wolf decided not to interrupt, nodded his head in agreement.

"And I'm more independent, perhaps, than many women, maybe because I've worked a man's job, hauling freight and mail, as you know."

"What's this about, Black Mary? I know you are upright. You don't need to tell me. Is there something wrong with the house?"

"No, nothing's wrong. I'd like to be a home owner, Mr. Herman." A muscle in her leg twitched. "I'd like to buy your house in town, the one I'm renting. But not the usual way."

Puzzled, the lines across her landlord's forehead deepened. He crossed one boot over the other and took a closer look at his guest.

"Just while I'm alive," Mary explained. "So, you see, it won't cost you anything, except a few years not living in it, which I don't think you want to anyway."

He scratched his head. "You propose to buy my house with contract to return to me when you die? Never heard of such a plan. I suggest you just rent. You have my word to stay all your life, Black Mary. Do you think I want to kick you out?"

"No. No, Mr. Herman, nothing of the kind. You have always been forthright. Everyone knows you are a man of your word."

"So, what is the problem?"

She leaned in, spoke in a softer tone. "Not a problem, so much as a goal of mine. I'm an old woman now. I have had a wish in my heart for a long time, and I want to see it through before I die." Her heart pounded as though it labored to speak, itself. At the end of a deep breath she asked, "Have you noticed any changes in Cascade atmosphere, lately?"

"You mean Mayor Hall and his ordinances? I say yes." He frowned and pursed his lips, tried to withhold disapproval that had intensified after reading articles reporting the "City Council progress." "Glad I am not there. Hall has more schemes than a rattler leading a pack of hungry wolves."

Gerlach, who had been listening in the hallway, stepped closer.

"Up to thirteen ordinances," Herman's voice cracked, "a baker's dozen—only cookies are not what they sell. Poor residents—that would include *you* if you bought my place—become poorer than church mice—one tax after another."

"Thirteen …" Mary uttered, reminding herself not to get emotional.

"They got to pay for water, for dogs, for business, for the right to live and mind all the crazy rules. People must be in home by eight-thirty curfew. Imagine!" His face had blushed to a disconcerting shade of red. "Still light in summer for *crying out loud*, as they say. Even they set a speed limit—not only for automobiles—for horses!" He shook his head repeatedly.

Mary's mouth parted.

Returned to calm, yet unable curb the course of his summation, Herman said, "According to the last law they baked up, no concealed weapons are allowed on any person unless they have a special permit from H.D. himself. All violators go direct to jail. And they have the gall to say, if you break an ordinance, you are committing offense against good order and God-fearing morals. A totalitarian dictatorship in broad daylight!" He rubbed his arm. "So no, Black Mary, you don't need to worry about *me* moving to town. Except for the mercantile, the train depot and my house, the whole shebang can burn."

"Mr. Wolf," Mary said, shocked by the number of changes added during her absence, "I was gone for awhile. I didn't realize it had gotten, worse, sorry to upset you." A tick of fear shook her resolve. Should she withdraw her proposal? She looked at Herman Wolf, clasped her fingers and said, "Sounds like martial law."

"Can say that again." Herman straightened, uncrossed his boot and met her gaze. "Oh, Mary, I forgot. They threw you out of the Q & L and Silver Dollar. I am very sorry—it was your eyes and ears, yes?"

She nodded.

"No women in saloons," he riled, "as if there were many. It is control. They plan some selfish thing, more than they are telling." Herman's perspired face began to pale. He unbuttoned his collar.

"So, what can I help you with, Black Mary? If I was you, I would give me notice, move far away. Maybe you would like to move out here, help Gerlach. I will pay you a salary."

"Mr. Herman, you're a saint. I agree with you about the council. They've gone wild, and to be honest, it makes me uncomfortable. And upset. But I have this dream, you see, can't get rid of it. Keeps coming back, no matter what. Know what I mean?"

"You said. What has this dream to do with my house?"

"It's not your house, exactly. It's about being a property owner, and a taxpayer."

"You know you can file for a homestead, Black Mary. Surely you know, and that costs no more than your rent if you add it all up."

"Yes sir. Thank you for helping me figure. You see, if I am a property owner, I can register to vote."

Surprised, Herman's shoulder hit the back of the chair. He sucked a long breath and stayed silent for what seemed too long.

Gerlach entered and asked, "Would you like some tea, Black Mary? You drove all this way. I'll get some."

Mary nodded, unable to speak.

Herman ran his tongue along his teeth.

Maybe I said it too plain, blurted it too soon, Mary gnawed. Should have said, *vote in City elections*, maybe—wouldn't sound like a suffragette demanding full rights—he's awful quiet.

"Why?" Herman asked.

She looked at him, baffled, wondered which of her points had not been clear.

"Why is it so important, Black Mary? You don't see Cascade women picketing for suffrage like in other places, demanding what they don't have understanding of—"

"Perhaps because I've done a man's work, Mr. Herman, listened to the talk in saloons—learned a thing or two, maybe."

This is as far as I'll grovel, she told herself. I could say, because I have every right as guaranteed in the Constitution—equal rights mean equal rights, including the vote. I will, if he's gonna say no.

"Black Mary, I don't support suffrage, but never voted against it, either. So, I guess you could say I have never been put to the test, until now."

Gerlach returned with a tray of tea and cookies, carefully placed it on the table. She sat down to serve. Having just gained insight into current events she was certain she had not heard of before, and her husband's opinions by means of their guest, Black Mary, Gerlach recompensed gratitude, and poured tea for the brave negress.

Adjusting the chair's cushion, Herman thought about logistics and potential repercussions. He wasn't for women wanting too much, but in light of the city council's insanity, this didn't seem such a terrible thing for an old negress to ask for—particularly due to the fact that she was stronger, better and faster than most men in the Birdtail. And she was there before them. Why not bear witness, give her a break? He wouldn't mind sticking a crimp in the council madness.

"All right then," Herman said, licking his lips. "Gerlach, did you hear that?" The sugar bowl slipped from her hand. Helpless, she watched white crystals splay across the carpet. She looked to him and replied, "Yes, dear," as though it were nothing.

"You're saying yes?" Mary asked, needing verification.

"Yes. I'll sell you the place. We'll make the deal like you said."

"Thank you, Mr. Herman, sir. I'm much obliged." She grinned, stunned. She'd never dreamed it would be given easily. How much will he ask for, she thought nervously—will I be able to afford his price?

Gerlach handed Mr. Wolf his tea, a cookie on the side. "Thank you, dear," she said. "Angels of mercy spoke through you just now. Black Mary has been faithful and loyal. She puts flowers in the altar, for years and years, and you've giv—"

"Let's not get carried away," he said, embarrassed. "Have one of your cookies, dear."

He bit into his ginger snap.

"You, we ... have to be careful, Black Mary. We have to plan this right. My brother is a lawyer in Idaho. I will have him write everything in a legal contract. The council and the dander they scratch up—it worries me a little. Are you sure you want to go through with this?"

"Yes, sir. Sure as I'm alive sitting here with you and your lovely wife. You're right though, I think. We can't breathe a word of this until each paper is ready and double checked, before we, I, go to sign the register."

"Tender, bill of sale, stipulations—he'll make it ironclad." Herman stirred his sugarless tea. "It's dangerous, Black Mary."

"Begging your pardon, sir, that's nothing new for me and the Birdtail."

The tick of the clock seemed to grow louder, as though underscoring its master's concerns.

"I'd like to give you a down payment, if you please. What do they call it, a mark of intent?" She knew very well it was called a security deposit or note of good faith; she was posturing naivety purposefully.

"A handshake will do, Black Mary. Mrs. Wolf is witness."

Mary freed her silver dollar, warm for the fiddling, from her pocket and stood. Opening her hand, she hoped his pledge was true. "Isn't much, but it's—"

"A shiny one," he replied, seeing it centered in the grooves and ridges of her dark palm. He calculated fast, estimating her life expectancy, measuring alms he would afford.

"Gerlach," Herman said with bravado, "listen and remember. I agree to sell my Cascade house to Black Mary Fields today for the sum of twenty-five dollars—to be paid at two dollars monthly. If Black Mary passes away, ownership will revert to me."

He looked at Mary. "You will bequeath the property to me in your will, or if you move, I shall buy it back for one silver dollar. When repairs or taxes need paying, I'll just happen to misplace some money when you're nearby, and you'll find it, use it to pay the costs."

"Don't remember that last part, Gerlach."

"Yes, dear."

"Is that agreeable to you, Black Mary?"

"That is less—I pay twenty-five dollars a month now."

"I know. Agreed?"

"Yes sir, Mr. Wolf."

He gave her a look.

"Mr. Herman, I agree to your terms for the purchase of your house."

She put her hand in his, and they shook on it.

Gerlach clapped. "Can the City Council undo your agreement?" she asked innocently.

Mary entered the hotel for supper that night and was immediately approached by Glover who welcomed her back, slapped her shoulder and requested a renewed promise to care for the team, the Cascade Cubs—cheer them on, he reiterated, the way she had during the last baseball season.

She had not forgotten her threat. *As for being your mascot, find someone else to give Cascade notoriety.* She had shouted those words two months ago, as she rode out of town—so now she was not going to acquiesce easily. She would make him wait, as she had waited for them to calm down. Whether they, the town men and some of the baseball players, had returned to their senses, she did not know.

As she slid the last bit of apple pie onto her fork, she told Glover she would think about mascoting, she was tired after her travels, and she would let him know. She knew his exuberant charm was being employed, in part, to save money on team laundry costs.

It was tiresome, analyzing motives unsaid. Edward and Louie aren't like that, nor D.W. or James Cornell, she brooded. With a pang in her chest, she realized it would be a long while until she made it back to Saypo, now that she had struck the deal with Herman Wolf.

Early the following morning, before customers had a chance to bring dirty clothes to her laundry, Mary made her way across town. She was surprised to see a work crew laboring on Central Avenue—sawing, measuring and hammering, sleeves rolled up before sunshine. It was easy to assess the project—sidewalks.

At the far end, where finished planks had been installed, indoor chairs had been placed onto the walkway facing east—ready for occupants seeking warmth and coffee sipping, she figured. Recalling Herman's account, she wondered if the council had gone so far as to govern who could sit where, when.

She turned the corner and stepped right again at the block's halfway mark, up the short gravel entrance, to knock on the Monroe's front door. She could hear children romping to get there first and Hattie's voice futilely calling, "Wait, your clothes—"

The door opened. Delighted screeches squealed. Her little buddies, naked from the waist up, tugged her skirt gathers, heralding, "Mama, it's Mary!"

Hattie rushed in, shut the door and embraced Mary, voicing teary relief and exclamations followed by an invite to sit at the breakfast table amidst the menagerie.

Coffee was set in place. Earl wiggled at Mary's side while Lester jabbered on the other, melling words, some of which, she was able to decipher: "fort—cannon balls—marbles—big bugs, I got there first," he recounted proudly.

"Why were you gone so long?" Earl demanded, having been quiet for minute, struggling to get his mouth to say what his mind had challenged him to understand.

"We missed you," Lester chatted.

"Quiet, Lester, let her answer."

"I went to visit friends of mine. A little girl named Mary who is younger than you, two years old."

"You spent all that time with a girl?" Overtly jealous, he pouted for a moment, until he had found a solution. "Why don't you bring her here so you don't go away?"

"That's a good idea, Earl."

Eventually they dressed themselves and were sent outside, cooperating only after Mary promised to stay where they could see her.

"I'm so glad you came back," Hattie said, scooting close. I wasn't sure you would."

Mary put her hand on Hattie's and smiled. "Missed you folks, and it's time for planting, too, and I was hoping the council would be calmed—"

"Oh," Hattie soured. "They've not calmed down nor slowed down. Did you know there was another election?"

"What?"

"Seventh of April. Re-elected all the same men, except for two aldermen who had to step down in order to do something else. Hall got sixty-three out of sixty-seven votes."

"Two-year term, right?"

"Yes. One of those four votes against Hall was D.W.'s. Said he hadn't expected H.D. to get so big in the head."

Should have asked me, Mary thought, waiting for Hattie to spill the news about ordinances.

"One good thing," Hattie said, "women have been speaking up. Now there's talk about women suffrage, in public. Most of us are talking out loud about it—to men, too. And Mrs. Marcum put a suffragette poster in the bank window. She invited a lady, Emma something, DeVoe, I think, to come give a speech for women's suffrage. Here, at the Methodist Church."

"Well, what do you know. Think I'll go to that."

"There's another vote in a couple weeks. A special election for a city water system. Imagine water coming through pipes, straight into the house."

Earl and Lester returned, complaining that there weren't enough stones for their slingshots, resting heads on Mary Fields' lap and shoulder.

"Had to have an election because it's going to cost three percent over the legal limit."

"How much is that?" Mary asked.

"I don't know. Twenty thousand dollars, I think."

"Twenty thousand dollars?"

"Yes." She tossed a dishtowel over her shoulder. "You look different, Mary. The rest must have done you good."

Lester, who understood they had been talking about the town council, pulled on Mary's sleeve. "Mary, Mayor Hall made a law against us kids," he riled, as though he were older. "We have to be off the streets, like a dog or a pest or something—be home by 8:30. It's not even dark yet."

"Oh, my Lord, Lester. Isn't that past your bedtime?"

"That don't matter."

"Doesn't matter," Hattie corrected.

"Okay, doesn't. It's not fair. He's not my mama or papa. He shouldn't get to make up rules like that."

"Mary, Mary," Earl shrilled, "Dogs have to get a license, or they get killed by the sheriff. And I heard Papa say he gets paid one dollar for every dog he kills!"

"Oh, my goodness," Mary goaded, "Is there a law against how many fish we can catch?"

He looked to his mama who said, "Not yet."

"Fishing!" the boys shouted, "When can we go, Nigger Mary?"

"Go outside now," Hattie said. "Work on your fort. No slingshots on your person, or you'll get arrested, remember? I mean it."

"We'll go tomorrow afternoon, fellas," Mary promised, thinking that in addition to fish, she would pick some dandelions and sorrel too, since she had spent all her money, except for the emergency cache under the boulder where she'd buried her '38 Smith & Wesson on the way home yesterday, due to the new gun ordinance.

She wondered how to get her pistol into town and, once accomplished, where to hide it. She had her rifle for home protection but needed a handgun to accompany her out of the house.

She looked at Hattie, who had begun washing dishes. "Are you kidding about the sling-shots?"

Hattie shook her head, raised an eyebrow.

"My God. What other ordinances are there now?"

"I saved the paper for you. They're not all there, though." She wiped her hands on her apron and grabbed the clipping from a drawer, passed it across the table. "I'll tell you the rest—think I can remember them all, fifteen total. I wish we'd never incorporated." She rubbed her eyes. "Do want the indoor plumbing, though." She eyed the stack of soapy dishes set in the big enamel tub she'd have to lug outside, pump icy rinse water over and carry back.

Struggling to think of something pleasant to mention before reporting the latest ordinances, Hattie poured cream into the bowl of food she had been preparing.

"Here Mary, have some shortcake—just baked it this morning. Before long we'll have strawberries."

Holding the Courier's front page close to her face, Mary sighed,

"Well, they've surely been busy." She folded the rag, put it on the table and looked at her friend, attempting to appear surprised. "Should call them the cascading reigning rules: r-e-i-g-n."

Hattie nodded. "Or r-e-i-n."

"If challenged, we'd say we meant: r-a-i-n: watering the parched, the uninformed."

Hattie laughed. "Ah, Mary ..."

"Let's hear the rest, and I'll help you with those dishes." She took a bite of shortcake. "Umm, I'm fortified."

As Mary listened to the punitive ordinance language riddled with egregious addendums and alarming repercussions, she wondered how the Chongs were holding up. She would stop by and see, compare notes.

She mulled over Ordinance No. 15, *"Relating to Offenses Against Good Order and Morals,"* the length of which had taken the majority of Cascade Courier's front page, three full columns, revealing, in her opinion, a manifest of intent straight from the council's tyrannical bench—constituents who seemed maniacally pre-occupied in a fictional future where they, the redeemers, were armed—all-too-anxious—to prosecute a broad expanse of cold-blooded, sinful criminals lurking on every Cascade corner—even the children.

Each violation ended with "... shall be deemed guilty of misdemeanor or felony charges, mandatory fines from one to one-hundred dollars and/or imprisonment."

The language gave her the willies—

"... any person maliciously or unnecessarily disturbing, threatening, quarreling, scolding, hallooing, provoking, annoying, frightening, uttering obscene, vulgar indecent ... shall be arrested.

... every person appearing in dress not belonging to his or her sex, or lewd dress ... guilty of filthy acts, uttering lewd or filthy words anywhere within hearing of anybody ... selling or offering to sell, or dispose of indecent or lewd books, pictures or things ..." And then, of course, "... inviting or soliciting entry into a bawdy house, house of ill fame or house of assignation ..."

And who would judge these broad infringements? The sheriff and the authors of the new laws—aldermen who had the audacity to call themselves "town fathers".

Why don't they just arrest each other and be done with it? Mary reeled. All this thrown into the same ordinance that begins temperately enough—with legitimate warnings for minor offenses "... making loud or unusual noises (vocal or instrumental) or making false alarms crying 'fire'."

But it was ordinance No. 8 that concerned her most particularly: prohibition of concealed weapons, including "knives, daggers, razors, dirks and slingshots" for all adult citizens except the select few (an elite membership that would surely exclude women).

"Hattie, think I'll get home, do some cleaning and take a nap. Tell the boys I'll be back to collect them around four o'clock tomorrow, if they have their poles and fresh-dug worms ready. All right?"

Mary felt a wave of comfort once returned to her own house, where everything had its place and, come what may, she knew where to reach for sugar, how to locate the outhouse half-asleep, where to search for things forgotten when she remembered, in the midst of soft air made humid by steeping laundry.

She noticed that the swelling in her hands and feet had eased and figured it was due to knowledge of her soon-to-come victory and the relaxing time spent with the Bruneaus. She wanted her extremities to stay like that.

Days later, on her way home from the hotel after breakfast, she saw Cornell and Monroe sitting on sidewalk chairs. The empty one between them looked inviting. Sore after planting in her garden, she considered resting a spell.

They waved her over, grinning.

James and D.W. listened as Mary described the grand vista she had witnessed standing on the rocky mountain precipice. She ended her depiction with an anecdotal observation of Cascade, how it looked like a mere fly spec on the grand Missouri River curve, supposing everything did if you got far enough away. She thanked D.W. for keeping an eye on her place, to which he insisted Hattie had done more, cleaning on occasion.

They relayed news of hotheaded local political debates and opinions on what they had tagged lumberjack lawmaking, as opposed to crackerjack. Cornell snickered.

Both seemed distraught about the changes and complained that Cascade would never be the same. Finally, with lament, they reported members' individual scores from the last rock-pile target practice—such events were now prohibited within city limits—and the location of the new bordello that neither of them had patronized, they added—along with candid admissions that they very much missed the perfume and singing and giggling that was currently and forevermore (at least until Hall was voted out of office) absent from all Cascade saloons. Such deploring prodded them back to grievances over more unjust regulations and the manner in which they had been composed and ratified.

Though Mary wanted the information, she grew tired of hearing it. She counted crows on the big grandmother cottonwood near Kraus's Sample Room, a block away. Deciduous splendor had returned; vibrant leaves decorated the branches.

Bent on finding the solution to keep her pistol on her person, she asked, "Either of you happen to get a concealed weapon permit from Hall?"

Unified scowls answered.

D.W. sawed, "Teddy would never have stood for an ordinance against pistols."

"Nope. Is he still on safari in Africa?" Cornell asked, "Man loves to shoot big game."

"Would you consider Hall big game?" Mary posed.

They chuckled.

Ruffled, Cornell sniped, "Too bad our mayor isn't more like Taft—cutting budgets frugal. Hall squanders our money, seduced like a woman in a hat shop, smitten like a heartsick toad—"

"Like an inebriated magpie," Monroe suggested, thinking "mule's ass" was more appropriate, but there was female company present.

"Hey, hang on there boys," Mary threatened, "you're insulting my feathered friends—"

"Sorry," Monroe cackled.

"Cockeyed as a drunk skunk spending every penny in the Cascade piggy," Cornell carried on. "Four months and we're drowning in debt. It's us who are going to get stuck with the council bar tab. Did you see the notice he put in the paper? 'Somebody is going to have their saloon license revoked if there is any more gambling or rough house.' What an—"

"What we need is common sense," Mary interjected, tapping the foot beneath her skirt to the beat of Humpty Dumpty.

Monroe took the bait. "What kind of common sense is that, Nigger Mary?"

"The kind women have, of course. The kind that keeps everything and everybody organized and on track," she said straight-faced. They chuckled, crossed their legs and chugged their joe.

The new sheriff swaggered toward them, slow stepped and heavy, intending to draw attention.

Spurred by his apparent interest, Mary cast defiantly, "Well, long as I'm not allowed inside the saloons, sure am enjoying sitting on our new sidewalk, our public sidewalk."

"Could be disturbing the peace with that troublemaker attitude," Sheriff Hoag taunted, "Might lead to an arrest." He slid his thumb up and down beneath his right suspender strap, stepping aside as a lady passed.

"No need for threats, Sheriff," D.W. warned.

The sheriff advanced and stopped in front of them, blocking the sun. "I heard what you said."

"What was that?" D.W. asked.

"Don't you go insulting our mayor and the town council."

D.W. replied, "We are citizens of this town."

"We have every right to our opinions," Cornell seconded.

"Didn't you go to sheriff school?" D.W. scoffed, aware that his taunt was below the belt—everyone knew Hoag hadn't made it past third grade.

A second, uninvited voice, spoke from the threshold behind. "*Common*, that's an interesting adjective you chose, Nigger Mary. That implies that we as a nation are common, as if we are all members of the same strata of society: women, men, black, white. A faulty precept."

There was no mistaking. It was Marcum.

She didn't turn to acknowledge him, nor did her friends. She tugged the bill of her cap and glanced to D.W., then to James. "Both these gentlemen know I meant nothing of the kind."

"That's right," said Cornell.

"Yep, and this is a private conversation," D.W. spoke louder.

All three kept their gazes straight ahead.

Mary said, "It's obvious that our country, and our town, for that matter, has more than one strata. I was not addressing that sorry state of affairs." She pressed her tongue against her teeth, stretching a pause. "I was referring to common sense, not common ignorance that can be had by any sex or color."

"You're a prime example of that," Marcum snapped, flaring his nostrils.

"In your common opinion," Mary replied, her hand groping for her pistol that wasn't there.

"Sheriff," J.E. Marcum barked, "you heard that. She has blasphemed my person."

The sheriff cocked his chin, trying to think which ordinance had been broken.

"Black Mary has an appointment," Cornell claimed in chilled haste, avoiding eye contact.

"We're late already, Mary," he play-acted, giving a deep nod as he took her arm in his. D.W. shifted to her other side, and the threesome ambled, clamored down the wood planks.

D.W. looked at Cornell. "Nice to have our Mary back, isn't it?"

"Thanks, fellas. That was fun."

As they chuckled, Mary suddenly had the answer to the mascot question. Yes. She'd do it.

That summer, Mary tended her garden, the laundry and the baseball players, in that order. Cheering the Cubs on revived loyalties to the players she liked and to the game in general. When conflicts arose, she envisioned herself standing at the ballot poll where she marked an X next to Hall's future opponent.

The Cub's first game had been advertised, and crowds flocked to town. Herman Wolf strolled among the many, carrying a folded sheet of paper in his buttoned shirt pocket. The Cascade band bugled a spectacular performance prior to the game, and sported new hit tunes, in order of requested sentiments: "I Can't Miss that Ball Game," "You're a Grand Old Flag" and "Take Me Out to the Ball Game."

Mary initiated a lively ceremony to commence each game of the 1911 season: the Cascade Cubs stood in line at the edge of the field while she, their "mascot" dressed in her finest, pinned a homemade flower boutonniere crafted from her garden's bounty, on each player's uniform. Decorated, the team jogged once around the plates, waving to faithful fans who cheered fervently. Anticipation buzzed in the dugout, in the stands, in buckboards and on automobiles parked around the perimeter. Home brew was discreetly passed along.

Enjoying the benefits of her hard work, Mary hunched with the boys on the bench and cheered, booed and hissed. At half-time, she served refreshments.

She had cajoled Mr. Bunnel, who managed the Cascade Mercantile Company, into donating lemons shipped clear from California, ostensibly, to keep Cascade Cub whistles wet and vitalize skillful hits. Afterwards, she'd crossed the street to John Thomas's Corner Store and wheedled Mr. Thomas into equaling Bunnel's generosity. A patriotic fan, John Thomas donated a crock, extra tall glasses and straws.

Rival team players grew jealous, forced to witness the Cubs enjoy first-class major league service, while they perspired and slurped cloudy water from canning jars, warm from the exposure.

Balls were pitched, dropped, fanned, hit and missed.

Mr. Wolf, who had not attended before, found the sporting event captivating. He didn't mind about waiting until half-time, or break-time, or whatever they called in baseball. In the interim, he learned that plays were fumbled on the rubber, off the rubber, stolen, pilfered, poled, grounded and tagged.

Shouting into the megaphone, the referee called a time-out intermission. Large numbers of people mingled. Glover was pleased, knowing that some of the crowd would stay the night in his hotel. Marcum distributed custom-made posters headlined, "Cascade Welcomes Good Business": a listing of "Professions Desired" filled the body, followed by a brief prospectus that directed interested parties to contact the Cascade Commercial Club. Women guild members huddled in well-dressed cliques, free to plan and say whatever they wished without worrying about time constraints. Hall sat alone, on the top row of the bandstand, surveying his kingdom.

Wolf made his way toward the coterie of fans who backslapped Cub players and slathered praise, swore allegiance to the team's success and dramatized count-by-count details of each thrilling point gained thus far, as if no one else in the crowd had just seen it.

Herman waved to catch Mary's attention. She hoofed it to the edge of the field where he greeted her with a hefty handshake and followed her lead to the row of cottonwoods that provided some privacy.

"No team can lose with you on their side, Black Mary," he declared. "You give them class."

He removed the note from his pocket and glanced at his list.

"Good news?"

"Well, yes, good progress."

She hid her disappointment. She knew there would be details to finalize but had naively hoped the contract would be ready to sign.

"He's written our agreement, my brother. Needs to know your legal name, how you want it."

"My legal name?"

"Yes, how you want it."

A baby wailed. Mary covered one ear. "Did you find out if I have to be in the house from now til the elections in 1913?"

"If you want to be sure, I mean, meet all the requirements—you need to be home from time you register until you vote. That's either six months or one year, not sure yet. You are not going somewhere are you?"

"Was thinking about a visit, maybe."

"Oh. That won't count. Write down whatever you want in your will—aside from, *you know*…"

"All right."

"You can give it to me at the next home game, Black Mary. Think I'll bring Gerlach."

"That's good."

"And your name. How you want it." He returned the paper to his pocket and buttoned it, tugged his hat and smiled. "Best be going, want to get a good seat. This is downright fun."

"Thanks, Mr. Wolf," she said as though nothing extraordinary had transpired. Grinning, she digested the information as she marched to the team bench, grabbed the ladle and poured lemonade.

"Mr. Wolf, wait!" she called. Ladle dripping in hand, she scuttled to his side and asked, "Do I owe you rent?"

"No, but you can make two-dollar payments toward the twenty-five, I mean twenty-four dollars, left on the selling price. I'll make a record. Keep those Cubs in shape. This is great fun, the game."

"And, Herman," she wiped her forehead, caught her breath. "Do I have a choice? For my name?"

Wolf pulled on his ear, considering. "Think you can make it whatever you want. That was my impression. See you at the next game."

Distracted from her duties, she could think of nothing but the chance to change her name. It was exhilarating, the freedom to choose. She wondered which one she would pick and whether it made sense to change one's name at seventy-nine years old.

After supper she lit her special candle, settled into her old rocker and rocked, thinking, if I do change my name, would folks call me by it? Will they add another in front of it, like they always do? That aside, would I like to have a new name?

She rocked some more, smoked the last of her cigar and listened to the wind whistling. Wonder what *their* names were—my women ancestors.

The candle crackled, its flame nearing the wick's end.

Names are usually chose special by parents—sounds and letters stitched into words, into a tapestry, a family tree.

It's important, those sounds that make the name, a brief cadence of notes ...

We can't help but respond ... as if we *are* those one or two or three or four-syllabled word-songs called at us. Black Mary—Nigger Mary—Stagecoach Mary—White Crow. Mother says the Christian name *Mary* means beloved ...

Anyway, I think it's true. Names become our identity. And these name word-songs, sounded over and over every day, our personal chorus, a life-long refrain, sets the tone of who we are, how folks treat us, and think about us, without realizing ... from the very moment someone names us.

Snapping a consonant, rolling a vowel, can change a person's tune from a gleeful chorus to a nasty slap—over and over. My ... Why *wouldn't I* change it ? Especially if I could rid myself of "Black" and "Nigger".

She got up for cookies and milk and sat at the table, tapped her foot.

I'm listening to the beat and melody and the feeling of Mary ...

"M-a-a-r—e-e." It has two beats and "m-a-a-r" is dominant. "Mare," like the horse—

Always liked more beats—think it would feel better to have three, maybe four syllable-notes. I like soft vowels like "ah" or "o".

"Hmmm, like Ahwao. Never thought about that."

Which consonants feel best? C or M, maybe D, with soft sounding notes: Amadora, Mariposa, Cassandra …

Could life really get better with the giving of a new name? I know it has strong affects—so maybe it can. No wonder names are revered by some folks, like the Indians, and the sisters. I bet they were important in my family's tradition, too.

It was nice to be given the name White Crow …

The master gave us his surname, to keep track of us. Guess you'd call it a name-tag. And forced us to choose English names for our first …

Wonder why I didn't consider picking my own name before? If a person's name—word-song—calls to our nobility or beauty or goodness, the kind we're born with—then each calling of our name-song nurtures our truth, our soul.

I'll listen for my soul name. Maybe hear it in a song, or in someone's conversation … I'll feel the hum in my bones … I'll know. Maybe the women in my line will bring it to me in a dream; sing my true given name across the galaxy …

She sipped the last of her milk and went to bed.

After days spent glancing at, and skirting around, the tidy stack of blank stationery placed at the head of her table—pages that seemed to stare like an uninvited guest plunked down in stiff repose, waiting for supper … Mary began, in exasperation, to make her displeasure adamantly known to the part of her that knew the right answers yet refused to come forth and speak. Bottoms of pots and pans were banged onto cast iron stove, and laundry was scalded with regularity, warp and weft the worse for wear.

Tired of wrestling with the need to rethink it after herding thoughts that insistently strayed off point and returned bushy-tailed, without the grailed advice she searched for from within, she shook her up-stretched arms and ordered, "Just do it—it's not that big a deal."

For the last time, she calibrated intent and summoned: you can face it, smart people do. Should I include my initial? It's my last opportunity to say so. Don't be sappy. I'm not sappy, and it is a big deal. Halted then, before the stark paper sheets, her means by which to ordain—she faced a future ready to receive her dictation. With pointed finger she drew a line through dust that had settled on top and headed for her bedroom.

She searched through every drawer, box and hiding place. After an hour, she had assembled a small collection that she thoughtfully separated into three groups. Aching head and rheumatism bullied into submission, she proceeded to compose, beginning with the answer to Herman's question:

Dear Mr. Wolf,

> *The name I would like you to use in our legal agreements is Mary F. Fields. I am also known as White Crow, Stagecoach Mary, and Mary Fields.*
> *And if you are wondering, no, I don't wish to use my full middle name. F will do just fine.*

> *Signed,*
> *Mary F. Fields*
> *June 2, 1911*

During her search she found the letter Onatah had sent years before, the one that included the suffrage section of the 1889 Montana constitution. She read it again:

Sec. 12. Upon all questions submitted to the vote of the taxpayers of the State, or any political division thereof, women who are taxpayers and possessed of the qualifications for the right of suffrage required of men by this Constitution shall equally, with men, have the right to vote.

"That's me," she said, smiling. "Now for the difficult deed."

Inspired by serenity, risen in the moment after a prayer-filled week of soul-searching, she readied the second blank page and penned the title of her declaration: *Mary F. Fields's Last Will and Testament.*

Composing directives, she scribed the list of her heirs, wrote an introduction and began her ceremony: words that would one day become her voice after death—last pledges and messages of love, tallied snippets of advice, and heartfelt wishes, general and personal … followed by instructions for the distribution of her modest legacy in specific detail … and a postscript requesting certain burial arrangements that specified the body's preparations, the location of the grave, proposed inscriptions and adornments … leaving the finality of such details to her personal representatives, Mr. and Mrs. D.W. Monroe.

In the section citing the inheritance of personal gifts and property, she reiterated the promise she had made to Herman: "Ownership of my house and its lot in Cascade, Montana, shall return to Mr. Herman Wolf. No cost is involved."

Sometime later, revived from the sanctioned ease with which she had completed her mission, Mary noticed that the day had nearly ended. She treated her hands and forearms to the luxury of store-bought lotion Hattie had given to her, rubbing it in as she circled the table.

Satisfied, she exclaimed, "So there, Grim Reaper. If you're around, you can leave." She glanced behind.

Belting in baritone bravado, she pitched, "See you later—much, much later."

She looked out the window to the ponderosa pine and said, "What a relief. I'll be having a cigar right after I finish this up."

Folding the answer regarding her name, and her will, separately, she inserted the packets into individual envelopes, sealed them tight with homemade glue. On each missive she scribed two lines front and center: *Mister Herman Wolf:* C-O-N-F-I-D-E-N-T-I-A-L. In the top right corner of the first she wrote, "N" and on the last, "W."

It was the morning of summer solstice when Mary arrived at the livery to pick up the horse and buggy she had bartered for a day's use, two weeks after she'd given Herman a note specifying her name of choice for the contract. They had rendezvoused briefly after one of the Cub's baseball games and set the date and time to meet again. Will and Testament tucked safely in her satchel along with a tin of oatmeal cookies and package of bobby pins for Gerlach, she snapped reins over the fine-looking palomino and traveled directly to the Wolf ranch.

After cordial greetings, Herman invited Mary to take a seat at the kitchen table where Gerlach had placed a small vase of wildflowers and a pitcher of cider next to John Wolf, who, pen in hand, reviewed fine print neatly executed.

"Look what Black Mary brought us, dear," said Gerlach, presenting cookies she had stacked on a delicate dessert tray from the old country. "Raisin oatmeal."

"My favorite!" Herman called, as he slipped into the chair opposite Mary, and helped himself. "John, you gotta have one of these—tastes like liebe Mutter's."

John Wolf, attorney-at-law, tidied his work and held it in his lap. "After we've finished your business. Refreshments and documents don't belong together."

"All right then," Herman said as he winked at Mary and grabbed another. "As you say, big brother, first things first."

Mary smiled, appreciative of the way Herman could put her at ease. She took a breath, enjoyed the family atmosphere and aromas of breakfast bacon and coffee that lingered.

Gerlach moved her cookies and cider to the sideboard and carefully removed ice cubes from the pitcher, saving them for later.

Mr. John asked Mary and Herman to read the bill of sale in its entirety; a painless task, as it was only one page with language fairly easy to comprehend.

He turned to Mary and advised, "Miss Mary, I assume that you wish me to review your will, for legal purposes only, of course, to make sure it will be executed without complication. There is no need to share the contents with Herman or Gerlach, as it is your private business. But I shall, with your permission, show Herman the section where you added—I'm assuming you included it—the clause stating that your home and property will revert to him, should he desire it, after you are deceased. Will that be acceptable?"

"Of course, Mr. John. I did include it and I want Mr. Herman to see I am keeping my word."

"Fine. And we will all witness you signing your will, though I will be the only legal witness thereof."

"Yes, sir."

"Now, if both of you will write your signatures on all three copies of the deed-of-sale—on the lines above your names. I will review the testament."

Both parties nodded in compliance, signed where indicated and waited, silently, passing the time with looks to each other and Gerlach, who sat erect, arms resting upon her checkered tablecloth, fingers crossed.

"Everything is in order, Mary Fields. You did a fine job."

Her shoulders eased, but she remained at attention, waiting.

"Herman, here is the section of Mary's testament that entitles you the return of your house. See here?" He folded the page and pushed it toward his brother.

"Yes. That was our agreement exactly," Herman confirmed.

Returning Mary's will to her, John asked her to sign again so he could testify and sign as her witness. She did so gladly.

"One more thing," he said with finality. "I recommend that clients make a copy of their legal documents. Before you leave, would you copy your will and testament exactly? I'll review everything and sign again, as witness."

"Yes, sir. Be happy to. Thank you, Mr. John."

"Are we done then?" Herman asked.

"We are, excepting the copy that we will seal this day and give to you, Herman, for safe keeping. Do you have a safe deposit box?"

"I have a safe place."

"Then I believe it's time for cookies and apple cider," John concluded with a smile.

Gerlach clapped her hands. The brothers and Mary joined in. Over the applause Gerlach spouted gleefully, "Guten tag! Guten tag!"

"She means it's a great day, Black Mary," Herman translated.

"It sure is!" Mary cheered. "Thanks to you all. I'm obliged."

"No, you are not," Herman said, "it is our pleasure. Let us eat the cookies. Will you give Gerlach the recipe?"

"Of course."

In order to avoid local knowledge of the transaction, Herman and John decided that John would register the property sale in Great Falls, the Cascade County seat located northeast, some twenty miles away, where the transaction had no reason to be noticed. John cautioned Mary not to breathe a word.

Safe at home, *her* home, that evening, Mary danced to a ditty spontaneously composed: "I'm a property owner, Mary F. Fields, a free woman, free citizen and landowner. I own this house and my little patch of garden." She swirled. "I have the right, the right to vote in Montana, land of shining mountains, same as any white man. Huzzah! Huzzah!" She kicked her heels and shimmied. "See me now, y'all," she called, eyes closed, eyes opened. "Come join the party. Your grand grand grand American granddaughter has won the right to vote!"

21

VICTORY

*C*ascade Cubs supplied stimulating excitement. After winning two trophies, word spread and fans multiplied. Patriotic locals and out-of-towners converged on designated Saturday afternoons, divided their collective mass in half and pitted feverish screeches and belched hollers—knee-slapping proofs of allegiance—from opposing sides of the ballpark. By dusk, one team of champions had been declared victorious, supplying days of baseball team maneuvers to celebrate or argue about at length.

News reporters published detailed accounts of every inning, including scorecards of each player, home and rival, depicting with gripping commentary, out-of-the-park plays and close calls that determined the final outcome.

Between hours of daily practice and official games scheduled every two weeks, Mary struggled to capture time needed to nurture flowers for the boutonnières, oil the bats, wash and iron the uniforms. She admired the sport's demand for perseverance and enjoyed watching muscular strength, agile moves and home runs—except when out-of-towners got drunk and indulged in catcalling—degraded her person, her race, her beauty. These behaviors bothered her more now that she had the right to register for the vote in more than school-related elections. Cub players had recently proved to be reliable; when a certain number of malicious remarks threatened Mascot Mary's safety, her teammates smacked fists into faces of the degenerate misfits and sent them limping. This was reassuring.

Mary had not written to Onatah as promised. Though she wanted to share good news about the house and her plans to register and vote with the very family who would keep such a confidentiality, she knew, also, that the congratulatory cheer they would surely send, would be laced with degrees of disappointment.

Specifically, Onatah's disappointment. Mary was well aware and very thankful that Onatah intended to take care of her when the time came, being the sweet girl that she always had been. And now there was time and a place, and Mary was asking her to wait. That she had asked her little bird to wait while she achieved this one more thing curdled an ache in her heart, so she had postponed sending another message that could hurt the person she loved as her own.

In early September, the Cubs and their mascot Black Mary caravanned west across three townships by motorized farm wagons to compete as finalists in the regional championship.

During their absence, Postmaster Rowe slipped Mary's mail, a letter and two circulars, under her door.

It was the first thing Mary noticed upon her return. She tossed the circulars and knapsack onto the table, grabbed her letter and a tin cup and headed out the side door, to the garden. She pumped cool water to sip and rooted herself on the tree stump in its center. Admiring blooms and scents, she listened to bees buzzing and took breath—the kind saved for ritual— and tore the flap.

Dearest White Crow,

> *I'm thinking of you and wonder if you are all right. Did the city council make more ordinances while you were here with us? If so, do they affect you terribly? I am curious also—did you decide to accept the mascot job with the baseball team? (I forget the name of the team.)*
>
> *We are well—all of us are working the harvest—drying, canning for winter, as usual.*
>
> *Are you coming before winter do you think? I hope so. We are waiting for your arrival, whenever that may be. Your choice. I realize that you are set on finishing whatever it is that holds you there. I will try to be patient. You know I was never good at that.*
>
> *I saw the enclosed article in the Choteau paper. Were you part of this baseball extravaganza? It sounds exciting all right, and oh, I see, Cascade Cubs is your team's name. Since they won, it should have been great fun for you? But I don't see any report of the most important team member, the mascot.*

If you were there, I'm irritated at no mention of you, the best, the most faithful …
Please let us hear from you.

Love, Onatah, Edward, Isabel, Louie and your Goddaughter,
in Saypo, your future home

P.S. Mary Ahwao keeps asking when we are going to have a new picnic with White Crow Aaáh.

Mary unfolded the clipping, read to see if the article was accurate.

Eleven Innings to Trim Augusta

In the Augusta's side of the ninth, Weisner fanned and Clover hit a hot grass trimmer to Berger who made a pretty throw to first but the umpire called him safe. It was there that the trouble began, for the fans assert that he was fairly caught. Mamix fanned and Clover who had stolen second, attempted to pilfer the keystone sack when the next man hit to short middle field. Thomas however, had caught the perfect throw of Rumney and stood over the plate, waiting for the runner who slid but was tagged fully two feet from the bag. Imagine the surprise of the fans when the umpire called him safe … Cascade went to the bat in the tenth with blood in their eyes … final score Cascade 12, Augusta 8 … leaving a bunch of fuming hostile fans to seek the nearest parlor of thirst … and an ecstatic pack of Cubs.

Mary's feelings were split. Winter, mentioned twice by Onatah, was sure to be lonely and isolated in Cascade. It was more than a year and a half until the Cascade mayoral election in April of 1913—plenty of time to meet the mandatory six-month resident-owner requirement. She and the Wolf brothers had decided that Mary would register for the vote in February, 1912. Esquire John Wolf would be visiting then, available to respond if there were any objections. She would write to him in Idaho, she decided, find out exactly how long she could be out of town and still retain her homeowner-resident status. Only then would she decide whether to commit to an extended visit with the Bruneaus.

Autumn colors fell to winter's grip. Mary spent most of her time coffered secure inside her house, with the exception of the daily slog to the hotel for a meal and small purchases at the mercantile. When she felt low, she reminded herself of the forthcoming registration and of her upcoming part in the city election, reassuring herself that things were coming together as planned. Not having heard back from Mr. John Wolf, she let the option of lodging with Onatah and Edward, fade.

Worn boot soles and slower reflexes changed the agility with which she moved about; she strained to hide indications of age or vulnerability. Saloons had to be passed by to reach the hotel, no matter which route she chose. When leers or slurs pitched from local barstool seats jabbed, she would pretend not to see them, or hear them, as though the taunting, goading sarcasms had the impact of small pebbles, an irritant, less than an irritant. When derogatory heckles did prick like Biblical thorns, she would culminate a response: decompose the trespasser into an ugly potato bug to be squashed immediately imagining its demise as she crunched her leather sole into ice, a satisfying crackle.

She yearned to share the glory of her first-stage suffrage triumph, but gushing about a suffrage victory to Hattie, her only close woman friend in town, could injure camaraderie that had taken a lengthy time to build.

Hattie was the wife of a property owner, not a property owner or taxpayer herself. Though married couple's property deeds often mentioned the wife's name, the titled "ownership" belonged to the husband. So Hattie's right to vote was limited to school district elections only. It wouldn't be fair, Mary decided, if she could vote in the city election and Hattie could not; not to mention it might rankle marital business.

She did ask Hattie for a haircut, her upcoming registration being the impetus. Hattie obliged and trimmed Mary's unruly salt and peppered hair as best she could, assuming that the do was meant to celebrate the New Year, as some wives were in the habit of doing. When Mary told Hattie that she had concerns about dispatching inferior laundry to her customers, along with the fear of consequence—losing her business if she were not able to identify the sources of the stains and, thus remove them, Hattie gave her an old pair of D.W.'s reading spectacles.

Mary was thrilled, grateful for her friend's generosity. Though the intended purpose for the new-to-her spectacles was to loop the temple tips over her ears when she registered, she tried wearing them while she scrubbed laundry and was surprised by the number of additional stains suddenly visible—a double win.

On some evenings Mary misplaced hours engaged in chimerical details of her future voter registration day and the privilege that would follow, the casting of her vote—an event worthy of holiday proclamation, to her thinking. Assorted versions of this suffrage saga were imagined, each ending with the soon-to-be franchised victory. Hugging the future, she wrapped herself in her bedspread (imagined as the American flag) and envisioned

Mary F. Fields signing the golden goose Montana Registry—proving up, as it were. Then, breasted in red, white and blue glory, she would march to the voting polls, plant an "X" next to Hall's opponent's name and light fireworks when Hall lost the election. And someday, she conjectured further, I will join a statewide congregation of women—we will post and proclamate our signatures and register for the national vote. Not someday. Real soon. Doppelganger victories—state and federal.

Hold your horses, she told herself, hands gripping her tea mug. What's that lawyer word? Digress. I digress.

Mr. Wolf will arrive to escort me to register, the morning of February 17th, the day after his brother John, our attorney, arrives to come with us. The entire event will be glorious. To start with, the sun will cut through any cloud cover, warm the weather's rough edges. I will wear a gown of gold and crimson and carry a parasol to protect my delicate skin. We'll stroll down the sidewalk. Birds will chirp and trill and caw.

When we enter Rowe's Cash Bazaar, our postman and registrar, Mr. Rowe, will usher us to his office, offer coffee and treats—and I will explain to him the purpose of our meeting. He will be astounded when I tell him of the royal connections I've had all along, second cousin once removed to Comte St. Germain, of the Royal Austrian Court in Bavaria, and how I had waited, until I felt like it, to claim my noble American right to vote. He will apologize for the town's oversight and ignorance and poor treatment and kiss my hand—then snap to it and process my voting registration with immediate efficiency.

In the background, patriotic band music is rousing to bravado, or is that crescendo? It's coming from outside, across the street on the sidewalk where the St. Angela's orchestra is lined up performing a concert of American tunes such as "The Star Spangled Banner" and "America the Beautiful" while I peruse and sign my signature and Mr. Rowe notarizes my guarantees.

When I emerge, a registered voter, a halo will be shining over my head, for all to see. The music will pause, and clapping will begin, heartfelt and spirited—whoops and cheers like the children made at my surprise birthday party after Bigg died.

Oh, before that, at sunrise, my parents and grandparents, alive and well, join me for breakfast. After handheld supplications, they remain with me tucked safe inside. I am fortified.

I'll be wearing an invisible garland of flowers in my hair—the kind young girls used to wear when they jumped the broom in Tennessee. My crow friends will be watching, cawing cackles that will resonate from trees and telephone wires; they will dive bomb anyone who wishes me ill. I am protected. It's perfect.

And if, per chance, the weather goes bad, things will still be good. There will be a reason. Nature in her wisdom will support my enterprise, send near-fatal temperatures to hinder other folks from going out—increase my odds of getting registered without interference—keep it secret.

"All this is silly," she nudged her giddy self, "I'm behaving like a nervous schoolgirl."

She got up, faced the mirror above the bureau and scrutinized her heroine.

"Crazy stories maybe," she said, "but they all have truth."

She fussed with her hair, turned her face side to side. "Registering to vote is important and you need to look nice, dress special for the occasion. I'll plan ahead."

When the actual day did arrive, midmorning didn't look much different than midnight. Dark clouds reached across all sight—and humidity, a relation who seldom visited high plains country, squatted beneath, blunting sharp quills of sleet hurled by an abounding tempest.

Mary pulled the kitchen curtain shut and realized that her plans to look good were incomplete. She had forgotten the coat. The old wool hand-me-down she'd been wearing, blemished by moth holes and missing buttons, wouldn't do.

She rushed to the closet. Pulling a faded extra-large hatbox from beneath a stack of mending, she tossed it on the bed, pulled the lid off, grabbed the garment and gave it a good shake. Fur flew airborne and tufts of beaver pelt ripped. Mary wiped her face and examined the damage. Mice had chewed and stolen valuable portions of fur, leaving naked patches of hairless gray hide blotching the surface of what had once been, an elegant full-length beaver coat crafted from beaver families trapped, traded and transformed into the best skin a human could slip into while traversing a wild winter wilderness.

"Those little monsters, I could—" She grabbed the box and flipped it over. Verifying the source of entry (a hole had been chewed in a corner she discarded it and examined her coat. "It looks ridiculous! And what is that smell?" she bellowed. Turning the wrap inside out, she took a whiff where the lining was stained. "Oh my God, decades of armpit sweat. Lord. Now what?"

"Should have thought about this before," she snarled, "Mother gave me this coat—just before Brondel excommunicated—could have fixed it, maybe."

She ran her fingers through the thick, shiny fur. "Was exquisite in its day. Stopped me from freezing to death more than once. Those damned mice." Catching herself, she remembered her pledge for this day: *Nothing is going to ruin it.*

"I'm wearing it anyway. I'll put my big wool scarf over it, try to hide the blotches." She took the coat outside, waved it as though it were a Union battle flag and brushed herself off, though it did no good, winds blowing catawampus.

Herman knocked at the front door.

"Coming," she hollered, stopping momentarily to cover her trimmed hair with her largest hat—a thick green fedora she had decorated with auburn and chestnut rooster plumes and a large red silk flower.

Leaving his going-to-town hat on, Herman Wolf angled his hands above the stove and told Mary to take her time.

Placing her envelope of papers into her pocket, she muttered, "Remember, I'm going to sign, Mary F. Fields. Where's my holster? Can't take my pistol, but I can wear my holster, can't I?"

They shuffled through snowdrifts laid down through the night. Crackling warned the pair of temperate thaw hid between thinning layers of brittle stratum, booby traps to be hopscotched across.

Wolf offered his arm, and Mary took hold. There would be no falling today. She held onto her hat with the other hand. Noses started to burn.

She quipped, "Great sakes, this cold is hard enough to break a town ordinance."

"Wouldn't that be grand," Herman chuckled, grabbing his own hat as a blast of wind slapped from behind. "Blizzard's coming on. Everyone's turned tail."

"I arranged it. No gossips to report our business. A regular ghost town, looks like."

She gasped from frigid air that had gripped her lungs and counted steps toward her destination.

Wolf pushed his weight against the Cash Bazaar door, unsure whether it was locked or stuck.

Sealed ice cracked and he lunged forward. Mary followed, struggling to reset the barrier, deter rifts of howling wind and people.

"Whew," she exclaimed, brushing snowflakes from her scarf.

No customers were present in the confectionary, or in back, at the Post

Office Third Class. She still couldn't understand how third class was an upgrade from first, though Mr. Rowe had tried to explain it.

"Smells like a carnival in here," Herman shouted, his hearing not yet attuned to the absence of elements whirring and knocking. He took off his muffler and gave it a shake.

Pretty electric globes reflected faceted angles of light into and upon bowl after bowl of colorful candy set in rows—perfumed taffy, candy canes, gumdrops, chocolates. Highlights bounced from one glass cylinder to the next, a dazzling sight that coaxed customers to come hither and choose sweet delights.

"A child's idea of heaven," Mary said, "a regular rock candy mountain."

Herman was not enthusiastic.

To Mary, the atmosphere seemed fantastical—she would register to vote in candy land.

He called, "Melvin, you here?"

Sounds from an adjoining room jumbled.

Mary pitched, "Howdy, Mr. Rowe, it's Mary Fields. Are you back there? I'm here to register … to vote."

A sound squeaked, and footsteps shuffled close together, the timbre of city folk.

Mr. Rowe came around the corner, from the post office section of his establishment. "What did you say, Black Mary?" Noticing Herman Wolf, he straightened. "Good day, Mr. Wolf, both of you. How can I help?"

He smells sweet too, like an orange, she thought, watching him fiddle with his spectacles. She felt for her own and the bill of sale in her envelope.

"Morning, Mr. Rowe. Smells good in here. I'm here to register to vote. Where do we do that? In the post office?"

Melvin got halfway through a chuckle before Herman's expression alerted him not to.

Confused, he asked, "Black Mary, you know you can't vote. Are you playing a prank?"

"Like I said, Mr. Rowe, I'm here to register to vote."

She arched her back, feeling strong and proud. Deliberately, she observed details of the exchange as if she were witnessing from above, recording every important word and action for history, her history—her victory to recollect at will.

Planted firm in her rightful place, she watched Mr. Rowe swallow his surprise and judiciously adapt. Reluctant to explain, she allowed Herman to clarify.

"Mr. Rowe, said Herman Wolf moving to her side, "Is it not true that women who own property have the right to vote, as wrote in our state constitution?"

Mary clasped her hands.

"Yes, as far as I understand it, women tax-payers can vote."

Ceremoniously, Mary adjusted her hat, lifted the spectacles from her skirt pocket and tucked the stems around her ears. Mr. Rowe, a body length away, blurred. She stepped closer and closer, until he was in focus.

"Mr. Rowe …"

Melvin jerked back. Had she gone mad? He straightened and looked to Mr. Wolf, who turned to Mary.

"It's these spectacles, Mary explained, "Guess they're only for reading."

"I assure you, Melvin, Black Mary is quite serious. And qualified," Wolf said. "She has purchased my house here in town, and I will sign to substantiate, if it be necessary."

Clearly, Melvin was stunned. "In that case," he said, looking to Herman and slipping a hand into his jacket pocket, "why don't you both sit at my desk, in my office, back here. Let me …"

"You know I wouldn't kid a busy official like you," said Mary. "Is this the first time you ever registered a woman?"

"No. Just a moment, please."

He scurried off, his mind racing: this is my first time to register a Colored, truth be told. Is a negress allowed? Never needed to know before—how could she afford to buy Herman Wolf's house?

He returned with a chair to parallel the one facing his desk—handed it to Herman who instructed Mary to sit. Glancing at his applicant, fancied in a fur coat and lady's hat, with an escort, it became obvious that she meant business. Melvin shuddered, imagined how H.D. would react and thanked lucky stars he wasn't an alderman any longer. How fortunate that the post office upgrade had required him to step down. He preferred the neutral position: Cascade's full-time Postmaster. At least he had thought it would be neutral …

"Do I have to fill something out?" Mary asked.

Rowe ransacked his memory: What are the stipulations? Race? Taxes? What prohibits … "Oh yes, I'm getting it."

He sat down, thumbed through the second drawer of his desk and removed a piece of paper. Pushing a stack of correspondence aside, he said, "Here you are Black Mary," and slid the single sheet toward her. "This is the voter registration form. You need to answer all the questions and print your full name here." He pointed to a line at the bottom left. "And sign your name there." He tapped his index finger on the lower right corner. "But not yet—I need something from the back."

He got up, cleared his throat. "Can you write?"

"Yes," she said flatly, keeping eyes to paper, insulted, letting it slide.

"Sorry. Some folks can't." He dropped his pen and retrieved it from under his swivel chair. "Should have known you could read and write."

Rushing to the bookcase in the postal supply room, he freed the key from his vest, unlocked a tall cabinet and grabbed a cloth-covered volume titled *The Montana Constitution,* published in 1889, and a thin bound addendum, *The Revised Codes of Montana of 1907.* He flipped both charters open to the short sections regarding suffrage—pages bookmarked with strips of deer hide. It took only moments to locate notations he'd jotted in pencil on the margins, the details of which he had forgotten.

He scanned "Rights of Suffrage, Section XII" and reread it, whispering:

… women who are taxpayers and possessed of the qualifications for the right of suffrage required of men by this Constitution shall equally, with men, have the right to vote.

He reviewed the male qualifications:

… twenty-one or over … entitled to vote at all general elections and for all officers … elective by the people … a citizen of the United States … resided in this State one year immediately preceding the election at which he offers to vote, and in the town, county, or precinct such time as …

Double-checking for racial qualifications, he found nothing that disqualified Colored women, only Indians and Orientals.

He concluded: If she owns property and paid the property taxes it appears that she has the right. How can I know with absolute certainty? There is no time. If I make a mistake, I'll get grief from everybody—lose my post, too. H.D will see to that.

His fingers were sticky.

Waiting for Melvin's return, Mary read the registration form. Only a half-dozen blank lines stood between her and suffrage rights. Once they were filled in, she was entitled, and titled. Beginning with "Name" she came to a sudden halt. Which was it? She had already given up on her soul name, there hadn't been enough time—but she had figured it all out and had come to a decision about her middle name. Now she couldn't remember.

Her heart raced. Should I include my initial F. as on the property deed, or stick with Mary Fields, the name everybody knows? If I add my initial and Rowe demands the rest of the letters, I'll have to divulge and I don't want to—it's my personal business. She printed, M-a-r-y and panicked again. What if the name on the deed has to match the name I wrote on the registration form, exactly? Her leg started to shake.

"Black Mary, what's wrong?" Herman asked, concerned.

She felt her face flush. Her stomach lurched and she swallowed a sour taste. Should she ask Herman? He'd probably consult Melvin and they'd say, add it to be sure.

"Nothing," she replied, and printed F-i-e-l-d-s next to "Mary."

When Mr. Rowe returned, Mary was leaning against the desk, fanning her face with the form. He sat down.

"Just getting the ink dry for ya. Here you are." She extended her hand. The bulk of her coat sleeve knocked the ink bottle onto his blotting pad. Black fluid flooded onto paper and wood, and further, toward stacks of books and periodicals.

"Gracious snakes!" she misspoke, trilling.

Each of them jumped, searching for something to stop the spillage.

The clock chimed—and chimed.

Rowe grabbed his postal apron from a shelf and pressed upon the saturated items, tossing unsoiled papers from surface to the floor behind.

Herman did the same with newspaper rummaged from the wastebasket.

Mary stared, dumbstruck.

Changing position, Rowe barked, "Bathroom down the hall. Rags!"

She leapt toward the door, careful not to knock anything else.

In syncopated time, she distributed handfuls of repurposed diapers, helped to sop up pigment before drips and dribble traversed to the floor. Half of Rowe's papers survived unmarred.

"Good. I guess," he muttered, trying to remain dutifully civil.

The store bell rang. Cold air rushed in and around the corner.

He frowned, handed the wet rags to Mary and left the room.

She trotted down the hallway to the back, dropped the wad into a bucket and after a short sigh, hoisted the proof of her clumsy mistake and carried it to the alley, leaving black prints on the door's latch.

She scooped handfuls of snow to the bucket's lip to diffuse, diminish—a natural laundress response. Raw crystals felt good and she rubbed her hands numb.

Wiggling to free herself from the coat, she braced her warm back against the sleet and shook the pelts, wishing that the stink and the loose fur would flee.

Everything's flown out of control. And I did it, she fumed, shivering.

Angry with herself and her beaver albatross, she returned her upper limbs into the silk lining and rejoined Herman in the office. He had tidied the disarray, stacked the stained papers behind the door on a broken footstool that Melvin apparently used as a doorstop.

Mary sat down and fixed her attention to the wall. She hadn't noticed its decoration earlier. She hadn't paid a pittance to anything except documents and ink. Now that she was noticing, she judged the large land-plat hanging in a rustic frame on the wall to her left, somewhat interesting. She breathed in the toxic scent of wood permeated in ink of tinctured oak balls, and sighed. The shop's doorbell tinkled, followed by a woman's seductive drawl undulating. Mary uncrossed her arms and hoped that the feminine presence would prove positive upon Melvin's mood, lend revitalized progress to her registration.

She let her shoulders down, remembered, and bounced to her feet.

"Where is my envelope?" she gasped, checking pockets, frightened that her papers had taken flight in the alley, destroyed. Or worse, in God-knows-whose hands. Blushed, she started for the door.

"Black Mary ..."

She looked at her friend who pulled the envelope and a paper, the registration form, from his pocket.

"Is this what you're looking for?"

"You're a lifesaver."

Hand placed upon her thumping chest, she wondered if a document such as the one Herman handed back, would retain validity once folded.

"It's all right, Mary ..."

"Thanks, Mr. Herman."

She sat down. Slumping against the chair's back, she closed her eyes and nudged her heart—asked her well-thought-out aspirations to come forward, ascend in order of importance. She was directed to courage: hers and her forbearers, the ones she had spiritually consulted before breakfast.

Rowe returned wearing signs of pleasure that diminished as he examined his stained workplace. He tilted his chin upward, extending a starry-eyed stare to the ceiling. Mary caught a whiff of toilette water, one particular woman's trademark. She sent her personal thanks to Claret.

Rowe loosened his bolero. "Where were we?"

"I'm real sorry, Mr. Rowe," Mary apologized. She handed over the envelope, her sleeve held well above the desk. "I think you might need this."

Herman had opened his mouth, assuming he'd take the lead ... then decided she was fine on her own. It's Black Mary's transaction, he thought, scooting back, noting then, the waxing tempest outside. He hoped Gerlach would send their dog, Neitzsche, to bring the milk cows in … keep them ready in the barn.

Rowe opened Mary's envelope and raised his head. "This is your receipt from the census, Black Mary." He looked at her, then to Wolf. "It doesn't apply."

"There's more," Mary said, pointing to the envelope in his hand.

He inspected and extricated another page.

"And neither does your laundry business license."

"How could I have …" Mary mumbled.

Rowe plopped the papers on his disfigured desk, clamped the inside of his cheeks between teeth and looked up, to his family's plat.

"Wait Mr. Melvin," Herman interrupted. "I'm sorry. I didn't know what she had in there. She must have been, well, distracted. This is what you want."

Rowe remained seated, forcing Wolf to rise and pass the documents.

Quick examination confirmed that the parchment in hand was indeed a registered property transfer. The deed of sale had been signed by both parties, witnessed, notarized, and drawn by an esquire with the same surname as the seller, John Wolf. No reason to question authenticity. The legalities were in order and he recalled meeting John at last summer's independence celebration. He also recalled the large sack of mail waiting for him to sort … Why did Herman sell his house to Mary?

"Have the property taxes been paid?"

"That was in the—" Mary tried to explain.

Herman leaned forward and pulled the receipt from his breast pocket, the paper he had taken from Mary's table when she was fussing with her galoshes.

"You will see that the taxes were paid in cash by Stageco—Black Mary."

"Did you complete the registration form, Black Mary?"

"Yes, sir."

"Go ahead and sign your name on the bottom line."

She signed her best signature, smooth loops with weighted hand, permanent ink.

Rowe reached across what seemed to Mary, an imposing boundary, like the thirty-foot ditch that had defined the specific place for slave shanties, like all boundaries that stopped designated outsiders from joining the ranks.

He took the completed form and checked each line carefully.

"Fine," he said, "fine."

Mary exhaled.

He swiveled to his bookcase, located the volume that exceeded the width of the shelf, grabbed its gilded-cowhide spine and laid the heavy weight upon new blotters he had placed to protect the official records.

She had never seen a book appear so regal.

As if responding to phantom accusations, Rowe defended his ethics, thinking, there is poetic justice to this; I took an oath. No one's going to stop me from executing my charge; I am the registrar. Black Mary has proven her right. We're all escapees from somewhere … Hall's bullied her long enough. She deserves this.

He opened the register and carefully turned one vellum page after another, until he reached the sheet where carefully penned entries ended, four lines down. He placed his special writing instrument between poised fingers. Under column one titled, "Precinct," he printed 56. Under column two, "Entry Number,"3490. Pausing as he glanced briefly at his automobile calendar to make certain, he recorded under column three, "Date of Registry," February 17, 1912. In the last column titled, "Name of Elector" he scribed in cursive, the spelling of words Mary had provided on the application: *Fields, Mary.*

Aware of Mary's rapt attention, Melvin Rowe lifted, balanced and turned the enormous opened ledger, placing it ceremoniously before her. Catching eye contact, he advised, "Please inspect the information, if you would be so kind, Black Mary. Make certain that the name and date are correct."

She heard the words. They felt like love. My name … look at it glowing … my name … taking its place. Mary Fields, an official registered voter in the State of Montana, Entry Number 3490. She drank the shapes of the words on the page, a sacred communion.

"Yes, that is correct, Mr. Rowe."

22

THREATS

*T*hree weeks had passed. It seemed to Mary Fields and Herman Wolf that all was going smoothly—until Herman was given the third degree by a hostile band of locals at the Silver Dollar. Implying revenge, they demanded to know when and why he'd sold his place to Nigger Mary, as though Herman were a traitor on trial for despicable crimes and they the self-appointed jury, ready to pass judgment.

Herman swallowed the last of his beer and brazed a poker face, thinking how wise it had been, after all, to employ his brother for the legalities. John had instructed Mary to pay the taxes on her house the previous November; he had learned that not doing so would provide the loophole these hooligans were seeking. Herman licked his lips, confident that the mob's coveted intent would fail.

Eager to demonstrate his advantage, Dan Hall, Mayor H.D.'s brother and leader of the wild-card pack of ruffians, flipped his jacket open. A fancy-gloved hand gripped his Long Colt. Herman wasn't surprised to see the holster's gaudiness—red rhinestones, no less, surely meant to indicate Dan's place in the pecking order, a regular peacock.

He hooked the heel of his boot over the bar's foot rail, and wished he was home with his Gerlach. How unfortunate that these hotheads didn't understand; he could not be swayed. His parents had undergone far worse; they had died in their plight, fleeing to America. He would not betray their memory by compromising his integrity.

Dan prodded, "Ain't it a shame when some farmers lose their rights to grain storage, cattle auctions, sheep shearing—don't know how—some reason or another—problems with the law maybe." He gagged on a smug snort and threw a glance to his cohorts, who hooted in tandem.

Herman scoffed, "Ain't it a shame when able-bodied men wallow their time scheming heartless cruelties—when they could prove up—homestead, make something for future—not waste years prancing to a pied—what is the word?" He scanned their trodden faces, pretending to recall. "Piper," he added.

Shaking his head, he slid coins off the bar, thinking, they are stupid donkeys.

"Dummer esels," he said plenty loud, taking pleasure in their ignorance of his meaning. "Dummer esels," he repeated.

Dan straddled his bulk between Herman and the door. He drew his double-barrel revolver, thumbed the hammer back, flipped the cylinder open and spun it.

A voice in the shadows twanged, "Ya know, in the South they have a club—K.K.K. it's called. I heard they hang coon lovers—ain't that a shame, fellas?"

"Rightly come-up-ins!" the youngest rouser squealed while the others snarled.

Dan slipped his Colt back into its holster but did not budge from his crest-chested stance.

Another heckler pitched, "Probably be alive, that coon lover, if he answered simple questions."

Idle grunts and spittle prolonged the exchange.

Herman looked to the barkeep, then to the door past the obstacle. "If you're done rankling," he said to Dan, "I have business to meet."

Dan whipped his six-shooter out again, glaring as he poked it at Herman, then aimed and shot five holes through the dartboard bulls-eye. Rounding his shoulders back, he flexed his mightiness, championed a paladin pose and spat sideways from beneath the newly purchased white Stetson.

"That's enough," the barkeep hollered. "Get out of here, Dan, and the rest of ya!" He slammed a shot glass down. "You'll be gettin' a bill for damages." He turned. "Not you, Wolf."

Begrudgingly, Dan and his cronies filed out, swaggering and darting coup de gras stares in Herman's direction.

Fed up and defenseless without his gun, Herman offered to replace the demolished darts and, after a few minutes, left for home, promising honor that he would return to town tomorrow—relay the bad news to Mary—that word was out—after he'd calmed down.

Unbeknownst to Herman, the following day was Mary's birthday. Trying to forget the council's made-for-her ordinance against throwing a party at the schoolhouse, she busied. To acknowledge her years and her good health, she baked a chocolate birthday cake, just for her—and perhaps the Monroe boys and their mother. She would eat the whole thing, if she felt like it, tomorrow, when she would be eighty-years of age.

During the night, Mary woke to sounds of labored coughing that shook her from her sleep. The room was sizzling hot. Her throat seized; she gasped to breathe. Smoke had taken the air and it was burning her eyes. When she opened them, torched peaks of red and black, the colors of death, brushed toward her. Flames jumped and devoured, and behind them, walls of fire blazed where the boundaries of her house had been.

She catapulted from bed, grabbed the shawl from the back of her rocker and covered her face. My house is on fire, her mind alerted urgently, also advising not to open her mouth. Get outside—that was its cry. Where? Heights of fire blocked her escape. A chunk of roof crashed beside her, broiling furniture. And flesh, too, if she defied the inferno. The hem of her nightshirt ignited.

She felt herself lift off, saw the color orange twist as she passed through it. The side of her smashed into burning timber, and her body propelled itself, launched like a baseball or a dart. She hit hard against a slab of ice and rolled—her face, helmeted by crossed arms. She curbed, compressed her form into a hiding cone, a chrysalis, where she would be safe until she could break free, a butterfly.

Someone's voice blurred too close. She started to feel. She could smell charred skin. She didn't want to. She heard the ravenous fire eating her house and cinders giving way—parts collapsing and sizzling on snow. She turned to see. Her shelter was gone. *Ashes to ashes*, a grouty voice in far recesses mumbled.

Her stomach spasmed. Her head pounded. She understood that she was seeing Hattie's face. Hands were squeezing her shoulders, and she felt shaking. Whether she was shaking, or someone was shaking her, she could not tell. She wanted to stay in the snow and listen for the fire's death.

"Am I burned?" she asked, staring past Hattie to the lone potbelly and its broken pipe, exposed in a pit of embers that cast an eerie glow.

A river of words whirled over her. "Mary, come with me," they pronounced. "Can you walk? It's Hattie. Hold on. I've got you. Try to stand up."

She tried to move. A burning in her legs prostrated her efforts. She tried again when she heard Hattie's voice change direction and holler, "Can someone help? Carry her for me!"

Sounds of men thumped through ice—running, yelling, crunching close. Mary strained. She staggered to balance her two feet, twitched and hunched. Grasping Hattie's arm, she whimpered, "I have to run," and covered her eyes.

"I'll hide you, Mary. Come with me. Sorry it hurts. This way."

Mary examined the words she thought she heard. She shook her head. "Not now. I have a cake."

"Mary," Hattie sighed, "I have a cake for you. This way, Mary."

When Mary woke, she felt the tips of her spine laid flat against something hard. She scanned her surroundings and rested her gaze on dark ash in a hearth. Where was she? She tossed the cover from her legs. Sight of bandages kicked her memory. She was burned. Her house was gone. She realized that she was, instead, at the Monroe's.

In a voice that sounded meek to her, she called, "Hello?"

Pale predawn light filtered through glass.

Small sticky hands from behind touched her neck. "Are you all right, Nigger Mary?"

"Everything's gone," she murmured.

She hadn't noticed Lester come in. Perhaps he'd been there already. She asked herself to remember, to think what was important. Pictures formed in her mind: Mary Fields standing at the ballot box, the red oak tree, silence, snow-capped mountains, driving her team on the mission route. I want them all. What should I do? She looked at the strips of cloth, gauze wrapped from ankles to knees, both legs. She wiggled her big toe. Why aren't my feet burned? Did I have my boots on? I don't remember.

"Are you all right, Nigger Mary?" Lester's voice twittered again.

"Yes. Yes, darling." Her eyes moved to the charred logs beside her. "I'm fine."

He came close to examine her face. "You look fine, Nigger Mary, except your hair is sticking out funny."

Earl wobbled in, carrying folded bundles of cloth in his arms. "This is for you, Nigger Mary. Mama is cooking your breakfast. Why did the ter'ble fire burn your house down?"

She gave him a teary-eyed smile. "Fault lies with the one who—I better get dressed." She hesitated, wondering if she could, in fact, get up. Her hands and feet were puffy and damp and hot.

"Word got out, no doubt about it," she said matter of fact.

She rolled slowly to the left, heaved up to balance upon the edge of a chair, shifted weight to her feet, wobbling until dizziness passed. Arms out for balance, she limped through the house and let herself outdoors, sidling barefoot to the outhouse, muscles cramped and stinging. She eased onto the ice-cold ceramic seat and shivered.

"Oh my God!" she uttered as her legs jerked. Does this take away my right to vote? Is it the house, or the land that counts? Have to talk to Herman.

Hattie watched as Mary picked at her breakfast. "We'll have to take a look under the bandages, Mary—second degree burns. You were brave."

She sent the boys out to build a snowman and recalled Mary's terrified plea, "I have to run." Who had inflicted such deep-cut scars—a cruel master, bounty hunters?

"Didn't have much choice," Mary said, struggling to scoop porridge with battered hands.

"Who would want to burn your house down, Mary? You've hardly been out. Bothered nobody. And it's the dead of winter.

"Well, you don't know the whole story."

"What?"

"I'll tell you."

She pushed the plate and bowl to the table's edge, asked if she could have a half-cup of Assam tea and began to recount her actions, beginning with her original challenge: how to get the vote. She then proceeded to the purchase of her house, and to the registration triumph, Mr. Wolf by her side. She made sure to mention, for Hattie's sake, the longing she had endured, aching to tell her—and why she had hesitated—for fear of dangerous repercussions, for both of them.

"Oh my God," Hattie shrieked. "I can't believe it!"

An electric response bolted her body upright. From there, she could grasp the magnitude of Mary's daring deeds, and realized how this woman had leapt beyond idle talk and wishful thinking—how Mary, with less, had done it. She could vote in more than just school elections.

"I can't believe it," she repeated. "You're astonishing."

Mary pressed her hand to her forehead, pushed on a tepid pulse that felt, to her, like molten lava colliding into cold sea. Where was that? Vesuvius, she thought, half-heartened, hoping distraction would stop the gushing queasiness that inched up her throat. She looked to Hattie.

Hattie's nerves shimmied. She darted random glances about the kitchen and realized she had forgotten to keep an eye on the bread dough that had since oozed over the edge of the bowl. Taking steps, she punched the glutenous mass with her fist and fumed: What hateful selfishness, trying to destroy an old woman's dream. Aren't we ever going to get rights?

She sat down, exhausted. "Mary," she said, "What are we to do?" Feelings of angst shot past each of the other's shoulder, to boundaries where vision loses focus.

Hattie put a slice of dried apple into her mouth and chewed, unaware of the silence, of her sons' whereabouts, of the source of her rising irritation. She looked at Mary and said, "Setting fire to your house doesn't eliminate your right to vote." She swallowed. "We'll rebuild it."

"Hattie, it's me they're trying to eliminate," Mary answered, "whoever it was."

Hattie winced, groping for the natural course of justice that should follow. Eyes closed, she wished for something tranquil. A damp thickness of moss and fallen lichens appeared to her, water trickling from cavernous rock cleft between spired mountain peaks—a beloved place she had visited once. She took a breath. Gravity seemed to settle her. Speechless and bare, she pressed herself into the imprint.

Admiring heights above, she mused, could the violent creation of mountains—converged continents thrusting, ruptured—be the catalyst for fountains of life channeled from beneath—precious drink coursed through fissures, slabs and shelves, elevated?

What was it like, the journey of water? Why did this suddenly matter?

She rode the surging reply. Fluid, she joined the gushing elixir and moved upward through darkness, squeezed by forces unseen in precipiced corridors, scraping dead matter from roots and centuries ...

Emerged to brightness, vast sky weightlessness, she and water touched the apex and splashed. Entwined, they tumbled onto earth. Infused and sparked by sunlight, color transcended their essence. Propelled, they transited.

Thinning, they stretched over polished arcs of stone—dropped far and fast into chiseled pathways, and corded, wielded into mass and swiveled through thickened webs of pebbles.

She touched one hand with the other.

Suddenly released, she and water leapt, and filled a glacier cirque— roaring, swirling, faster, bubbling, slowed—a blissful repose.

Pooling, they explored new form and a level surface, they themselves the fold between above and below. She breathed.

Refracted prisms glowed in spherical drops, upon and in the water, on rocks and trees and clouds, sparkling. Kinetic coupling danced in the cove, the loch, the basin, the place reflecting movement of orbiting planets and galaxies, mirroring, miring indigenous sight to a linked heritage.

A clearing coursed through Hattie's heart. She felt her rapid-river veins surge. An element transformed, she would change as needed, adapt and join the women ushering change. They would congregate with open hearts, glide upon ancient currents of knowing—a confluence—navigate to prismed inlets, oceans and reservoirs that would sustain, nourish and replenish …

Women are the sustenance by which human life exists, her consciousness rose to speak.

She opened her eyes and followed one thought: a woman's body designs life, labors to birth, and suckles the children. Without voices from our bodies that experience such creation, life is sure to fail—our nation, our frontier, will topple.

We must forge together.

She quivered from the quickened resonance, insulated memories of pregnancy and birth and an unbid spark of clairvoyance: things to come if humans did not embrace compassion. In this vision she saw bodies emerge from treeless shadows shouldering burlap sacks of pain, arms flinging seeds that would ravish rather than propagate.

She looked up. Mary was seated across the table, eyes closed. Hattie aborted her earlier impulse to feverishly cite the harsh severities of Mary's situation. Rather than exclaim, "This is horrible, Mary," as she had intended, she doused her words and waited.

Mary opened her eyes. "Can't wait to vote against Hall next year," she stated, as if she'd been asked.

Hattie wiped dry hands on her apron. She pushed her chair back, stepped to the window and watched Lester and Earl duel with sticks. Siphoning memory, she searched for faces peering through the previous night's darkness—faces delighted by the flames—perpetrators.

"Meanwhile," she said as she sat down and touched Mary's hand with gentle reverence, "we need to take care of you. I'm going to clear out D.W.'s study, put a mattress in there. You'll stay with us, until we get your place rebuilt."

Mary didn't respond to the generosity of her friend, yet. Such an invitation would need to be approved by a husband. Accepting now would be awkward if D.W. was not of the same mind.

In a bedraggled voice, she asked, "Would it be all right if I lie back down by the hearth?"

The floor grabbed a chill from her, but she didn't mind. Cold felt good against the heat of burned skin. She wanted her comfrey-hypericum salve and some valerian, and realized they had been consumed. And my cigars, she grieved, the last of my Whizzers—and my tattered case, my box with the picture of Homer the Pigeon who protected my treasures, my keepsakes.

She told her thoughts to change direction.

They didn't mind.

How did word get out? Who hates me this much? Why do they have to hoard all the rights and the land when there's so much free for the taking? She wrestled it in her usual way—roped it, flipped it, mulled over it again, dozed off when pain eased.

Waking sometime later, she felt grateful for measures of luck received. Postmaster Rowe could have denied her right to register and sent her packing. What would she have done? Gone to Helena, picketed the capitol building? Herman Wolf had foreseen the need to tie legal knots, and they'd been graced with good timing, passing Marcum on the way home, after the registering was done. Am I really a threat? Little old me, eighty years old? Guess I should be happy that I'm not barbequed, like Tennessee chick—oh, wait—

Today is my birthday!

She heard a murder of crows cawing, swooshing and flapping. Play, it sounded like, somewhere above the chimney passage. She thanked them for being near, wondered if maybe they were squawking happy birthday wishes, personal.

Monroes insisted that she join them for dinner, and D.W. spoke for the family—invited her to stay and told her not to worry—that he and Herman had already started organizing volunteers to rebuild her house.

Mary sighed with the realization that she could relax, for awhile. Hattie presented a chocolate cake with candles. Teardrops dampened the frosted edge as Mary efforted to eliminate more flames.

The next afternoon D.W. went to the Post Office, as usual, to get the mail. Melvin Rowe handed him two parcels for Hattie and a rolled-up-tied-with-a-string newspaper addressed to Miss Fields.

Returned home, he joined Hattie in the kitchen, opened the newspaper he'd not heard of, scanned the headlines and read the leading article.

"That's right!" D.W. exclaimed, "I said that, just this morning. Scoop has no right to leave Mary's fire out of the paper." He took his hat off. "Discriminated news coverage, blatant absence. Finally, someone who agrees with me!"

"What?" Hattie asked, busy baking cookies for the Lady's Aid meeting.

"How in the world did that reporter get the news, those details, so fast?" he muttered.

"The fire?" Hattie asked.

"Listen to this."

Cascade Flames Demolish House & Constitutional Rights?
James P. Ball

Cascade resident Miss Mary Fields, who on February 17, 1912, became the first colored person to register to vote in her district, awoke to a blistering inferno last night. Jumping through a wall of fire, she made it outside in time to witness flames burn her house to the ground. Though she did not suffer serious injuries, the loss of her home and business will, no doubt, cause considerable suffering to the only colored resident of Cascade.

Cascade's newly appointed magistrate, C.E. Hoag, reports that the cause of the fire is unknown, and no further investigation is necessary.

The timing of this unfortunate event leads inquisitive minds to ask: Does the victim's new status as a registered voter have anything to do with the life-threatening incident? If proved to be a heinous premeditated crime, who did it? These are questions that law enforcers, our keepers of the peace, normally investigate.

It is common knowledge that some people living in the Birdtail-Sun River area, dispute civil rights as guaranteed in the United States and Montana constitutions. Miss Fields has been encouraged, on more than one occasion, to relocate.

"Who wrote that? Couldn't be Scoop," Hattie interrupted.

"It's a colored newspaper, The Colored Citizen, it's called. Was in Mary's box. "Right on the money isn't it?"

"Read the rest."

Cascade's first Mayor, H.D. Hall, and his council, created twenty-two ordinances immediately following their election, one year ago. Among the first was a law prohibiting persons of the female sex from smoking or drinking in public: including restaurants and saloons and shade under grand old cottonwoods where it is said that this same woman had occasionally in the past, enjoyed conversation and a smoke with friends during her eight-year post as the United States Star Route Mail Carrier, and prior to that, nine years while she labored for the Ursuline nuns at Saint Peter's Mission.

One cannot help wonder why this perilous event, in which Miss Fields came close to losing her life, was not deemed important enough to report in the Cascade Courier newspaper by Editor C.W. Tierney, alias "Scoop" Tierney.

Well here's a scoop for Tierney and Courier owner, W.F. Berger: it is irresponsible and unprofessional not to report local news, in this case, a fire within city limits—particularly when flames border local businesses and residences, including the Cascade Courier's office. We encourage residents to ask, "Why?"

D.W. folded the paper carefully, set it on the shelf where Mary would find it undisturbed.

"It just isn't right," D.W. pained, "All of it."

Hattie moved close and took his hand. "We're losing moral decency. What's become of love thy neighbor?"

D.W. and Herman sought volunteers—offered a free drink of choice for each hour labored on Mary's reclamation. They convinced young bucks that ladies' hearts flutter for chivalrous men, then called upon the older crowd to show those whippersnappers how it was done—the remodeling.

Hattie canvassed the compact Cascade neighborhoods, soliciting solidarity from each and every woman, including wives of aldermen, females occupying the house of ill-repute and Presbyterians, pointing out that this project represented a united responsibility for everyone, seeing as Mary Fields was a Cascade cornerstone in need of tending, as one would for one's grandma, or the baseball mascot, or the valiant, former territorial mail carrier. She also mentioned that the fire had been reported in a Helena paper, and eyes were on Cascade—all the more reason to demonstrate Christian morals.

When recipients of her solicitudes didn't volunteer immediately, she continued chatting, reminding that Mary had laundered most everyone's clothes for years—or babysat, making it possible for husbands and wives to get out on occasion. Hattie could draw a connection from Mary to almost each resident, though some were quick to deny any implication of reliance. Her heartfelt closing rang, "Just do what's right. Mary would help you, and you know it."

Aldermen Wedsworth and Atkinson organized an emergency city council meeting. After passing a copy of *The Colored Citizen* around the table, Atkinson demanded, "What are we going to do about Mary Fields spotlighted on the front page? It sounds like no one did anything to help her."

"That's right," Wedsworth barked, "this can ruin Cascade's reputation. We worked hard to build it."

Mayor H.D. Hall, irritated to have been called away from poker-night with brother Dan and the simple-minded riffraff, brayed, "We're going to do exactly nothing. I already thought about it. Any action or comments from us will make us look like we've got something to defend."

"Like our honor?" Dr. Russell posed.

"Like I said," H.D. repeated, "Our honor doesn't need defending. That news article was writ by a colored editor for a colored newspaper, in Helena. He pulled a cigarette from his pocket and tapped its end. "Just about no one will see it, and anybody reading that nigger rag will find his own self, suspect—" He struck a match. Odor of sulfur riffled his conclusion: "Don't worry about it."

Alderman Briscoe, long-time resident and new incumbent (replacing Charlie Lemon, who had moved to New York) reported, "I heard that Monroe is organizing a charity drive to get Black Mary's house rebuilt."

"Good," said Hall with a twang of sarcasm. "Perhaps we should contribute. That would be fine publicity. Right, Wedsworth?" He shot a glance to Wedsworth and his thick spectacles, expounding, "We'll discuss this later. Do you realize we have less than a year til re-election?"

Atkinson jumped in, "That's not much time to get the waterworks finished. We won't win unless that's done; we're over budget by thirty-plus percent, and—"

"Did we get the bill of sale from the realty," Briscoe asked, "for the land and the water rights we bought from Taylor?"

"Don't forget the forthcoming onslaught of women suffragists and temperance goody two-shoes, who might, God forbid, get the vote before then. That would be—" He slid a finger across his throat.

"Did you hear what Marcum's wife Ida did?" Wedsworth tossed into the new business free-for-all. "Invited some woman suffrage leader to come give a speech."

"Does anyone know when?" Hall demanded. Rubbing his thinning hairline, he tried to remember whether it was a flush or a full house he'd had in his grip before all this hoopla.

"Too bad some women got the right to vote on city measures," Briscoe whined. "People keep harping at me, want to know how we let Black Mary buy her house in the first place."

"We didn't *let* her," Hall barked. "Wasn't under our authority and, furthermore, we didn't know about it." His indigestion cranked up a notch.

"Could we have stopped it?" Rowe's replacement, Mr. Gregory, blurted, concerned that his reputation could be blundered by association.

"Whoever sparked that match should be arrested," Thompson grieved. "Had to be consumed by hatred; a monster."

The truth momentarily disabled tongues.

"Well, let's get on with it, then," Russell, who had a patient waiting, grumbled. "We'll have to decide what projects to promote—publicize all the good we've done and remind our citizens that this is the best place for Christians to live and prosper. We need some new ideas for our platform. We'll have competition this time."

Tired brows narrowed.

"Yeah, but not tonight," Hall dismissed. "Did anyone ask Scoop why he didn't report the fire in the first place?"

Dr. Russell sighed. "Yes. He said, and I quote, 'If I reported her in the paper it would give her validation. I prefer to think that she doesn't exist.'"

J.E. Marcum, who had burst into the council chambers moments earlier, stood arms crossed, disheveled and irritated. "Since this isn't an official meeting," he initiated, striking his prima-donna pose, "I want to present a question—if you haven't solved it already."

"Have a seat, J.E.," Hall said, trying to keep a lid on his temper. "This is an official meeting, on schedule or not." He waited for J.E. to lower himself head level to his aldermen. Wielding top-dog authority, Hall turned to Marcum and asked, "What is it, your question?"

"Why is Wolf rebuilding Nigger Mary's place?" he demanded, drumming his fingers. "Monroe's been sermonizing moral duty, paying workers with whiskey. Got the frame halfway up already, a regular snowman construction crew, busy as picnic ants."

"Least he's patronizing the businesses we all but killed," Thompson cracked, "The saloo—"

Marcum cleared his throat loudly. "Second question. Think. If Wolf really sold it, he shouldn't have such an interest in the house anymore. I wonder if he really did, sell it."

Looks swung.

"Here we go," Thompson muttered, rousing speculations from Mr. Gregory seated to his left.

"Well?" Marcum cavaliered, eyeing each council member in turn. "No one knows anything?"

Heads shook, wearing varied amounts of concern.

"Can't you all pass some kind of ordinance that prohibits building in winter? Or a mandatory city permit they must apply for—an inspection or something that would, you know, delay things?" Marcum plied.

"I don't know about that," said Hall, "sounds kind of obvious."

"Like our ordinance wasn't?" Atkinson drawled.

"Like our Mayor said," Russell rebuked, "we have an election coming up. Should have come earlier, Marcum. The matter has been discussed already."

"Yes. That agenda item was closed," Hall said proudly, feeling equal to his mentor, J.E.

"Wolf's interest is suspicious, all right," Wedsworth commented. "How can we get a look at the bill of sale? It must be registered. Where?"

"I told you something fishy was going on," Atkinson hooted, as though he'd just won the cakewalk.

Russell said, "Even if the deed is on the up and up, doesn't mean …"

"I wonder who paid the taxes," Wedsworth posed, "I told you all before—property values will rise without a nigger living in town. Just a fact we should consider, as the council."

"If and when she leaves," Atkinson said, "we should arrange a spot for future ones, across the river—"

Thompson stood. "I thought we all agreed to support our Christian community." Surprised his voice wasn't shaking, he bravely insisted, "I think this meeting needs to end. And another thing. Our council meetings are still not open to the public. It's wrong." *Sinful* was the word he really wanted to shout.

Shocked to hear Thompson speak his mind but uninterested in rebutting, Hall, lacking his gavel, slapped a fist on the table and declared, "Meeting adjourned, fellas."

Members of the Bruneau family were seated at Louie and Isabel's table for supper. Louie pulled a letter from his pocket and handed it to Onatah, explaining that it had arrived earlier, that he had forgotten to bring it to her.

"It's from White Crow," she exclaimed, "maybe she's coming at last!"

Everyone watched her nimble fingers rip the flap. She scanned. Her face contorted, then paled. She leaned against the chair's back.

"What's wrong?" Edward asked.

She looked at him. "There was a fire." Eyes returning to the page, she felt her throat constrict.

"Is she all right?" Isabel shrilled.

Onatah fought the welling tears. "She made it out somehow. Doesn't say how …" She sipped air and looked up. "Both of her legs are burned."

"And the house?" Louie asked.

"Burned to the ground."

"Oh my," Isabel said. Searching for solace, she added, "Will she come here now? Is anyone tending her?"

"There's more," Onatah said. "She registered to vote last month. And word got out. The fire happened on the eve of her birthday."

"She's lucky to be alive," said Louie, "Poor woman."

"So that's why she wouldn't commit to living with us," Edward said thoughtfully, "She'd made a plan—a plan to get the vote. It wasn't just the ordinances—"

"How can you be thinking about that?" Onatah yipped. "She almost died, and you're talking about her stupid plan."

"I don't know whether to cheer or cry," Isabel commiserated. "Is anyone tending her?" she repeated.

Mary Ahwao started to whimper.

Edward stroked his daughter's hair, as though his touch would shield her from her mother's distress.

Onatah turned to Isabel. "She's staying with the Monroes, friends of hers. They say they'll rebuild her house."

"She's put everything at risk," Louie said.

"Yes," said Edward looking at his father, "but I can understand. It may be awhile until she comes to live with us, unless things escalate again."

"Edward—" Isabel said, shooting him a look.

"Did she say how she did it?" Louie asked.

"Did what?"

"Escaped the fire."

"And registered to vote," Edward uttered, admiring such courage.

"No, she didn't," Onatah snapped, as she stood and headed for the door.

Hattie visited the women again, this time in their associations: church societies, secular clubs and guilds. She cited their civic duty as members of humanitarian organizations, provided a schedule of necessities, and asked for pledges, clipboard in hand.

Items needed by Mary Fields included clothing, soap, towels, laundry tub, washboard, clothesline, dishes, pots and pans, kerosene lanterns, throw rugs, curtains, bed, bedding, dresser drawers, table and chairs, rocking chair, coat, coat rack, shoes, boots, hats, gloves, paper, pen, books, yarn, crochet hooks, reading glasses, and niceties of personal cheer such as doilies, quilts or afghans and, last but not least, caps, a variety of caps.

Most women rallied, committing to contribute with compassionate verve.

Hattie ignored the inevitable few who patted themselves on the back, indulged in and perpetuated snobbery; they spewed and spouted versions of, "Poor old Mary, getting indigent, can't take care of herself … we're helping her out again … I gave her … I remember when …"

"I don't care what name they call Mary or what they say," Hattie complained to D.W., home and out of earshot, "as long as everyone contributes, and we get the poor dear what she needs—at least the bare bones."

It took Hattie awhile to realize that the side-swiped glances darted her direction were generated by ill will. At first, she dismissed the rude behavior as reactionary—disgruntled citizens who hadn't appreciated her assertive petitions, necessary to make things right for Mary Fields. It will settle, she told herself, doesn't it always?

When time proved her wrong, she groped to comprehend the harsh attitudes, short retorts peppered with scorn. She considered the word *shun*. Were they shunning her?

It was D.W. who had the heart to break it to her. "Don't you know why they're avoiding you? he pressed. "Think. What has changed?"

When Hattie came up empty, he confided, "It's because we have Nigger Mary *living* with us. You know, eating at our table, using the same dishes, the same outhouse."

Hattie's jaw dropped. She was no fool. Of course, help had separate quarters, if one had help, but this had been an emergency—one soul helping another.

"Makes me all the more proud that Mary is here," she declared. "How can people be so backward?"

23

NEW FRONTIERS

SPRING 1912 - FALL 1912

"Dear Lord," Mary mumbled, waking in the night. "Please let me live long enough to realize my goal. Then I'll live and let live." She tossed and fretted until, at last, she dropped off and dreamed: herself and Mary Ahwao playing in water; the child takes a breath and sinks; Mary reaches out and suddenly all strength vanishes; paralyzed, she watches the child fight for life. Time to sustain breath passes yet the innocent babe kicks a somersault and rises, breaks the surface, smiling. They embrace.

Mary heard herself gasp and pulled the covers to her neck, listened for, but heard only, the absence of sound she sought. Succumbed to haunted feelings that pulled her back into the dream, she revisited her inability to move, panic stricken, and skipped to the ending—the emergence of joy and relief. She probed for the dream's meaning. Was it a warning? Was she in danger—of murder—of losing the chance to be part of a family? Did Mary Ahwao need her help? She rubbed her forehead and worried: Maybe I'd better get to Saypo. Isn't it smarter to go where I'm welcome? Will Onatah still have me after all this dillydallying? Maybe the dream came from my injuries—the pain, it's terrible enough. She lay, eyes wide open, until the first sliver of dawn arrived and was startled, again, to realize she was in the Monroe's house.

She tramped to the hotel for breakfast, and then to Rowe's Cash Bazaar where she retrieved the post for which she had been waiting. Hands clumsy, cloaked in oversized church gloves since the fire, she decided to open her small package before it, or the news inside, slipped from her grip.

She chose the Q & L to lean against (the establishment was closed until noon) and pulled the dingy cotton sheath from her right hand. Undeterred by drops of blood, as scabs caught and tore exposing raw makings of new flesh, she read the single page letter as though in a race and every second mattered.

Onatah did care.

"I still have a home to go to," she uttered. She looked to the steady steel-gray sky, allowed a small smile to emerge. Centering her gloved hand to her chest, she rubbed, sending pent-up heartache away.

Yearning for both things, the vote in Cascade and the family in Saypo, she agonized over the choice at hand, felt her very soul would split. "Look at me," she stated. "A lifetime spent fighting for freedom of choice and I can't decide! Each choice gives me freedom, but different kinds."

She hoofed it to Monroe's—witnessed upon entry, a riveting scene: Lester and Earl, transported pirates clad in paper hats and homemade eyepatches, engaged in an altercation over a chest of treasure: rubies and gold doubloons and goblets. Each claimed ownership, and they advanced, on guard, thrusting shields and swords in a duel to the death for Fortune, Queen and Country.

"Watch out! You'll Drown, Matey," they shouted as Mary tiptoed through what anyone could see was the deep Caribbean Sea. Mighty waves threatened to crash the three-chairs-in-a row ship crowned with a broomstick mast and a handkerchief flag. Lester used both hands to turn the vessel's imaginary wheel, nearly missing the jagged rocks, otherwise known as the fireplace.

Chimerically soaked to the bone by the time she reached the kitchen, Mary sat down in a chair to enjoy currant scones, baked by Hattie that morning, with raspberry jam—until Sir Earl and Captain Lester prevailed upon her for assistance.

Captain Lester saluted and implored, "Queen Mary, we need you to be our hostage so we can barter you for our release! The King has arrested us, and we will be hanged on the gallows if you don't!"

"You can stay where you are," Earl said.

"We just need to tie you to this chair." Lester clarified, rope in hand.

"Oh, my. Gosh!" Mary shouted, jumping from her chair. "How could I have forgotten? The King's coach awaits me—a matter of utmost urgency—our kingdom depends upon it. I must be off!"

She swam across the ocean, to a small isle near the door, slipped her boots on, grabbed her sweater and bellowed, "Ahoy Mates, shiver my timbers!" and slammed the door. Headed for her boulder, anxious to reread the contents of her treasured letter, she slowed and eventually aborted her mission due to the relentless invader she had become most familiar with: pain. Claiming a moment of solace, she leaned against the wind-worn Catholic altar, oddly placed and still anchored: one lone sail in an open sea, like herself, she thought.

Feeling better but not resolved, she complained, "Lord, do I have to choose? Persevering on willpower alone, is wearing thin."

She pulled Onatah's note from her pocket and listened to the words as she read aloud:

March 20, 1912

Dearest White Crow,

   I am so sorry, upset about the fire and the implications. That goes for all of us.

   I am so thankful you don't have more injuries. How bad are your burns?

   Congratulations for becoming an official registered voter. I am proud of you.

   How did you manage it? Perhaps you will vote your cruel mayor out of town, at least out of office.

   When you come home, we'll give you the 80th birthday party you missed.

   Here is the photograph Isabel promised, from our picnic.

   Hurry up. Before it's too late.

Love,
Onatah, Edward and Mary Ahwao

"Before it's too late," rang in her heart. The weight of her swayed and she leaned into her walking stick.

When the Monroe house grew quiet that night, Mary lit a candle and unwrapped the photograph she had forced herself to wait for, since morning. Holding the precious gift by its sides, she brought it near to her hand-me-down spectacles. The May Day picnic on the mountain one-year past, came to life. Mary Ahwao, Onatah and herself twinkling with glee. Such a splendid afternoon they had shared under the red ash lounging near the babbling brook, listening and talking and shouting exultations of spring—a genuine family jubilee. Promising to spend her first future earnings on a pretty picture frame, she re-wrapped the image and slipped it under her mattress.

Mary's house was restored three weeks later, thanks to efforts contributed by Herman, the Monroe family and volunteers who donated their time and many of the items posted on the *Mary Fields Necessity List*.

Cognizant of her growing attachment to another college-educated independent-thinking white woman, Mary realized the extent to which the emotional loss of Mother Mary's friendship had affected her, and was moved, acknowledging a dormant part of herself, rekindled.

Hattie worried that another attempt on Mary's life would occur. She asked D.W. if he and his buddies would patrol the neighborhood.

The rebuilt flat board house had no divisions—no walls within the four sides that stood between Mary and all that was outside: a rectangular structure with an old iron wood stove in the middle, multi-purposed to service heat, cooking and laundry.

Her last pennies and postage stamps had been spent days ago. She hummed, thinking, now is the time to subscribe to homespun horse sense: *worry gets you nowhere*. Externalizing energy from her concerns, she asked: What projects can I catch up on? Recreate? Replace? My Whizzer cigar box and its treasures can't be duplicated; what about the new assortment of caps and clothes? Most are too big, too little or worn out in spots. I could alter them to fit, or cut them up and patchwork shapes into improved, useful clothing more to my liking—save the strongest fabrics to sew functional aprons reinforced with extra-deep, extra-lined holster pockets, or hidden pockets. I have more than enough time, between injuries and ordinances keeping me held-up.

"Least I won't have to rewrite my will," she spoke aloud, startled to hear her voice echo and sink flat somewhere, between the scarcities of objects. "Thank goodness Herman has a copy," she mused, listening more intently to the way sound moved. She thought how glad she was that Mr. John had been gentlemanly, hadn't let Herman read her "last words" scribed to Nadie and Onatah.

"Oh no! My gift to Nadie," she cried out. "My diary of gardening secrets and seeds for each of my special flowers and vegetables ... it's gone!" She squeezed her hands, not feeling the pain inflicted. "And my beautiful dolly that Onatah, little Annie then, made all by herself." "Saved all this time," she mumbled, "for Mary Ahwao. If only I would have taken it last spring ... I wanted her to have it and wanted Onatah to see it again. Only thing left from her childhood, the egg face, painted, the darling dress she stitched. I'm so tired. Time for bed."

❧

The desperado who had failed in his attempt to rid Cascade of Mary Fields, once and for all, was disturbed that his vision had been foiled. Convinced that he was an instrument of God's will, he had persuaded two others to participate in his assignment, a mobilization of moral forces synchronized under his command. They had ignited three corners of Mary's house, never considering that she would wake and leap through walls of fire.

The self-appointed soldier was not accustomed to defeat and therefore maintained vigilance, waiting for auspicious signs, messages or prophecies to appear—the next strategic insight that would arrive by virtue of his devout preparations.

Exercising principles of mortality, his manly rights of passage, he traveled through the moonless night, as was his weekly ritual, to the whore house where he would cleanse himself of earthly impurities—sexual passions in need of purification—so that he would remain a reverent vehicle of virtue, the knighted disciple who protects his community from association with unclean, degenerate creatures cohabitating within City limits.

Knocking on Claret's door as he pushed it open, crossing her privacy without regard, he tossed his overcoat her way, plopped onto the bed and raised a muddy boot for her to pull. Harlots had their place in the Bible, too, he acknowledged, gracing her with recognition.

She collected payment in advance and placed her shoeless foot in his crotch while slowly unhooking and sliding her black, fish-net stocking down, noting his hardened response and a nauseous smell—kerosene and smoke that seemed to ooze from the lily white skin, thinning hair, and attire that she pitched to the furthest corner.

Providing copulative relief with flawless ease, rendering her client twice diffused and vulnerable, she petted the head pressed upon her breast. Angling seductive charm, she alluded to his masculine wit and virile abilities, then innocently inquired why his clothes carried that unusual scent—what ingenious mission had he been supervising this time?

He took the liberty of an over-time lick and nibble and replied, "It was preordained, and the fire was glorious, monumental."

Suddenly pricked by suspicion, he pulled her hair, assessed the nature and degree of her alliance. He pulled harder, bending her neck precariously, and watched for contractions of fear—of which he saw none. This pleased him. He blew breath into her parted lips.

He is alluding to something criminal, Claret considered as she swallowed. A large fire ignited—it thrilled him, his dark side, and he calls it glorious. Must be horrid, for him to call it monumental—he himself soaked in kerosene, in the act—the wild look when he recalls it. He can almost taste it—lurid, depraved, vindictive … Her stomach turned and she knew. It was he who tried to burn Black Mary alive.

Posed demure and vacant, she ordered her countenance to perform. "Same time next week my, shining knight?" She raised an eyebrow and dispensed a proprietary smile, indicating the need to be released from his grip.

The following Friday night, Claret offered him the opportunity to become her benefactor: she would generously allow him to receive her services quid pro quo, once he had agreed to her terms. Investment in her enterprise would conceal his identity, that of the arsonist behind the Mary Fields tragedy. His anonymity would be preserved as long as contributions were paid. He would agree to this arrangement and provide, immediately, a substantial endowment followed by fixed monthly donations.

This would enable Claret to procure more suitable quarters, redecorate and relocate the bordello further north, nearer the river—a better location, more convenient for customers who, like himself, preferred to remain anonymous. He would be her financial cornerstone. She would provide professional services, facilitate his freedom and keep her tongue.

An interesting choice of words: *keep her tongue*, he considered, allowing his mind to contemplate the alternative. He swallowed a smirk and pictured her disabled, mute, hands cuffed to the bed rail. "A fallacious proposition," he replied, stroking his chin. "You only had to ask for my help." He reached for his hat. "Tit for tat, Madam Claret." He extended a hand, then let it fall as hers rose. Aloof, he turned toward the door.

"Wait," Claret said, unnerved, "Before you get any ideas … I will disclose the cautionary measures I took already."

He pivoted.

"My full testimony has been written, notarized and locked safe in a bank deposit box. One key is in the hand of a member of Montana's State Legislature, a close friend of mine. Someone else has been instructed to pass their key along to the county prosecutor and Cascade's sheriff, if any harm comes to me. My will permits the senator to open those papers. And that reminds me. If Mary Fields or any of my girls are harmed, everything is off, and you go to jail."

He snickered. "Are you done? I'd say so. Well? As if you give a hoot for the old nigger."

Dank end-of-winter moods began to lift as mud and muck domineered sinking levels of ice. People emerged, pale and permeated by months of indoor smoke. Pores opened. Conversations bloomed like shades of color that would soon stroke the landscape.

The women who had shunned Hattie coalesced, encouraged her to resume attendance at the weekly Sacred Heart Altar Society meetings.

Hattie, emotionally bruised, concluded that the invitation was not an adequate apology. Realizing it was as much as she was going to get, she forgave but did not forget. Equipped with a heightened awareness of innuendo—ticks of the lip and brow, parried banter, stilted glances— she observed each acquaintance as though they had never met and re-evaluated her loyalties.

New discussion and discontent over high taxes hen-pecked the town council. Though Hall and his aldermen steadfastly enforced the City's twenty-two current ordinances, they held back from authoring new ones and set course, supervising the construction and engineering of improvements they had initiated: projects that had cost the citizens a bundle in bonds—the water system, the sewer system, extended telephone and electric service—all of which needed to prove successful, or the odds of commandeering Cascade's future would surely dwindle.

Mary's daily intervals at the House of the Well Fed were lonely. Friends didn't patronize the hotel unless they were celebrating a special occasion, and most days she sat at the same table, folding and re-folding her napkin, waiting to eat and leave. Restaurant customers, the few who came and went, were strangers on their way to or from somewhere else. Overhearing incessant chatter, she felt all the more alone. Sometimes she left before dessert, aching to be home, wherever that was.

Upon the arrival of each day, however, she embraced hope anew. Rinsing her burned legs and arms with sagebrush tea, she applied salve of comfrey, plantain and hypericum—wrapped them with cotton strips when needed, and inspected for layers of new skin. Yearning to visit the vista marked by the first curve of her legendary mail route, also the location of her guardian boulder, Mary declared herself ably recovered and headed up Mission Road gripping an old flour sack that contained a hand-me-down harmonica, a handkerchief-sized piece of deer hide and a dented serving spoon she had resurrected from the rock pile.

Spring grass coated by Jack Frost's final appearance crunched under her oversized rubber galoshes. Wishing she had worn two layers of socks, she looked up and no longer cared. "There you are," she cooed, rising with the road. "My favorite granite boulder bench. I spent many an hour sitting on you, waiting for Bigg Too—he'd eat all day if I let him. Always had a handy flat top, you."

She stood before its coarse bulk and patted its side, smiling at the captive pink quartz crystals that sparkled in early angled sun. Pulling the spoon from her sack, she maneuvered a squat (legs too tender to kneel upon and began to dig. A red-winged blackbird trilled from a reed-bogged hollow nearby. "You probably know this already," she rambled, "Birds that visit our neighborhood have changed over the years, but the mountains —they'll be here long after all of us." She looked to a majestic peak she loved, one of the biggest and tallest, and took a deep breath.

The earth was harder than she had expected. It took nearly an hour to gain sight of the tin. Relieved, she looked around, wiggled the deposit box loose and shook the topsoil off. Metal clinked. "More room for my pistol now," she muttered, "wrapped better." The cache box safely tucked inside her sack, she withdrew the pliable hide, used it to replace the old rag that had covered her pistol temporarily, and tied the bundle with leather straps, hoping to protect it from marmots until she figured a way to keep her gun closer at hand. "Watch over my pistol please, boulder."

After rearranging dirt and stones to look natural, she tossed the sack over her shoulder and moseyed home, affectionately reminding Mary F. Fields that residing in what had become a claustrophobic town, was only temporary.

As planting time neared, Hattie purchased more flower seeds than she needed. She knew Mary wanted to retain her reputation as the best flowerbed gardener, and she knew that Mary would only accept seeds if they were presented as extras.

She and her boys arrived at Mary's with hoes and shovels, ready to be ordered about until the planting was done. When Earl and Lester grew restless, Hattie promised treats if they could figure a way to get four discarded milk cans (the large ones, each as tall as Earl) from the rock pile to Mary's kitchen. Sometime later, the cans were arranged as pedestals to support the extra door D.W. had instructed workmen to leave in Mary's backyard. Seated at each side of their friend's make-do table, four cheerful gardeners toasted with full glasses of milk, washing down over a dozen sugar cookies, extracted from Hattie's satchel.

1912 politics seemed to rattle the core of everything. National news reports briefed Americans on the latest developments concerning suffragists, conglomerates, commissions, investigations and the proposed agenda of each presidential candidate. It was hard to keep up.

After homestead plowing, planting and calving was done, more farmers found reason to come into town and join political debates with local cohorts—fellow voters who had until November to select a blue-ribbon champion from amongst the six thoroughbred candidates competing to win the presidential race. Campaign issues included corporate anti-trust suits, tariffs, federal investments overseas, railroads, public utilities, suffrage, education, the penal system, health, labor unions, banking reform and ministrations of paper currency.

After harvest, these registered men would line up at the polls and place their personal preferences with ballot marks that would endorse Wilson (Democratic), Taft (Republican), Theodore Roosevelt (Progressive), Debs (Socialist), Chafin (Prohibition) or Reimer (Socialist Labor)—each voter hoping that their contender would triumph and guide American citizens to their collective destiny of prosperity and political power. Surely the Twenty-Eighth Chief Executive of the Nation, the President of the United States of America, would reform and regulate the economy, expand U.S. influence abroad and protect the welfare of the ordinary people.

By mid-summer, debates were as brittle as the record-breaking heat, choking throats and acres with little relief. On Saturday afternoons, men compassed around the new Westinghouse "amplitude modulation" cabinet radio displayed at the Cascade Mercantile Company, the emporium that sported a red, white and blue banner in its window and advertised, "Honest Goods at Honest Prices and a Square Deal to All." Iced tea was guzzled with and without measures of moonshine.

They shushed each other when a man's voice burst across the airwaves —announced the candidates who would debate national issues, followed by commentary and rhetoric—information that was interpreted, discussed and argued over afterwards, with west-of the-Missouri-horse-sense, at length, through the work-week until next Saturday when the throng reconvened for more.

All this political discourse, along with Hattie's newfound fervor for justice, inspired D.W. Monroe to examine his patriotic responsibilities. Two years of Hall was all that he and the community could tolerate, D.W. believed. Progress had been made, but at what cost? Folks seemed to be up in arms, and selfishness was spreading—a side effect of greed, in his opinion. He was quite sure that a few council pockets had been lined. That had to stop. Cascade had only just incorporated, and already it was—we are, he corrected—up to our knees in debt.

Christian ethics and moral principles must guide the family, community and country—fundamental conviction that will endure as cornerstones—actualize cooperation, communication. Our town used to be so friendly, he mused. People must be able to trust their mayor and aldermen—then things can be set straight. Unjust laws need to be reviewed —by everyone. Folks should participate, attend council meetings, speak up, and watch out for each other. Ordinances in other towns could be investigated, compared. Laws have to be fair—equitable to women and children, too. Can the mess be untangled? Can we, as a community experiencing rapid change, remain faithful to our forefathers' original goals?

He had asked James Cornell if he would run against Hall, but James had adamantly refused. I agree with you, D.W., he had said, but I'm not the one —don't have the taste for it. Why don't *you* run, Cornell had insisted.

Glover had suggested the same thing—after he had fallen out with Marcum.

D.W. supposed that he would cause less damage than others he could think of, but still he was not resolved. He decided to speak to Hattie. If they were of the same mind, he would do it, run on the Democratic ticket, if he was nominated.

When he shared his thoughts with his wife of ten years, she kissed him on the lips, in public, then reminded him of Cascade's hurtful and unjust ordinances—how they exemplified the sorry, stereotypical representation of the American West—*towns where freedom is sabotaged by renegade town leaders interested in prolonging or reviving wild outlaw legend days,* she emphasized. In her opinion, the council had done exactly that and, in so doing, reduced the rights and dignity of all Cascade citizens: women, children *and* men. It had become an embarrassment to be a sabotaged citizen—the absolute opposite of how one should feel.

"You are perfect for the job," she exclaimed. "I think you can win. You have to do it!"

"Actually," he said, stepping back, "You should run for mayor, Mrs. Hattie Monroe. Listen to you."

"Sorry. You know me." They smiled at each other, aware that neither cared about the stares coming their way, pleased that they had made the decision together: David W. Monroe would run as the Democratic opponent against Hall—launch a campaign to become Cascade's next mayor. They strolled, arm in arm, from dinner at the House of the Well Fed, to their home, Lester and Earl trailing close behind.

"I would consider it, if I had the right to run," she said, watching for his response.

He stopped and looked into her eyes. "That needs to change, doesn't it?"

The following morning, D.W. stopped by the hotel and told R.B. Glover that he'd decided to do it, run for mayor. He asked R.B. if he'd join him in the Democratic camp, run for the office of alderman in his ward, help him strategize and roundup the best candidates Cascade had to offer— mates to join their platform—moral, honest men.

Delighted, R. B. accepted—lavished congratulations with a deep-throated, jolly voice that thundered through the lobby. Slapping D.W. on the back, he ushered him into his office where they sipped celebratory brandy and perused the marketing campaign Glover had drafted in advance.

They deliberated over the subject of local government—the tarnished state of Cascade affairs—agreed upon the importance of replacing the present council (the ones who kowtowed to Hall's delusions of grandeur) with businessmen who knew how to prioritize and visualize the future while managing to exercise economy, opportunity and wisdom.

Exiting the building in search of young Mister Harry Ludwig (H.W. for short), the first man on their list, D.W. and R.B. located him in the cellar of Ludwig's Dope, reorganizing the inventory of his newly purchased drinking establishment.

After moments of small talk, Monroe and Glover got to the point, both assuming that Ludwig would jump at their invitation.

"How does it feel to join the ranks of Cascade businessmen, Ludwig?" Glover asked. "Good to have you."

"Well, thanks," Ludwig said, turning a dusty whiskey bottle, looking for a maker's mark. He met Glover's gaze. "Good to be back. Been a year or so since I been gone."

Monroe took over. "Don't know if you realize how badly Hall and his aldermen have mishandled our tax money, Ludwig." He pushed his hat up to see clearly. "Most of which comes from business taxes."

"I heard rumors."

"That's why we've sought you out, Ludwig. We know you to be a decent, law-abiding businessman of sound judgment."

"So we're here to give you first opportunity."

"For what?"

"To join us in our Democratic campaign against Hall," D.W. clarified.

"Our brother, D.W. Monroe, here," Glover boasted as he backslapped his constituent again, "has agreed to run for mayor." Recalling Ludwig's rural upbringing, he added, "Best news I've heard in a coon's age."

"Well, congratulations, Mr. Monroe," Ludwig said respectfully.

"Thank you, Ludwig. Will take more than announcing, of course. I need good men to stand up with me." He held Ludwig's attention with a penetrating gaze.

Glover took the lead. "How would you like to join our campaign, honor Cascade by running for alderman?"

"Our? Does that mean you're running, Mr. Glover?"

"Yes, for alderman, as well. I can't let Monroe or Cascade down," Glover pledged with conviction as he crossed his arms.

"Well, one thing—" Ludwig disclosed, "I'm a Republican. Signed up when I was in Oregon." He stepped back. "So I'm afraid—"

"Don't let that get in your way," Glover said.

"You may not realize, Ludwig," Monroe began, "A Republican vote won't count for much of anything this election. Remember Cascade's first? Only one party—the Citizens' Party." Ludwig nodded. "Hall and his men, some of whom might choose to be Republicans in the future but haven't changed over yet, are currently still members of the Citizens' Party— so it's the Citizens' or the Democrats. You're the only Republican I know of."

"The point is," Glover summarized, "there will be so few registered Republicans, a vote for their team will be wasted. I'm sure you'll want to make your vote count."

"Even better, make your business experience count by joining our platform—be one of the men who shapes Cascade's future," D.W. invited.

Glover riled, "Ludwig, did you know that Hall and his council left $14,000.00 sitting in an account that doesn't accrue interest? That interest could have paid for City improvements or salaries or expenses. Such irresponsible, wasteful mismanage—"

"All right, R.B," Monroe said, patting his constituent's shoulder.

"It's not that they haven't done good things," Ludwig said, "They say we'll be getting water this fall—and who doesn't like electricity and sidewalks?" He set the bottle on the shelf next to him. "But they do seem to have their noses stuck up in the air. Wasn't easy to get my saloon license."

Monroe jawed in a comfortable rhythm, "Ludwig, are you aware that the Republican Party has changed? It's become far too liberal of late.

'Distracted' is the word business analysts use. Swarms of Republicans have converted to the Democratic Party because it's the Democrats who are pragmatically building our country's foundation through business."

"That's right," Glover confirmed.

"It's business that provides innovation and support for our present and future economy," D.W. vocalized, noticing how important the situation was to him, in earnest. "You've just become a business owner. It's the Democrats who will cast their votes to help you realize more profit—and make America the strongest country in the world."

Glover stepped back, thinking that he'd picked the best contender for mayor, all right. He listened to his friend, his party constituent, exercise thoughts that would, with a little practice, evolve into great speeches. A natural.

"Down to earth businessmen have become hard to find in Cascade, Ludwig. We need you—an honest man who thinks before he acts—a trustworthy businessman who takes pride and invests in his community. You'll be a respected Cascade alderman. Join us on the Democratic ticket, Ludwig. You won't be sorry. Take a stand."

"But I just registered to be a Republican," Ludwig said, unable to relinquish its importance.

D.W. reiterated, "As responsible Cascade businessmen, we can't afford to let Harvey Hall get re-elected. Our public—property owners, renters and businessmen—are browbeaten. We are, all of us, thousands of dollars in debt now. Citizens have been left holding the bag. And business owners pay the most tax."

Ludwig shivered, unaware that so much money had been involved.

Glover emphasized, "We're going to give Hall a run for his money—regain the good faith of people—foster goodwill and fiscal security!" He slapped his knee and ballyhooed, "It's easy to switch parties, Ludwig. Just fill out a simple form. It's the smart thing. Don't know how the Republicans got so crazy anyway—maybe Teddy did it when he started the Bull Moose Progressive Party. The point is, we need you. Cascade needs you."

Ludwig scratched his head. "I've always been happy staying out of politics—hard enough deciding who to vote for in the national election."

"That's easy," Glover thrust, "vote for Wilson."

"Gentlemen," said Monroe, "that's another can of worms." He shot Glover a look. "Are you with us, Ludwig?"

"I feel obliged, now that I am a businessman. I guess so—since all businessmen should be leaders in their community. To make business grow, we need to make responsible decisions and keep track of every penny. And I see now, that includes tax dollars that I never worried about before. Count me in."

Suffragette activist Emma Smith DeVoe arrived in Cascade by train, early on a Saturday morning in August. Ada was there to meet her, and they strolled beneath stylish parasols in church-going attire, back to the Marcum house where Ada served the esteemed suffragette leader-organizer-speaker tea and delicate cakes.

Ada welcomed the opportunity to exchange privacies with such an accomplished woman. "Is it true that you knew Susan B. Anthony?" she asked.

Emma, a kind and cultured lady, impeccably well dressed, the epitome of Ada's vision of strength, answered, "Yes, I met her when she gave a speech on women's rights. I was eight years old. When I married, Susan came to live with my husband John and myself in the Dakota Territory. Under her tutelage, we campaigned for moral reform, temperance, women's suffrage and statehood for the Dakotas. That was the first of many campaigns in thirty states."

"How can you be so brave? Isn't your life in constant danger?"

"My father was an abolitionist. He taught me to stand up for my convictions, regardless of what others may think."

Ada's brown eyes flickered and she leaned forward to say, "I wish I lived in Washington or Idaho or in any of the states where you have helped women gain the vote—where suffrage is won and women have rights under the law."

Tired from the long overnight journey, DeVoe answered, "I can see you have aspirations, Ada. I hope you will achieve them. I should be honored to help you, if ever I can. But first, may I rest for a bit, prepare for the activities that you have, so bravely, had the courage to organize?" She patted Ada's hand.

"Yes, of course." Ada blushed, reveled in the compliment. "I've never met a woman like you, Mrs. DeVoe."

"Please, call me Emma."

A few men and almost every woman residing in Cascade and the surrounding Sun River Valley arrived to hear what Emma Smith DeVoe, president of the National Council of Women Voters, had to say.

She stood on a simple stage that local women had decorated with red, white and blue streamers and began by speaking as though the women's vote was sure to prevail everywhere—a benefit come to grace the nation —that had in fact, enriched the lives of all who lived within those enlightened states—including the individual family unit.

As a consequence, she informed her audience, women with the vote live happier, more productive and dedicated lives, their patriotic efforts having improved schools, civic organizations and the economies of towns and cities—thus expelling husbands' unwarranted fears that their women would, once equipped with the right to vote, find reason to leave. Quite the contrary, Emma assured.

With congenial charm, she mentioned her associations with governors and senators and congressmen who had called upon her for assistance, and she them, during her suffrage efforts, thus gaining respect from the majority of the Cascade assembly and reducing the possibility of protest (disgruntled attendees frequently loitered, ready to agitate.

Sharing a brief overview of the Washington State Suffrage victory in 1910, she suggested that publicity—prudent action designed by suffrage leaders to guarantee that all Americans become aware of the suffrage discourse and the political choices at hand, had been and would continue to be essential—that the NCWV had employed a publicity bureau to organize mass rallies, bands, posters, parades and stump speeches, and furthermore, had maintained a feminine approach and appearance during these crusades—policy endorsed and supported by its male and female membership.

Elucidating further, she relayed an anecdotal story about the "Suffrage Special," a train that had toured the State of Washington for the purpose of transporting renowned suffragists to deliver caboose-platform speeches at every railway station during the final campaign effort—a method proven to facilitate bipartisan victories.

She expressed gratitude for the dedicated pursuits of women suffrage leaders, mentioning each by name, and emphasizing that these insightful women personified the "still hunt," quiet and non-confrontational efforts to advance the cause for freedom for all—the best method, in her opinion, to achieve the Union's suffrage goals. She thanked the Methodist Women's Guild for the kind invitation to share her experience and encouraged active involvement toward realizing a future protected by equal rights, which included, certainly, national suffrage for all Americans.

Ada was beaming.

J.E. was furious.

After punch and an array of desserts, an inspired group of women escorted Emma DeVoe to the train depot where they conversed until the *Great Northern* arrived and she, their personal representative of national acclaim, stepped on board and vanished.

Home alone that evening, J.E. Marcum had his say. He accused Ada of ruining his reputation, of violating his position as her husband by inviting the scandalous woman to town without his permission, of negating the very pact of their marriage by means of her unforgivable behavior that was neither compliant, ethical or religious in its brazen and heinous disdain for all that is Holy, emphasizing that she would be punished by God the Almighty and it was her own fault. He added that he was ashamed of her, and she should be, too, if she had only the slightest remnant of self-respect. Further, that as she knew, women existed for the sole purpose of childbearing and child rearing and she had failed on that front, as well.

Embracing successful suffrage tactics, Ada responded, "I am in agreement with the majority of male and female populations in Washington, Colorado, Utah, Idaho, California and Wyoming," turned her back and marched to her sewing room, upstairs. She closed the door, angled the spine of a chair beneath the doorknob, and deliberated.

After this marital altercation, J.E. spent most of his time at the bank. He sold his store and made a unilateral decision: he would invest the money in something profitable—something that would irk his wife—something to do with men and power—a tobacco shop or an exclusive men's club, perhaps.

Ada decided to run for the open seat on the school board. The election was in four weeks. Everyone knew she had managed accounts in the Marcum bank for years; there could be no doubt of her qualifications. Who would the town residents support? Women could vote in school elections.

She began to canvass.

The heat wave continued. During Mary's two-block walk to the New Cascade Hotel, she was surprised to run into Ada Marcum, who addressed her by name, Black Mary, and chatted, soliciting her vote for school trustee. Surprised and a little suspicious, Mary said she'd think about it and thanked her for her time.

Turning the corner, she was further detained by two acquaintances from days gone by—times when she used to frequent the saloons—play checkers, smoke an occasional stogie, sip a lemonade.

She didn't know that the two men coming her way had been approached to run for city council. All persons involved with the Democratic campaign, under wraps: Hattie, Glover and prospective contenders, had been sworn to secrecy by D.W. who planned to announce his candidacy immediately *after* the presidential election.

"Howdy, Black Mary," George Woods called.

"Nice day, don't you think?" Ludwig added.

"I guess so. Haven't seen you boys for awhile."

"Just moved back to town, Black Mary, setting up a saloon. Sorry to hear about the ordinance. I don't feel that way, just so you know."

"Thanks, Ludwig."

It had become unusual for men to jaw with her. Thinking about it, she decided it must be because Ludwig hadn't been badgered by Hall and his gang yet, and relaxed.

"I'm on my way to the hotel for supper," she informed, keeping her gait.

They matched her pace, flanking close. "We'll come with ya, if you don't mind," Ludwig said. He thought he'd test out the limited amount of presidential campaign lowdown he'd accumulated, in hopes of keeping his own with the boys.

She nodded.

"Black Mary, we've been talking about the president candidates—we can't agree whether President Taft is a stand up leader or not. I mean, I'm a Democrat—well, a new Democrat—so I should be voting for Wilson, probably." He looked at her. "Woods, here, says that Taft ain't gonna take care of us businessmen, and I heard Wilson's been telling about the 'new freedom' we're all gonna get when he's in the White House—how he's going after big business corruption—but I thought Taft did a good job the last four years. Do you?"

"Gracious," she said, undecided whether to reveal her opinions. Deciding not to, she turned instead to Woods. "What do you think?"

"Wilson is the best," he said, skirting a skip. "He's against those crooked lobbyists and wasting government spending." He pressed the dimple of his chin. "Taft shouldn't have made income tax. Now we have to pay more money. Wilson says, 'Divided power makes it impossible to see who is accountable for ill-doing,' and ya can't argue with that. Call a spade a spade and get rid of corruption. Specially in the committee system."

"What committee is that?" asked Ludwig.

"I'm not real clear," Woods replied.

Mary snuffed a chuckle. "I think he means the Senate and House committees that debate the issues that are put forward to Congress for a vote." She hoped they would remember. The hotel entrance was a few yards away.

"What about Teddy's Bull Moose Party?" she asked, curious to hear what they'd say.

Ludwig started, "I think Teddy's gone progressive, cause now he's courting the Women's Suffrage vote—least that's what R.B. says." He shrugged and kicked a stone. "I won't vote for Teddy—too much squabbling in the pig pen, if you ask me. Don't understand why Teddy and Taft were at it so much," he rattled.

Mary shook her head and admired the hollyhocks standing tall next to the confectionery. "Did you know that there are campaign radio broadcasts at the Cascade Mercantile on Saturdays?"

Woods blurted, "Teddy's done good for us before, led our country into stronger business, protected the welfare of ordinary people. But he's outdated."

"Was a real baseball fan, though," Ludwig boasted.

She wondered if Ludwig knew how to read. Surely, he must … Maybe he's been busy, Woods, too, she considered as she piece-milled the men's words together. Two months left—they'll get up to speed. Think I'll order apple pie. À la mode.

On a lovely afternoon, the second-to-last day of August, the day marked with an "X" on most Cascade women's diaries, Hattie walked over to Mary's, and from there they managed the familiar route untrod by Mary during the past year—the short distance up the hill to Cascade's dominant three-story brick schoolhouse—the building that offered panoramic views, a place most suitable for watch towers or forts in earlier times of conflict.

"Do you know how you'll vote?" Hattie asked.

"Yes," Mary said, "You?"

"Yes."

There were three measures at hand—yea or nay on funding for new textbooks and curriculum supplies, a proposed increase for primary teacher salaries and the selection between two candidates running for the position of school trustee: Mrs. Ada Marcum, Marcum Bank employee; and Mr. Harry Newhouser, a tailor, recently relocated from Milwaukee, who had set up shop in the backroom of Berger's Toggery. At present, the Cascade school board of trustees had no female members.

Hattie could tell that Mary was excited. So was she. It wasn't often that a woman had the liberty of exercising her vote. She pulled the heavy-springed door, the one with the notice "Election This Way" posted eye-level, and waved Mary ahead.

"My word," Mary muttered, "Never thought there'd be such a line." She braced herself.

"Goes all the way round the corner," Hattie added.

They took their place at the end, wishing that it wasn't risqué to wear sleeveless blouses.

Waves of chatter reverberated. Voices seemed to circle, tip and roll, out-sounded by repetitive thuds from behind closed doors—school boys clad in shorts, who bounced basketballs to and fro across hardwood floors—practicing athletics, they called it—in the "school gym," a recent innovation contrived by the new generation—a crazy unnecessary expense according to crotchety old-timers whose answer to trials of life was simple: *keep working—good old-fashioned elbow-greased labor will make you strong*. Many among the crowd would have articulated as such if able to decipher the background source of persistent rumbling—the cause that had prompted them to speak louder and louder, hands cupped to hear their neighbor.

The broad width of Mrs. Riley turned around.

"Good morning, Hattie and Black Mary." She looked at Hattie. "Voting for our woman candidate?"

"I'm voting on all three measures," Mary volunteered.

"Oh?"

"Yes. Unbiased by sex."

Mrs. Riley, forced to confront the word *sex* in public, was appalled—assumed it was due to a lack of education on Mary's part—crossed herself and forgave the trespass judiciously.

Hattie changed the subject, commenting on an item discussed at the recent Sacred Heart Altar Society meeting.

"How long are we going to have to wait?" a loud shout leapt overhead. More voices repeated the query—then rejoined nearby chitchats: "Got to get back to work—I insisted—vote for the new tailor, what's his—Newhouser—what kind of name is that? Country was better when it was territories—can't trust nobody—"

An authoritative woman called for attention and shouted, "Did all of you register before the cut-off date four weeks ago? If not, your name won't be in the Register Book here." She held it above her head. "And you won't be able to vote."

A spatter of grunts responded, followed by footsteps and doors slamming.

I wonder if there's a voting poll place in Saypo," Mary pondered, distraught by the growing number of voters crowding closer. She extended elbows to protect her still-healing body.

Mrs. Riley leaned in. "I'm not the only one who notices your good deeds, Black Mary. I put my son Charlie's flower in my pretty crystal vase after every game last summer. It was my mother's."

Mary blinked, unclear.

"Thank you for decorating our team with the pretty boutonnières."

"Oh," she said, "You're welcome, Mrs. Riley," pleased to hear there were folks who thought well of her.

"Babysitting and flowers at the altar, too. You're a good soul."

"Yes, she is," Hattie said.

"Are you allowed to vote here, Black Mary?"

They turned the corner, movement that provided distraction. Mary pretended to look for something in her satchel. Which answer needs explanation, she irked: whether I have the right to vote or am allowed to vote in Cascade? I'll let her see for herself.

Behind them, the line had grown, amassed at the door. Odors of perspiration, tobacco, perfume and hair oil blended and propelled a sweaty stink. Legs in the crowd shifted weight from one foot to another, rocked onto toes to assess progress.

It's a gossip cacophony, Mary mused, like when you step into the hen house with a sack of feed. She lifted her head and overheard, "This new corset is killing me," and smiled.

Most conversations are mashed, like potatoes, each of us hearing something different, I bet. Mary closed her eyes and asked herself to hear the best parts, not the loudest—see if such sifting could work.

…"Taft is squashing the little guy—all women can vote on school ballots, regardless of marital status or color—women don't need—Ludwig's Dope—terrible name for a saloon—should have an audience, I mean, an ordinance against rude things like that—been to the Amusement Company?—don't seem right that the council lets this election be in the schoolhouse but denies our Commercial Club—a new meeting place before next month—What goes on—moving pictures accompanied by Minnie on the piano—the latest from Hollywood—Taft was making deals to keep tariffs high—promised us farmers he'd lower them—indecent for young eyes—Roosevelt made the mess—compromises with the big guys—"

"Almost there, Mary," Hattie said, thinking Mary had dozed off.

A hostile voice wafted into earshot and bombarded, "Women don't need to clutter their minds with political rhetoric, jumble to them." More conversing outsounded: "Does anyone have a fan? Common sense—course a woman is better suited—what the children need—education of our children will build—those women cluttering the country with homestead filings are getting in the way—What?—and grazing land and—"

A nasal inflection bemoaned, "Next thing you know," its owner, Marcum forecasted, unaware that his voice carried, "they'll be wanting their names on property deeds, business titles and leases—as joint owners!"

Flushed, Mrs. Riley prayed that bystander irritation would germinate and swing more votes to Mr. Marcum's wife.

J.E. Marcum would never admit it, but he had just cast his ballot for Newhouser.

A chubby woman who worked in the school office moved to the head of the line and announced, "Everyone needs to know how to read and write to vote."

It was Mary's turn. The women running the poll verified Mary's registration status—her name was in the book—they asked her to identify her ward in the district. After supplying the correct information: Ward Three, she refused assistance offered, took her ballot and stepped behind the curtain to an old pulpit.

Carefully reading each word, Mary marked three squares: Yes; Yes; and Mrs. Ada Marcum. She shook her head thinking: can't believe I spent my first vote getting a white woman into office. That's all right. It's for the children. She folded her paper in half, as instructed, placed it into the large wood box at the end of the room and waited for Hattie in the hallway—saving the big grin in her throat for later.

Mary and Hattie dashed out—Hattie to her boys and Mary to implement a plan she had configured earlier. At home, she snacked on a raw potato and changed into what she thought of as patriotic style to be paraded on days like today.

Serendipity smiled. Band music drifted from Central Avenue, as promised in the paper. Finessing final details, Mary tucked her hair into the second-hand Union Army cap she had recently acquired in trade for laundry services.

Facing herself in the mirror, she took a long look and urged herself to remember this face of victory—hers—victorious. Today the school vote— soon, the city vote, she promised, giddy.

"Caps like this one," she announced aloud, "headed the brave men who fought on the right side, won our freedom, freedom from slavery, freedom for a chance to live right."

She grabbed the patriotic accoutrements she had purchased—two American flags, each the size of a dainty dishtowel hoisted upright with pencil-width wooden dowels.

"Now I'm ready!" she declared, and marched to the corner of Front and Central, two blocks up from the band assembly—where the sheep dip yard had been, years past—renovated now, into two city lots, both for sale.

Mary appeared larger than life—an apparition—a tattered page of history.

She wore a battered pair of creased shoes, well-polished, the tops of which were shrouded by a skirt made of carpet-weight cotton, navy blue, gathered loosely, an uneven hem, aged, as evidenced by moth holes here and there—coupled with a white blouse, of which only the well-starched ironed cuffs were visible from under a hip-length jacket, also blue, a lighter, faded shade, buttons pulling from the tight fit, responsible for some of the small tears, perhaps—accented by a double-knotted bandanna, a red paisley pattern, and her navy blue cap—patriotic attire inspired by Union Civil War soldiers, the victors of the War Between the States.

No one could be uncertain of Mary's loyalties during the War Between the States—nor of her lack of regard for H.D. Hall on this particular day. Hooked onto a wide black belt buckled about her waist, was a holster. In plain view, the holster housed an unloaded Ladysmith pistol, the grip of which extended above the leather. Bullets or not, possession of the firearm was against the law and violated City Ordinance No. 8.

The weapon was simply a detail of a patriotic costume on a patriotic day, was it not? Or would she be arrested by Sheriff Hoag? She had considered this and had decided to throw worries to the wind this once, in celebration of victory so elusive, and so long in coming, a victory for which fear would have to prostrate itself.

"It's Election Day," she hollered, waving her American flags under an azure sky speckled with puffy white clouds. "Vote in the school election! Three measures to vote on today … will determine Cascade's quality of education … Our children's future teeters in your hands. Vote! Come one, come all … its voting day… *All registered women can vote today!*

As though on cue, the Cascade Brass Band tooted the "Battle Hymn of the Republic." Mary tapped her foot and called, "Do your duty! Choose your candidate for School Trustee. It's all right if you don't see eye to eye about everything. Vote for who you think cares most—about education—our children's! Vote! Today! School election! Up at the schoolhouse! Make your opinion count!"

She waved her flags high and joined the hymn's refrain, "*Glory, glory hallelujah, His truth is marching on,*" feeling warmth from the sun and warmth in her heart.

Claret rounded the corner.

"Miss Claret," she called, signaling her to her side. "Have you registered? Have any of your associates registered? If they did, please send them to the school to vote. Women know best about children. Let's get our votes heard!"

"Yes, Black Mary, I'll do that," Claret promised. "You're right, of course. Voted myself early this morning."

An advocate of human rights, Mary continued her mission. She snagged passersby, not caring why they listened—whether they were drawn in by disbelief, curiosity, struck by gumption, hers, or something else—didn't matter as long as they voted: women, in particular.

Pausing to catch her breath, she realized that she felt happy—through and through happy!

Across the street, a young man leaned against the Thomas Corner Store, arms crossed, fedora tipped, to get a better view of the patriotic canvasser and local response. When his boss, editor at The Great Falls Tribune, sent him to cover the Cascade School Board Election, he had moaned, sure the assignment would prove to be dull as dishwater. Enthusiasm regained, the newshound darted across the intersection, leaping to avoid collisions with automobiles, carts, and horses, keen to interview the passionate anomaly who had positioned herself near the center of the thoroughfare, effectively drawing attention to her cause. He asked her name, asked why she promoted the vote, why the school election seemed so important to her, if she lived in Cascade and whether she, herself, had cast a vote.

The handsome lad reminded Mary of Jack, Nadie's husband—the spirited charmer who had been such good company when she owned and operated Mary's Café. She asked for his name. When he replied Jack, her knee gave way and he caught her. He brought a chair and glass of water and encouraged her to rest momentarily. He pulled a camera from his case, and for some reason, wasn't surprised when the astute woman asked what model of Brownie it was.

He asked permission to take her photo and include it in his newspaper article. She agreed. When traffic eased, they stepped from the sidewalk, and he snapped a few shots—claimed that her patriotic enthusiasm shined bright through the lens.

He promised to send her prints. She thanked him and walked home, having decided that she had pressed luck far enough. It had been a miracle to remain unscathed, uncontested and unharmed on an election day. Perhaps it was the presence of Jack the reporter who had kept her safe, or spirits of Jack and others in the spirit world, she mused. "Thank you," she offered.

A month later, Mary entered The House of the Well Fed, as was her habit on Sunday afternoons. She noticed a robust appetite surface after months spent bickering with a tired stomach, shrunk from her insistence that it didn't need more than one daily meal, that it had been too much bother to make the effort.

She chose the table by the window and waited for Madeline, the chipper waitress who liked to chat. Opening the menu, memorized now, she examined the fancy serif type style headings until a glass of water slid into view. She returned Madeline's grin and asked, "What's today's special?"

"Mary, you know the Sabbath Special, never changes: roast beef, mashed potatoes, corn and fresh apple pie."

"Oh, yes, sorry. Forgot what day it was for a minute. One Sabbath Special, please, and some hot tea."

As Madeline scurried off, Mary lifted her glass of water and proposed a silent toast: Mr. Stickney, wherever you are, I am forever grateful for these tasty gratis meals that relieve me of tedious labor.

She listened to the conversation nearby: three portly men argued over whether women were intelligent enough to vote in national elections. She was about to tell them off when a hand touched her shoulder.

"Good afternoon, Nigger Mary," D.W. greeted.

He was wearing a dapper three-piece suit with a bright red tie and cuff links. Good thing he loves Hattie so. He's a looker, more handsome the older he gets, or maybe it's my eyesight.

"Golly, didn't see you there, D.W. Pull up a chair, sit down and take a load off."

He laughed. "Don't mind if I do, thank you."

"Where's Hattie and the boys?"

"On their way. Promised them supper out."

"Good for you."

Keeping an eye on him, she said, "Wonder who's going to run against Hall for mayor next year. Every time I ask one of the fellas, they turn tight like someone told them to zip their lips."

D.W. stirred his coffee. "Have to be someone that'll give him a good fight—save what's left in the City Treasury." He glanced down.

Realizing that he was not going to spill information, she said, "Getting close to Election Day. National Election, that is." Primed with information from Hattie, she baited, "Know who you're voting for?"

"Haven't made my final decision. Most likely will stick with my party, Nigger Mary, the Democrat, Woodrow Wilson."

He helped himself to sugar cubes, a culinary treat.

"Well, there's more debates coming up," she said, inferring there was time to amend inclinations.

"Yes, I want to hear those. Believe it or not, I voted for Teddy last time. But now I have a family, need to think of the future. Did you see in the paper that America is the wealthiest country in the world?"

"Yes, I did. Speaking of our economy, Taft is strong on business. He's been streamlining corporations for the past three years. Just because he's not a braggart, folks don't realize all he's done." Her throat tightened. She didn't like Wilson, believed him to be a racist and a snob, though he always said the right thing in speeches.

"I like Wilson's stand on streamlining the government, reorganizing," D.W. announced.

"Yeah. Think he called the problem 'too many foxes in the hen house.' I agree that tightening checks and balances for government agencies (she thought of Mother Mary's struggle with the Indian Bureau) is a prudent course."

"Teddy says Taft made a mess of his anti-trust suits—caused all kinds of mayhem," D.W. sawed.

"But those anti-trust measures are exactly the kind of laws we need to regulate big business. Same as Wilson talks about," she pressed.

"I don't think he's done enough. Chaos is still rabid."

"Well, wait a minute—"

Madeline set Mary's Sunday Special into place.

Ignoring the heat of rising steam under her chin, Mary replied, "Taft fixed railroad rates so we aren't taken advantage of—by the railroad moguls. He set up the Interstate Commerce Commission to regulate fees, passenger and freight—so prices will stay under control." She stirred her tea again. "Those anti-trust suits: his administration filed eighty suits—penalized those big-boy monopolies for stealing profits—protected us and our money from greed gone berserk."

"Impressive." He tapped his saucer. "Wilson is for labor unions, Nigger Mary. How can you not support that?"

"I do support labor unions. So does Taft." She pushed her fork and plate aside. "He started the Children's Bureau, a federal agency, to protect children from being worked to the bone—you can imagine unlimited hours of labor. Deplorable." She wet her lips. "And he made it better in the mines, including Montana's. Mandated safety equipment and safer operation rules. Saved lives. Why hasn't our paper reported this?"

"I didn't know that. Good question. Do you think Taft is doing enough, though? He hasn't addressed streamlining the legislative fat, like Wilson."

"I don't know. I think Wilson seems sincere about streamlining—reduce the number of fingers in the federal pie and that. I just don't think he cares about all the people. I think he's a bookworm type—a serious student of law from the South."

And talk about trimming fat is awfully vague, she kept to herself.

"Well, I guess I need to read more. You still have your papers?"

She nodded.

"There's Hattie." He pushed his chair back, patted Mary's hand, "You let me know if there's anything you need, all right?"

Signaling him close, she whispered, "D.W., while you're doing your political reading, let me mention a Wilson quote you may find of interest. He said, 'Segregation is not a humiliation but a benefit.'"

Stunned, D.W. straightened. "So that's why you don't like him."

"Well, of course I don't care for hatred … but believe it or not, I wouldn't eliminate him for that shortcoming alone." She scooted to whisper, "If you were colored you would know that none of the white men candidates are thinking that colored rights are an important issue. I gauge actions more than words, try to decide who's the most humane under all of the rhetoric—and who seems to best understand all the many American peoples and what they really need. Course I do hope that kind of person will pass legislation to protect colored rights, too."

"My God, Nigger Mary, you never cease to surprise me. You've become a scholar."

"Hardly. Been cooped up—have to do something with all the time. But keep my comments to yourself, would ya, please? And could I ask you a favor?"

"Of course."

"Would you mind, if it doesn't grist you one way or the other, calling me by my Christian name, Mary Fields?"

"Mary, Mary," Earl and Lester squealed, lassoing arms around her. Can we have a treat?"

A week later, Methodist Reverend W.W. Van Orsdel stood at his pulpit and sermonized from the heart: "Political rhetoric is buzzing across our American prairies louder than locusts!"

He let a beat of time lapse and nudged his flock toward the message of his Sunday sermon, "Moral Proprieties," admonishing, "Just remember, everyone is entitled to their own opinion. We must respect each other and be kind, whether we agree with our neighbor or not. Let us sing hymn number 237, 'Holy, Holy, Holy.'"

This chorus of singers was heard by Mary, outside enjoying the sunny morning with her congregation of flowers. Reminds me of Mass at Saint Peter's, she reminisced. Gotta say, the nuns really taught the girls how to sing beautifully, even when they were singing French or Latin. Wonder how

Mother, no, Mary Amadeus, is fairing up in the icebergs. She's working on her third Alaskan mission. Hope she's not hurting too bad.

She invoked the prayer, "God bless all my friends. Love them no matter what." What was it Onatah told me? One of her Onondagan chiefs translated the Lord's Prayer from English into words Iroquois peoples would say, spoke it to a group of congressmen. Instead of, "Thy will be done as it is in heaven," it goes, "The forest and flowers are in prayer …" I love that. "The forest and flowers are in prayer …"

"Love these beautiful tiger lilies, too. So dramatic—orange with black freckles." Surprised they bloomed the first year, she thought, with all that ash from my burnt-down house. And my giant sunflowers—some people call them weeds—they are happier than people—birds and bees love them. Wonder where those bumblers are hiding the honey. Sure would taste good. Reminds me, this is roast beef day, and Madeline told me there's a shortage of apple pie. Better get dressed for dinner.

On the second Sabbath of November, Mary wiggled into the small straight-back chair in the hotel dining room, and shifted her weight just so, to avoid the annoying pain in her hip.

Focusing her thoughts on the making of a Thanksgiving centerpiece, she considered using some of the sunflower heads she had dried—how she believed them to be stunning, in and of themselves, with or without seeds, hardened into position, a dark umber shine, like oak or mahogany, varnished. Perhaps the Monroes would invite her for Thanksgiving—if not, she would savor the arrangement for awhile herself, then place it in on the Catholic altar, surprise some folks. Madeline appeared and asked, "The usual, Mary?"

She nodded. Two days til Election Day, November 12, 1913, she mused. Wish *I* could vote. Next presidential election I'll be voting for sure. *And I will* be voting against Hall in five months.

The "after church crowd" pushed through the opened, beveled-glass doors. Voices clamored, and hungry customers organized in rounds. Men discussed the election, ignoring their wives, whose opinions were of no consequence, at least in public.

"Hard to keep my mouth shut so close to the polls," Mary whispered, pushing cheers of patriotism down. "Wait. Here comes D.W."

Arriving at her table, he hailed, "Just have a minute, Mary. Must get back. I wanted you to know that your comments made me look into details—of speeches and debates—and I've changed my mind. Though I am a democrat, this time I'm going to vote for Taft. He really has accomplished more than has been advertised. You were right."

Mary's mouth dropped.

"Hard to believe?" he asked.

"What was it that swung you over?"

"Reading about the anti-trust suits Taft filed against those greedy sons a … monopolized 'trust' companies. I didn't know that as many as ten companies could be hidden under one company name. Call it a tax umbrella made to manipulate market prices. That really burns me. And Taft went after them, relentlessly. Not just a couple times, like Roosevelt."

He caught his breath. "That, and Wilson's repeated ambitious promise to reduce government legislative controls. I'm not sure he can. His campaign emphasizes individual freedom as 'the new freedom.' Most of those federal agencies just got established—now we're gonna take them apart and instantly have new freedom—I just can't—and well, that's the thing—he talks about it over and over—and doesn't respond to Taft's achievements. Streamlining and new freedom sound grand, but it's all become too abstract and singular. Thanks for pushing me to investigate, Mary Fields. Got to go, excuse me."

"Bye," Mary called, flushed that he had remembered to use her Christian name, proud that she had swung a vote.

Monroe seated himself at the large round table at the far end of the room, the one circled by men only, most of them smoking cigars and sipping liquor, cackling over designs to celebrate when their "man" won on Tuesday next.

Really steams me, Mary stopped herself from declaring. *They can smoke cigars in here, and I can't, cause of the stupid ordinance. Well, anyway …*

Her roast beef arrived, and she attended to ladling gravy over thick slices of beef, buttering corn on the cob and thanking Madeline for the extra-large slice of pie. In principled protest, she got up and changed chairs so she didn't have to watch the men's assembly.

"Terrible about Vice President Sherman passing away, isn't it?" the baritone voice belonging to R.B. Glover plied. "Taft will lose votes because of it."

"Well, that's good, ain't it?" Woods asked.

Silverware clanked, making it harder to hear above boisterous laughter. Bits and pieces slipped: "Teddy is the best, and we can trust … Are you kidding? Said in his speech that women who work should have equal rights with men, including the vote … Too progressive—"

Mary fumed: *Women who work … like any of us don't.*

"Wilson is Top Hat," someone boasted.

"You mean Top Drawer?"

"Oh. Yeah, I guess."

"A trust is just a conglomerate for small companies, saving resources by joining together," Marcum's snooty voice clarified.

"I thought a trust was a saving account," said H.L. Rowley, a new member of their group.

In her mind, Mary stood up and yelled at them: No, dopey, a trust conglomerate is equivalent to a pre-war, family-owned multiple-plantation network, specializing in slavery and theft!

"Hey, Woods." Laughter snickered. "Was that a square deal or a square meal you ordered?" Fingers pointed to Wood's lasagna.

"How are we going to dress suffrage and temperance?" Rowley posed, screeching above the rest. The punch line followed, "With as little as possible."

Mary fisted her napkin and shook her head thinking, oh, my God.

"… it's clever, George, because a politician would say *address*, not dress—understand?" Glover boomed again.

"Oh, so *never* would be the right answer?" Woods efforted.

Mary closed her eyes.

"I got one," a high-pitched voice posed. "How did Taft get so fat?"

No one took the bait.

The joker climaxed, "He brung his own Holstein cow, name of Pauline, to the White House to make sure he gets plenty of butter fat! No, honest, it's true. He really did! Has a special housemaid just to make butter and cheese from old Pauline's givings. She grazes on the White House lawn, pretty as a picture. I saw the picture, in a pamphlet, in Helena."

Madeline cleared Mary's table, commenting, "Full of themselves, aren't they? Think it's time to stop giving them liquor?" Crumbs fell to the floor. "Mary, is that true what they say about the Holstein?"

"Yes, it is. I think of it as practical, and frugal. Don't you?"

"I think it's sweet. Probably reminds him of home."

Mary said, "Waste not, want not. That's the kind of president we need."

She heard Monroe respond, "No, I *am* serious. Taft plans for America's future economy—he looks at the big picture."

"Big picture," Mary muttered, "*my* words." She thought of places that had sparked those same words, *big picture*: the bluffs, the buttes, the mountains.

"… and he got," Monroe explained, "American companies to build a railroad in China! That's a man with foresight."

"No, Wilson is our man," Glover insisted, thundering, "We need a conservative democrat in the White House. Now more than ever. A president to concentrate on building business in America. Wilson will fix it all."

Glancing at his company and further to his patrons, Glover noted significant numbers of his restaurant crowd staring. Deciding that his group should relocate, concerned that he in his enthusiasm may have caused potential damage to his *own* future campaign, he prompted, "Let's take this over to Ludwig's Dope, fellas. First round is on me."

24

CAMPAIGNS

*P*atriotic aftershocks quaked across America. The results of the national election were conclusive; the number of exuberant voters who celebrated victory equaled combined totals of the disappointed who hadn't marked their ballot for Thomas Woodrow Wilson, the new Leader of the Union. Never before had six candidates made it to the presidential finish line. Reporters claimed the race, historical. Losers grated their teeth while the winning patriots piped final hoorays and reveled about the electoral margins with which Wilson had triumphed.

In Cascade, reactions were split.

My heart was beating in my throat, Mary recounted to herself late that night in bed. We all watched Mr. John chalk the total number of votes cast for each candidate on the slate board outside the Thomas Corner Store. So close: Wilson 6,296,184; Roosevelt 4,122,721; Taft 3,486,242. If the Republican Party hadn't split between Taft and Roosevelt (Teddy should have retired in 1909), our incumbent, Taft, would have won, even without the votes that went to Debs—901,000, and Chafin—208,000, and Reimer—29,000. Darn!

She tossed and turned, replayed the diverse arsenal of shouts that had followed and surmised: Wilson fans (businessmen and conservatives mostly) are crazy certain that profit margins will soar with their president-elect at the helm, whereas us loyal Roosevelt and Taft enthusiasts are sad to lose the president that already proved up to our expectations. Not sure exactly what Debs and Chafin and Reimer fans are thinking, but they must be disappointed, too.

There I was, she memorialized: chagrined, twisting my mouth when the final numbers came in—I wanted to wail my opinions like everyone else—well, like the men—didn't see any women hooting. But some day, all women will be able to throw whatever we want out with the bath water, and yelp about it, too.

Days later, waning political clatter on sidewalk corners moved indoors when perennial snowstorms returned and thrust frigid magnitudes of drift onto sidewalks and under eaves, everywhere.

Shortly after sunrise the next morning, Mary bundled herself with a hand-me-down overcoat and scarf and stepped cautiously across new layers of ice, slippery from melt reconstituted during a starry night. Still experiencing pangs as a disheartened Republican, and still adamant in her belief that Taft was the better choice, she decided it was best to shift her attention toward the immediacy of an equally important campaign—the Cascade City Election.

Was there anything she could do to improve the odds of *decent* men winning the majority of council chamber seats? The elected mayor and aldermen would predicate crucial parameters of her lifestyle over the next two years. Was it legal, she wondered, for aldermen to fabricate whatever laws they wanted? Wasn't the state supposed to set limits?

She'd think on it more once she got into her warm chair at the House of the Well Fed. She crunched through the last length of ice, then wiped her boots on the metal grate and proceeded to the lobby entrance. Who would it be, she pondered—the President of our United States—if all us women could vote?

Biding time while her side order of bacon sizzled, she examined the lifelines creased deep across her palms. Frustrated that she couldn't recall which palm was said to foretell the future, she decided it didn't much matter, glanced across the room and identified the back of D.W. by his height and particular way of hanging clothes on the coat rack.

"D.W.," she called, inviting him over with the twist of her hand. "Come sit down, have some coffee."

She righted a cup on its saucer and slid the universal symbol of friendship across the table, ever the gracious hostess when she wanted to be. Though many years had passed since she had run Mary's Café, to be on the receiving end of food preparations still felt odd. Smiling, she announced, "Coffee's coming, directly."

"Just for a moment. Am on my way to—"

She patted the tablecloth, coaxing, the way she had patted many a horse or child entrusted to her care.

Once the coffee was poured and sugar was stirred, she seized the opportunity for which she'd been waiting. "Ya know, D.W., a couple months ago we were having a conversation, right here."

He looked up. "What?"

"You said that Hall's opponent for the mayor's seat would have to be brave enough to slug it out and save what's left of our City Treasury."

"I doubt I said, 'slug it out,' Miss Mary."

"Same thing, and I agree. Been waiting forever for that courageous soul to announce his, or her, candidacy."

D.W. Monroe chuckled as he conjured an image of Hattie, a gavel gripped in her smooth hand.

"A lone sandhill crane passed through here and told me a rumor—that the courageous hero who's gonna reform the wrongdoing and resuscitate our town, is you."

Unequivocal confirmation met her steady stare.

"I'll give it my best, Mary. I want our people to feel proud—"

"I'm proud of you," she interrupted.

He cleared his throat. "Proud to be members of an incorporated city in the West. Sophisticated or not, we will gain a reputation for being just. Politically, Cascade can be as solvent and forward thinking as the big cities in the East. We will govern our own community from the heart—Christian, in the true sense."

"Hallelujah!" She lowered her voice and giggled unabashed, grabbed the napkin from under her fork and fanned her blushed relief with vigor.

"Shush, now," D.W. suggested, handing her his glass of water. "Our announcement is this Sunday, after church—in front of the hotel, when folks are walking home or coming here to have supper.

"Our?"

"Yes. The Democratic ticket candidates—me and my fellow constituents who are running for the aldermen seats."

"Ah, music from Heaven," she teased, "You've been planning this a long time already, haven't you?"

Glover's voice interrupted. "D.W., are you coming?" His coat flaps brushed against the tablecloth as he marched, preoccupied, toward the front desk.

"One of yours?" Mary asked.

He winked. "I can trust you to keep this under your hat?"

"All my hats. Thank the Lord. We're gonna be rescued."

She scooted her chair back and sighed. Looking at her cold bacon, she signaled the waitress, ordered a three-egg omelet and crossed her arms. So that's why Hattie changed the subject whenever I started talking about who should run.

It was snowing on Sunday, which ruined Glover's plan to place the orator's platform he'd had built, in front of the hotel. Instead, he instructed his staff to store it in the basement and to hurry, stitch a length of sheets together and paint the words, "FREE CAKE & COFFEE—COME RIGHT IN— IMPORTANT SABBATH ANNOUNCEMENT—11 A.M. TODAY" and fasten it to the hotel outside, at once.

Cascade residents were surprised when they discovered that the purpose of the Sunday social was political in nature. Most couldn't figure why these men were politicking for votes that wouldn't be dropped into a coffer til spring. They wondered why the hurry when no one would remember campaign promises months back, except that they were contrary to H.D. Hall and the council.

Nevertheless, a boisterous round of applause shook the fine hotel china and kept the crowd buzzing for another hour. This encouraged the hosts: Monroe, Glover, Ludwig and Woods, intent upon priming their public to prefer them, the Democratic nominees, who would soon be elected as the official Democratic candidates for mayor and aldermen at the Cascade Democratic Convention and Primary, four months hence, and would, with passionate and dedicated zeal, campaign onward against the incumbents Harvey Hall ... and realize a landslide victory and thereafter celebrate as the new mayor and aldermen-elect, the people's choice in the second Cascade City Election, scheduled to take place on April 7, 1913.

The altruistic announcement of intent inspired a resurgence of interest in current ordinance affairs that would, inadvertently, watchdog the behavior of the present constituents—an unanticipated plus, Glover opined, when he met with Ludwig and D.W. for coffee the following morning. "We're off to a great start, fellas," he affirmed, "Don't want to ballyhoo legislative proposals just yet ... *you-know-who* would just copy ... behooves us to let him muddle along on his own. Does such a fine job of it."

"I was heartened by the genuine interest and, well, felt relieved, I guess I have to say," Monroe added. "Several said how glad they were, to have been presented with new options, an alternative."

"Yeah," said Ludwig. He ran his fingers through his wavy hair and furrowed his brow. Composing a phrase of words learned from his new comrades, he promised, "I'm gonna work hard to make our aspirations spark renewed patriotism. Thanks for inviting me to join ranks."

"Listen to you, H.W. You're speaking my language!" Glover patted him on the back and, with his other hand, snapped fingers for another round of breakfast pastries.

Ludwig voiced an afterthought. "I'm glad Hall wasn't in town yesterday." He looked to Glover, wondering momentarily, whether the clever manager had arranged it somehow. "Did you see Alderman Thompson, Briscoe and Russell leaning against the wall, saying nothing?"

Later that afternoon, Hattie advised D.W. of residual feedback that had traversed a grapevine to her door, which included, she articulated: wishes for kinder and more compassionate regulations for children and animals and the criminally insane, the removal of ordinances that were prejudiced toward women and other unprotected non-voters, active fund-raising support for better schools, temperance, and last but definitely not least, woman's suffrage.

She mentioned that it was her opinion that they, the intended public servants who held the power to vote and run for office, should feel flattered to have received such extravagant interest given the faux pas they had committed, breaking a well understood rule of etiquette—promotion of something other than religious and meditative activity on the Sabbath—and had in so doing (according to several husbands undermined head-of-household authority, employing trickery—a devilish sin. She paused and straightened his lapel, reminding her dear-heart that she was merely the messenger and was sure this information could prove helpful.

"Trickery?" he repeated.

"Yes," she confirmed, explaining that said parties alluded, further, to the deceptive means of engagement: enticement by means of desserts and socializing—an advertisement without full disclosure, a legitimate source of irritation.

Cake should not be used as bait, she had been told by one particular woman—yet accolades had followed with a request for more cake in the future, perhaps on Saturday picnics, inside or out, with political speeches advertised in advance, the neighbor had suggested.

Mary had babysat for Hattie earlier in the week and, afterwards, let her know there were no hard feelings about keeping the fact that D.W. was running for mayor secret. She thought it gracious of herself to say so and accepted Hattie's sincere apologies because she truly believed that Hattie had withheld only because of her characteristic devotions as a faithful wife—though honestly, it had stung a little, in retrospect—herself going on about how great it would be if D.W. would run, when all the while, Hattie knew and didn't say—couldn't say, Mary accepted.

Feeling embarrassed, more so now that her trespass was out in the open, Hattie baked three batches of Mary's favorite oatmeal raisin cookies and invited her over on Saturday afternoon. Licking their lips over ham sandwiches and vegetable soup, the two of them indulged in gossip and conjecture and sunk forks into Hattie's surprise dessert, warm from the oven: deep-dish apple pie, dressed with vanilla ice cream.

Undeterred by the two mischief-making boys, who were, as usual, on the move begging pennies, permissions and exceptions to the rules, Hattie and Mary discussed events that had recently occurred in town—activities that neither of them had anticipated. Most dramatically, a mystery: the fancy-lady Madam Claret and several of her girls had disappeared without a trace last Thursday night, between the hours of two and five a.m., Marshal Hoag had reported.

Claret had recently redecorated her parlor, Mary stated. She knew this because the strawberry blonde woman, Fannie, had delivered two exquisite red cut-glass chandelier style kerosene table lamps to Mary, with Claret's compliments, last week, reporting that her employer had special-ordered art-nouveau lights that would arrive that same day by train.

"Last Wednesday, I think it was—upside-down cake day. So Miss Claret wasn't planning to leave town," Mary premised, relaying her point-by-point vestige of deductive facts that she was akin to personally.

Hattie chewed another forkful of pie, pining for an imagined faraway place where nutmeg and cinnamon scents lay heavy in warm, thick air. Had another woman known to her face-to-face, fled for safety from who knows what and what kind of past after having scraped a semblance of independence on this frontier? What had necessitated the calamity? The tapping sound, realized finally to be Mary waiting for a response, forced her into action. She got up and ruffled through the newspaper bin by the stove, located last week's issue. She turned to the State Capitol section.

"I remember reading this, Mary." She creased and folded the paper, gave it to her friend. "The article says that the House and Senate passed stricter laws against prostitution. Makes being a madam against the law, in any location, at all times." She rubbed her hands, thinking that it would never happen—the absence of prostitution. "Look, Mary," she said pointing, 'for the purpose of preventing licentiousness and prostitution … anyone who solicits, encourages or maintains a place for such purpose is liable for arrest and conviction with felony charges and can be sentenced to years in prison.'"

"Maybe certain men are trying to take all of the property owned by those rich madams in Helena," Mary said, re-reading the posting in the *Montana Daily Record*. She looked up. "Those madams own most of the buildings in the red-light district and some property close to the best parts of the city." They're taxpayers, too, she thought, the women. "Laws never seemed to bother Claret much, here, course she's always been friendly with the marshal and H.D. Hall."

"So why leave like a thief in the night?" Hattie posed, thinking aloud. "She owns the house, doesn't she? She didn't have time to sell it, get the equity to go." A number of wicked possibilities came to mind, none of which resulted in outcomes she would wish on any woman.

"As far as we know," Mary grumbled, frowning. "What if someone had something on her, something bad, and threatened to expose her—could be anything—or maybe she was colluding with somebody and this new law would put him in trouble …" She rubbed her hands that had gone cold and clammy. "We should find out if someone has just gotten title to her house. Might lead to answers. The important question is—is she still alive?"

"Mary! That is too horrible."

"And how did she leave town? Not on the train if it was during the night. Let's check to see if her Model T is still here."

"Let's change the subject for now. I can't … Would you like some more tea?"

"Have you got any spearmint?"

"Yes." Hattie massaged her temple, then filled the water kettle. The front door slammed, and heavy footsteps sounded along with the usual scurries belonging to Earl and Lester.

"Is that apple pie I smell?" the manly voice called.

"Come and see," Hattie flung. "Mary's here."

Steps rounded the corner. "Miss Mary Fields! How are you?"

"Just fine, Mister Future Mayor." She let her buoyant greeting dangle keeping eye contact, getting after a moment, the Cheshire grin she had anticipated. Motioning to Hattie she bragged, "Best apple pie west of the Missouri. Course, you know that."

"By the way, Mary," Hattie sparked, "what did you think of D.W.'s candidacy announcement?"

"I thought it was superb! That's what."

Wonder if Claret would have voted for D.W., she pondered.

Hattie slid the newspaper off the table and into the bin and cut three slices of pie at the counter.

"Will you cut me a slice, dear?" D.W. asked, making himself comfortable at the head of the table.

"Just when did you decide that you were going to run for mayor?" Mary half-teased.

"Can't remember exactly. Awhile ago, when you were talking about Taft."

"Would you and your team like to borrow my nickname for Hall and his camp?"

D.W.'s fork, in route to his mouth, stopped.

"Thought it up during the presidential race. I call them," she made him wait, "Cascade's Bully Council who suffers from Square Deal delusions!"

D. W. guffawed, and Hattie, having heard it more than once during the presidential campaign, chuckled.

"That's clever—sounds just like you," he said, feeding his appetite, wiping his mouth with his napkin. "I'll keep that in my 'sly remark' pocket. Thanks. The men will get a kick—" He noticed a slight tremor in Mary's hand, causing him to study Mary's face and note how she had aged—he hadn't paid attention, he realized, a bit ashamed of himself. He leaned back and asked, "Will you be my unofficial campaign manager?"

"Yep. Long as the terms don't require any mascot duties," she barbed.

"Think we have a chance of winning?"

"I think hearts are aching for a politician they can believe in. As your unofficial campaign manager, she winked, "I've got a great idea, D.W. First action you and your team should do when you win. Gather round the council table and make a brand new ordinance that says: all old previous mayors have to leave town, forever!" She laughed, unabashed.

"You'd ... We'll make sure you're there to notarize the decree!"

"Let the record make it so," she trumpeted.

"Speaking of fish stories," D.W. said as he pushed himself away from the table, I promised the boys I'd take them to Dowdy's place, Hattie. Pond is iced, and Harold cut the hole already." He handed his plate to her. "Only a couple hours of light left. Going to meet Russell and some other potential democrats."

"So, you'll be bringing dinner home, cut and cleaned, then?"

"Yes, Mother Monroe."

Mary remained in place on the table's bench until the winter sun angled streaks of blue twilight across the Monroe kitchen. Cap in hand, she scooted over and announced, "I best be going."

"No, Mary," Hattie asked, "stay for awhile, please?" She couldn't rid herself from imagery—a woman running in darkness, refracted light from red crystal lamps—a gypsy with long dark curls shaking her head, ringed fingers turning tarot cards over, a blank card.

"All right."

Hattie sighed. "Good." She forced herself into the present, glad for the companionship, thankful that she had a good husband and two sons, and that she had been protected, somehow, from frontier disasters. She brewed a new pot of mint tea and placed it center, between dessert plates with second helpings of pie, untied her apron and sat down. "I was thinking, Mary—when you and D.W. were talking—about you realizing your dream. Will you be voting in the Republican Primary, then?"

"Primary? What are you talking about?"

"There will be a party convention and a party primary, just like the presidential ones."

"Are you sure?" Mary squeezed her cap, still in hand. "I hadn't thought … Is that cause there's more than one party now?"

"Yes. State legislators passed a new law. Candidates for all electoral seats have to file petitions with the City Clerk and supply signatures of registered voters who support them. That's before they can be nominated at their party's convention to become a candidate. Then the members vote, choose their contenders in separate primaries."

"Oh. So, will the Citizen's Party be a thing of the past? The one-fits-all-party is over?

"I think so. Seems like each party has separated, like the presidential campaign: Republicans, Progressives, like that."

"My Lord, don't want to be part of the Republican Convention if it's the one Hall will be running with. Wait. This is confusing. If they *can* still have a Citizen's Party, they could be hostaging Democrats that are supposed to be at the Democratic Primary, right?"

"I guess so. I'll ask D.W. I think the Democratic Primary will be in March—March twenty-fourth, I think."

Mary quivered from a sudden chill. "I'm only interested in voting for D.W. and his team at the final election. They can't stop Republicans from voting for Democrats at the ballot box."

She collected the plates and utensils and stood at Hattie's newly installed sink, washing china with Hattie's dishcloth in a speckled enamel dishpan, enjoying most of all, the novelty of water bursting forth from pipes and disappearing down a drain, another pipe.

Between the time Mary got home, lit the fire and snuggled beneath the coal-warmed blankets of her bed, she rocked in her rocker and wrote a quick note to Onatah, who she imagined was faring well … safety in numbers, she assured herself, unlike Nadie who had struck off by herself—to Helena—never heard of again.

She had meant to share the memento in her lap, the evidence of her victory, sooner, but it had slipped her mind. *Onatah will be so proud,* she thought as she held one of her photographs, the framed picture gifted by Jack the reporter. *Bless his heart, sending three, each the same, mounted professional.* "*… for the purpose of sharing your grand day with loved ones,*" he had written. *Mighty generous.*

I voted one time so far, as a United States and Montana Citizen. And in the doing, I helped an educated, qualified woman get into public office, she commended. *All future American women will have suffrage rights, and I hope each one of them will understand what a God-given, woman-battled-for-right they have. Hope they never take it for granted.* She scratched her head. *How long til Onatah can vote, I wonder? Maybe same time as me, if the government calls her white.*

She stared into the sepia-toned image, mesmerized. *Look at me, standing in my destiny, flags in each hand. God bless that young reporter Jack, and God bless Nadie and her Jack, and Onatah, and Edward and Little Mary and Hattie, and Claret and every person I ever cared for. No one knows the future.*

D.W. Monroe and Glover agreed. They would invite all Cascade men and women to campaign get-togethers that they, the Democrats, would host whether members of the assemblies were eligible to vote or not. On the second Saturday of each month, they presented the nearest likeness to outdoor picnics they could pattern indoors and called the events "Political Coffee Clutches," replete with refreshments and unlimited cups of coffee.

They introduced subjects that they believed to be of utmost importance to their attendees: education, taxes, business growth, city expenditures, safety, ordinances, utilities, roads and supervision of elected officials—concerns for a moral and decent community—thereby initiating conversation, a partnership between residents and the candidates they could choose to protect their future.

They asked: What are your concerns? How can we be of service? What is your vision of Cascade in one, two, four years' time? They contributed thoughtful suggestions, such as: What if we were to increase our City revenue by depositing our tax dollars in an earmarked account that would acquire interest and reduce the need for future taxes?

Then they revealed, with due diligence—that under the guardianship of the present Council, the public's hard-earned money was stuck in a no-interest account, doddering like a bump on a log, accruing nothing but ill-will.

They emphasized the importance of choosing wisely: selecting well-experienced businessmen: visionaries accustomed to the application of strategy, expedience and economy: men who would organize and operate with pragmatism and govern with goodwill and wisdom—much like a compassionate father, a head-of household. Unlike those who allowed *less than honorable* motivations to be greased by personal interest and greed.

Implementing clever modus operandi, they purported means to cultivate a voter's level of knowledge and, hence, his or her participation in the political system. So that they, the voters, would, in the future, effectively evaluate the performance of their public servants, prepared, in part, by fundamental input the Democrats had provided. For example, the Democrats asked: What defines a City, exactly? A wholesome community? How should such a place be governed? What services and maintenance should be provided to protect our good, clean, moral standards?

R.B. Glover purchased the newest type of amphitheater blackboard that rolled on wheels and placed it strategically in front of the restaurant's exit. With his chalk stick, he outlined highlights from the coffee clutch discussions into feasible proposals, edited and bulleted for community perusal.

Cascade's personalized compendium would be addressed further and eventually formalized into resolutions or ordinances that would be implemented and assimilated into the community by their soon-to-be civil servants, the Democratic candidates—*the most experienced, dedicated and committed contenders* for the Cascade council. Such was the Democrat's plan.

Monroe reminded his friends and neighbors to look for evidence of their own insightful contributions in the newspaper and to help themselves to seconds and thirds at the dessert table.

As winter passed, D.W. had begun to think of himself as the incumbent mayor, having talked as though he were, for several months. He kept records of those chalkboard outlines in the top drawer of his desk. He would indeed draft some of those mutually created proposals into ordinances if he won the mayor's seat—and he would not forget to credit the originators—his earnest public—when brainstorms had evolved into City codes.

Glover, ever the prolific marketer, continued to outline highlights from each homespun luncheon and made sure every resident in Cascade and the outlying neighborhoods received circulars of picnic minutes and campaign notices that were also, as promised, published in the *Cascade Courier, the*

People's Paper: available for free in the New Cascade Hotel lobby, the Pastime Theater and the Methodist Church office.

Overcome and overrun by the extensive publicity and the community's participation with the Democrats, Harvey D. Hall and his incumbent aldermen floundered. Though mismanagement of funds was difficult to argue, they insisted that they, as the original visionary founding fathers of Cascade, had demonstrated remarkable prowess; they had supervised the installations of new public utilities successfully. Not only had they pulled Cascade up by its bootstraps, configured it from cow-town to metropolis, they would continue to dedicate themselves in the spirit of the Citizens Party's mandate: to guide Cascade's development with wisdom, prudence and justice for all.

They also exercised caution to the voters. Watch out, they warned: because historically, aspirants to civil office made hot-air promises ballooned out of proportion, whims based upon what they believed the innocent public wanted to hear. Warning further, they claimed: the Democrats' crazy campaign promises would disintegrate without the wherewithal to carry them through—without prior governing experience.

"We, you and us, built this prosperous City," the council incumbents cock-a-doodle-doed to their constituents. "And now its future growth, or lack of it, teeters in your hands. Remember, we made Cascade something to be proud of. Let's keep it that way!"

In the privacy of Council chambers, Hall emphasized a confusing hand signal and claimed crassly, "The Democratic plague is spreading faster than a loose woman!"

Thompson pressed upon his stomach, beginning to believe he had an ulcer, resolved that Charlie Lemon had had the right idea, moving to New York.

Alderman J. Harris Russell, M.D. decided to switch parties. He would run on the Democratic Ticket, if they'd have him.

"Listen boys," Hall regaled, gavel in hand, refusing to close the meeting, "They think they're so smart. Uppity goosenecks. Let's show them while we still have time. Should we make a new ordinance?" His mind dove for crackerjack ideas.

In March, registered members of the two opposing parties, the Democrats and Citizens, attended their long-awaited pre-election political galas that commenced with party-conventions held at opposite ends of town. After nominations and elections of official party candidates, the respective primaries concluded later that same night.

The Citizens, who stubbornly persisted in representing a political party that didn't actually exist, presented the same ticket of candidates: Harvey D. Hall for Mayor and Alfred Briscoe and J.C. Thompson for Aldermen, minus Russell, who had deserted.

The Democratic Convention and Primary produced no surprises either: the final ticket designated the names of the active Democrats fast on the lips of every Cascade resident, pro or con: D.W. Monroe, R.B. Glover, H.W. Ludwig and J. Harris Russell.

The Cascade Courier encouraged citizens to come out and vote, emphasizing that such duty was critical, due to the fact that the town was on the eve of phenomenal growth. The paper endorsed the Democratic Party, claiming that the incumbent Citizens' Party had conducted a far from flawless administration, citing several questionable ordinances that typified, in their judgment, tyrannical dominance over an innocent community.

Like the democrats, *The Courier* stressed the importance of electing a progressive mayor and City Council who would conduct business in a prudent manner, en rapport with the spirit of the times. Commentary urged Cascade voters to select "the best and most public-spirited men within their ranks—gentlemen imbued with high ideals for a bigger, better, more economical and more harmonious city government—a government not for a few, but for every resident, be he a big businessman or a common laborer."

Three days before the election, Mayor Hall issued an official proclamation that instructed voters where to vote in their respective districts. Ward One: the City Jail. Ward Two: Hall's Livery Barn. Ward Three: Askew's Livery Barn. He informed that polls would be open between the hours of eight o'clock in the morning and six o'clock at night.

On the same day, the official Democratic candidates advertised their policies: in *The Courier*, in storefront windows and in House of the Well Fed menus, providing a written promise to their public:

The Men to Vote For on April 7th— Policy of Democratic Candidates

Resolved, that peace and quietness be maintained in all places of business within the limits of the city, and that no disturbance of the peace will be tolerated on the streets, or in the city.

That we advocate the best of schools, more churches, and the maintenance of a good clean moral standard.

That we believe in the upholding of the highest standard of health, by keeping the city in a clean and healthy condition, and that the health officer be required to attend to the duties imposed upon him to the letter of the law.

That we believe in equal rights, and justice to all. That we extend a welcome invitation to strangers to come within our midst, in order that they may avail themselves of the bounteous resources which may be found in the city for numerous lines of business.

That we will do all that lies in our power for the upbuilding of a good clean modern city within which all may enjoy health, comfort, and prosperity.

That we will avoid all unnecessary lawsuits; publish all council proceedings in the local press for the public's inspection; that we will be guided by the laws enacted by our legislature which are applicable to a city's government, and that we will manage the city's government just as economically as may be consistent with good government.

That we will carefully consider any proposition which will require an extensive outlay of money believing that the interest of the taxpayer would be jealously guarded, knowing that we are burdened with as large a taxation as the business interests and property owners can stand, and that heavy taxation tends to retard the growth of our city and works a hardship upon the property owners, increasing the cost of living among those who are compelled to pay rentals and depend upon a monthly salary for a livelihood.

That all public moneys which heretofore have been left on deposit with banks, on open accounts, with full knowledge of the members of the council that it would not be expended for a period of at least six months, and drawing no interest whatever, shall be placed on interest upon good security from time to time, as such public moneys accumulate in the general or special funds, and which is not in contemplation of immediate use.

D.W. Monroe
J. Harris Russell
R.B. Glover
H.W. Ludwig

Democratic City Candidates
For a Bigger, Better, More Harmonious City Government
Vote For Monroe, Russell, Glover and Ludwig

Mary promised herself: she would remember everything about Cascade's Election Day. When she woke before dawn on April 7, 1913, she squinted at her home's tiny interior, as though she were visiting, and began taking notes … impartially, she told herself, the way Reporter Jack had done, but without pencil and pad.

Rattles knocked outside. She got up to investigate. Howling winds pitched eager lilac branches against the windowpane, opaque from sinking depths of cold. The racket bugled a message—worse weather coming.

"Men candidates like to use that word, impartial," she muttered. "I think it's a little cold—the word impartial, and my house."

She rushed to find her slippers.

Never mind. This is *my* day. Going to vote.

"Polls open at eight."

I'll eat later, she decided as she splashed frigid water from the pitcher onto warm cheeks and an ice-cold nose. Even with pleasing globes of red color that spread from her new crystal lamps, it was not possible to discern the colors of her clothing that hung a short distance away. She finagled balance to get her legs into wool trousers and a wool skirt assumed to be navy-blue, a patriotic choice.

When the stove fire had begun to flame strong, she added more logs, tucked her unruly hair under her rebel cap, slid feet into boots and arms into overcoat sleeves and charged directly to Askew's Livery, the Ward Three Polling Place.

She didn't know the time. She would wait if the poll takers weren't there.

A strip of light glowed beneath the livery barn door, so she knocked, pursing chapped lips to fend off a chill.

"What time is it?" she inquired to the man wearing a bright blue ribbon tied around his coat-covered bicep.

"Almost eight. Name's Mr. Joseph Jones. Come on in." He opened the door.

He doesn't know me. That's good, she decided, used to applying strategy, hoping that someday there would be a time she didn't have to.

"Name's Mary Fields, without a middle initial. Looks like I'm first."

"Yes, you are. I'm one of the judges appointed to this ward, and that's Mr. Parsons over there." He pointed as he pushed the door shut. Tugging the hem of his jacket he said, I don't know you, but I've heard of you, course. I live across the river. Are you sure you're allowed? This isn't a school election."

"My name's in the book. I'm a taxpayer." She touched the piece of letter Onatah had sent, the State Constitution Suffrage Statute Section Twelve, copied in Onatah's hand years back, safe in her skirt pocket.

"I'll see," he said, unconvinced, wishing that the other two assigned judges would show up. He flipped the large ledger open, scrolled his finger along page margins, scanning names that were listed by date, surprised the names were not in alphabetical order. "Parsons, is the coffee ready yet?"

Uncomfortable, he scanned through past election pages, searching to see if things were listed differently then, and formulated a complaint that he would register at day's end: an objection to his bestowed title, *judge*, which implied cardinal knowledge of constitutional law. It was well known that his expertise lay in business and crosswords.

He knew that some women were allowed to vote, but he had not been made aware of requirements that would pertain in a situation such as this.

"Here you are," Mr. Jones muttered.

He kept a steady stare on the characters and numerals as though they would solve his dilemma. Removing his spectacles, he pretended they were cause to tarry, and wiped the lenses heedfully, glancing down, listening for footsteps that did not come. "Do you have the ballots ready, Clerk Parsons?"

"Yes, I do, sir." Parsons, a young lawyer just graduated, tread the short distance to his senior advisor, browsing through papers in hand. Looking up, he stopped abruptly, his jaw parted, three gold teeth exposed. He crimped, as though he had a cramp.

"What's the problem?" asked Mr. Jones, knowing full well it was sight of a black woman that had snatched his acuity.

Parsons glanced to his stack of folders, to the rafters, the bales of hay, the coffee pot, noticing for the first time, the odor of manure that wafted.

"Judge" Jones hoped his clerk would execute some folly, do something to waste more time. Mary sighed.

Parsons set the ballots next to the ledger and returned to his post. He turned the radio on. A male voice announced a forecast of rain and more rain for the next week. A chorus of women sang about Borax, the mighty twenty-mule-team laundry additive.

"May I have a ballot, please?" Mary asked nonchalantly, instructing her heart to remain calm, advising prudent discipline to assist her in her mission—assuage the dilemma—allow miracles to materialize.

Mr. Jones asked, "Can I see some identification?"

"I'm the only colored woman in this town, city. Everyone knows me ..." Shut up, Mary, her better sense admonished—just show him your receipt.

"Here's my registration receipt, sir," she added, politely.

She clenched her teeth and felt the dampness of her clothes. She remembered her morning pledge—to record, make a memory photo album.

Keeping one eye on Mr. Jones, who surveyed her paper for too long, she wondered, where is Herman Wolf? He promised to meet me. And where is Mr. Rowe, who could bear witness?

Mr. Jones sighed, having made his decision. He looked to Mary in earnest and asked, "Republican, Democrat, Progressive, Citizens Party or other?" He would comply, professionally, pragmatically. He had made a pledge and would ascertain solutions if defined protocol was lacking.

"Republican."

He printed Republican on the top line of the ballot and handed the single paper sheet across the wide table. "Can you read?" he asked, hoping she would say "no," and thus, cause him to adjudicate ignorance as a reason to delay.

"Yes. Any place behind there?" She glanced to the blankets tacked across the north end of the barn.

"Pick any stall."

She locked onto his green eyes until the correct meaning sunk in. Stall, as in horse stall, of course, dividers between voters, privacy.

She proceeded. Kind of like where the baby Jesus was born, she associated. Think of it as sacred. Yes, it is. She reached for an army blanket edge.

A coarse voice hollered, "Stop! What the hell is she doing here?" A flash of cold air coursed across her ankles. Papers flapped. Straw flurried.

Clerk Parsons moved toward the female voter in question—readied also, to confiscate her ballot if duty demanded. This was his first time as a poll clerk, and he intended to add it to his curriculum vitae.

Mary kept her position, her back to the voice.

"Mr. Berger, about time you got here," Joseph Jones chided. "I'm sure you have a valid excuse." He extended his hand to his colleague elector, the second of the ward's three judges to arrive, and detected the scent of alcohol.

Bill Berger from our baseball team? Mary wondered, listening closely.

"I said, stop her." Berger demanded, his unavailed hand fisted in his pocket.

Jones pulled the ward official aside and whispered, "You have no more authority than I, Mr. Berger, and you have not made yourself acquainted with the situation."

"She's a colored woman. Good mascot, but that's beside the point."

"You're here to act as a judge, an impartial arm of the law. You best remove yourself before everyone realizes you've been tipping the bottle."

Parsons touched Mary's elbow. She turned, slowly, elevating her height, instructing herself to behave like an experienced American voter, or royalty, like that regal Saint Germain.

Both livery doors swung open and a gaggle of voices, men's voices, entered. Mary angled her eyes to the floor, fixed sight toward the shadows, placed confidence on a pedestal, engaged in selective listening and disregarded all that was of no import.

Deliberations between Jones and Berger paused as the newly arrived men voters got into it—the quagmire of her presence and their objections to it. They, intruders upon her victory, thrust demands and dared each other snout to snout. What would they do? She eavesdropped, filtering chinks from daubs, malarkey from sense, threats from violence. Opinions split. Demands yapped.

The resolute Mr. Jones delegated, once more. "Mind your own business," he ordered.

A familiar voice came close and asked, "Miss Mary, what's—" It was Herman.

She took a breath and slipped the ballot into her overcoat pocket, unnoticed.

"She can't vote," Marcum shouted. "No way, no how."

"She has papers, registration papers. Says she owns property," Joseph Jones explained.

"What the hell are you talking about? She doesn't own anything."

"You are quite incorrect," Herman defended.

"Damn it, I warned you," Marcum charged, darting accusatory glares at Hall and Thompson. "I knew it!"

Flushed, he turned to Herman. "You sold her your house! Why did you—"

"Gentlemen," said a woman's voice.

Mary looked up to verify its owner.

Ada Marcum reprimanded, "This is a polling place. If you can't respect your privilege, and the law ..."

"Mrs. Ada," Mary spoke, "I have, in my hand here, a copy of the State Constitution, Section 12, the political suffrage code as relates to the rights of women." She stepped close, handed the wrinkled paper to Ada and faced the crowd, reciting from memory:

"Article IX. Rights of Suffrage. Section 10: Women have the right to vote at any school district election."

"Yeah, and that's all the voting rights they have," Marcum shouted.

"Section 12," she continued. "Upon all questions submitted to the vote of the taxpayers of the state, or any political division thereof, women who are taxpayers and possessed of the qualification for the right of suffrage required of men by the state constitution, *equally with men, have the right to vote.*"

"She made that up. No such thing as equal with men," a rusty old chameleon hooted.

"No, gentlemen, she has orated the Article IX sections perfectly," Ada confirmed, pressing upon pleats that hid her trembling legs. She raised her chin.

"Listen, fellow voters," Mary dared, "in case you're not clear about women taxpayer rights, the 1907 Code, Number 3680, explains it. 'Taxable property includes but is not limited to: real estate, mines, timber, stock and bonds.'"

J.E. demanded, "Who registered her?"

Ada extended her arm, silencing her husband and anyone else who dared to dispute her authority, known by most residents as the keeper of their bank accounts and the new school board trustee and J.E.'s better half—in addition to guild chairlady at the Methodist church.

"The way I see it, electing City officials who hold the power to make our laws is very serious business. A council holds the power to interpret legislation from the constitution, to some degree. More to the point, in our case, they are allowed to create city laws, ordinances that could determine, just or unjustly, what measures taxpayers are allowed to vote on—potentially eliminating a citizen's right to vote on issues that directly impact their life, our lives, personally, as relates to men and women and children." She looked from left to right, and stated, "You men, whether you own property or not, will also be affected. Assume nothing."

Disbelief raised hair on the napes of necks. She could tell by the widening of eyes.

"What are you doing here?" someone barked.

Undaunted, Ada raised her voice. "Our Council determines the levels of taxes, negotiates interest rates on our debts and assets, authors the nature and parameters of ordinances and contracts that affect acquisitions of real-estate and business agreements and, to some degree, regulates the fees incurred with them. Tell me, how can voting for our mayor or aldermen not be tax-related?"

That is the point of Ada's oration, Mary understood—that and distracting their attention from me. In her heart she applauded the brave wife who knew, same as she, that a City Election *was* tax related. Had the fact flown over the heads of her audience? She stood her ground.

Thompson, who had come in just before Mary's reciting of the constitution, said, "We talked about that at the Council meeting. Remember H.D.?" He swung around, locating Hall. "We decided … Well, you did mostly, to do it the way you heard other cities do—not to let the women taxpayers vote in municipal elections—just the special elections—like the water bond. Remember?"

Hall hacked through the pulsating crowd and placed a heavy heel on Thompson's toe, zinging, "That's the way it is in state elections, Thompson."

"But women don't vote in state elections," Thompson replied.

Hall barked, "We're supposed to do what the state does. All you aldermen know that. It was a Council decision. Who the hell told you there were any options?" He scanned the group, searching for aldermen other than Thompson, to back him up. "Where's Briscoe?"

"But you said we had a choice, as the founding fathers," Thompson fired, defending his innocence.

"Excuse me," Herman bristled. "Are you saying that you had the *choice* of inviting women tax-payers—some of your wives, included, I assume—to vote in this election? And you didn't tell them? And just as bad, you didn't give City voters a say about it?" He took his hat off. "Didn't those same women taxpayers vote on the incorporation measure? The measure that gave rise to a City Council?" He searched for acknowledgment under the cloaked heads. "I'd be in hot water if my Gerlach was one of those ladies."

Tension escalated.

Women had not been allowed to vote on City Incorporation.

"Why is Mary Fields' name on the qualified list?" Hall yelled, distancing his person to the registration table. "Where's Rowe? Or Glover? Who is responsible for this list?"

An irritated voice from behind answered, "Right here, H.D. And I'm not one of your councilmen anymore, in case you forgot," Melvin Rowe spurned. He fanned his arms, as if stopping a train. "Just so everybody's clear on this: Mary Fields met the qualifications to register to vote last year, as you know very well. Her house got burned down right after, remember?"

Voices conferred, muttering.

The livery doors swung open again, giving non-voter passersby a chance to participate in the pivotal controversy.

Mr. William Berger was nowhere to be seen.

Hall straightened his agate bolo tie and pulled himself together. Winning the election was looking less likely if this kept up, he calculated.

Misters Parsons and Jones concluded their whispering.

Ward Judge Joseph Jones announced to the crowd, "I believe, ladies and gentlemen, as one of the judges of this polling place, that the rule is: if a person's name is on the specific register compiled for a specific election—in this case, our Municipal Election, today—he, or she, has the right to vote."

"That's what they call a technicality," an unidentified man called out.

"Nevertheless," Jones insisted.

"Where's the City Clerk?"

"Who is the City Clerk?"

"That's irrelevant," said Jones wishing he'd declined his nomination. "It's done already, no matter who registered the voters."

"Are there any other women's names on the list? Mine, for example?" Ada Marcum demanded.

The women who had gathered into the hazardous throng pressed forward, transfixed, as Ada studied each register page.

Mary Fields elbowed Herman Wolf and slipped into the stall.

J.E. Marcum blared, "Who compiled this registration list for this election? That person's in the wrong. Should be prosecuted," he insisted.

Voices hammered. Heads turned back and forth, exasperated. Grumbles persisted. Everyone remained standing. Digits were beginning to numb.

Mrs. Bernice Hall arrived and was quickly informed by the female conclave that encircled, of the City Council secret that had just been divulged accidentally: a purported woman suffrage right that had been allegedly debated inside closed Chambers, followed by the Council's execution of an unacceptable illegal policy bullied to finality by her husband, the Mayor. Unmarried tax-paying women and tax-paying wives who owned property independently might have had the right to vote in this Municipal Election, they reported. Further, women *may* have had the right to vote in all of Cascade's municipal elections thus far!

Attention split. Curt remarks cauterized.

Men targeted their outrage upon the subject of Mary Fields, who was registered but shouldn't be, according to Marcum and Hall, regardless of the past Council's alleged illegalities. The majority present argued that their endowed arsenal of rights as men, the heads of households since America's beginning, had been violated—and might be restored if the black canker that had contaminated their election was thrown out on her ear—immediately. The minority insisted that she could vote, since her name was in the register.

The women, particularly the tax-paying women, were infuriated to realize that they possibly, probably, had been betrayed by the selfish obtuse conclave of governing Cascade representatives who had promised unequivocal equity according to Montana State Law.

Bernice Hall considered the nefarious charge. Cascade women voters who were tax-payers, had, during the past two years voted on Cascade water and electricity measures—*in City Elections.*

Had her husband and his bedfellows fabricated these electoral limitations? Had she and the other women been tricked into believing that they were not allowed to vote for Cascade City officials when in fact, they were? How could she have been so naïve?

Property values and taxes were undeniably affected by the business of the Council: the contracts, the utilities, the choice of City land deals, the ordinances. As aldermen, they had set the actual rates of tax, for God's sake. Were we women eligible to have voted on the Incorporation Ballot, too? she quested. Her flesh burned.

She felt betrayed. Again.

Twenty years past, a young and desperate married woman, she had had to swallow her pride, humiliate herself and petition the Montana courts for "sole trader" status. Such an act was socially degrading. Wives were stigmatized though the necessity to eliminate debt was most often caused by irresponsible husbands. Disgrace and exclusion followed—which was why Bernice had agreed to start over in Cascade in the first place. Would she be shamed again, today?

There had been redeeming benefits that came with sole tradership status: financial independence from Harvey, the legal right to employ one's own intelligence and execute independent decisions in regard to business affairs: buy, sell, contract, negotiate in her name, solely, with no repercussion to, or from, her husband's legal affairs. All this, resulting from H.D.'s failure to provide. He had forfeited his silver mine claim to creditors, failed at saloon keeping, bee keeping, coffin construction and everything else he had tried, accruing enormous debts, placing his wife and children at perilous risk.

She had readily agreed to sole trader terms: among them, payment of taxes and acceptance of full legal responsibility for the maintenance of their children—now a moot point, since all three had died from smallpox five years afterwards.

She had kept her sole trader qualification a secret, all these years, and could no longer contain her resentment. Interned rage escaped with a sinuous shriek, shocking to her own ears.

"Harvey Hall, if you stopped me from voting in this election—if I had even the slightest possibility of doing so—I'm going to murder you."

She grabbed a cane from beneath an old man's arm and lunged forward, landing a mighty smack on Harvey Hall's shoulder before others intervened, confiscated the weapon and implored her to sit down.

Thompson, who had jumped high to rescue her feathered hat, returned it to her, speechless. Mr. Jones provided his chair.

Aching for the egregious things that must have fueled her friend's exhibition, Ada spoke calmly from her post at the registration table. "Bernice, I'm so sorry my dear friend, but neither you, nor I, are listed in the register."

Bloodshot eyes gazed into Ada's.

"I don't know if we could have been. We'll find out."

Bernice gazed past her, to memories that stabbed.

Ada said, "Let us scrutinize this issue at length, elsewhere." She leaned in and helped the mayor's wife to her feet. They locked arms and took their leave.

An ambiguous silence squeezed vocal cords. Men glanced at Harvey, then collectively watched the pair of beautiful women, female pillars of the community, traverse a distance that seemed to swallow them.

Mary, peeking from behind the blanket-curtain, took the opportunity to slip out and deposit her folded ballot into the antique alms box, the makeshift repository provided. She sidled next to Mr. Rowe and Mr. Wolf who were engrossed in what appeared to be a serious exchange.

Rowe shivered and looked at his watch. Unaware that Mary had just cast her vote, he patted her hand and offered his solution, "Mary, without debating the politics, let us concentrate on the fact that you are here, your name is in the register, and however it came to be is irrelevant. I'm glad for you. Let's get you a ballot."

"Did you hear that, Mr. Jones?" Herman called out.

Mr. Jones jerked askance. Sweat indicated his angst.

"Hear what?" he said, gripping his pencil, sure, after checking again, that no other women were listed in the register.

"Mr. Melvin Rowe, here," Wolf patted his comrade's shoulder, "just spoke the very words I was feeling. Let's do what we came here to do, stop this legislative logrolling and vote. I've got errands, and I'm sure these good people," carefully including glances to the sensitive sex, "do, too."

Thompson barked, "Women should have the vote! It's just and right, and they're entitled!" Facing aggrieved expressions, he defended, "We need them!"

The women who had remained, applauded. Apron-stringed compliance had lost all appeal.

"Are you nuts? You certifiably are the most ignorant S.O.B. I ever met," H.D. squalled, losing his temper again.

Marcum seconded, "You have no idea what you're talking about. You're like those jungle palm trees, Thompson, swaying wherever the wind takes you."

"I've had it with you two," Thompson blasted. "It so happens that Montana's House of Representatives and Senate agree with *me*. Not *you*. Maybe you've been tumbling in the throes of arrogance too long," he charged, surprised at his valor. "Are you even aware that our state legislators passed the suffrage bill? That's suffrage for women. Unanimous, almost."

J.E. laughed.

"We *men* ..." Marcum shouted, "are you hearing me, Thompson?" "We *men* still have the power to vote that suffrage bill down in the public State election that won't even get on the ballot until the end of next year!"

Women gasped.

"Excuse me, everyone," Clerk Parsons intervened. Mr. Jones and I would like to point out that it's nine o'clock and we've already wasted an hour. It is illegal to prevent voters from voting. Do we need to call for Marshal Houg?"

"How did Nigger Mary manage to twist Rowe's brain in the first place?" someone churned.

"There's no Goddamn way I'm gonna stand for letting a coon vote—women aren't supposed to be voting in the first place," a disheveled lumberjack slumped against a slatted stall threatened.

"You there, hiding in the shadows," Mr. Jones dared the rabble-rouser. "Is your name registered?"

Parsons stepped forward, straightened his tie and roiled, "All the women, tax-payers or not, will have equal rights to vote any day now, regardless of anything any of you say. And I doubt that one woman's vote is going to tip this election one way or the other. The Senate's vote on the measure was 74 to 2, in favor of suffrage. Get over it, gentlemen."

He nodded to the ladies who had remained just outside the barn's entrance.

Jones gave his clerk a nod of respect. "Everybody who wants to vote—rather, is *registered* to vote—form a line, please."

Recumbent anger continued to ripple. Muscles twitched. Someone pulled the doors shut.

"Have your registration receipts or other identification ready," Parsons punctuated.

Mary felt like she was floating. Not only had she just voted, unbeknownst to everyone but Herman, she was being shuttled into line to vote again. Now what?

Should she mark a ballot in honor of Ada, or Hattie, or Mrs. Hall, in honor of all tax-paying women who were supposed to have suffrage rights, according to the Montana Constitution, Article IX: Rights of Suffrage, Section 12 who for some reason had been banned, at least here?

Why was the statute worded so vaguely? Was it to let each city do what they wanted? It was wrong either way. And so was voting a second time. She remained in line for awhile, to participate in the first part of the voting experience, thinking she would slip away unnoticed, and realized suddenly that she couldn't leave. They would think she'd chickened out, run away like a scared nobody who thought she didn't deserve to be treated like a human being—proving everyone who despised her and thought she was useless, justified. She owed it to her sex and her race to embrace declaration of independence pride and undertake her patriotic duty.

Shortly after six o'clock, shrieks of democratic victory reverberated. Shouts louder than church bells bellowed from one ward to the other. It seemed a chorused score. An hour later, after final counts were tallied, a second wave of glee caught fire, clamor declaring the official win from City Chambers at the Opera House.

Democrats had prevailed across the board—ballot counts averaging close to double in their favor. Patriots cheered. Fireworks cracked the gloomy skies.

Polling results were posted on the Thomas Corner Store chalkboard: Monroe 60, Hall 36. Final tallies for aldermen: Ward One, J.H. Russell, victor—no challenger, uncontested; Ward Two, Glover 30 versus Briscoe 15; Ward Three, Ludwig 20 versus Thompson 14.

"Glad you got to vote, Mary Fields," D.W. bravadoed, as he opened the door to his home and waved her inside.

"Sounds like *you* had a close call?" Hattie asked.

Mary nodded, donning a broad smile.

"You did it. Hoorah!" Hattie shouted.

"You can imagine who I cast my vote for … Now let me think," Mary teased, miming hand to elbow, finger to forehead.

Hattie gave her a peck on the cheek. "Come in the kitchen, Mary."

She had been invited for supper and had agreed to baby-sit, just as happy to celebrate her political victory in the company of Earl and Lester who would spend the evening playing marbles on the carpet by the glow of a crackling fire in a real fireplace—preferable, in her mind, to entering throngs of triumphant democrat supporters at the hotel.

Rushing to join his colleagues, orate the toast, shake the many hands of loyal voters and bask in the landslide glory of an unstructured evening where his only obligation was to distribute cigars and accept gratitudes,

D.W. shoved forkfuls of Hattie's corned beef casserole into his mouth, too distracted to taste.

"Say hip-hip hooray to your parents, boys, one last time before they go," Mary directed, watching the couple pin miniature American flags onto the lapels of their coats. Both she and her candidate had won, eliminating the past two-year-pain-in-the-derrière term, once and for all.

"And congrats to you again, Mary Fields," D.W. reciprocated.

Hattie gave Mary a big squeeze and said, "Out of all the tax-paying women who might have voted, I'm glad Providence picked you, Mary. It was meant to be."

Scurrying to match her husband's pace during the two-block distance, a clear view under lighted street lamps, Hattie, chilled by the dampness, called, "You know, it's a wonder that the uproar at Ward Three didn't turn into a violent brawl, D.W. Mary could have been injured badly, the way some men are."

The freshly minted mayor couldn't switch his attention toward one of Hattie's present concerns, valid or not. "Uh-huh," he muttered, his pace propelled by the passel of voices heard trumpeting behind the New Cascade Hotel doors.

Hattie's thoughts visited the additional second hand news she'd heard about that afternoon: Bernice's scandalous physical attack upon her husband. She felt sorry. So many of her friends living with fear that strangled. And they never talked about it. So many secrets we women keep behind closed doors, she considered. As if we are the guilty ones.

Stepping into the lobby, the couple was immediately engulfed by elated well-wishers assembled to cheer and celebrate a democratic victory and their new leader, Mayor D.W. Monroe. Swarming, citizens felt what it was like to be united, mirroring virtuous patriotism as they mingled and convened into the banquet suite that had, under Glover's direction, been transformed with twinkling lights and colorful streamers and blue-ribbons attached to broad pedestals crowned with cut-glass punch bowls.

The soiree's consummated mood waltzed buoyantly forward, serenaded by modern live music provided by Indian students from the Fort Shaw Industrial Orchestra.

When Hattie and D.W. returned home, they found Mary curled asleep on the sofa. The new mayor-incumbent insisted on escorting his advocate home, aware of large numbers of intoxicated men gallivanting in the streets.

Hattie draped an extra coat over Mary's shoulders and said her goodnights.

Walking in the darkness, Mary noticed her bodice cutting tight. She'd worn her best clothes to the polls, a little too tight, and had forgotten to change when she could have. She distracted herself by admiring her favorite constellation and silently reported another of her journeys to the Big Dipper, one that had concluded in safe victory. She thanked those particular bright stars, as she often did, for the compassed guidance they had provided so reliably, and thanked them again for watching over her, as she liked to imagine.

D.W. opened the door, glanced around, made sure enough logs were stacked near the stove and departed after thanking Mary once more for her vote and for her dogged encouragement.

Soon tucked into bed, Mary felt contented and cared for—gratified, as though her name had been added onto a cosmic scroll of grace—worthiness—absolution—equal to those men who had signed the Declaration of Independence—equal to anybody and witnessed as such. She fell asleep smiling.

During the night, an unknown perpetrator loitered, waiting until everyone was long gone before proceeding to falsify the polling numbers posted at the Thomas Corner Store. Using his shirttail, he erased the tallied total for D.W. Monroe—changed it from sixty to fifty-nine.

It was blatantly obvious to Mr. John Thomas the next morning—the intended meaning and the specific person whose vote the perpetrator had wished to eliminate. He promptly corrected the misdemeanor before anyone saw and decided to cancel Harvey Hall's running tab.

25

LOVE AND GRATITUDE

SPRING 1913 - SPRING 1914

*M*ary sat in her garden, navigating from the place she'd been in her dream—in timeless morning—worlds away from Cascade and the dramatics of yesterday's election. It was a different land. Maybe Africa, she reckoned. Colors bright and alive. With music. Deep beats of drums and whistling flutes baiting all kinds of rhythm crisscrossing into pulses that swept everyone, all the happy people, to their feet.

Jumping. Swinging. Singing. Celebrating. Earth to Stars.

Reaching to the morning sky, she swayed, thinking. In the dream I felt euphoric, felt like I could dance forever. Leaping! Then … Standing on the shore. A huge white sandy shore. Facing. Meeting the ocean. Gentle, lapping. Colors of turquoise and jade.

Walking into. The ocean embraced me.

I knew how to swim. I swam beyond the waves. Saltwater holding me. Raising me up. Offered. Like a newborn babe. I spread my arms and legs. Floating. Like a star. Sparkling.

Drinking blue sky.

This dream, together with an emerging need to remain rooted to her soul, quaked an underpinning, a sixth sense that would not be ignored. She wasn't concerned that she didn't understand why.

It was in the House of the Well Fed an hour later that she overheard news that disturbed her quenched tranquility. According to local men jawing, it would be another month before Monroe and his aldermen officially took office and gained the right to govern. That left a rat's nest of time for Hall to get into lathers of falderal or bitterness or who knew what, she thought, sighing.

One more month …

Sorting things out at home, Mary processed J.C. Thompson's laundry order, dress shirts and long johns, with vigor, elbowing worry against the ridges of her washboard. Upset still, she scrubbed the floor. It wasn't until late afternoon, when she stepped outdoors, clippers in hand, that she calmed down as she cut sprigs of lilac and yarrow and arranged the juxtaposed scents into a lovely bouquet—for herself—a prize for the first colored woman to vote in Cascade, Montana—an American who shouldn't have to fret anymore, she thought, congratulating herself.

Warming weather told her it was time to plan her garden: design the pattern, choose the seeds, ready the soil for planting. This year it needed to be smaller, she reminded, in consideration of her knees that did not giddy-up and down the way they used to. Flowers were essential. Vegetables, delicious and also beautiful, would have to accept secondary positions.

She strung strings and twine that she had saved and tied together during winter, around nails she hammered into place on her fence, equidistantly high and low to fashion the warp of an acute-angled web. She stretched the lines taut. Sweet peas and green beans would share this lattice, flourish in the heat of the sun, as she did.

The Courier posted a Cascade city announcement, the date and time for the transfer of stewardship from council incumbents to the council elect. On May 5th, at seven-thirty in the evening, a small crowd pressed through the Opera House doors and into the chambers.

Mayor Hall, dressed in his finest, announced, "We, the Citizens' Party, the *first* elected officials of our fine City, Cascade, pass the torch of justice to D.W. Monroe, the second mayor, and his aldermen."

Stepping away from the chair at the head of the grand triple-leaf maple table, the legislative seat of the Council, Hall rolled a theatrical wave to the new incumbent, indicating transference of his authority.

As D.W. came forward, Hall, neglecting to shake the incumbent's hand, relocated to the folding-chair section. He watched as Monroe stood proudly, chivalrously gracing each of his aldermen with anecdotal compliments and pausing to provide brief intervals for applause before he extended invitations to come forward one at a time, and take the honorable, consummate place at the Council table.

Mary, who sat in the front row, clapped the loudest and the longest.

"Thank you for coming, everyone," Monroe finalized. "I'd like to take this opportunity to promise that my Aldermen and I will actualize our campaign initiatives during this term. Beginning now."

The new mayor grabbed the gavel to emphasize his pledge. The mallet did not budge.

Hall, who had cemented Cascade's symbolic sword of leadership to its block, and the table, snickered. Attention swerved in his direction. Groans of contempt were cast and thudded, it sounded to him, like clods of dirt falling on a coffin. His. He closed his eyes, furious that his disloyal aldermen had not laughed along with him.

Two days later, new gavel in hand, Mayor Monroe sidled up to the refinished table and struck three blows, commencing the first session of Cascade's new Council. "I call this meeting to order," his voice boomed, "the evening of May 7, 1913. Who is taking minutes until we have a Clerk?"

Appointments of officers and City employees were assigned. Demonstrating economy, D.W. consolidated the offices of City Attorney, City Clerk and City Treasurer into one position and selected Esquire E. B. Parsons for the prestigious post. George Woods, the Democrat who had withdrawn from their slate early in the campaign, was appointed Cascade Police Magistrate.

Past due contractor claims were scrutinized, then approved for payment.

An innovative resolution was passed: "Cleanup Day," an incentive for Cascade residents to tidy their yards and alleys, annually, beginning seven days hence, on May 14th; the article of said announcement to be published in *The Courier* the following day.

The Opera House grandfather clock struck ten tones, the agreed-upon number for closure. One last item of new business, an addendum D.W. had been plotting for months, was proposed, seconded and unanimously passed. A single gavel strike, followed by "Meeting adjourned," concluded the proceeding.

Mayor Monroe headed directly to Mary Fields' house and knocked several times before he heard footsteps coming near.

Clad in slippers, robe and a flannel sleeping cap, Mary, after insisting and receiving identification of her caller, opened the door.

"D.W.! What brings you over?" She rubbed her eyes. "Is Hattie—are the boys—"

"Everyone's just fine, Mary. May I come in?"

"Of course." She stepped back, watched to see that he slid the lock shut.

"Miss Fields," he began and then paused, suddenly aware that he had woken her. After clearing his voice, he announced, "With heartfelt congratulations, I bear good news from your new City Council."

She took another step back.

"An amendment to Cascade's first Ordinance has been passed. I quote: 'Ordinance Number One is amended as follows: As of today, May 7, 1913, one woman and one woman only, Miss Mary Fields, is hereby awarded unconditional access to all saloons in Cascade, Montana.'"

"Oh, my Lord, D.W.! I thought you—Just me? I—Thank you." She pressed her heart. "I'm free to go into any saloon? Anytime?"

"Yes. Long as you'd like. And you can smoke your cigars, if you please."

Words seemed inadequate for such welcome news. She offered her hand, shook his with a sagacious pioneer grip.

"And," he titillated, "As Mayor and as the new proprietor of the Silver Dollar Saloon," he raised his thick eyebrows, "I'd like to invite you over to my establishment for celebratory toasts in your honor. Whenever it's convenient."

"You bought the saloon? Well. I hardly accept." A girlish grin of innocence, given her years, glowed. "My Lord. Unanimously. On all counts."

"Goodnight, Mary. And God bless you for being so good natured about the unjust barrier that is now, finally, rescinded." He tipped his hat.

Fire in the potbelly hissed. "Oh. That reminds me. Ordinance No. 2 will allow birthday parties. Yours, anyway, at the schoolhouse." He closed the door, making a mental note to see it through.

Mary remained standing; stunned, warm. Her heart welled as though the morning star had risen in her honor. She'd go to the Silver Dollar tomorrow, in the afternoon, when checkers and chessboards would be laid out waiting. Customers would be happy to see her. There would be celebrating. She hoped it would be hot. Hot enough to fry eggs on a rock.

"Whoopee!"

What was it I said? Frosting on the cake will arrive once I vote and D.W. wins? Maybe better times are here to stay. Buttermilk, instead of plain.

"Yippee!"

D.W. chronicled his civic activities to Hattie: acquisition of a new gavel, Council progress, unanimous votes that would please her. "We amended the first Ordinance. Made an exception to it. Mary Fields is allowed in the saloons now. She was so thrilled when I told her—thought she was going to keel over. Let's go to bed."

"Only one exception?" asked his wife, "I'm surprised you didn't include all women. Didn't your campaign promise equal rights?"

He glanced her way, unsure if she was jesting, and unbuckled his belt. "Wanted to get it through fast. Besides, good Christian women would have no desire to enter saloons. You're the wife of a saloon owner, and you don't harbor inklings to go inside dim lit drinking holes, do you?" Shivering, he turned the pendent light-switch off and slipped under the covers.

"I'm glad for Mary," she uttered, in bed and rolled to her side. She pulled blankets over her eyes and planned a future with independence.

The imagery she summoned refused to crystallize.

She changed then, to the sounds of water pooling, swirling and bubbling. Saw herself, attaché case in hand, wearing success and an exquisite feather hat—a future in which Hattie had, in addition to exercising her state and national suffrage rights, actively introduced local change. She searched her mind for the vocation—the civic contribution she would make and profit from—a typing service—a business college for young women?

D.W. started to snore.

She thought of her parents and of the importance for preparation—training to allow for opportunities—like drops of water filling a reservoir. *A natural vision*, she heard her inner voice say as she dozed off.

Spring and summer of 1913 were good seasons for Mary Fields. Her garden grew rich with flowers—enough for the Catholic altar, herself, Hattie and the Silver Dollar. Wounds of exclusion began to heal.

When she felt the need to socialize, she would saunter to a Cascade drinking hole, where she would orate one or two personal episodes from the legendary Star Route Mail Carrier era, edge-of-the-buckboard-seat frontier narratives animated with scintillating flare. Details of perilous mishaps or mysteries or triumphs that took place in the region's mountains, buttes and prairies in wilder days: tales known by the Birdtail freighter who had survived all kinds of danger during the past three decades.

She had grown to like being addressed as Mary, without *Black* or *Nigger* stuck to the front of it; and reinforced this preference by referring to herself as *Mary Fields* or *Star Route Mary* when engaged in the telling of her stories and when introducing herself to strangers.

In late September, during the gold rush of autumn color when beloved aspens shimmied, Mary suddenly panicked. She couldn't remember when she'd last heard from Onatah. How could months had slipped by without her noticing? She had sent news to Onatah, hadn't she? Heralded the important school ballot victory and her supreme success as she placed her vote in the Cascade municipal election?

Unsure, she scowled, took a sip of water, set the glass down and hurried to her dresser. After digging through nightgowns in the bottom drawer she located two identical photographs. "Yes!" she declared, "I did send that photograph to Onatah. Me waving two flags, the resident school board voter."

She knew that Onatah had always responded quickly, and began to worry: had Onatah received my letter and forgotten to reply? She sat down and tried to remember writing that letter. Unsuccessful, she massaged her temple, trembled and fought off tears. What if something happened to Onatah or Edward or little Mary Ahwao? Or Isabel and Louie, and she had been fiddling around, preoccupied with her new saloon rights, telling stories. Was it time to leave? What had she promised? Winter was on its way.

After breakfast, she went to Hattie's, asked for a sheet of paper and envelope and single-footed, like her steed Lightning, she imagined, to the Silver Dollar, to the back table that she had claimed as her own. She scribed with fitful penmanship:

Dearest Onatah,

> *Where are you? I was listening to our music shaker trees, dozing off, when suddenly I woke up frightened. Worried about you. It was the worst feeling.*
>
> *I'm sorry if you wrote and asked me something and I don't know. I haven't gotten a letter from you for ages. More than a year I think.*
>
> *Last fall I voted in the school election. I sent you a photograph. Did you get it? This spring I was double victorious. Managed to be the only woman who voted in the City election.*
>
> *It was grand!*
>
> *Hall lost. My D.W. Monroe won.*
>
> *But that all means nothing if something has happened to you. My beautiful Onatah. Are you well?*
>
> *If someone else is reading this, what has happened to my Onatah?*
>
> *D.W. is Cascade's new mayor and the Council amended the bad ordinance. Now I am free to go to any saloon I want—a wonder as glorious as yellow glacier lilies busting through ice. I've been living it up, to be honest. Smoking a cigar once in awhile and telling stories from the Birdtail days. Free meals at the hotel. I do a little laundry and babysitting for cash. People treat me better now, mostly. I am very worried. Please write when you get this.*

> *Love always and forever,*
> *White Crow Fields*

P.S. Please write soon.

"Oh my God!" Onatah screeched, envelope in hand, "It's another letter from White Crow. Her third letter. She doesn't remember getting mine." Shoulder blades tightened. She twitched.

"I know she got my letter because she talked about it in her earlier letter. Her letter to me!" She grabbed Edward's work shirt, forced his full attention.

"Could she have suffered some kind of attack? Apoplexy?" he said, concerned.

"No, she can write. See?" She turned the inked page to him. "She's just forgotten …"

"What do you want to do?"

She pressed her lips together. "I would have gone to White Crow right after I saw that photograph of her—*last year*. The one of her wearing tattered clothes, looking absolutely indigent!"

"I know. I'm sorry, Onatah." He touched her shoulder.

She clasped his hand. "It's not your fault." Regrets stirred memories of the fall harvest that had been destroyed by fluke hail, and then, little Mary's fever in the spring that followed. Now she ached double-fold. Her frightened Ucsote believed that she, her little-bird daughter, had not answered. *For more than a year.*

She leaned against the counter, rubbed between her eyes. "*I did write*," she grieved. "But I didn't do as a daughter should—go find out what happened. She was wearing rags. And now she's scared. She's forgotten my letters, and she thinks something terrible has happened to us."

She pulled on her hair, looked to Edward. "We have to do something!"

Her unrelenting stare charred. "God only knows what shape she's in. And we promised. At least *I* did—to take care of her."

"I promised too, Onatah. I love her, too." He stared blankly at the small calendar tacked on the wall behind the counter.

"It's been over a year, Edward. I am so ashamed." She studied the lines of her uncared-for hands. "Now she talks about going to the saloon, telling strangers about her Star Route days." Onatah set the crumpled letter on the counter and pressed it open, gently stroked from center to each edge, tears welling. "My Ucsote is reduced to finding solace in her old age in a saloon. All she has left are her stories."

"Aaáh," Mary Ahwao called.

"She has us," Edward said, his voice trailing as he turned toward his daughter's voice, missing the heated angst in his wife's eyes.

"We have to go get her."

Footsteps pattered. "Ahwao, in here," Edward called.

"I can tell by her writing," Onatah said. "She's failing." She wrapped her unbuttoned sweater tight around her bodice and held herself. "Edward?"

"I'll find a way to get there, Onatah. As soon as I can. It may be spring."

She folded the wrinkled message of love and returned it to its envelope. "White Crow's worried about *us!*" she shouted, turned from him as she lifted Ahwao into her arms.

"What's wrong, Aaáh?" Little fingers wiped her mother's wet face.

"Spring may be too late." Onatah handed Mary Ahwao to her father, slipped the envelope, a pencil and an expired invoice taken from clutter on the counter, into her pocket and headed for the door.

Edward remained, listened to the door bang and ignored his daughter's babbling, watched Onatah grab some rope and streak across the field like an arrow, toward Bigg Too.

She slipped the makeshift halter over the gelding's ears and across his nose, and in one motion, slid onto his back. They galloped toward the mountains; her destination, the place of the May Day picnic.

Once arrived at the murmuring creek, she perched herself on the boulder where Mary had admired her "big picture." She sharpened the pencil and scribed on the back of the invoice:

October 5, 1913

Dearest Ucsote,

You are the very best woman I know. Don't be sad. Edward will come to get you as soon as he can. Meanwhile, I want you to remember to eat more than one meal a day at the hotel and enjoy yourself with your friends.

She stopped, wondering whether to explain to White Crow that she had forgotten—that she had, in fact, received and read a previous letter from Onatah, perhaps two. She began a second paragraph:

Not all mail carriers are as reliable as you, Mary F. Fields. It appears that something may have happened to the letters that I posted to you—my letters that contained my heartfelt congratulations for your success in the school election. I received your photograph and will always treasure it. I stare into your ever-kind eyes and send you my love—my beautiful Ucsote who celebrated her American citizen right to vote. Hooray to you, Mary White Crow Fields.

When you wrote to Edward and I last spring, to announce your second remarkable feat, we held our breath, amazed. You told us that you were the only woman allowed to vote in Cascade's official municipal election—the same election that enabled you, White Crow, to place your vote for the mayoral candidate of your choosing. You were part of the pivotal force that created your newly gained, entitled freedom.

You must feel unharnessed. Like a crow, flying free. How I long to see you. Now you can stroll about Cascade, come and go as you please and choose your company. Have they changed the ordinance to reinstate your birthday parties at the school? I'm sure the children are looking forward your celebrations as much as I did, and still do. You have had twenty-seven birthdays in the Birdtail, White Crow. Don't forget how many of us love you. If you need help, call upon Hattie Monroe, or Mr. and Mrs. Wolf, or Mr. Cornell.

Is there a special place, a tin or a cigar box where you can save the letters I send to you? That way, you can read them again when you wish.

I have exciting news. Edward and Louie will soon set to work, building you a cabin next to ours. When you arrive in Saypo, you will have your very own house, and you can do whatever you wish. All right? I am looking forward to having you with us. Mary Ahwao can share stories with you. She is learning how to read! You two can take turns imagining, reading cloud stories and playing games on picnic blankets in the sun.

Please remember to stay warm. Do you have a winter coat? And winter boots? Please tell me, so I won't worry. We will be together soon. As soon as spring flowers bloom. Perhaps before, if we can manage. I love you, White Crow. May you always have sweet dreams, and always remember that we love you dearly. Soon we will all be together.

Hugs and Kisses,
Your loving daughter, Onatah

P.S. State suffrage will pass before we know it. We will go to the polls together. Won't it be grand? Why were you the only woman allowed to vote in the City election? That's a story I want to hear.

Mary borrowed Lester's magnifying glass and sat at her kitchen table, determined to read Onatah's words that looked so small; writing that, at first glance, looked to her more like chicken scratch than cursive handwriting from one of Saint Angela's best pupils.

Employing great lengths of patience, she persevered through each paragraph, thinking it was a lot like freighting a buckboard wagon through rough terrain, landing bump upon bump followed by brief straight-aways where she sometimes sighted buffalo scat or deer drinking in waterholes. She wished J.T. was still alive to help her find things. She reread two important sentences: *Edward and Louie will soon set to work, building you a cabin next to ours. When you arrive in Saypo, you will have your very own house, and you can do whatever you wish.*

Dizzy from the news and upset to think she had doubted, or forgotten, she reeled, stood up and straightened herself, stepped outside to find fresh air and greet the crow perched on her dried sweet pea vines. Relief settled, and she sat on the tree stump.

From the core of her being, a sliver of happiness began to rise. She reviewed: Onatah was proud of her. Happy for her. Interested in all of her Ucsote's life. Most of all, the whole family loved her so much they were building her a house, a cabin safe and warm, next to them, for her to live with them, forever.

The immensity made her quiver. Did she dare to embark on this quest for happiness? The freedom of love in a family? She would. There was no longer any reason not to.

It was a secret. She would not tell anyone. When spring came, she would pack and be ready. Edward and Onatah would come get her—she would settle up with Mr. Wolf—kiss Hattie and the boys goodbye—and be on her way. She sighed a deep sigh. The sky smiled. The whole universe smiled, it felt like to her.

Following Onatah's suggestion, Mary refolded the letter from her little bird, placed it in the cigar box that Mr. John Thomas had given to her, (a poor replacement for the Great Whizzer Pigeon, but functional) and hid it under her bed.

As holidays neared, Mary found herself turning more often to the devoted family that was constantly available: her steadfast ancestors. She invited them in for solstice (the longest night of the year) to join a candlelit ceremony and share company beneath midwinter's cloak. She hummed, lonely for the sound of an intimate human voice.

Centered in solstice darkness that night, she intoned: I am the lucky one who received the answer to your prayers, my beloved family. I am here in America embracing what many of you had in Africa. Freedom. I think that's true. You other precious souls whose lives were captured … I want to reach you through this flame: candlelight to starlight, to heavens that sparkle and connect us. You—and me, our shared destiny.

I want you to know that I thank you deeply for the steadfast strength and faith it must have taken for you to carry on … for the risks you took to make a better future for your children and grandchildren … You set the fires to free our lives, fought for us before we were even born.

We did it. Tipped the wrong back towards right. I want you to share the bounty. You can be proud. You hear me, don't you?

Yes. I know you do.

Please, don't worry anymore. Me too, I am not worried. I hope you are resting, and I hope you are free.

Some days later, after a frightening Birdtail sleigh ride championed by his old bay workhorse, Herman Wolf trudged through Mary's yard of hard-cracked ice that had proved too difficult for her to clear. He knocked a familiar chorus of repeats, dubbed by Mary as Herman's red-bellied-woodpecker improvisation.

She rushed him into the warmth.

"Black Mary. This is for you, from Gerlach." He handed her a large oval tin, the object he had clutched under his arm.

Herman's coat, hat and gloves shaken and hung, Mary directed her guest to the chair by the stove, the center of her house. She dragged another chair to sit close.

"Gerlach says to say Merry Yuletide Christmas and many returns. She wants to know if you are well and if you're getting enough to eat."

Mary pulled the lid off. "Sugar cookies!" she cooed, "with frosting. Umm. How beautiful."

Gerlach can see so well, she thought to herself.

"Like to admire them as much as I like to eat them," Herman disclosed and pointed. "See the trees? And Saint Klaus?"

"Yes. Pink and green and white frosting. They're like paintings or ornaments on a tree. Lovely. Have one, Herman." She handed the tin back to him and got up. "What kind of tea would you like? Got assam and mint."

"Whichever tastes more like coffee."

He stayed longer than she thought he would, and she appreciated it. Gerlach seldom came to town anymore, and Mary hadn't been out to the Birdtail since she had signed the legal house and will papers at their kitchen table.

Herman talked about bushels of wheat from the fall harvest, his cattle and his new Jersey milk cow. She filled him in on local gossip—the men's. Both agreed that things in the town—city, rather—had changed for the better under the new council's rule.

When he mentioned his brother, John, the lawyer in Idaho, and his brother's wife who had just given birth to the couple's first son, name of Gunther, Herman's first American nephew—Mary decided to entrust the letters she had written to accompany her will, into Herman's care. She felt they would be safer with him.

"Mr. Wolf?"

He raised his head. "Mister? Name's Herman to you!"

She laughed. "Would you put this envelope with my last testament? In your safe?"

"Don't have a store-bought safe, Black Mary, but just as good." He could see it was important. "Don't you worry, will see to it when I get home."

"And will you give something to Gerlach for me?" She'd been racking her brain to come up with a suitable reciprocal gift. "Just a minute. Wait here."

Rushing to her wardrobe, she dug for the raccoon hat she had received in the box of hand-me-downs from the Methodist ladies two years ago. It was too-fancy for her, she had decided, and she'd saved it, sure that it would be perfect for someone needing to keep warm in the elements, while milking cows or doing some other chore in the frigid winds.

She smiled, thinking she'd found its rightful owner at last, and thumbed through a stack of papers she had neatly pressed with her heavy coal iron. Locating a large sheet, she wrapped, folding the ends into a design of pleats, double tucked, her back to Herman so he couldn't see. Finishing, she wrapped the bundle with pink string, string from the Hong Chong Laundry, she recalled, struggling to undo the original knot.

"Here, Mr. Herman. Please tell Gerlach, Mrs. Wolf, Merry Christmas from Mary with hardy thanks for the artwork cookies!"

He put the bundle on his lap, set his cup and saucer on the stove. "All right," he said, "I'll tell her. There's something I've been meaning to ask."

"Shoot." She sat down.

"On election day, when you got shuffled into line after you'd already voted—did you vote, again?"

"Oh. I wanted to tell you and forgot."

She took a sip of tea. "I started to leave the line and go on home." She sipped again. "Then I realized: I can't do that, they'll think I was bullied and gave up—think I kowtowed to them and groveled home, tail between my legs." She rubbed her neck. "Couldn't do that. So I waited in line, got a second ballot, as you know. Waited a whistle-stop of time in the stall, and then put the blank ballot in the box." She crossed her leg. "Couldn't have lived with myself, otherwise. Wasn't right to take advantage. Specially of something so important." Her eyes met his. "Ya know?"

"Thought that was what you'd say. Was curious how you went about it. They'll never know." Smile lines creased, and he winked. "Best be going."

Herman outfitted his winter layers into place, flipped one earflap down.

Mary handed the pleated package over and asked him to protect her letter, same as if it were a ballot. "Put it inside your overcoat, please," she added, and wondered why he had homesteaded in the Birdtail prairie, exactly, wondered if he had told her already.

"Be safe, Mr. Herman," she said as she held the door open.

He pulled his wool hat down, crunched on old snow and into new slurries—signaled her to stay put. "So long," he shouted.

Inside, she stood facing it, the door she had latched shut, the front of her cold, her backside warm. An odd feeling nudged her attention and she strolled across the room to her table, slid her finger along its length and across, inhaling confidence from years gone by, a grand number of them, when she could whup whatever darkened her door with relative ease.

"Home is where the heart is," she said, and opened the tin of cookies. She set two on a plate, poured a large glass of milk, sat down and took a bite of Gerlach's Saint Klaus. As she tasted its sweetness, she stared at the empty place where she had stood by the door, as if observing her personal-self as it waved goodbye only moments earlier.

Inspired, she gathered some pine branches she had clipped earlier and crafted a simple centerpiece, lit the candle she had placed in its center and returned to her chair to admire the arrangement—lush greens garnishing the brightness. She pulled her shawl tight and breathed the pungent scents. Raising her glass, she toasted, "I'm happy. And I'm free. And people love me."

She tipped the bill of her cap, took a deep breath and said, "Mary Fields, why don't you fix yourself some oolong tea and have another cookie?" She raised her chin and replied, "Why yes, I think I will."

A measure of time later, weather warmed. Hattie tried patiently, as only a mother would, to explain the purpose of May Day again: wading through innocent peak-and-valley lapses of attention, corralling Earl more often than Lester, back to her point: "You need to show people that you love them. So they know, because it's usually those same people, who love you. You're old enough. It's part of becoming a good man."

Lester reddened, wretched invisible hairballs from his gut. "Ew. Hearts and flowers ... Mother!"

Earl grinned, tickled to see his brother upset, until his shin took the brunt of Lester's kick beneath the table "Ow! Mama, Les—"

"Lester, you want to become a good man, don't you?" Hattie asked, standing up. "I almost hate to tell you," she emphasized as she stepped to the stove, her back to her boys. "It's a lot of fun. Children your age used to have to win a lottery to go on the May Day Picnic led by your very own babysitter."

"What's a lotter?" Earl asked.

She turned to face her eldest. "I'm not sure you're ready to be a May Day giver."

Lester glared at the floor and spurred, "I can do it if I want, like Papa. But there's nothing fun about picking flowers."

He considered the picnic part he hadn't heard of before, keeping his upset feelings buttoned until he knew more.

"You see, dear, after one has picked the flowers, one has to figure a way to be invisible. If you are seen, you have failed your mission. One has to make a fast getaway." She chattered on, extolling the risks and challenges that were many and could only be met by the cleverest athletes and the most expeditious—like baseball hall-of-fame players, or pirates, she mentioned.

Lester laced his fingers together, feigning indifference. Gaping askance, he pretended he could take it or leave it, since he was already the bravest pirate in the world, although invisibility did sound exciting.

He waited it out, hunkered over an empty plate, scraping the floor with his foot. Eventually, when he thought his mother would be teary for the wait of his decision, he lifted his head and saw that she was wide-eyed, as calm as he. He offered to do the deed, for her, if she would yield to his buccaneer conditions: *that Earl and he do it alone.* And that their rightful booty included *a picnic with trout fishing.* And she could come, too.

"We are perfectly able," he summarized, glancing to his brother, speaking words that his father had spoken with apparent success, "I'll take care of it. As you wish, Mother. Will you make us the picnic, and we'll go fishing?"

"Agreed, young man," Hattie said, hiding her pleasure. "Bring the flowers home, and I'll put ribbons on them. Better get going. Take your pocketknife, Lester."

The boys marched out the back door, the elder instructing, "Look for the best flowers, Earl. But we can't take them from the neighbors. I promised."

"They have to be wild," Earl said, repeating his mother, stopping to look at a fat-bellied robin that pecked its yellow beak, pulled a worm from the section of newly tilled earth that would soon transform into his mother's vegetable garden.

They walked south. Lester wished he'd had the foresight to bring something in which to hide the sissy items and hoped he would not run into any girls from school. He took Earl in hand and headed toward the creek bed tucked in a gully not far from city limits.

"It's May Day," Earl sang as they lumbered along. "Lester, did you ever go on one of those May Day Picnics with Mary, like Mama was talking about? I'm hungry."

"It was before we were born, Earl."

It occurred to Lester to pick extra flowers to give to his mother. He decided not to share this idea with his little brother who always got his way by simpering, clinging to their mama's apron, and blinking what she called, "those big brown eyes," in order to get hugs and kisses on his cheek. No, Captain Lester would capture that May Day happiness his Mother had described as delectable treasures one could measure only by gratitudes pledged from the receiver.

"De-lick-able," he considered. It sounded sweet, like a lollipop.

The pirates returned an hour later, undetected—Lester giving Earl, the mate he had instructed to carry the loot, a slight push through the back door as they entered their house.

"Mama, we got them," Earl said proudly. "The violets are the prettiest." Hattie kissed Earl's blonde hair, her babe who was growing up too fast, and patted Lester's shoulder, her first-born who already pretended to act aloof and unaffected by her expressive overtures—though his love for her remained true, she was sure—and she was proud.

"Lester, would you hold the posies in a bundle while I tie the ribbon," she asked, and he complied. "These are so beautiful, and so many, a good variety for this time of year," she praised, shaping a double bow.

"Those are violets, Mama," said Earl. "Does Mary like violets?"

Hattie reminded them how important it was for the receiver not to discover who the giver was: a benevolent exercise, she thought, to give without expectation. Rich by means of moral amplitude, her husband would say—

"Now, when you've accomplished your May Day magic, your successful endeavor, having witnessed how delighted the receiver is sure to feel ...

Remember what she says and come home to tell me all about it. I'll be preparing our picnic," she prompted.

"Here, Earl," Lester instructed, "Take the box of flowers to the front yard and wait." He rushed toward his room before Earl could object and when his brother was out of sight, turned about-face, scurried past his mother and out the backdoor. He grabbed the balsam sunflowers he had stashed behind the outhouse, put them inside a crate under his father's worktable in the toolshed and ran out front where he found Earl sitting cross-legged staring at puffy clouds.

"The flowers need to be in the shade," Lester said as he swooped in, grabbed the box and placed it under the eve of the house. "There." After a sigh, he pointed to the apple tree and ordered in a throaty baritone, "First mate Earl, report to the apple tree!"

Earl, distracted by distant sounds of whirring metal, waited for the long shrill that reliably sounded between breakfast and dinner. He hunched to the ground, hoping to catch the timbre he knew by heart.

"Earl—"

Earl listened to his brother's voice fuse into the steam engine's wail, heard it give way before the *Great Northern's* final toot.

"Do you want to have an adventure, or not?" Lester bated.

"Yes, sir!" Earl grinned, jumped to attention and saluted.

"See this?" Lester pointed the large tree, full leafed and in blossom. "It's not our tree today, it is our lookout, our crow's nest." He shot a glance, unsure if Earl remembered what a crow's nest was. "We'll climb up there like pirates setting sails high on the ship's mast. And we will be very quiet, surveying people coming and going."

"You mean, spying?"

"Race ya," Lester kicked off his shoes and scrambled up the tree's trunk using practiced toe grips.

"Wait for me!" Earl screeched.

"Hide yourself in the leaves, Earl—I mean, mate. And don't make a sound."

"Help me up!"

Lester extended an arm, pulled Earl to the first branch.

"Smells pretty, like Mama's perfume."

"I said, be quiet. Pretend you're invisible and don't move. If people see us it won't work."

Earl, confused about what exactly wouldn't work, didn't ask. He did as he was told and scooted onto the strong branch nearest the one where Lester had mastered a leg-lock and leaned back against the ragged trunk, nonchalant, as usual. Earl hugged the tree with both arms and pressed his face to its cool surface, hiding apprehension that eased when he noticed the expansive view.

Are we really invisible, he wondered, deciding they must be if Lester said so. Passersby strolled beneath them and across the street, unaware of their presence. It was magical—the people walking, pausing, talking—so close he could hear their words, yet they did not see him. He questioned whether it was only voices that needed to be silent, having noticed that people often turned when he stared, and decided that he should just pretend to be a bird, like the robin, and sun himself, carefree.

Minutes later, he whispered, "Lester, are we watching for Nigger Mary?"

"Mama said to call her Mary Fields, Earl. Yes. Shush."

"There she is," he exclaimed, releasing one arm to point. "She's coming to town."

"Hurry. Get down. We have to go," Captain Lester ordered.

On the ground, Lester grabbed the cardboard treasure chest, checked the condition of their bouquet and hurried his sidekick through the alleys. Minutes later, he instructed his first mate to climb a second tree and watch for Mary Fields again.

"Stay in the lookout post until you see her return *and* go inside her house."

Earl was getting hungry but didn't say.

"We can talk," Lester said after awhile, bored for the waiting, lounging on the tree's lower limb, "until we see Mary Fields. Then you have to be quiet. All right?"

"All right."

They clung to their mission and the graceful elm, wishing that it had apples or apricots or something to chew—then played the "I spy" guessing game their father had taught them: a player described an object (within view and unidentified to the other) by its general size and shape until their opponent guessed the specific item correctly—Earl interrupted Lester's puzzling depictions to remind his brother about the picnic and the fishing and the need to dig for worms.

After endless lengths of time, Mary Fields came into view. She unlocked her door and stepped inside, whistling a song Earl did not know and tried to memorize so that he could ask her about it later.

"This way," Lester charged, having thought it through during the wait. He took his brother by the hand and dashed a short distance before huddling in deep grass again. He explained, "We have to sneak up, the way we do at a fishing hole. We can't take any chance of letting her see us."

"All right."

"Follow me." Lester adapted his pace, allowing his brother to keep up—advanced through the willows and around the back of Mary's house. He took the posy from the box and passed the container to Earl—then paused and traded the hand-held objects—pressed the bouquet into Earl's soft hands and whispered, "Set it careful, by the door."

Earl felt the damp stems in his palm and sniffed the delicate blossoms that had been, a short while ago, part of the outdoors in grassy clefts they had discovered. He noticed how each half of the pretty bows perfectly matched the other, all loops the same.

He felt a nudge on his shoulder.

Alerted, he began his mission—trotted slowly toward the corner, then stalked—one step, then another, each with care, until he reached the door and set the May Day bouquet at its sill.

He glanced behind for his brother, who, to his surprise, leaned over him and knocked, employing the strength of a mighty sword wielding captain—loudly, so Mary Fields would hear. His mother had been specific.

"Run!" he cried.

Lester let Earl get a head start and was proud to watch him sprint like a spooked deer—limber, agile, only short legs slowing his propelled speed. He raced past, an arm's length ahead, to guide Earl's route—leaping, moments later, flat into tall reeds where they would be camouflaged yet maintain a clear view. Earl plopped beside him, catching his breath and Lester's order of silence made clear by pressing a finger to his lips. They waited.

Their personal own babysitter opened the door. To their delight, she turned her head—one way, then the other, shrugged her shoulders—started to shut the door.

They bit their lips and held breath. Willed her to look down.

She did.

"Oh, my Lord," she exclaimed, bending over. Gently she grasped at the blooms, lifted them to her face, oohing and aahing as she did. She looked around.

They ducked. Chins on damp dirt, they peeked between blades of grass; still, like hunted grasshoppers or rabbits.

"Happy Mary Day!" Earl belted.

Lester shoved him, shushed him with a threatening scowl and shook his head.

Mary camouflaged her recognition, stopped a jubilant grin from cracking the face she had tempered to appear stoic, and stood there, pretending to be perplexed for the benefit of her beloved holiday posy givers.

"I wonder who gave me these beautiful gorgeous May Day flowers," she cheered with glee.

Cupping hand to brow—she looked left, right, up and down, and repeated the enactment with due sincerity, twice.

"Whoever gave me these absolutely lovely colorful spring flowers, I thank you from the bottom of my heart and send you wishes for a very very happy May Day!"

Lester put his hand over Earl's mouth.

She had spotted them, her darlings, and turned the other direction, hollering once more, "Happy May Day, wonderful posy givers!"

She stepped inside. The door shut.

The boys were gripped by her absence, and the silence, and the honey-sweet feeling that accompanied their choice to disavow credit for their honorable deed. They looked to each other and smiled.

"Stay put for awhile," Lester advised, "She might come back," secretly hoping she would; it had felt so good.

They waited.

Mary knew better than to open the door again, take the risk of altering May Day protocol. "My favorite holiday," she said hugging her shoulders, admiring the gift already slipped into a cobalt glass jar.

A flash of delight swept her—weakened her knees, kindled her heart. She was still loved by someone. More than one. Waterfalls of memory flooded—the many wondrous May Day expeditions she had shared—the contagious joy that children, by their generous natures, expressed, giving flowers and good wishes and cheer.

Expertly backtracking and remaining out of sight, Lester and Earl headed home. Meandering through willow branches, touching slender bright green leaves that decorated agile branches arched low, past their shoulders—and seeing in a distance, the thick steady current of the *Missouri*—they lollygagged, savoring secret treasures.

"Mama was right," said Earl.

"Yeah," Lester shucked. He put his arm around his brother, his very own brother, and they walked side-by-side. The May Day giving of sunflower posies to his Mama would include Earl, he decided, standing tall—more like a mayor than a pirate.

26

ANTICIPATION

SPRING - FALL 1914

Around the time Mary tossed her dried up wilted May Day flowers into the compost heap, she began to wonder when her cabin in Saypo might be ready. If the constructing hadn't begun last fall, she considered, it was unlikely things would be underway until about now. Maybe she'd be moved in time for the turn of aspens, in time to cozy up by winter fires with Mary Ahwao, the way she and Nadie and Onatah had done, way back when.

She sipped tepid tea from the cup she had left on the tree stump, earlier, when she decorated the fence and the ground beneath her clotheslines with a mazy trail of sunflower seeds and waited to see when the local crow clan would come to investigate. Excited to see the birds swoop—arranging toes and talons to perch with agile finesse, twisting necks to get a good look— Mary chuckled, knowing her presence would not deter their fondness for puzzles and food.

Leaning against her house, she watched a youngster clutch one seed at a time, tilt the position of his beak and cast a swing-toss to his friend who after several attempts, snagged a treat, circled left, cracked the shell and crunched with great satisfaction. Another adolescent hopped along the fence. Mary thought the fellow looked as if he were dancing a jig, sporting his strut and twist moves without knocking a single seed from the ledge. Others tipped their fine glossy bills to scoop seeds into open mouths, totes to carry the cache, intent on dining in private locations or sharing with family—chicks and eggs nestled in treetops nearby. Elders placed themselves at cornerstone outlooks where they flapped and squawked advisory warnings, as needed.

Mary's favorite, Granddaddy B.O.B, had arrived. Stationed out of sight, on the ridge of the roof where he sunned himself, he perused the goings-on and waited for the food she brought to him every morning without fail. The ritual had begun three springs past when he had injured his leg.

On cue, Mary placed his allotted pancake on the stump, lifted a smile and sang out, "Good morning to you, my Big Old Blessing ... I know you're here ... thanks for bringing your clan to grace my little garden today."

B.O.B. coasted down, spreading an enormous span of graphite wings above his property. He snatched a nibble and piped melodious caws of approval. Having perfected a system, he folded one edge of the soft disk to the other, repeated the exercise once more and transported his breakfast to his roost, the highest fencepost. He rotated his head to spot Mary and squawked again.

His favorite human warbled back, "Life would not be the same without you, B.O. B. Yes sir'ee, my fine feathered friend." She swallowed the last of her tea, hefted the sack of seeds onto her hip and wondered how she would ever tell him she was leaving when the time came.

That afternoon, absorbed in her game of solitaire at the Silver Dollar, someone approached and tapped her on the shoulder. She looked up, startled not to have noticed, and leapt from her chair to give him a hefty hug. "Edward, my dear Edward," she cried. Slipping her deck of cards into her apron pocket, she said, "Let's go," pulled his arm and led him toward the door, waving to the barkeep as she spouted, "This is my friend, Mr. Edward Bruneau."

Edward nodded, hand to hat brim, grinning.

"He's come to visit me."

The door slammed. Heads turned to the window, mulling the unexpected news.

"Is Onatah all right? And everyone?"

"Yes, White Crow, fine. It's good to see you, as always." He put his arm around her.

"Lordy, you sure surprised me." She had forgotten earlier thoughts about the cabin. "Why are you here?"

"Business and pleasure. You're the pleasure."

She laughed.

Minutes later they arrived at her house. He noticed that the sign in her window, "Mary's Laundry," had slipped—a neglected presentation that could cause new customers to hesitate, he thought—he would fix it when she wasn't looking. He watched her push the door open nonchalantly; she had lost the key weeks earlier and the need to dawn a search had continually slipped her mind. She, of all people, should know she's putting her safety at risk, he tallied.

"Come on in," she invited, swinging the door ajar, stepping back to wave her guest ahead.

"Ladies first, White Crow."

"White Crow, like the sound of that." She straightened her cap and walked through, toward the cupboard.

"It's chilly," said Edward, as he set his case down. Proceeding as if he were at home, he crumpled sheets of old newspaper stacked next to a small pile of wood near the stove. No kindling in sight, he told her he'd make some, grabbed the hatchet by the side door and stepped out.

Mary poured water from pitcher to bowl, splashed to rinse her face, swung a quick glance at the mirror, too fast to acquire detail, pinched her cheeks to look pretty. She heard B.O.B. squawk as she opened the lid to her cookie jar. It was empty. She filled the water kettle, scowling, and bit on her longest fingernail, scanning the room for ideas.

Edward returned, made a fire and a mental note that the woodpile was near gone. Though it was spring, there was still need for another cord for evenings. He thought of Onatah and the list of things she had asked him to examine and went outside to wash his hands at the pump. Upon his return he saw Mary spooning dried herbs into her teapot and slipped by her to retrieve a gift from his leather case.

She turned.

"Close your eyes and put your hands out," he prompted. She felt cool metal on her palms, looked to see a shiny square tin and smiled. "Can I open it?"

"Of course. All three women had a hand in it," he said, watching. "They all send more love than you can imagine." He thought he saw blushing rise.

"Yum! My favorite! Onatah knows, doesn't she?"

"Nothing would please her more than to provide you with all your favorites, White Crow." She held it to her chest as though she was hugging her little bird, then arranged the delicious looking oatmeal-raisin cookies on a plate, doubly grateful—a gift and a solution to her hostess dilemma. She let her shoulders down, poured boiling water into her china teapot and motioned Edward to her rocker. Been ages since I had an oatmeal raisin cookie, she thought.

He grabbed a chair from the table, set it next to her rocker by the potbelly, leaned back and waited.

"So what was your business about?" she asked.

"I delivered hardware to a store in Great Falls. Turns out we have several blacksmiths in Saypo—they forged a collection of latches, handles and hinges of varied size and application. I helped to negotiate a contract so that the enterprise has a better chance of remaining solvent. Exquisite work, really—European, American and original design."

"You knew how to do that from working with your father?" she asked.

"Mostly. It provided the opportunity Onatah and I had been waiting for—to see you." Sitting close gave him time to examine the state of her clothes, a high priority in his wife's opinion, and a valid indication of certain health and economic issues."

Mary chewed on a second cookie, decided not to ask why Onatah had not come with him, figured there were plenty of good reasons and advised herself not to take it personal.

Edward was glad that Onatah had not insisted on coming. Mary's house was in disarray, just as his wife had feared. Levels of clutter, dust, ash and wood chips altered an indisputable history of tidiness. Onatah would have gone frantic at the implications; he could do as much as she for the time being, he determined; his wife had enough to do caring for the family, designing school lessons, teaching classes ...

"I have great news, he announced, sharing a satisfied grin as he tipped his chair on back legs. We got our official Homestead Owner Certificate. After five years of proving up, meeting all the requirements, we have the patent, signed and sealed, validating one-hundred and sixty acres as our property."

"Yea!" Mary cheered. "Nobody can take it away from you. It's yours forever, and you can pass it down. Little Mary won't have to move anywhere unless she chooses to."

As Edward let his chair down, Mary patted his knee. "I'm mighty proud of you and Onatah. Your own land. And you're taking care of your parents and everything else. You chose the high road, Edward—you're committed to your family and your community. And you're a good man. Always knew that. You sure you need an old lady to take care of?"

"What old lady?" he swung around, agape. "By any chance are you referring to the legendary ageless Star Route Mail Carrier? The woman we've been begging to join us for years?

He leaned in. "Speaking of care, there is a family waiting for you to join them on the homestead, White Crow." We want Little Mary Ahwao to know you, as we have. She still asks for you, by the way." He mimicked the little voice, "Where's—ite Crow?" and took a proud breath. "You should hear her chattering fragments of French, English and Blackfeet into her own prosaic verse.

Mary warmed from the confirmation she'd been seeking. Thoughts of Mary Ahwao delivered joy and a familiar ache. "Want to help me in the garden today?"

"Yes, ma'am. Put me to work."

Edward rolled up his sleeves, glad to do something physical after parleys of business negotiations the day prior.

She laughed. "Got a hefty compost pile outside, needs big muscle for turning."

"Is that the secret to your grand flowers? They must love you, White Crow—always twice the size of everyone else's."

Outside, he grabbed the shovel propped against the house, held her hand as they walked to the end of the garden plot. "Onatah always says you're the life and breath of plants; she claims that you have an intimate understanding."

He enjoyed showering her with compliments; knew they were well deserved.

She loved hearing his praise, free from the need to be wary. Blarney or no, it fueled her spirit.

He looked at the pig-sized pit. "This is what you want turned?"

"And chopped, if you don't mind."

She carried her bucket to the other side, flipped it over and sat down while Edward dug the shovel into the heap of food scraps, leaves and vegetable discards that had been dumped but left to decompose without assistance.

He added straw and manure from separate heaps nearby. The unpleasant stink of rot indicated that she had not been turning the ingredients—which implied, to him, a physical limitation to do so. The wet mass was heavy, concentrated. He wondered how she got these leftovers home from the restaurant. Did she walk the streets carrying a bucket of restaurant garbage? If so, she would be ridiculed.

He borrowed her bucket seat to gather wood ash from the stove. While inside, he noticed the empty laundry pots stacked on the floor, dry and caked with mineral residue. Supposing the clothesline would be likewise empty, he glanced through the kitchen window, and allowed his eyes to rest, momentarily, on lengths of limp rope undressed. He thought about asking if anyone helped her with heavy chores—wood, for example, and decided against it. Returning with the bucketful of ash and burnt charcoal, he dumped it into the compost mix and returned the container to its place, bottom up.

Mary reclaimed her seat.

He grabbed the rusted pitchfork he found leaning against what had been a doghouse and bore its prongs to aerate the coarse weight. Afterwards, he used the tip of the shovel to chop and cut the mass into smaller pieces and covered the half-full hole with a piece of scrap wood.

"I had to live in Cascade, here in this house, until I got the city vote. You understand?" Mary announced in a serious tone.

He paused. "What do you mean?" He speared the shovel's tip into the earth, rested his boot upon it, gave his full attention.

"I mean that's why I didn't move like Onatah wanted me to, before. Just saying that's why, is all." She rubbed the back of her neck, stretched the soreness left and right, stopped to look into his eyes. "Still like to come live with you folks, if you'll have me." She hawk-watched his response.

"I thought we settled all that. Onatah says you agreed. I'm going to build your cabin, soon as possible. It would have been built already, had it not been for father's fall. I'm managing the store now. And I have acres of fencing to put up and projects on both homesteads.

"You said everyone is fine. What happened to dear Louie?"

"He will be fine. He broke his leg in a logging accident last November. We hired a neighbor to help, but there's enough work for—"

"An army, I imagine," Mary filled in. "I don't feel right about coming empty-handed, Edward."

He took his hat off, wiped sweat from his brow with a bandana pulled from his pocket. "Nothing about you is empty-handed, White Crow."

"Should you and I barter a contract like you did with the businessman in Great Falls?"

"If that's what you want, but there's no point. Our invitation is not contingent upon services provided by you. You've been Onatah's mother all her life—I don't think she can truly remember her parents' faces. It was you who protected her, watched over her. She wouldn't be the person she is if it hadn't been for you."

He pushed the rim of his hat back. "She wants to take care of you. Has nothing to do with charity or you earning your keep. Has to do with love. Shall we leave it at that?"

"I'd be a kept woman," she proffered with a wink that Edward did not respond to, maintaining a gaze of earnest intent.

"Seems to me, White Crow, you're just the right age to be retired and loved." He stepped across the pit and squatted next to her, gave her the kind of hug reserved for mothers, rocked her with gentle motion.

She closed her eyes, felt the sun and his embrace.

He remembered Onatah's last words before he had left: *Thank you for being my eyes and ears ... get to the heart of it ... make sure the decision to move is truly hers ...*

"What do you say to a big glass of lemonade, Edward? I'm parched."

"Sounds perfect." He swished at the diminished number of flies, carried the shovel and rake in one hand, extended the other arm for Onatah's Ucsote to grasp as they walked back to the house, stopping to wash at the pump.

Inside, Edward tossed a small log into the potbelly.

Mary leaned over the cooler. "These lemons came all the way from California," she bragged, thinking of Mr. Stickney in the orange groves and Mary Amadeus walking on a stretch of sand. "Maybe you'll go there someday, Edward."

"I'd like to take you to the hotel for supper after our lemonade, White Crow."

"I usually go mid-day."

"That's past already. Today you have a supper partner, an escort. I need to check-in, anyway."

"You're not staying here? You're welcome—"

"Under orders. Onatah's. We don't want to cause you extra work, and I'm not going to argue with you about sleeping on the floor."

She smiled at his foresighted knowledge of her and the consideration. She nodded toward the water pitcher. "Would you get some fresh, from the pump?"

"Yes. And thank you for your invitation, just the same."

Quickly returned, he set the pitcher on the counter and sat at the table, positioned to observe, as promised.

Nothing seemed out of the ordinary. She poured sugar into the pitcher without measuring (he had never seen her use a measuring cup), placed a sieve over its top and squeezed every last drop of juice from the yellow orbs, then dropped them into a can for the compost. After adding water, she reached for two glasses and filled them at the counter. Moving in front of the vessels, he saw her do an odd thing: as she poured the lemonade from the pitcher, she slipped her idle hand over the lip of each glass, placed her index finger inside and held it still until the height of liquid met her touch.

She's seeing with her finger, he realized, surprised. What a clever adaptation. Onatah was right—Mary's vision is more than just a little compromised. He tried to think of ways to assess the quality of her distance sight—he would point out a bird, an automobile, a mountain peak, later.

"We're having dessert first," she said offering more of Onatah's cookies with their lemonade.

After chatting awhile longer, Edward got up and grabbed the pitcher.

"Can I pour you another?" he asked, filling her glass to the level she had marked previously.

"How long can you stay, Edward?"

"Until tomorrow or the next day," he said. "Will you take me to play checkers at the saloon, White Crow?" He didn't say … where I can investigate another of Onatah's requests, ferret whether you *really* have friends in the saloons as you claim.

"Yep. Best get ready. Maybe you'd like to water my seedlings in the garden?"

"Yes, I would. I'll wait for you outside," he said reaching for his hat. He watered her seedlings, cleaned his boots with a rag.

They walked the distance, three and one-half city blocks to the House of the Well Fed. He told her how nice she looked, that the colors of her skirt and blouse and scarf were cheerful, like her flowers. He carried his leather valise of clothes, papers and toiletries, cupping Mary's elbow to steady the gait of his family's unique relation.

After she was seated, he checked-in at the front desk and hurriedly changed clothes to rid himself of lingering compost scent, then returned to her company in the restaurant, wearing his new plaid cowboy shirt, blue jeans and a silver bolo engraved with the Bruneau brand, seventy-seven bar: 77.

She winked. "Must be handy to be seen as white once in awhile. I would have liked to have that chameleon trick up my sleeve a couple of times."

He chuckled, opened the menu, perused for a moment.

"What will you have, White Crow?"

"Thought we agreed—a new life with y'all, thank you, sir."

"Um, sounds delicious." Best news I've heard all day. "What would you like for an appetizer?"

"The roast beef special. Wait, that's only on Sunday. I'll have fried chicken."

Madeline the waitress arrived, raised an impish eyebrow at Mary and listened carefully to the gentleman who articulated their order, and went about her business.

"I always wondered, White Crow, if you don't mind my asking, why didn't you move to Great Falls, Helena or Seattle when you left the mission? Where you might have enjoyed a community with people of your race? That's why many people move to Saypo, for the comradery."

"Came to Montana in the dead of winter. Never seen so much white. Temperature low enough to snap anything—railcars, even. Arrived in

Helena." Her hands remained gripped to the opened House of the Well Fed menu. "Took the stagecoach to Dearborn and a wagon from there ... The crotchety 'ol geezer, owner of Stone Inn, was kind enough to drive us on what would've been a deer path if you could have seen it. My introduction to glacier wilds ..." She looked at him. "So cold, it drew breath from my bones. Couldn't stop shivering, and my skin burned from the dry. Anyhow, we came around this bend ... I'll never forget ... my jaw dropped and I was mesmerized, struck like lightning by the full view panorama of those gigantic majestic heart-stopping peaks—length of endless wonder that bamboozled my previous understanding of landscape." She sighed. "I'd been in such a rush and hurry, clutching my satchel of herbs, devising a healing plan for Mother Mary. The moment I glimpsed those Rockies—pinnacles of rock raised up in glory, more brilliant and God-like than anything—I guess my life changed, then and there. My very soul jolted."

"I grew up with them," he said, "the Rockies," aware that she had sidled from his question deliberately. "Always had them looking over me, a reassuring reference point—her interior, a privilege I had to wait for—wait until Father said I was old enough. I yearned to go there when I was little. The entry, exploration, emersion into the unknown, the search for answers I knew she had for me. It's hard to describe. Father spent much of his life there, and spoke of her like a woman, ever since I could remember. Still get goose bumps when we saddle up to go in."

Madeline hovered, set two plates of fried chicken and vegetables under the intimate conversation and slipped away wondering who he was, the handsome man whose voice drew her in. She would ask if he were taken.

After devouring a chicken thigh, Mary put her fork down. "There's a suffrage parade in September, Edward. In Helena. Hundreds, maybe thousands of women marchers will participate, the Men's League too—men who support our cause. I want to go."

"Onatah says you two are going to vote together, in the state elections, after the suffrage bill passes. If they let her register, a fifty-fifty proposition. I'm voting in your favor, for woman suffrage, of course."

"That sounds fine. Both things." Her mind had wandered, imagining. "Where will I sleep in Saypo?"

Encouraged by the question, Edward said, "In your cabin, remember? I'll draw it as I see it—" He pulled a pencil from his jacket pocket and excused himself to get a sheet of paper from the front desk, reconsidering whether he should add an addition on their place rather than build separate lodging.

Reappeared, he seated himself and drew carefully—a simple square with three dividing walls inside, noting the placement of a stove, a fireplace and south facing windows—and sketched an armoire, a rocking chair, a bed and kitchen table.

She studied the picture, stroked it with her finger. "Where's the mountains?"

He drew them in, suddenly recalling that he had forgotten to put Onatah's special surprise in his jacket pocket. "While you're looking at this, White Crow, I have something for you upstairs. Wait here, I'll be right back." He hurried to his room, retrieved Onatah's present and returned minutes later.

She was gone. Guessing that she probably did not frequent the hotel's powder room, he paid the bill and headed directly to her house. Had she forgotten she was waiting for him? Would she be surprised to see him now? "Ah," he uttered in response to an epiphany that flashed—did she leave because she couldn't read his drawing and would be found out?

He located Mary in her garden, bucket in one hand, ladle in the other, watering her seedlings—the ones he'd already watered. The sun had set, and dusk afterglow was nearly gone.

"Howdy, Edward," she greeted, apparently unsurprised by his arrival. "Come look at my baby hollyhocks." She chatted on, introduced him to each variety of flower and vegetable sprouts—in some cases, providing lineage, the location where a particular plant's great great great great grandmother had been rooted and the descendant's migration before arriving, at last, in the Birdtail—most often at the mission where she had nurtured, she explained, enormous crops of vegetables, including a smaller reserved garden of specialized herbs that she transformed into medicines.

"White Crow, let's go inside. I'll make a fire. I have a gift for you, from Onatah."

"You do?" she asked. She made herself comfortable, wrapped her shawl around sore shoulders and eased into the rocker that Edward had moved close to the potbelly's warmth.

He filled the cast iron kettle with water and joined her, offered the present wrapped in brown paper. "From Onatah," he repeated.

"Oh, how sweet she is. She always was ... And so clever." Mary held the gift in her hands, turning it from side to side. "Sometimes when I can't decide, I ask myself, what would Onatah do, or what would Onatah say ... when I'm not sure."

She pulled the string that extended around two of four corners and paused, resting her hands on the gift. "I remember the time she hid in my wagon, all day in that sweltering heat, from Saint Peter's to Cascade, to Fort

Shaw and back to here, my house, hiding because she wanted to live with me."

He nodded, knowing the story well.

Unable to unfasten the bow, she tore the paper recklessly and held a framed photograph at arm's length, scowling. "How can this be?" she demanded. "It burned in the fire! Edward—"

"White Crow," he spoke softly, "It's all right." He patted her shoulder. "You remember that Onatah used to work for the Cascade photographer? That same photographer took this portrait of you in his studio. You knew him." He patted again. "Onatah wrote to him, asked if he had taken the photograph with dry plates—I think that's what she said—so he was able to make another print. This is a new print, but it's the same picture."

She examined it, brought it close to her face, tipped the image toward potbelly light. Having stopped listening halfway through Edward's explanation, she stated, "This is when I was the Star Route Mail Carrier. And J.T. was still alive."

"Yes."

"I always loved this photograph. Marked a time I was proud of." She wanted to pull off her cap, shake her hair free, but didn't. She studied the image of herself: posed, rifle in hand, her dog J.T. at her side. "I was so strong then. I loved the challenge and that I did it." She stroked the wooden frame, felt the carved furrows that traveled the perimeter between edges. "This is a fine frame," she said, trusting the wisdom of touch.

"I carved it for you. It's a winding vine, like beans climbing a pole."

"Or sweet peas. Will you hang it on the wall for me, same place as before? At eye-level. Mine?"

"Happy to. Where was that exactly?" Edward hung the portrait as directed—a patient endeavor due to Mary's repeated change of mind. They said their goodnights and Edward walked, his heart reaching for Onatah as he gazed at the night's stars.

Upon his return to the hotel, he asked the clerk to arrange an appointment at the oculist for the following day and headed to his room.

Edward laid awake for hours. It wasn't the tufted mattress nor the absence of cricket chirping that kept him tossing and turning. After wrestling one worry after another, he pinpointed the real source of his distress. If, God forbid, his father's injury left him crippled, Edward dared to imagine, he would need to support the entire family, including White Crow. Heat gripped. How could he realistically achieve such a daunting responsibility?

He turned to the legacy that had given him courage in the

past—Bruneau family history as told to him since birth. *When I was ten years old*, his father, Louie, would begin the chronicle, *my parents died. I had nowhere to go, so I walked three days to get to, Le Havre, the port. Signed a contract with a ship's captain. The next morning, we left France, the country of my birth, for the new world. I worked as a junior seaman, cleaning the decks, doing what I was told. Our crossing was rough. Storm after storm pummeled our ship. Four mates died of the scurvy, but I survived. We landed in Nova Scotia. Winter. Next day I was sold—an indentured servant for seven years—that was the price of my passage. Day I turned seventeen, I packed my knapsack and left for America.* This was the point where Edward usually interrupted, captivated by his father's journey, how he had survived alone. He had memorized these details as told by Louie—a life traversing the wilderness, scaling ridge after ridge of mountain range, earning coin as a trapper—and had dreamed of the day he would strike out on his own, like his father.

A child's dream, Edward told himself, suddenly aware that he had calmed, his breath steady, deep within. He heard his father's closing words in his mind: *I settled here in Montana when I fell in love with your mother. Once you were born, my wanderlust was over. I wanted you, my son, to have the stability I never had.* A heavy cant of rain drummed. Edward closed his eyes and slept.

The next day began with a clear thought: *I have to delegate my time wisely.* Refreshed, he spoke to the concierge and joined Mary in the House of the Well Fed.

"Want to play checkers later, at the Silver Dollar?" came words from the woman who had already sipped several cups of tea, anxious to spend more time with her Edward. She looked so happy.

Edward grinned, slipped into a chair. "Sure."

He glanced at her skirt and blouse, the ensemble's condition in dire need, similar to the patriotic outfit that had caused such angst to his wife—fabric marred by the occasional moth hole, stain or tear. Onatah would call it an unacceptable condition needing to be remedied, as she had pointed out to him many times during the past year.

"White Crow, I meant to say congratulations again for voting. Onatah and I love your patriotic photograph—you, holding two American flags, victorious. It's grand."

Madeline came and went with their order.

"That was a great day," she reminisced. "A fellow named Jack, same name as Nadie's husband Jack, made the photograph and mailed it to me from Great Falls." She beamed from the memory. I knew I sent it when I found two in my dresser drawer."

"Oh. It sits in honor above our fireplace, on a cedar mantle I carved. Each day we all say hello to you and send you our love."

"Did you make a frame for it like the one you gave me?"

"Yes, with flowers."

She smiled.

"White Crow, we love that photograph because it shows your bravado and spirit. To be honest, though, Onatah has been extremely upset about it."

"Why?" I thought she would be proud."

"She is very proud of you—she couldn't be more proud. It was the condition of your clothing that caused her concern."

"What are you talking about?"

Ham, pancakes and eggs arrived, delicious aromas circling between them.

"That was my patriotic outfit."

"Yes, the outfit was handsome, indeed. But the small tears and holes in the fabric—she was overwrought. She insists that something is affecting your vision because you were always a good seamstress. She says that you mended clothes with meticulous care, immediately, at sight of the smallest imperfection. She's been upset about it ever since."

Mary fiddled with the scrambled eggs, twirled her fork. "Tears and holes? Way back then?"

"So, I have a gift I hope you will allow me to give you today."

She looked up.

"I've made an appointment with the eye doctor. It will please us to provide you with a pair of spectacles, if you need them. We missed your birthday … It will help your checker games, I imagine." He smiled with all the cheer he could muster.

"I don't like going to doctors, but I accept. I guess I do need spectacles. Tired of squinting, anyway. Thank you, Edward. Can we go somewhere else, first?"

Stomach full, she led him out of town, to Mission Road, to her boulder just past the cemetery. She pulled a trowel from her bag, asked if he would dig beneath it. He burrowed around and beneath the granite rock, finding only smaller rocks and a few lethargic earthworms. He did not ask for reasons, nor did she offer any.

He refilled the holes.

She apologized for the fruitless exercise, and they returned to downtown Cascade, to the eye doctor who, after a lengthy examination, invited them to take a seat by his desk. He explained her symptoms, gave a diagnosis and prognosis of what he described as an eye disease called macular degeneration for which there was no known cure. He apologized for his profession's inability to solve the problem and recommended that he supply lenses for the mild variance in her peripheral vision and recommended the ingestion of carrots and an herb called eyebright.

She seemed to take the news well—picked out silver-plated frames that looked quite attractive—pretended to be unaffected by the bad news; sudden reserve and the hunch of her shoulders suggested otherwise.

"I'm very sorry, White Crow," Edward said. "If Onatah were here, she'd offer to stand in for the center field that's gone dim. And she'd be chomping at the bit to get you to Saypo." His words reminded him of his nighttime epiphany, and he shrugged his shoulders.

"I do all right. Can still see most things."

As they were passing the lady's toggery, Edward stopped to look at a poster in the window. "It's a group of suffrage women, White Crow, making a speech somewhere."

"Is it about the parade in Helena this September?"

"How did you know?

"Hattie helps me read the paper sometimes.

Edward said, "They're all wearing the same style of hat—straw hats, quite stylish." He admired the image a tick longer and straightened to examine the window dressings.

"Look, White Crow, they have the same hat right here." He motioned to the object of her pointed gaze, grinned another of his beguiling grins. "I think our patriot extraordinaire needs a new hat. You can wear it to the parade at the State Fair, White Crow. I insist."

"No wonder Onatah loves you so," she teased. "If you really want, I'd like to have such a hat, if it fits and if it looks good. You have to be honest how it looks, Edward. I mean it. Now that you know my business."

"I promise," he said, hoping that she would get to the suffrage parade in Helena. "September 25th. Will you remember?"

"Calendar's marked."

Minutes later, they strolled arm and arm, up and down the entire distance of Central Avenue sidewalks. She could feel the heat of tongues waggling, pleased to be the center of something again, innocuous as it was.

Edward suggested that they sit on the bench at the train depot. It was a beautiful spring day, the kind celebrated by spontaneous removal of coats and scarves. Mary remembered the first reunion she'd had on the very same bench—how against the Bishop's rule, Mary Amadeus had brought Nancy and Annie to see her. She smiled at the memory.

"White Crow, I need to ask you a question."

She turned, attending the sincere tone. "All right."

"After Onatah wrote to you last fall and told you that we would be building you a cabin, we never heard back. Onatah assumes that you are ready, waiting and wanting to move to Saypo, but I need to be sure."

She bowed her fashionable head, nodding.

"So tell it to me straight, no fooling, skirting around. What do you feel about it?"

"If I've been quiet about it, it's because I want to come so much, Edward. When I didn't hear, I thought maybe you changed your mind. Then, yesterday, when I learned of all the extra work you have to do," she put her hands in her pockets, "I don't want to cause more hardship for you and Onatah." She looked into his green eyes. "Time slips by—I guess because sometimes I forget. It appears that I forgot to write back to Onatah and say I was thrilled, which I am. I was so excited when I got her letter... Ever since, I've been holding it like a valentine next to my heart. I want to come. But you need to take care of your business. I don't want to be an albatross." She leaned against him. "That's the God's honest truth."

"I'm very happy to hear you say it, White Crow." He took a deep breath and sighed. "And you're not going to change your mind?"

"No."

"All right. I can't promise when I'll start on your cabin, but I will as soon as I can; it may be close to first snow when it's finished, cause I'll have all the haying—you understand."

"I understand," Mary said.

"... at least ready enough for you to move... if you need to stay with us a couple weeks while we're finishing that'll be fine." He tapped his boot on the platform.

"So, it sounds to me like we have an agreement?" she asked.

"Yes. We have an agreement."

Edward opened his arms, and she leaned in, surprised at her involuntary gush of tears—tears of relief and joy. He hugged her tight and said, Onatah will be so happy. We all are."

The following morning, Edward retrieved his team and wagon from the livery and drove to Mary's house to say goodbyes. She admired his horses, a fine roan and a dark bay. She stroked their brawny necks, breathed in scent that flushed a kaleidoscope of feeling, and tidied their manes while he wrapped and bundled his belongings close behind the wagon's cross-seat.

They hugged and lingered over a handshake, fusing promise to promise—he would build; she would come to join her family at last, regardless of her voting status. By first snow, at the latest.

He settled his hat, stepped up and set the reins ready, then leaned over to say, "Don't worry when you notice that your closet is almost empty. I sent your things to the seamstress, and it's taken care of. Onatah's orders. And wood will be delivered and stacked. We love you, White Crow. We'll write when the cabin is ready. You write if you want to come earlier. We'll come get you."

He waved her a kiss, and she watched until he had disappeared from her sight.

Five months later, the string of summer travelers subsided. Mary had savored the interim of time, idling … welcoming sit-a-spells, tea and checkers, weather, lapses from laundry, visits from birds and casual conversations with Cascade friends, this being the last days as their neighbor, though they didn't know it.

Light shifted lower in the sky. After declaring that autumn had officially arrived, Mary bantered, "Folks are battening down the hatches," her thoughts turning to riverboats and barges and the endless caches of food she didn't have to process. Soon she would do-si-do and promenade to her new life in Saypo, when Edward came to get her.

The single event that Mary had been most eager to attend before she departed, arrived. Thrilled to join crowds of Montanans who had traveled long stretches of time and miles to get there, she tucked extra pins into and out of her straw hat and slipped her arm through Hattie's. Today is September 25, 1914, she minded to herself, and here I am at the Montana State Fair Parade for Suffrage!

"Hold tight," Hattie hollered as the crowd pushed forward. Concordant sounds thrummed to a strident quarter-note beat; rows of musicians, uniformed in color, were sighted two blocks down. "Here it comes, Mary."

Waves of cheers marked the progress of the band as it marched closer. Masses of excited onlookers packed in, positioned between the curb and storefronts along the one-mile route from the south end of Main Street to the Helena City Auditorium.

A popular tune, "The Washington Post March," blasted from players trumpeting horns, flutes and piccolos in pitched unison. Swift and roaring beats of drums set the rhythm and the Anaconda Band demonstrated exceptional skill as they marched in regimented formations. Hundreds of patriots, Mary and Hattie included, clapped and sang along.

A little girl and boy headed the procession holding the American flag above their shoulders—the same silken banner that Montana's suffragette leader, Jeanette Rankin, had carried throughout the state during the ongoing woman suffrage campaign. The suffragettes' intention was to introduce their cause with a symbolic message, implying that by passage of the bill, men and women alike would thereby carry Old Glory to new heights of democracy.

Next came three distinguished suffragettes: Dr. Anna Howard Shaw, forty-year suffrage veteran and current president of the National American Woman Suffrage Association, who led the assembly, followed by Dr. Maria Dean, former NAWSA president, and Jeannette Rankin, present chairman of the Montana Suffrage Association. Each revered leader exemplified the suffragette look designed to further the campaign—a signature yellow gown and hat. The trio strolled in unison, greeted the crowd and gracefully waved suffrage banners left and right. Mary and Hattie recognized them from photographs in the newspapers. Cheering, they saluted the freedom fighters' sustained political courage.

Most onlookers were familiar with suffrage movement symbolism portrayed by color: white representing purity of purpose; purple designating courage; green, renewal and strength; black, disparity for non-suffrage states; and the dominant color prevalent at events such as this—*yellow,* representing hope for enlightenment, and consequently, full suffrage rights for women.

Countless numbers of yellow balloons were released from building tops. As the orbs floated down over the festivities, afternoon sunrays stretched and dollops of blinding light bounced from silver and brass instruments, dramatizing the parade's objective—to create national treasure more valuable than glitter or gold.

Representation from all States of the Union followed. Ten young women wearing white dresses carried the national suffrage banner—each one representing an enfranchised state. Then, states with partial-suffrage demonstrated their status quo—suffragettes and banners decked in mourning dove gray, a hue that best signified the half-won victory.

"Look!" Mary cried as she tugged on Hattie's coat. "The next ones are wearing black!"

"States with no suffrage," Hattie exclaimed, struck by the visual impact, so far, the largest assembly of demonstrators who, most assuredly, mourned for their lack of equal rights. The suffragettes marched in formation—dignity and pride held high symbolizing the female majority, the thousands of American women citizens who deserved and demanded rights that had been denied for too long—women who, like herself, remained politically and judicially powerless, excluded from the running of a country whose claim to greatness was based on the premise, and the promise, of a true democracy: equal rights and privileges for all.

Black banners signaled by women dressed in black continued to move past, and bystanders could not help but associate the passel with members of a dirge. Heartfelt sympathies surfaced from the crowd, followed by optimistic hopes that the number of these state representatives would be reduced at least by *one* at the polls, weeks hence.

Mary squeezed Hattie's hand, and they listened to the band coming up that hailed, "The Liberty Bell March." Moments later, ear-splitting cheers cried for the Montana participants, female patriots who personified home state suffrage pride. Over one hundred women outfitted in yellow dresses, sashes and headbands marched, representing local support from each of Montana's thirty-nine counties. Banners bearing the names of each county waved high above the yellow river of suffragettes that flowed between banks of the revitalized crowd.

A second ward of yellow clad suffragettes demonstrated for Montana cities. Livingston, Great Falls, Butte, Helena, Culbertson, Big Timber, Forsyth and Chinook displayed the most elaborate banners.

"Mary," Hattie shouted, "each of those headbands and sashes says, *Votes for Women*."

Mary nodded, eyes on the next banner that stretched across the street's width, a white one with red letters carried by group of girls and boys. The message read, "Mother, dear Mother, come vote for me now." She felt her pride aspirate, regaled to witness thousands of like-minded human beings marching, clapping, cheering, whistling and rooting for the better world woman suffrage would deliver.

"Hattie," she hollered, pointing at more rows of women strolling in unison. "Over there. The big hat with flowers. Isn't that Claret? I think it is!"

Hattie tipped on toes to get a look. "You're right! She's marching with the group from Helena. I'm so glad she's alive! She's wearing green to symbolize strength."

Their attention turned to the next attraction, regiments of men coming their way—patriotic platoons of dedicated woman suffrage advocates whose numbers equaled that of the women—over six hundred. They strode to music muffled from beyond the boulevard's corner. Men of all ages displayed their support: members of The Men's Equal Suffrage League, the Clerks' Local Union of Great Falls, the Electrical Workers' Union and a large group of unaffiliated independent fellows who hoisted banners titled, "Just Men."

"Wouldn't it be grand if all the men dressed in yellow?" Mary posed.

Hattie thought of D.W. She understood his reason for refusing to come with her: "As Mayor, I don't want to tip the apple-cart just yet—" She had disagreed—insisted that he should be proud to show his support of woman suffrage—be an example. But he had not acceded.

Again the crowd erupted into cheers. "Boy Scouts," voices shouted, grins of pride glowing on many a mother's and father's face. Row upon row of Boy Scout troops high-stepped as they swung salutes, touching hand to brims of uniform caps—America's faithful young men, hearts pledged to the Boy Scout Oath: *Do my duty, to God and Country.*

Hattie swooned when she read the message worn on each scout's red armband: "I want my mother to vote." Teary eyed, she wished Lester and Earl were present to witness their peers.

Mary didn't care that she couldn't see parade details: she was present, one of many voices declaring the united message: *Our time has come. Women must have equal rights.* Trumpets resounded. Banners rippled.

More "Just Men" marched past, by the dozens. The endorsement was inspiring.

A band from Helena performed more bandstand favorites. The players marched in place as two women musicians outfitted in yellow stepped to the forefront and launched into melody, bugling, "The Stars and Stripes Forever." Members of the crowd placed hands over hearts and sang along.

The momentous parade continued, no end in sight.

A quarter mile length of women rode by on horseback, mostly quarter horses—more visions of beauty dressed in yellow with colorful flowers accenting their hats and headbands. The sounds of horse hooves clip clopping delivered comfort to Mary and many of the old-timers.

Soon after, the last section of the parade, drones of modern motor cars came near—transportation that would accompany the era of woman suffrage. Automobiles and engine-powered floats ornate with streamers and archways of flowers putted along as the occupants, prestigious legislative suffrage leaders, waved to the crowd, to a future that included the vote for women. As the last car passed, the massive crowd hooted and raved with satisfaction. From start to finish, the march for suffrage had proceeded in harmonious unity—male and female citizens promoting a better future—an essential political statement.

The crowd spilled into the streets and followed, making their way to the rally that would begin in an hour's time. Prestigious leaders from across the Nation had come to address the merits of suffrage before Montana men who would decide the fate of state suffrage when they placed their mark on ballots in thirty-nine days, on November 3, 1914.

Mary and Hattie were too tired for rhetoric. The parade had surpassed their expectations, and they walked until they found a park bench where they rested until sunset. Mary arranged the details of September 25, 1914 in her memory, planning to share her State Fair Suffrage Parade experience with the Bruneau family, in detail.

On the day of the state suffrage vote, November 3rd, Mary and Hattie met at the Cascade schoolhouse, where Hattie, using her political connections, had arranged to secure a room in the basement—available due to repairs in progress—from which all women could monitor the results of the day's election without interruption. *The Suffrage Ballot Ladies Lounge*, Hattie called it.

Ada Marcum had volunteered the use of her radio, and it had been placed on an old desk at the head of the windowless chamber. Mary helped Hattie move ladders and sawhorses and cans of paint aside before they arranged folding chairs in circular rows facing the radio's swatch of fabric from which the political broadcast would sound. Lastly, they covered a worktable with Hattie's Thanksgiving tablecloth and a crystal vase of greenery, designating the spot for potluck contributions.

By two o'clock, a half dozen women had arrived. Hattie slipped potholders under casseroles and watched her friends plop satchels containing projects to prevent idle hands on chairs in the front row. Aromas warmed the otherwise bare looking lounge, and casual chatter helped to relieve the subject on everyone's mind.

Anecdotes poured forth: I couldn't do anything right this morning, burnt the toast, got shells in the eggs—I sent the children off without their lunch boxes, had to deliver them—I forgot all about choir rehearsal. Testimony encouraged comradery once individuals learned that their personal trepidation resonated with neighbors and thousands of other Montana women who, this day, would share fate-driven hours waiting for the verdict.

By three o'clock the room had filled. Ada rushed in with apologies, explaining that J.E. had delayed her departure. Hattie was surprised that the turnout included most of Cascade's female population, even though some husbands would, no doubt, perceive attendance as an act of defiance. "We're going to win this time," she exclaimed. "You should have seen the thousands of people at the suffrage parade. All those numbers can't be wrong."

A moment of doubt resonated.

"Does anybody remember why it took two years to get this suffrage bill to the ballot after the legislators already passed it?" Mrs. Thomas asked.

"Men politics," Bernice Hall replied, shrugging a shoulder.

"Why did the bill require a general election majority vote in the first place?" Miss Smith, a newcomer from Utah, a franchised state, asked.

"All I know is, the bill better pass this time. My health depends on it," overweight Mrs. Riley boomed as she tossed her cable-stitched wool sweater onto a chair and fanned her face with a hankie, ignoring Mrs. Little, the preacher's wife who, out of habit, pointed to the pegged rack by the door.

"Me, too," several voices chorused. The atmosphere relaxed.

"When does the report come on?" Mrs. Thomas asked.

Ada looked at the radio. "Four o'clock."

Hands pulled at watch chains.

Hattie suggested, "Why don't we eat? Everything smells delicious."

Utensils clinked against plates piled high. Conversation converged toward points everyone could agree upon: our time has come— predictions say it will be a landslide in our favor—the weather is good, perhaps that will help—Hattie, thank you for organizing this respite— Montana will be a better place when we can vote.

Deep sighs proceeded footsteps for seconds and dessert. In the background, the radio droned—a man's monologue itemized crop prices and stock reports.

Mary sat on the chair nearest the radio, wishing she had brought yarn to crochet, then remembered why she hadn't. She couldn't figure the reason for her inertia, as of late, and huddled, stationary in her chair for more than two hours. She dismissed explanations: no wind for sails, dog-tired, misplaced my beauty sleep. Her body felt heavy and content to be, just be. Waiting was an adequate exercise, she had decided.

Children released from school burst into the room, charging the atmosphere with heightened decimals of noise. Ada busied herself at the radio dials, filtering through static in search of ballot news. An attractive schoolteacher joined the conclave, clapped a settle-down-signal to her students with mediocre result. Hattie grappled over whether to return home in time to cook supper, and formulated an idea. After conferring with other mothers, she called the older girls into a corner and gave instructions: "Take the children to the Silver Dollar, and ask Mayor Monroe to distribute them to their fathers who should watch over them until unequivocal ballot results are in. The women will be home when suffrage is won. Can you remember all that?" The girls nodded, eager to participate in such audacity.

Ada shouted above the noise, "It's on, the report is on. Quiet!"

Girls rounded up the children and quickly herded them out, grabbing coats and hats and goulashes in tandem. Each woman found a chair and huddled to listen.

"Ladies and Gentlemen, I'm Raymond Daniels speaking to you from the Montana State Capitol in Helena, reporting the results of today's suffrage election." Mary opened her eyes, glanced to read faces across the circle. "Word just arrived from our State Capitol. Election officials in the City of Anaconda have refused to obey Montana State law. Protocol dictates that polltakers must provide up-to-date ledgers of ballot tallies upon request of state officials who administer public records, in addition to providing a sealed duplicate copy of the tally with the actual ballots. This procedure ensures that results will not be tampered with. Today, Anaconda polltakers refused to hand over the ballot tally for public record."

Fear seeped into the schoolhouse basement.

"Suffrage supporters are rightfully concerned because this refusal allows opportunities for the ballots to be falsified—to swing the election one way or another after results from other counties are reported. This fraudulent act is of grave concern, listeners, because recent reports provided by other Montana counties, confirm that votes for and against equal suffrage are running neck and neck. Suffragist Jeanette Rankin alerted the National American Woman Suffrage Association headquarters in New York. The Associated Press has put news of the alleged Montana State Election security-breach on the wire. A team of guards has been posted at the Anaconda polls."

"Oh, my Lord," many of the women gasped.

"As I said," Mr. Daniels emphasized, "It appears that in most counties, the race for equal suffrage is running extremely tight. This race has proved to be much closer than legislators and suffrage advocates predicted. Of course, nothing is final, yet. Votes for woman suffrage outnumber those against in Mineral, Ravalli, Flathead, Cascade and Missoula Counties. Just barely. Stay tuned for later updates. This is Raymond Daniels signing off."

Nervous tension flared after the account of illicit exploits. Cries of "oh no," and "what if," reverberated. Scorched expectations steamed as the assembly confronted the possibility: Montana woman suffrage might be denied for the sixth time!

Rising from their seats, the women paced about, conferred with those closest. When emotions cooled, they returned to the chairs that faced the radio, a refreshed collective. Further discussion generated a consensus: *planning counter actions against future subjugation did them no good, presently.* Rankin would tether the Anaconda criminals—they would ride the storm.

Mr. Daniel's voice hurtled over the radio waves again. "And here I am with the latest suffrage vote news, Ladies and Gentlemen. It's a cliffhanger. With one hour left until the polls close, the rights of seventy-five thousand women voters are dangling in the lurch."

"We have the right! It's in the Declaration of Independence," Mrs. Riley reeled. "How long must we endure?" She fanned herself with a paper, a suffrage parade poster grabbed from the floor. Jessie Bickett rushed to her side.

Mr. Daniels spoke through the radio, "Reporters at polls across the state have relayed quotations from men voters who waited in line to vote this afternoon."

A paper riffled.

"Here's the anonymous sampling: 'Of course I'm gonna vote no. Got to protect from women turning into men. If we give'm an inch they'll forget about housework and be caring more about dogs than babies.'"

"Another voter says, 'I'm proud to say I'm voting in favor. My wife deserves the same legal privileges as me, works every bit as hard and knows more about paperwork.'"

"The next opined, 'Montana women are in violation of every propriety—suffrage is an invasion of sacred ground and wanton disregard of the tender sentiments of home.'"

"And thoughts from an old-timer," Raymond Daniels announced. "He says, 'Couldn't decide at first, cause I don't want them taking my job. But I voted yes in the end, cause turnabout's fair play.' The old-timer's younger brother commented, 'The Holy Bible decreed that man should rule. Those females who usurped man's kingdoms like Cleopatra, Bloody Mary and Joan of Arc provided disastrous proof—enough for us to know better.'"

"And one more, folks. 'Women are the moral compass of humanity and we need their guidance. I'm voting yes and recommend that all Montana voters do the same.'"

"This is Raymond Daniels speaking. As I said, it's neck to neck." Clicks of a telegraph sounded in the background. "Wait a minute, folks. We have an update." The air went silent for ten long seconds. "As of 4:30 p.m., pro suffrage votes are ahead by approximately three percent, a lead too small for guarantees. Polls will remain open until 6 p.m., and not all votes have been tallied, meaning the results are unknown and anything can happen. Hold onto your hats. Each of you take an Indian Head from your pocket, toss it with your company and count'em up. Heads-for, tails-against. Your tally is as good as ours. Tune in at six-thirty for the next suffrage vote update."

Cascade wives who had planned to leave in time to prepare supper, changed their minds. News of this proportion demanded definite results, and they would do their best to get it, tonight. The conclave held their position at The Suffrage Ballot Ladies Lounge. Suppressing visions of bondage, they finished the rest of their buffet, exchanged recipes and talked about children. When the evening stock report interrupted, Ada turned it off saying, "Sorry, I get enough of it at home." The atmosphere felt tight but supportive and protected—as long as they remained together.

Mary opened her eyes and said, "Don't worry. We're going to win."

Doubt, responsible for the hesitant silence, tapered and a renewed optimism gained ground—the clatter of knitting needles hastened, and women spoke in deeper tones, crossed their hearts.

Eventually, 6:25 p.m. arrived. Ada readjusted the dials.

Mr. Daniels' familiar voice erupted, "Good evening, Montanans, and welcome to today's final report on the suffrage vote. It's been a day of uncertainty, as many of you are aware, because the City of Anaconda in Deer Lodge County has refused to supply the ballot tally—their report of yeas and nays—leaving us unable to give you accurate predictions in regard to the present standing of the suffrage bill."

Droning in steady rhythm to sound neutral, he recited totals canvassed from a sampling of counties as of six o'clock: "Missoula County 62% for, 38% against; Lewis & Clark, home of the Capitol, 47% for, 53% against; and Cascade County 48% for and 52% against."

"Those dirty low-down conniving—" Bernice muttered.

"...Added up," Daniels continued, "excluding Deer Lodge which is believed to be anti-suffrage in general, total figures from all counties indicate a 2% lead in favor of suffrage. I wish I could give you a definitive call, folks, but no one can. The State Election Office has advised us that they will begin a thorough recount tomorrow. That final count will include all ballot votes from Deer Lodge, including Anaconda's, whose sealed ballot box will be removed from their polling place at seven o'clock tonight. I'll be back tomorrow to report progress as it comes in. My mother would say, 'Patience is a virtue.' Let's give it a go. This is Raymond Daniels, reporting the status of the suffrage bill from our State Capitol, on November 3rd, 1914, signing off."

"I want to shout, *victory!*" Mrs. Riley hailed, shaking her dominant arm in the air. "But I don't dare," she growled, voicing unanimous sentiments.

A tick of silence lapsed.

"We are triumphant," Hattie spired.

"Yes, we are. I believe equal suffrage has won," Ada declared.

"We can't know that if it's one or two percent apart!" someone in the back of the room hollered.

"Maybe this will give unenlightened men a few days to adjust," Bernice said.

Mrs. Rowe sighed, looked left and right before chortling, "I wish we could know for sure."

Heads bobbed in agreement.

Hattie stood, motioning volunteers to do likewise. "Let's stand up and hold hands."

Over thirty women rose and formed a palm-to-palm circle, a wavy configuration due to their numbers, complete and firmly pledged when last hands squeezed. Smiles emerged.

"I'm so glad we came together," a sincere voice offered. Mm-hmms filled the room.

Ada proposed, "Let's live the forthcoming days—until the count is final—in confidence that our suffrage rights have been won. When our victory is affirmed and our governor stamps the state seal, amending the Articles of our Constitution to ensure women's equal suffrage, our cheers will ring triumphant, and we will celebrate a jubilant victory!"

"And we'll register!" Mrs. Riley cheered, breaking her clasp to begin what became inspired rounds of applause.

"We should hire a band," Mrs. Rowe spirited.

"Hooray for us!" Mary called.

"Hooray," the group repeated, savoring the flavor of women's strength in unity that indicated, ostensibly, the power of equal suffrage with which they, collectively, would magistrate compassionate change. After tying their shoelaces, they stacked folding chairs into the closet, buttoned buttons and redressed hair with adroit fingers.

Mary waited for Hattie, who gathered forks and spoons and cups and her tablecloth. Last to leave, Hattie turned the recently installed wall light switch to off, locked the door and escorted Mary home before proceeding to hers. They strolled, admiring stars, shared goodnights and semi-sweet congratulations.

27

HOME

*P*ulling her dressing robe tight, Mary pondered the old saying: good things to worry about come in pairs ... or was it bad things come in threes? "Oh well, doesn't matter," she consoled. "I know they are both coming, on the way right now, the good things."

She looked through the window at white clouds stretched tight like drum hide, reckoning whether this day would bare the weight of snowflakes she had done her best to ward off. Before first snow, Edward had promised.

"State suffrage and a new home," she muttered, shuffling across the hard-chilled floor to rummage through her wardrobe, dress for breakfast and hurry the fire. "Where are my birds?" She searched tree limbs. "Something's brewing. So still, like a contrary child pouting."

She stepped outside and a wallop of cold clutched her, stole a moment of her time. She proceeded to her destination.

"Stop at the post office on the way home," she whispered, clutching hopes that her letter from Saypo had arrived with details of her impending journey. She could see herself in her new cabin, strolling from one room to another, looking out that window Edward had mentioned, admiring her beloved mountains close by—walking distance, touching distance.

A wind picked up. Mary gave it a kick, figured it had born itself from ice country, north. Squalls slid low along the ground, spinning fallen leaves into wheel-sized twisters that swept the street and spilt apart.

After breakfast, she amended her earlier directive and hurried home instead, holding a pancake-currant jelly sandwich she would place on the stump for Big Old Blessing, unsure if he would come, given the mounting turbulence. He's probably seen it all, she mused as she pulled her cap down, contriving simpatico with those she loved.

Inside, she bolted the door, looked at the stack of wood by the stove and divvied it in her mind. "Three good fires and then Edward will be here, or I'll have to use my savings, buy a cord." She shivered, added two chunks of larch and waited, stretching hands above the iron stove, gazing to claustrophobic shades of gray that hung on the other side of glass, grudging the return of winter cold that sucked moisture from her skin, movement from her limbs.

Turning to warm her back, she hummed as the fire crackled, closed her eyes and swayed, wondering who was stronger: that culprit outside whirring into a bona fide tempest, or the sun—the glorious, most longed for star. Considering strength, she uttered, "Put what I learned to good use," and reminded herself to ask Hattie if news of the suffrage bill had arrived. In print. She decided it would be all right to break her routine this once, take a nap. Her bones ached and there was nothing to tend. She would stow energy and pack up when she woke, revitalized.

It was a howling gale that wakened her. Confused and blinking into darkness, she could tell by the absence of firelight and by the chilled leathery feel of her uncovered flesh that the temperature had plummeted. Instead of rising to start a new fire, she willed herself to ignore the scraping scratches that gnawed against her house—then tried to find the rhythm, match it to a melody—and in the doing, slumbered past sunrise.

Wakened by a gasp, hers, she flung her quilts further than intended and sat on the edge of her bed, dizzied. Hot pulsing of her hands and feet verified swelling. Her tongue tasted sour and baked, the chill in her chest sore and burning. She covered her lips to ease a broken cough and hurried to the wardrobe to search for her robe, socks and wool britches—and the leather slippers the Monroe boys had given to her last Christmas.

She peeked above frost on the window, surprised to see that the dreaded snowflakes had not fallen. Not up to sparring winter for breakfast, she decided to eat later. She allotted four of the remaining eight logs, stacked them separate on the floor.

"Hattie gave me one of those rubber hot water bottles," she muttered, squatting to grab its box from beneath her bed. She struggled to hold the iron kettle steady as she poured boiling water across the funnel-shaped lip of red rubber. Tightening the vessel's plug, she sighed for her aching back and slipped the heat under bedcovers she had straightened.

After arranging slippers where she could step directly into them, she realized that she was playing hooky—just like those rare coveted times she had grabbed her fishing pole and trotted off, returning at day's end with a mighty rainbow trout. Enjoying a satisfied grin, she tucked blankets round her neck, pulled her nightcap over her ears and pushed the hot rubber beneath her feet. Drifting, she was overtaken by sleep in seconds.

She remained so, though she fitted and tossed—past closing time for The House of the Well Fed, past a vibrant magenta sunset overtaken by pewter cold that had staked its claim on the bank of the *Missouri* and advanced west toward the Rockies, past a series of dreams that repeated over and over, as though she had to get something right before she could open her eyes and return herself to Montana, to the Birdtail, to Cascade, where her body lay wrung out, sweating, chilled to its core, restrained by exhaustion … and where she, her consciousness, was mercifully unable to comprehend that the temperature of her house had submerged to minus integers and that the luminous stupor in which she currently lavished might not serve her if she coalesced in its company much longer.

Madeline, waitress at the House of the Well Fed, reported to her boss, R.B. Glover that Mary Fields had not come to eat for two days. Certain that such an absence was cause for alarm, since Mary hadn't missed breakfast or supper during the past three years, to her recollection, she requested permission to deliver a meal to Mary's house and find out what was going on.

R.B.'s upper lip, masked beneath a thick mustache, twitched as he regarded cold-country lore that measured seasonal loss based on the number of old-timers taken by Grim Reaper once winter arrived. He patted Madeline's shoulder and told her not to worry—he would take care of it. He rushed toward the front desk and proceeded, a short time later, out the door wearing a sheepskin work jacket and an old pair of cowboy boots. As he strode up the icy grade towards Mary's house and her laundry, he noticed the absence of smoke billowing from her chimney. Nearly out of breath after trudging through thigh-high snowdrifts that obstructed access to her house after the night's blizzard, he pounded his fist in thrums of five, each time louder and harder, rattling the door from his force. A still quiet persisted. Kicking ice from the threshold, he shouted, "Mary Fields, open up," and pounded again. "If you don't open up right now, I'm coming in!"

He grabbed the knob and to his surprise, it turned, and the door swung open. Lunging forward, his throat spasmed. Soot and dank smoke tainted the air. "Damn winds," he muttered, "Must have pushed the damper open. Sounds like she slept through it." He stepped cautiously to avoid thrusting ash.

As his sight adjusted to dimness behind closed curtains, he shivered, alarmed by chill that equaled temperatures outside. He touched the stove and opened its door. The belly was empty, barring a layer of ash. He held his breath and peeked around it, to the bed where he spied Mary covered only by her pink dressing gown, limbs sprawled, mouth agape.

Berating himself for staring, he cleared his throat, rolled his shoulders back and tried again. "Mary Fields, it's R.B. Are you awake?"

When she did not rouse, he shook her shoulder and called, "Wake up, Mary, it's R.B." He squeezed her wrist and searched for a pulse, which to his relief, he felt beating, though he was unequipped to know whether the count was fast or slow. He pulled the bed covers up, called to her again and noticed that her face was pimpled with sweat. His hand trembled.

Stepping away, he told himself to take charge. He returned to the stove, stacked the last four logs with kindling and straw, readjusted the damper, lit the crinkled tinder and stomped out the side door to restock her wood supply. Finding no wood whatsoever where several cords should have been stacked and covered, ready for winter, he lifted his hat, stroked his hair and uttered, "Has she lost her mind? No wood? What do I do first?"

He rushed indoors, oblivious to black waves of ash that whirled in his wake, ignored the charred smell and took the liberty of opening her wardrobe. He searched for all garments warm and heavy, adding lastly to the weight strewn over his arm, a pair of clean folded socks from the closet's bottom corner. Searching further, he grabbed her overcoat and shawl from the coat rack by the front door and returned to her side.

Disappointed that she had not woken after all his racket, he slipped her socks over her ice-cold feet, took mittens from her coat pocket and drew them over equally freezing hands (limp and weak to his touch) and draped her old fur coat, a patched-up wool jacket and her shawl across the length and width of her body, aware that it would take two or three hours to warm the place, requiring more wood that he would need to supply pronto.

Thinking then, that hot water would be needed whether for bathing or for pressing compresses upon her forehead or whatever else women did with simmering water when nursing the ill—coffee rose to mind—he grabbed the kettle from the stove and after realizing no plumbing had been installed to connect Mary's house to the city water pipe lines, rushed outside again, to the old pump where he labored briefly, wishing he had thought to put his gloves back on.

"Mary Fields, he announced as he slammed the door, it's R. B. Glover here. Are you awake? I'm coming in." He turned past the potbelly, quivered when he met the empty stare. "Mary?"

"Who are you?" she hollered, scooting against the wall. She yanked the covers over her chest.

"Mary, you know me. R.B. Glover. I came to bring you food." He realized then that he had forgotten to bring the meal. Fearing that she would not believe him without evidence, he moved out of view and said, "I'm going to get Hattie for you, Mary. Stay where you are."

He sprinted from the house, fraught with concern and haunted by memories of his mother's death the winter before. Frantic, he tried to remember which details he should convey to whom and in what order, gnashing his teeth until he had instructed his staff to deliver a cord of wood to Mary Fields, immediately.

From there he hurried to the Monroe house, explained the situation to Hattie and D.W. as thoroughly as possible, asked Hattie if she would go straightaway, bring Mary back to her senses, get a big fire going and stay to nurse her. He added that he thought Black Mary had a fever and that Madeline would be delivering chicken soup and whatever else the cook opined to be helpful, within the hour. He rushed off, anxious to catch Doctor Vanatta, the osteopath relocated from Toronto, in her office so that he could retain her service to assess Black Mary's illness, and tell them what to do. Then he could have that coffee he'd been longing for.

Hattie leapt from her sewing, grabbed a bar of soap, towels, teas and a wash pan, wrapped herself in winter garb and took off.

When she arrived minutes later, the sun had set and winds whipped at savage speeds. She knocked as she entered, shut the door and called to Mary who did not answer. Dismayed by black soot streaked across the floor, she paused to add wood to the fire, grabbed a log from a supply stacked in an unfamiliar metal container next to the potbelly.

Calling Mary's name again, Hattie rounded the corner. Relieved to see that she was breathing, though rasping as she inhaled and damp from sweat, she seemed to be succored in a deep sleep. Hattie rested the back of her hand on Mary's brow and grew more concerned.

Returned to Mary's side minutes later, a washbasin filled and positioned on a stool next to the chair she had arranged for herself, Hattie wrung the cloth that she had been soaking in lukewarm, sage-infused water and gently wiped Mary's forehead as she spoke in soft reassuring tones.

Mary mumbled but did not open her eyes, and Hattie thought it just as well, hoping that rest would heal the affliction though an ache inside urged her maternal sense to keep a close watch. What herbs had Mary given the boys when they were down with a cough last winter? She untangled Mary's hair from her face and eased the nightcap found beneath her pillow, over her head, tucking, as Mary would request if she were awake, all of her hair inside.

As the house grew warmer, Hattie removed Mary's fur coat, shawl and overcoat, returned them to their places. Locating Mary's mop, she did her best to clean the floor. Afterwards, she refilled the kettle with water from the pump and sat waiting by Mary's side.

Heavy knocks sounded, and three pairs of feet entered; Dr. Vanatta followed by R.B. and D.W.

The men stood by the stove. Hattie clasped her hands and observed Dr. Vanatta examine, answered questions put to her. The doctor mentioned a deep rattle in Mary's lungs and noted swelling throughout her body, her legs in particular. She stated that Mary would likely be laboring from a heavy hacking cough when she woke, and to keep her upper body elevated. She gave Hattie some homeopathic pellets to administer, asked her to keep Mary hydrated, warned that the patient may be confused or disoriented and recommended that someone stay with her until she was out of danger. When pressed for a diagnosis, Dr. Vanatta said that she was sorry to say: dropsy, with suspected pneumonia, and volunteered to return in the morning. She looked to Hattie and added one more directive: get her temperature down.

R.B. and D.W. were of the mind that if Mary needed twenty-four hour care, she needed to be in the hospital. They began to formulate plans. Hattie overheard and told them to stop, insisting that they honor Mary's choice to stay home, no matter what lay ahead. "Mary and I have discussed 'at death's door' preferences," Hattie explained, watching the men's jaws drop. "In advance, so I would be Mary's voice, if need be. I promised."

The men bade their goodnights. R.B. escorted Dr. Vanatta, and D.W. returned home to take care of the boys.

Hattie managed to change the sweat-soaked sheets and pillowcases and carefully redressed Mary in a flannel nightgown she had found ironed and folded in the bureau. Arms and legs jarred in the process, Mary cried out and coughed—deep-throated barks that sounded ominous. Hattie dropped the homeopathic pellets beneath Mary's tongue and continued to apply compresses, reciting poems to pass time and offer comfort.

Hours later, the flush of fever yielded.

Mary opened her eyes. "Are you all right?" she asked Hattie. "Is Onatah here?"

Speaking provoked a slurry of coughs. Eyes watered and hardened mucous prevented air from entering nasal passages. Dodging the act of breathing, as it burned to inhale, she pulled the sheet above her mouth and parted her lips, sipping in thin breaths, as little air as possible. She reached to the pillow behind, realized she was sitting rather than lying, looked to the window and to the colorless light behind it—to Hattie, to the washbasin and back to her friend who said, "You haven't been feeling well. You had a fever, but you're awake now. Would you like some chicken soup? R.B. sent it from the restaurant."

Mary shook her head. "Did I get a letter?"

"I don't know. I'll check later. I'll make you some chamomile tea. It will settle your cough."

"Don't forget," Mary whispered.

"I won't," Hattie said, "I'll go to the post office."

Another rush of craggy coughs jagged, leaving Mary worn and exhausted. She closed her eyes and yielded, reluctantly, to carouseled swirls of sparkled light beneath eyelids. Dizzy, she tried to find center.

Sometime later when Hattie came close, she uttered slowly, "Yarrow … in bowl, pour boiling … water … towel over head."

"All right, Mary." That was it, Hattie thought, the decongestant she gave me for the boys, striving to recall if she had any left. "I remember, I'll get it for you, soon as someone comes."

"Who?"

"Let me get your tea. I'll explain." She patted Mary's hand, got up to pour simmered water from the kettle to the teapot she had readied with dried chamomile flowers.

As the infusion steeped, Hattie returned to Mary's side. "You must have caught a chill, Mary. We need to keep your fever down."

Mary felt her forehead.

"You had a high fever last night but it's lower. I'm going to stay here with you, until you're feeling better."

As Mary efforted to reply, bile inched up her throat. She gagged and swallowed it, covering her mouth.

"Spit it out, don't swallow," Hattie said as she rushed to the cupboard, returned with a bowl that she placed by Mary's side. "Here's a bowl for next time."

Boots tromped to the doorstep followed by heavy-handed knocking and cold air entering. "Hello," three voices called, the same visitors who had come the night before. Soles scraped and linings of heavy garments swished as arms pulled from sleeves.

R.B. was first to round the corner, holding a platter covered with towels. "Black Mary," he barked, "You look so much better. Got chicken soup, scrambled eggs, mashed potatoes and orange juice when you're ready. I'll put it on the potbelly."

Dr. Vanatta listened to Mary's lungs and instructed when and how to prepare the herbs she had prescribed: feverfew, yarrow and comfrey to draw the fever and build strength; tinctures of lomatium, balsam and grape root for inflammation and congestion; a mustard poultice for her chest.

Mary scowled, distressed by the realization that she'd lost control of her privacy. Smacked queasy by aromas of food, her stomach wretched. She waved a hand at Dr. Vanatta and attempted to say something. The words dribbled out scrambled and she couldn't fix them. She tried again and gave up, allowing the weight of exhaustion to close her eyes and ears, wishing that rain would extinguish the fire in her body, imagining cloudbursts.

Hattie pressed a glass of water to Mary's lips.

The doctor asked Mary to tell her how she was feeling. A door slammed. Footsteps thundered. Mary cringed and waited for the noises—logs tossed, one against another, the creaky stove door closing, latching, a long sigh heaved over boot soles shuffling, chair feet scraping the floor and a heavy plunk landing body weight—to stop.

"Fine," she forced, hacking for her effort, patting the place on her bed where she thought her old dog J.T. should be.

When Dr. Vanatta left, D.W. handed Hattie's coat to her and signaled that she should follow him outside. Stationed by the woodpile, he crossed his arms and initiated the discussion Hattie had hoped to avoid, explaining that his primary goal was to keep Mary alive and that the means by which the dear old woman's recovery was to be achieved was secondary. He reached to pull her close.

Hattie, regretting her foolishness at having contradicted her husband in front of a colleague, kept her ground and crossed her arms, waited for her temper to cool before she acknowledged his sincere intentions and alleged that her goal was the same: to keep Mary alive and well. She stated unabashed, that she would neither be loyal nor responsible, had she not spoken on Mary's behalf.

After a pause she confessed that she would continue to speak the patient's words of intent that she knew for a fact had been deeply considered and composed with conviction. A large crow perched on the tree stump, flapped his wings and flew to the pines, cawing.

Hattie dared to elaborate upon Mary's precarious situation, professing that Mary needed someone as near and dear as he was to defend her old-age-life choices when unfortunate turns of events rendered her unable to speak for herself … adding that, in her opinion, there were few things in life that one had control over, and that if one stayed true to oneself, the golden years should, ideally, personify one's character and the accumulated merit of their achievements.

"In Mary's case," she said, "—she being an individual who has always thought for herself and wrestled egregious situations without fear—it is all the more crucial that we protect her, and make certain her wishes are honored so she receives the dignity and respect she deserves."

She stepped closer, embraced D.W. and said softly, "Her choice to stay home is difficult for both of us to honor, particularly since we, by default, must bear witness to suffering—but we can only imagine …" She leaned her head on his shoulder. "She bade, and I promised, that when the time for her final journey arrives, I will stay with her, in her home, to protect her as she embarks, on what she refers to, as her biggest adventure."

Having given her handkerchief to Mary, Hattie stepped back to wipe her tears with her sleeve and gazed at her husband, who looked as though he himself were bruised and stricken. "I don't know if her time is near," Hattie tendered, but I do know she wants to remain in her home. We are duty-bound."

"It is my heartfelt concern and duty that guides me," he replied as he touched her on the cheek and told her to find someone to watch the boys if she intended to remain, and to find someone to take turns with the nursing.

Hattie sighed, wondering if D.W. would adhere to Mary's resolutions if and when things escalated. "Let's see how she's doing in a couple days," Hattie suggested as D.W. turned to leave.

That evening, Mary's cough worsened though she sipped the chicken broth and swallowed teas and submitted to the various remedies and procedures, including the tented-breathing of infused yarrow.

On the day that followed, D.W. took his boys to the House of the Well Fed. When R.B. joined the father and sons' after-dinner card game, D.W. enlisted him, in short whispers, to find a woman to relieve Hattie from Mary's bedside, divulging that this couldn't go on much longer—the absence of his wife and him having to watch Hattie's grieving.

Between blackjack hands, Madeline treated Lester and Earl to hot fudge sundaes, and R.B. debated to convince D.W. that they should return to the original plan: deliver Mary to the professionals whose business it was to heal, armed with the latest medical advancements, adding that he'd already asked all the waitresses and that none of them were able to help out.

Earl had been listening and asked when Mary would be well enough to play with him and Lester again. He suggested that he deliver a posy to Mary—paper ones since no flowers were in bloom—and could he please go to visit because he knew it would make her feel better and it would make him feel better, too, he admitted, and besides, he implored, he wanted to see his Mama before bedtime.

Lester elbowed his brother, cupped his hand over Earl's ear and whispered that he'd better leave Papa alone and be quiet because Mama had told them both it was very important not to disturb her because she had to stay at Mary's to take care of her.

R.B. arrived at the Monroe house two hours later, after Lester and Earl were sleeping. D.W. percolated a pot of coffee. Stirring cream and sugar, they discussed the matter of Mary Fields' sickness, D.W. conveying Hattie's opinion about the importance of following a patient's wishes.

After some time, they came to agree on one thing: that often, when a person was ill, they lost the ability to assess what should be done, not being able to comprehend the severity of their condition nor the options available—options that they may not have been aware of previously—moreover, options that might not have existed at the time of Mary's decision-making.

Hattie was furious when D.W. woke her at five a.m. and informed her that Mary Fields was to be transported to Columbia Hospital in Great Falls on a train that would depart in two hours.

She had a choice, he stated, after presenting the summary of reasons for his decision: she could help Mary endure the trip, which meant that she had to hurry and pack her things as well as Mary's, and also, she could remain with Mary at the hospital for a few days, if she'd like to (he volunteering to take responsibility for the boys upon his return later this day). Since Mary Fields might be able to be saved, he insisted, live for years longer—it was their, at least his, responsibility to do everything possible to meet that goal—Mary's recovery. Would she please respect his decision that was compassioned for her, Hattie, as much as Mary—after all, she had nursed her friend for three days and still there were no signs of improvement.

Hattie's brow knit lines that deepened.

Ninety minutes later, R.B. parked his automobile, honked the horn and left it idling while he rushed into Mary's house. He greeted Hattie with information: he had borrowed a wheelchair in which Mary could rest at the depot, and or, on the train. A glance from D.W. informed R.B. that the marital discourse had not gone well, but Hattie appeared cordial enough to him, her voice cheerful as she eased Mary's arms into the fur coat, her demeanor calm as she explained to Mary that she was not to worry, that she would return to her home in a few days' time and she, Hattie, would not leave her side.

Frigid air slapped Mary's face when she was lifted, perched upon the locked arms of D.W. and R.B. She yelled, "Get your hands off me! What are you doing? Let me go!" and doubled over, hacking, her throat scorched, lungs on fire, independence stolen.

Once Mary was in the automobile's back seat, Hattie pushed her satchel into D.W.'s hands and scooted in, reached an arm around Mary, averted her guilty eyes and heart and prepared herself for the tremendous blame she deserved, having proved her ineptitude by failing her dear and honest friend miserably, unforgivably.

Minutes later, the car stopped, its running board flush to the depot platform. R.B. was relieved that most people wouldn't see, it being so early on a winter morning. They lifted Mary again, this time into the wheelchair, and, after hailing the assistance of the conductor once the train had arrived, routed its wheels over what appeared to be a cattle ramp.

Mary, knowing she would incur charring pain for the right to express herself, yanked her arms free and screamed, "Stop!"

Flinging wrath toward D.W. and R.B. and anybody else who thought they knew better, she gathered spit to lubricate and yelled, "Know you're trying to help, but I want to stay home!" She swallowed, easing the burn slightly. "My choice. No hospital!" Twisting to locate her friend, she cried, "Hattie!"

The wheelchair bumped over the last ridge of the ramp and was backed into the aisle between red velvet seats, to the back end of the railcar. Knowing she couldn't escape on her own, she closed her eyes and evacuated from the turmoil, asked herself to prioritize, care for herself however she could while ignoring what she believed to be a cruel and devastating absence of compassion launched upon her during a moment of vulnerability. She placed her hands on her cap and rocked.

D.W. slung two suitcases, Hattie's and Mary's, onto the rack above the women's seats. Hattie dropped her head and listened to the screeching train whistle that sufficed the opportunity R.B. took to excuse himself from the situation he'd had a hand in creating. D.W. folded himself into a seat toward the front of the coach.

The Cascade school bell rang in the distance.

Aware that chances were slim, Mary demanded, "Then take me Saypo. I want to go to Saypo!" No one acknowledged. "Won't cost anymore. I'll pay." She convulsed into a grievous episode, pulled her coat lapel across her face, encumbered.

"I'm sorry," Hattie apologized, knowing better than to offer her hand, or a string of sympathies after having failed to defend her confidant's wishes, rights and freedom to choose; after conceding—conspiring, actually—to a husband's demands. She hung her head but kept an eye on her friend's cardinal symptoms.

The dreadful cough, and its alternate wheezing, rooted.

The act of breathing seemed to break Mary apart. She hacked the entire one hour distance to Great Falls, her body shaking, weak and fragile. Relieved momentarily when the abrasive rattling and chugging of locomotive wheels ceased, she forced herself to sustain. Hands pulled her from her position, opened her supine and latched her onto a stretcher.

Transferred in and then out of an ambulance, a remodeled milk truck without amenities, her head throbbed, accosted by further handling and delivery—slamming, jolting, scraping, honking noises. She evoked will to fight for breath—more difficult to capture, strapped as she was, horizontal. Tirading in her mind, she hurled: I asked for nothing but peace and quiet from which to gather my last ruminations—prayers—ancestors. Not this.

Inside the Great Falls Columbus Hospital, she strained at further caustic discord—more screeching wheels and bright lights exacerbated by irritating and redundant accounts of, and questions regarding, her condition. Agitated by the poking and prodding, her body the subject of examination, her knowledge and opinions dismissed as superfluous, she pulled the sheet over her face.

Hattie stood by, ignoring the presence of her husband who had caused this needless suffering. Silent in her fury, she accused: she's been forced to fight for her freedom again at the most inappropriate time. It is so wrong. She forced a smile as he left for the depot.

When the last door shut, the door to the little room Mary was placed in—a sterile hollow she refused to lay eyes upon—they stripped her of her clothing and yanked a starched, scratchy cloth around her—a gown, they boldly called it. Detecting cadaverous scent beneath two odors, iodine and quinine, Mary refused to injure herself further—she would not speak. She opened her eyes and glared, pointing to her throat. Aware that Hattie's guilt hovered, she returned to her self-attained privacy where she struggled to nurse her pain, find the place from which she could relax and listen. Was it nighttime yet? Were the stars out?

She dozed into a liquid feeling until a new voice barked from above her, a voice with hands attempting to remove her cap. "No!" she screamed, flinching from the pain and the nurse's terse threat of reprisal. Repositioned, cap intact, she visioned a barbequed pig on a rotisserie spit, an apple in its mouth—which helped to form saliva.

There was no miracle cure, Hattie discovered quickly. While advances in science, medical education and diagnostic equipment like the stethoscope, had created hope for miracle cures and had generated an increase in hospital construction, patient care at Columbus Hospital seemed regimentally basic and lacking in therapeutic procedures. Hattie learned that familiar tried and true remedies had been banned—cures that had worked for decades, centuries, perhaps—the homeopathics that Dr. Vanatta had prescribed, for example, and the poultices, the herbal tonics, diuretics and decongestants. She fantasized: if only I had known, I would have barricaded the doors to Mary's house, stayed inside with her no matter what—or taken her to Saypo, the place she asked for and mumbles about in her deliriums. After gaining permission, she eased Mary's torso forward and gently thrummed a fisted rhythm on Mary's back to stimulate congested phlegm upward, purge unhealthy mucus from the lungs. Unsuccessful, she placed pillows under Mary's swollen legs, tucked an extra blanket to keep her warm.

The head nurse and doctor insisted that their goal was to make Mary as comfortable as possible yet they offered no treatment plan or details regarding her illness. Hattie bit her tongue. When the staff asked if she would like transportation to her lodging, she informed them that she, Mrs. Monroe, the wife of Cascade's mayor and the patient's personal friend and advocate, would be staying in the room. She refused to back down, even after the three-hundred-pound matron threatened to call the police.

As a result, the hospital staff seemed to enter the shiny white chamber less often, and that appeased both of the women who found themselves sequestered within a rigid antiseptic system, unable to negotiate further. Hattie decided to administer the remaining homeopathic pellets she had packed in her suitcase.

Several times each hour, Mary jerked from traumatic coughing and wheezing that shook her vitality as if chaffing grain from its staff, her honeycombed lungs squeezed until sucking for breath became a primary objective. Fever returned, ensnaring her further, and she lay depleted, heavy as stone.

Arrived home in Cascade, D.W. threw his hands in the air. Earl had wailed for over an hour, demanding to know why his Mary was gone, why he and Lester and not been told, and why they couldn't go to visit her, screaming when his father came near. Lester was equally disturbed, feeling betrayed by both parents, his father in particular. He dared to accuse, "Now Mama and Mary Fields are both gone," and ran out the door.

Onatah posted the long-awaited letter: the cabin was ready and waiting.

R.B. explained to those who asked, that he had been able to get Black Mary into the highly esteemed Columbia Hospital that normally did not accept coloreds, due to the old-timer's past affiliation with Saint Peter's Mission—omitting that he had contributed a large donation along with his request for her admittance.

"Bring me a warm compress," Hattie demanded as she had regularly over the past three days and nights, "and a bowl of hot water, please."

Groggy, Mary tried not to cough but couldn't help it, explaining in mumbles that she just needed a little rest and then she would harness the team.

Hattie held the warm cloth to Mary's head and repeated with her soothing voice, "Everything is fine, Mary … you might like to close your eyes and rest for a moment."

Mary's slumber fell deeper, her body weak from its labor, her breathing somewhat eased. A slight smile emerged, and this reassured Hattie, who kept her hand in Mary's grasp for fear of disturbing the peaceful interlude.

After a time, Mary's eyes darted beneath lids. *The day was sunny in her dream. She rode bareback upon her black horse, Lightning, and she remembered a beautiful place she had been to once, and how to get there.*

She rode the familiar trail up the slope of her beloved mountain, toward the pathway that meandered to a beautiful glacier lake. But the turnoff cut to the right instead of the left, and led her beneath a canopy of deciduous trees. Dappled shade soothed the heat of her skin and she felt rejuvenated. She knew it was spring because birds trilled and flitted from branches to unseen locations, their beaks full with twigs and lichens and fluff for nest building.

Soon she arrived at a clearing and realized that she had been there before— the scents familiar—though she did not recognize the lake when she spied it, the shores obscured by cattails and other reeds. Eager to explore, she slid from her horse and stepped quietly toward its glittering surface. Admiring long rays of light low in the sky, she felt sure that the lake's depths had been quickened— supple and pregnant with trout and frogs and minnows.

She sat cross-legged at its edge, her eyes closed. A forthcoming vision delivered a smile. As if she were a bird gliding upon high thermals, she witnessed the expanse, the big picture from above. First, the quaint oversized pond where she sat, and close by, two larger lakes, a knoll of open green between, and new vistas beyond. Intrigued, she got up and pushed through an overgrown deer trail, certain that her destination lay straight ahead.

Eventually, the earth became sandy—remnants of a great lakebed from the past, she reckoned. What seemed like hours later, she dropped into another switchback, a gradual decline bordered by trees and shrubbery petite in stature.

Seized by the sound of voices, she listened. After identifying several distinct sources, tones harmonious in nature, she continued with caution. Cornering the next bend, she was startled to witness a group of people gathered at the pebbled edge of a huge, undulating body of water—crested waves of water, like an ocean—yet it had no sound.

They turned toward her and smiled, motioned her to come forward. Surprised more by the quake in her heart, the absolute joy at seeing them, she did not hesitate. She joined their company, let herself be hugged and greeted; hugged in return, gleeful and delighted. The people spoke many languages, none of which she understood, but she loved the shapes and sounds of the words. There was no need for apprehension, and she was in no hurry—nor were they, it seemed.

She saw a little girl run into the water and chased after her, fearful for the child's safety. Saltwater splashed upon her body. Her bared feet and strong hands fueled her mission. She lunged.

As her arms embraced the girl, there was only light, life in the light, timeless.

Hattie felt a change. Refusing to release Mary's hand, she fumbled for Mary's pulse with the other. Compelled to breathe, she took a breath and, in that moment, knew that Mary had died. She wanted to cry but surprisingly, felt exhilarated, awed by an unseen resonance.

"Mary," she whispered, "God bless you on your journey. You have my love … and prayers for eternal happiness."

In the morning, Hattie located a telephone, anxious to fulfill the promise she had made to Mary. Pleasantly surprised when the woman who answered at the Saypo General Store identified herself as Onatah, Hattie relayed the sequence of events: Mary's illness, her remarkable fight to survive, fueled in part, she said, by the goal she, Hattie, had just learned of: Mary's wish to spend the rest of her years with the Bruneau family; and finally, the moment of Mary's transcendence, her spirit released at sunset, yesterday, December 5th.

"Mary asked me to say," Hattie gripped for breath, "that she was sorry she didn't get to come live with you and your family. Several times during the last days, she called your name in her sleep. In a moment of clarity, she told me to say, exactly: 'I love you forever, Onatah. You are in my heart and soul and I'll be there when you call.'"

Time passed before Onatah could answer. "Thank you, Hattie," she said.

Hattie expressed her sincere condolences before inviting Onatah and her family to stay at her home, the Monroe house, if they chose to attend the funeral that would take place in two or three days and advised Onatah to leave a telephone message with the Cascade Mercantile if she and her family were coming—then added that the storekeep would be able to provide her with the date and time of the services.

Three days after Mary's passing, on the afternoon of December 8th, Lester counted over one hundred and fifty people come to pay their respects at Mary Fields' funeral, heartened by the fact that her beloved youngster friends outnumbered the total of adults. He could not identify some of the mourners and decided that Mary Fields must have known everyone from everywhere.

He peeked inside from the doorway where he stood with his father, down the auditorium's aisle to the coffin, frightened to think of his Mary inside the claustrophobic space. He stroked the softness of his lucky rabbit's foot hid deep in his pocket and asked God if Mary Fields could please have all the fresh fruit and candies she wanted up there in Heaven.

Prodigious quantities of flowers: wreaths, sprays and bouquets, had arrived by train—some before and some on the same train that had transported Mary shrouded in a pine casket and Hattie pushing an empty wheelchair. Wasting no time, Hattie instructed the undertaker to dress Mary in her patriotic outfit and provided the exact garments after checking the details of Mary's photograph found on the nightstand by her bed.

Herman hurried to craft a well-built coffin with brass handles and dovetailed corners that would replace the indigent model provided by the hospital, and advised Mr. and Mrs. Monroe that he had taken the liberty of opening Mary's will. It had been stored in his safe on Mary's request, he explained, and the document asked the couple to oversee her burial arrangements. He provided them with a copy of Mary's instructions, a moot exercise perhaps, he commented, as they had already been acting on Mary's behalf. He mentioned further that his brother, Mary's lawyer, would administer any other business pertaining to her testament when he arrived.

D.W. and R.B. selected four more pallbearers in addition to themselves and mandated a dress code: black three-piece suits to be accessorized by special custom-made boutonnieres they would provide, artistic arrangements similar to the ones Mary had crafted for the baseball team all those many years.

Mayor Monroe also made it a point to speak to the owners of *The*

Cascade Courier and *The Cascade Echo,* strongly recommending that they do their professional best and get busy composing noteworthy tributes to the woman who had become a Cascade Birdtail legend.

Hattie revisited the undertaker and viewed Mary's body to make sure that the Union Cap was placed ever so slightly toward the right, the way Mary liked it, before acquiescing to the final closure of the coffin lid, completed by Herman Wolf.

Madeline had provided Mrs. Arthur McCollim, a renowned soprano who frequently donated her talent at funerals, and her piano accompanist, Miss Mamie McDonald, with titles of hymns she had heard Mary humming over the years.

Gerlach purchased a second red rose bouquet for the Catholic altar outside of town and placed it there in Mary's name along with a hand-printed card upon which she had written: *In loving memory of Mary Fields who buck boarded to Heaven on December 5, 1914.*

Ada Marcum spared no expense when she telephoned to a Helena florist and ordered an extra-large stand-alone wreath, requesting a wide yellow ribbon to be stretched diagonally across the circular arrangement of white camellias. *Our True Patriot* was the message she assigned, thinking how unfortunate it was that Mary hadn't lived to celebrate the state ceremony she felt certain (as Mary had proclaimed a month earlier) would arrive shortly: the legislative enactment of Montana's Woman Suffrage Rights.

She stopped by the auditorium early to be certain that her visual tribute had arrived as she had articulated and that it would be prominently displayed, along with many others, next to Mary's coffin—which, she discovered, was gracefully strewn with ornate sprays of gorgeous colorful flowers and was, as she had anticipated, centered at the front of the auditorium. Satisfied, she helped her reverend from the Methodist Church arrange an elaborate shoulder-high wrought iron candleholder upon which a great number of votive memorial candles would be lighted. She caught Lester's stare.

Lester's grief was plain to see. D.W. had tried to distract his son by assigning him the position of head-usher, instructing him to lead his friends and neighbors to their seats. "Anywhere you choose," he had advised, patting Lester's shoulder and inserting a red carnation into his progeny's lapel.

"Lester will take you to your seats," D.W. said after greeting each person by name, clasping hands and waving them forward.

Guiding those who had come to show their respects, systemically filling each chair from front to back in the hall's raised seating, Lester efforted to keep his eyes off the coffin though he noticed more and more flower arrangements delivered onto the stage—creating a garden, to his thinking, like Mary's.

Sister Gertrude, who had come by train from Great Falls, insisted that Lester seat her in the front row, deeply saddened not to have known Mary's whereabouts the week before, as her residence at the Great Falls Ursuline Academy was located just blocks away from the hospital where Mary had spent her last hours—where Mary could have received loving words from her faithful friend, Gertrude. She squeezed the hankie in her pocket and glanced for familiar faces.

Mr. and Mrs. Chong broke tradition, attending an American funeral dressed in formal Mandarin ensembles. Lester, taken by the beauty of dark silken fabric and startled when an ominous dragon raised upon its sheen appeared to glare at him, ushered the couple to the reserved section in the front row. Suddenly overwhelmed, he was relieved to see his mother signal him to the empty seat beside her.

Father John Casey began the service. He offered prayers for the repose of Mary Fields' soul and afterwards, requested a moment of silence for private supplications.

Mrs. Arthur McCollim and Miss Mamie McDonald skillfully performed three hymns: Amazing Grace, Rock of Ages and The Enchanted Isle, a song from Verdi's opera, "Ernani." Inevitably, emotions wavered, and tears fell.

Members of the assembly, many of whom had become somewhat tipsy from inhaling profuse fragrances of non-native flowers, were invited to contribute personal eulogies. One friend after another came forward and testified to Mary's character, shared stories of affection and told familiar tales, many of which regaled grand and gregarious adventures. Anecdotal recollections citing Mary's eclectic humor were also imparted. Chuckles quaked a communal core.

A reflective length of silence followed before Father Casey asked if anyone else would like to speak. Earl Monroe stood up, waved his hand and suggested that everyone sing the song Mary Fields loved best. Without waiting for a response, he caroled, "Happy Birthday to you—"

Youngsters sprang up and joined in, as if on cue, followed by the adults, who rose one by one, inspired, like their children, by good memories. Breaking formalities, someone began to clap, and the congregation engaged in spontaneous applause. When zest waned, Father Casey announced that interment would follow directly, for those who wished to participate.

The pallbearers stepped forward, hoisted the casket upon steady shoulders and proceeded up the center aisle and outside where they eased the Birdtail heroine onto a flatbed wagon that had been garnished with carnations, evergreens and pinecones.

The Pastime Theater, Cascade's temporary funeral hall, had emptied. Because no surviving family members were present, the multitude of flower wreaths and arrangements were carried by those who chose to participate in the burial service. They joined the formal procession that slowly advanced to Cascade's Hillside Cemetery on the outskirts of town. As the two-horse team made the last turn, sunshine split the overcast chill and shades of sapphire blue heralded from beyond.

Once the coterie of mourners had made their way past familiar headstones, the pallbearers—Misters R.B. Glover, J.H. Jones, F. N. Askew, James Travis, J.W. McKay and D.W. Monroe—lifted the flower-laden coffin onto their shoulders and slowly crunched across yesterday's ice, carefully setting the farewell case beside the open grave headed by a small, unmarked, tin cross.

Finding themselves without officiating clergy, Mary's friends looked to one another and fell silent. Gerlach reached her hands to those beside her, initiating a hand-held circle that spread to encompass the coffin, the empty grave and the cross. Eyes looked skyward and back to a shared profoundness inspired by mutual love.

Hattie spoke, "Let us pray that Mary's new life is filled with joy. May each of us strive to match her grand goodwill."

"Amen," the ring of voices quelled.

Onatah cried for days. Having chosen to honor White Crow's passing in her own way, she snowshoed up the mountain where she built a modest altar from stones and sticks and feathers, climbed upon her Ucsote's "big picture" boulder and faced east. Life without the beloved elder, eluded her.

She parted through personal memories of White Crow and wondered what had taken place during Mary's half-century of life before arriving in Montana. What had it been like to be a slave—as a child, and as a woman? What had happened and who had she loved? So many years.

She whispered a special prayer of gratitude, ever thankful for Mary's decision to come to Montana, to the place where their lives had intersected. She sent a kiss upon a waft of glacier wind and gave herself time to grieve until she had shored peace she could hold onto—love shared, alive still, love that would last forever—her love, ready to release heartstrings so that Ucsote White Crow could soar, free.

She sang a soulful song without words, reached for her knife and cut her hair—a tribal act of mourning.

That night, she baked a chocolate cake and lit candles, and the Bruneau family shared stories of life brightened by their beloved White Crow.

EPILOGUE

The official canvass and recount of the Montana State Woman Suffrage Bill was completed at last, and on December 9, 1914, four days after Mary's passing, the woman suffrage rights amendment was signed, sealed and officially entered into the Montana State Constitution.

Governor S.V. Stewart stated: Now, therefore, I, S.V. Stewart, as governor of the state of Montana, pursuant to the statutes in such cases made and provided, do hereby declare and proclaim that a majority of all the votes cast at said election for and against said amendment was and is in favor of said amendment, and that from and after this date, said amendment will be in full force and effect as a part of the constitution of the state of Montana.

IN WITNESS WHEREOF, I have hereunto set my hand and caused the great seal of the state to be affixed.

DONE at Helena, the capitol, this the ninth day of December, in the year of our Lord one thousand nine hundred fourteen and of the

independence of the United States of America the one hundred thirty-nine.
By the Governor:

S.V. STEWART

A.M. ALDERSON,
Secretary of State

Some years later, Earl Monroe replaced the original unmarked tin cross that
headed the grave of Mary Fields with a handsome granite stone inscribed in
her honor, the way he believed it should have been done: "Mary Fields,
1832-1914".

ACKNOWLEDGMENTS

Many people helped me manifest this chronicle. I give my heartfelt thanks and appreciation to Sister Kathleen Padden, Sister Francis Xavier Porter, Sister Debbie Lloyd and archivist Julianne Ruby; librarians Judy Ellinghausen, Nancy Royan, Jackie Strandell, Deana Wirkus, Ann Brooks and Nancy Callan; Molly Holz, Molly Kruckenberg and Lea Solberg at the Montana Historical Society; Pat Wardinsky and Jan Thompson from the Great Falls Genealogy Society; Mr. Earl Monroe, deceased, a former Cascade resident and the last living acquaintance of Mary Fields; Megan Ault Regenerous, Bruce Glasrud, Michael Searles, Kathleen Robison, Illia Thompson, Nancy Ashley, Michael McConnell, Harfijah Oliver and Elizabeth Trudell. A very special thank you to Rofiah Breen for her countless hours of wise expertise, and to Jennifer Lynch, United States Postal Service Historian.

This book would not have been realized without contributions from each of these supportive and enthusiastic individuals. Others have also invested generous amounts of time and attention. I thank you all.

AUTHOR'S NOTE

I could never have written this book had it not been for my Montana heritage. All four sets of my great-grandparents were homesteaders, three of whom "proved-up" in Montana not far from Cascade and the Birdtail prairie. As a child I listened to my grandparents' conversations with friends and neighbors as they leaned back at grain elevators, quilting bees, cattle auctions and county fairs to enjoy momentary respites from continual hard work.

When I became aware of Mary Fields, a black woman who lived outside of the norm in rural Montana during the same time period as my great-grandparents and grandparents, I was captivated. How had she managed to survive? Racial prejudice ran deep back then. And remained so, judging by hostile points of view I had overheard as a child. Delivering mail meant that Mary Fields' location on an isolated route was public knowledge. Those with ill intent had ample opportunities.

I wanted to know: who was she, and how did she survive such perilous odds? Why did she choose to put herself at such risk? Scoundrels and outlaws committed murder without consequence during Montana's turbulent seventeenth, eighteenth, and nineteenth centuries.

Brief Wild West articles published throughout the twentieth century characterized Mary Fields, also known as Black Mary, Stagecoach Mary and/or Nigger Mary, as a sharpshooter who drove the Cascade-Birdtail stagecoach, rifle gripped in one hand, pistol in the other—a six-foot tall, two-hundred pound match for any two men, a notorious cigar smoking legend who, as an impoverished old-timer, felt innately proud to serve the white population as laundress, babysitter, mascot and local landmark.

Surely, Mary's true story stemmed from her remarkable character—traits that included confidence, endurance, ingenuity, humor, and generosity. How had her presence created a lasting communal imprint upon peoples of diverse cultures?

Mary Fields was not only a well-respected wagon freighter and mail carrier; she was a good-looking, goodhearted multi-tasking pioneer and entrepreneur, an astute strategic planner with tenacious patience and the ability to ignore, sustain and persevere in order to manifest her unique personified vision of independence.

It is my wish that Mary Fields' contributions be acknowledged, regionally and nationally. May her life story live on, preserved in annals of American history—an inspiration to all peoples—past, present and future.

I'm grateful to have been the lucky one who unearthed documents that proved Mary Fields was, in fact, the first African American woman star route mail carrier in the United States. USPS archive historian, Jennifer Lynch, announced Mary Fields' official status after receiving documentation from me in 2006.

I was thrilled a second time in 2006, when I discovered that Mary Fields had registered for the vote. I located the evidence in "Cascade County Official Register No. 15." Proof of her voter registration authenticates Mary Fields as the first African American person to register in Cascade, Montana.

More discoveries came my way, many of which are included in this book. If you are interested in additional facts about Mary Fields, Sister Mary Amadeus, woman suffrage, early Montana politics and other related subject matter, I invite you to visit my website, where you are welcome to make comments, ask questions, check for author events and sign up to receive giveaways, book news, and reader opportunities.

www.miantaemetcalfmcconnell.com

Write a Review

If you enjoyed reading *Deliverance Mary Fields*, please take a moment to give a review at your online book site of choice. Your comments will help to spread the word and encourage others to learn about this extraordinary American hero.

Library Requests

Next time you call or visit your local library, consider asking your librarian to add *Deliverance Mary Fields* to their collection, another way to introduce Mary Fields to readers.

Thank you

SELECT BIBLIOGRAPHY

Books

Abair, Sister St. Angela. *A Mustard Seed in Montana, Recollections of the First Indian Mission in Montana.* Toledo: Self Published, 1938.

Anderson, Martha. *Black Pioneers of the Northwest 1800-1918.* Publisher unknown, 1980.

Belafonte Enterprises, Inc. *The Long Road to Freedom, An Anthology of Black Music.* U.S.A.: 2001.

Bittner, Rosanne. *Into the Wilderness, The Long Hunters.* New York: A Forge Book, 2002.

Burt, Olive W. and Messner, Julian. *Negroes in the Early West.* New York: Simon & Schuster, 1969.

Capps, Benjamin. *The Old West Native Americans.* Alexandria: Time-Life Books, 1995.

Code, Joseph B. *Great America Foundresses.* New York: The Macmillan Company, 1929.

Cushing, Marshall Henry. *The Story of Our Post Office, The Greatest Government Department in All Its Phases.* Boston: A. M. Thayer & Co., Publishers, 1893.

Doherty, Craig A. and Doherty, Katherine M. *The Iroquois.* New York: Franklin Watts, 1989.

Duffy, Consuela Marie. *Katharine Drexel, A Biography.* Philadelphia: The Peter Reilly Co., 1966.

Foster, Martha Harroun. *We Know Who We Are, Metis Identity in a Montana Community.* Norman: University of Oklahoma Press, 2006.

Garceau-Hagen, Dee, Editor. *Portraits of Women in the American West.* New York: Routledge, Taylor & Francis Group, 2005.

Glenbow Museum. *Nitsitapiisinni, The Story of the Blackfoot People.* Firefly Books Inc., 2001.

Graymont, Barbara. *The Iroquois*. New York: Chelsea House Publishers, 1988.

Hunter, James. *Glencoe and the Indians*. Edinburgh: Mainstream Publishing Co. Ltd., 1997.

Hunter, James. *Scottish Highlanders, Indian Peoples, Thirty Generations of a Montana Family*. Helena: Montana Historical Press, 1997.

Jackson, Curtis E. *A History of the Bureau of Indian Affairs and its activities among Indians*. San Francisco: R & E Associates, 1977.

Jackson, John C. *Children of the Fur Trade: Forgotten Metis of the Pacific Northwest*. Missoula, MT, Mountain Press Publishing Company, 1995.

Jackson, W. T. *Wells Fargo Stagecoaching in Montana Territory*. Helena: Montana Historical Society Press, 1979.

Jacobs, Harriet A. *Life of a Slave Girl*. Harvard: Cambridge: University Press, 1987.

Judson, Katharine B. Montana, *The Land of Shining Mountains*. Chicago: A.C. McClurg & Co., 1909.

Jung, A. M. *Jesuit Missions Among the American Tribes of the Rocky Mountain Indians*. Spokane: Gonzaga University, 1925.

Kallen, Stuart A. *Native American of the Great Lakes*. San Diego: Lucent Books, Inc., 2000.

Katz, William Loren. *The Black West*. New York. Harlem Moon, Broadway Books, 1971.

Lindesmith, E.W.J, Chaplain, U.S. Army. "August 15, 1887 entry." *Father Lindesmith's Diary of 1887*, Fort Keogh, MT, (1880-1891).

Lincoln, Sister Angela, editor. *Life of the Reverend Mother Amadeus of the Heart of Jesus, Foundress of the Ursuline Missions of Montana and Alaska*. New York: The Paulist Press, 1923.

Mahoney, Irene. *Lady Blackrobes, Missionaries in the Heart of Indian Country*. Golden Colorado: Fulcrum Publishing, 2006.

Mahoney, Irene, introduction. *Far from Home, Letters from the Ursulines, Montana Missions, 1884-1918*. Self Published, 2001.

McBride, Sister Genevieve. *The Bird Tail*. New York: Vantage Press, 1992.

McGuffey, William Holmes. *McGuffey's Eclectic Reader, Second Reader*. New York: American Book Co., 1879.

Morgan, Lewis Henry. *League of the Iroquois*. Secaucus: Citadel Press, 1984.

Palladino, L.B. *Indian and White in the Northwest*. Lancaster: Wickersham Publishing Co., 1922.

Palladino, L.B. *Forty Years, A Missionary in the Rocky Mountains, Memoir (1884)*. Helena: Geo E. Boos & Co., 1884.

Peterson, Jacqueline. *Sacred Encounters: Father De Smet and the Indians of the Rocky Mountain West*. Norman: University of Oklahoma Press, 1993.

Petrik, Paula. *No Step Backward*. Helena: Montana Historical Society Press, 1987.

Rowe, Jean Conrad. Editor. *Mountains and Meadows, A Pioneer History of Montana 1805-1925.* Great Falls: Self Published, Blue Print & Letter Co. Printers, no publication date.

Samek, Hana. *The Blackfoot Confederacy 1880-1920: A comparative Study of Canadian and U.S. Indian Policy.* Albuquerque: University of New Mexico Press, 2011.

Sanders, Helen Fitzgerald. *Trails through Western Woods.* New York: The Premier Press, 1910.

Schrems, Suzanne H. *Uncommon Women Unmarked Trails, The Courageous Journey of Catholic Missionary Sisters In Frontier Montana,* Norman: Horse Creek Publication, Inc., 2003.

Shirley, Gayle C. *More Than Petticoats, Remarkable Montana Women.* Helena: Falcon Publishing, 1995.

Sun River Valley Historical Society, *Pictorial History of the Sun River Valley.* Shelby: Promoter Publishing, 1989.

Taylor, Quintard and Moore, Shirley Ann Wilson. *African American Women Confront the West 1600-2000.* Norman: University of Oklahoma Press, 2003.

Terrell, John Upton. *Black Robe: The Life of Pierre-Jean DeSmet - Missionary, Explorer, Pioneer.* New York: Doubleday, 1964.

United States Postal Service. *An American Postal Portrait, A Photographic Legacy.* New York: HarperCollins Publishers, Inc., 2000.

Ursuline Sisters of Toledo. Mahoney, Lelia, editor. *A Tree in the Valley, The Highlights of the Annals of Ursuline Convent of the Sacred Heart, Toledo, Ohio, 1854-1979.* Toledo: Self-Published, date unknown.

Wagner, Tricia Martineau. *African American Women of the Old West.* Helena: TwoDot, 2007.

Wong, K. Scott and Chan, Sucheng. *Claiming America, Constructing Chinese American Identities during the Exclusion Era.* Philadelphia: Temple University Press, 1998.

Wooten, Dudley G. *A Noble Ursuline: Mother Mary Amadeus.* New York: The Paulist Press, 19--

Newspapers

(Baseball, Cascade Cubs) *The Cascade Courier,* June 23, 1911, April 26, 1912, May 30, 1913, Sept. 19, 1913, May 22, 1914, May 1, 1914.

"Cascade City Election." *The Cascade Courier,* Jan. 27, 1911 and Feb. 19, 1911

(Cascade City Election) *The Cascade Courier,* Feb. 7, 1813, March 28, 1913, April 11, 1914.

"Death of Mary Fields." *The Cascade Echo,* Vo. 3, No. 5, Dec.13, 1914.

Dwyer, Jennifer. "The Legend of Stagecoach Mary." *Toledo Blade,* June 7, 1981.

(Fort Shaw) *The Rising Sun,* June 12, 1889.

Hutton, Charles W. "Tales of School on the Prairie in Days When Montana Was Young." *Great Falls Tribune,* Nov. 29, 1936.

J.B. Bass, Editor. "REPUDIATED! REPUBLICANS DENY THEIR LOYAL ALLY THE COLORED VOTER ANY RECOGNITION WHATEVER IN THE DISTRIBUTION OF PATRONAGE, The Colored Voters of the State Are Righteously Indignant at this Unfair Deal." *The Montana Plaindealer,* Helena, Montana, Jan. 11, 1907.

Jones, E.R. "The Cowboy's Corner, 'Mary Fields.'" Montana Cowboy's Association. *The Cascade Courier,* July 6, 1944.

"Mary Field, Well Known Old Timer who Is Known All Over the State." *The Cascade Courier,* March 18, 1910.

McBride, M. "'Black Mary' Labored Long at Old St. Peter's Mission." Montana Newspaper Association, *The Cascade Courier,* Aug. 7, 1939.

"'Nigger Mary' Fields, Early Day Resident of Cascade, One of State's Noted Characters." *Great Falls Tribune,* May 22, 1939.

"Old Timer Passes Away." *The Cascade Courier,* No. 47, Dec. 11, 1914.

"Ordinance No. Eight." *The Cascade Courier,* May 5, 1911.

"Rancher Remember Mary Fields, Pioneer." *Great Falls Tribune,* April 18, 1975.

"'Stagecoach' Mary Fields 1832-1914." *Chicago Tribune,* Section 8, March 3, 2004.

Talwani, Sanjay. "Frontierswoman and Former Slave was a Mission Character." *Great Falls Tribune,* Parade Section, Jan. 30, 2000.

The Colored Citizen, Helena, Colored Citizen Publishing Co., Sept. - Dec., 1894.

Periodicals

Bates-Tompkins, Angela. "Leaving their mark: African American women of the West." *Cobblestone* 20, no. 2 (1999) 18-20.

Behan, Barbara Carol. "African Americans in the Montana Territory 1864-1889." *Journal of African American History,* 91, Winter (2006). 33-34.

Berndt, Christina Gish. "Kinship as strategic political action: The Northern Cheyenne response to the imposition of the Nation-State." (Doctorate, University of Minnesota, 2008) 149-154.

Boeve, Eunice. "Past Times, Mary Fields: The Tough, Tender Legend of Cascade." *Montana Magazine,* Jan/Feb. (2001). 70-74.

Campbell, Fred. *The Native American* 22, No. 21 (1921). 158, 252.

Cascade County Gazetteer 1896-1897, (Business Directory). (1897). 210.

Cascade County Directory 1903. (1903). 381.

Cascade County Directory 1906. (1906). 380.

Cascade County Directory 1908-1909. (1909). 383.

Code, Joseph B. "Mother Mary Amadeus of the Heart of Jesus: The Teresa of the Arctics." *The Epistle*, Vol. XXVI, Summer (1960), No.2.

Cooper, Gary, as told to Marc Crawford. "Stage Coach Mary, Gun-toting Montanan Delivered U.S. mail." Ebony Magazine, Oct. (1959). 97-100.

Everett, George. "Ex-slave Mary Fields felt at home in Montana, whether working in a convent or managing a mail route." *Wild West Magazine.* Feb. (1996).

"Explore the Homesteading Timeline." *U.S. Department of Interior, Bureau of Land Management.* (No Publish Date).

Fitzpatrick, Frank. "The Disturbing History of Baseball's Mascots." *Inquirer,* June 23, (2014).

Greer, John T. "A Brief History of Indian Education at the Fort Shaw Industrial School." (Thesis, Montana State College, 1958).

Harris, Mark. "The Legend of Black Mary." *Negro Digest*, Aug., (1950).

"Heroic woman of Montana protected Catholic school and carried U.S. mail." *Negro Digest*, Aug., (1950). 86.

Miller, Don. "Mary Fields, Freight Hauler and Stage Driver." *True West,* Aug.,(1982). 55.

Northern Cheyenne Tribe. "Northern Cheyenne Reservation Timeline." Northern Cheyenne Tribe, Indian Education Montana Office of Public Instruction, March, 2010. Ch. 2, 14-17.

Sources of Historical Information on Post Offices, Postal Employees, Mail Routes, and Mail Contractors, USPS Pub 119, Sept. 2004.

Taylor, Quintard. "The Emergence of Black Communities in the Pacific Northwest: 1865-1910." *The Journal of Negro History* 64, No. 4 (1979). 342-354.

Underwood, J.M. "Deceased Ursuline Missionaries." *Indian Sentinel* VI, no. 14, Oct. (1919).

The United States Postal Service: An American History 1775-2002, USPS Pub100, Sept. 2003, 18-19.

Van Rennselaer, H. "Sketch of the Catholic Church in Montana." *The American Catholic Review,* (1887).

Government Documents & Research Facilities

Board of Indian Commissioners. *Indian Affairs, Jan. 26, 1894.*130.

National Archives at Denver, CO.

National Archives, San Francisco, CA.

National Archives, New York City, NY.

Northern Cheyenne Tribe. "The Northern Cheyenne Tribe and Its Reservation," A Report to the

Office of Indian Affairs, Washington, D.C., *Report of the Commissioner of Indian Affairs*, Aug. 27, 1892. 86-87.

Report of the Secretary of the Interior, Fiscal Year End. June 30, 1891. 59 - 60.

Report of the Agents in Montana. *Report of Blackfeet Agency, Oct. 1891.* 64.

Report of the Agents in Montana. *Report of the Blackfeet Agency, August 31, 1892.* 97.

Steell, George, U.S. Indian Agent. Report of the Agents in Montana. *Report of Blackfeet Agency, Aug. 15, 1893.* 119,166, 188.

U.S. Bureau of Land Management and the State of Montana Department of Natural Resources and Conservation. April 2002.

U.S. Congress. *The Homestead Act of 1862, 37th Congress Session II 1862.* 20 May, 1862.

U.S. Department of Commerce. *Federal & State Indian Reservations & Indian Trust Areas.* 1974.

United States Postal Service. *United States Postal Service: An American History 1775 - 2002*, USPS Pub 100, Sept. 2003. 18-19.

United States Postal Service. *Sources of Historical Information on Post Offices, Postal Employees, Mail Routes, and Mail Contractors*, USPS Pub 119, Sept. 2004.

Letters

Author unknown. "Mary Fields". Typewritten account, Helena: Montana Historical Society Archives, vertical files.

Letter from Joseph Bandini to Mother Amadeus, June 1884, Jesuit Oregon Province Archives.

Letter from Mother Amadeus, St. Peter's Mission to Mother Stanislaus, Convent of the Sacred Heart, Toledo, Dec. 19, 1884. Toledo Convent Archives.

Letters from Mother Mary Amadeus to Mother Stanislaus, March 29, April 2 and April 20, 1885. Ursuline Centre Archives, Great Falls.

Letter from Quigley, P.F. (Pastor of St. Francis de Sales Church, Toledo), sent from St. Mary's Seminary, Cleveland, OH to Reverend Mother Sacred Heart in Miles City, MT. March 21, 1885. Ursuline Centre Archives, Great Falls.

Saint Peter's Ursuline Annals, Ursuline Centre Archives, Great Falls, MT.

Saint Peter's Ursuline Annals Volume IV. Ursuline Centre Archives, Great Falls, MT.

Interviews

Lynch, Jennifer, USPS Historian, Washington D.C. Phone interview by Miantae Metcalf McConnell. Sept. 2014.

Monroe, Earl. Personal interview by Miantae Metcalf McConnell. Great Falls, MT: 13 May. 2006.

Padden, Sister Kathleen. Phone interview by Miantae Metcalf McConnell. Sept. 2014.

Made in the USA
Middletown, DE
15 October 2020